GEOLOGY IN THE SITING OF NUCLEAR POWER PLANTS

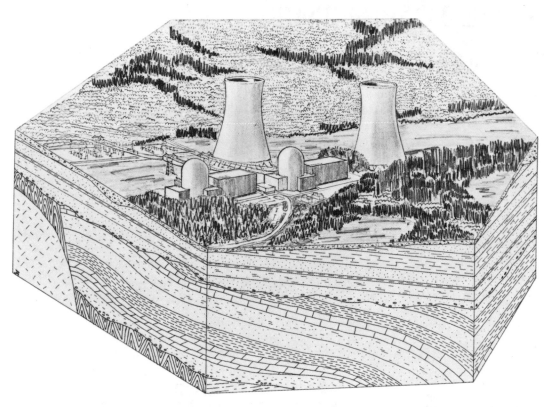

A hypothetical two-unit nuclear power plant, with its characteristic domical reactor containment buildings and giant, hyperbolic cooling water towers. Nuclear power plants bring to a sharp focus the profound interaction between works of Man and the geological and ecological environments. Plants are carefully located on terrain found to represent a suite of least-impact natural conditions, and the site is then carefully explored by engineering geologists to prove a hazard-free subsurface. Many potential nuclear plant sites have been found wanting in the course of site-specific, safety-related explorations and have been abandoned by the sponsoring electric utilities. Artwork by John Ross, courtesy of Bechtel, Inc., San Francisco, California.

REVIEWS IN ENGINEERING GEOLOGY
VOLUME IV

GEOLOGY IN THE SITING OF
NUCLEAR POWER PLANTS

Edited by
ALLEN W. HATHEWAY
AND
COLE R. MCCLURE, JR.

The Geological Society of America
Boulder, Colorado 80301
1979

Published by
THE GEOLOGICAL SOCIETY OF AMERICA, INC.
3300 Penrose Place
Boulder, Colorado 80301

Printed in the United States of America

rev. 2-25-88

Contents

*To the many young men and women geologists
on their first professional employment,
who supplied creativity and muscle during the
great decade, 1965–1975, of siting and construction of
nuclear power plants for electricity generation.*

Preface

The construction of nuclear power plants and associated licensing activities reached an all-time high in 1975. More than 50 generating units were in operation, and another 164 were under construction or in early licensing stages. The nuclear industry had mustered the largest geologic task force in this country's history. Those of us involved kept informed, to a large degree, by contact with fellow workers; the science developed at a rate that exceeded its ability to formally document or disseminate the vast new storehouse of geologic knowledge. Each new site investigation seemed to turn up challenges that led to the development and application of exciting new geologic techniques.

Recognizing a need for professional communication, the management board of the Engineering Geology Division of the Geological Society of America asked for and received permission to hold the 1975 annual symposium on "Geology in the Siting of Nuclear Power Plants." Twelve authors presented state-of-the-art papers at the well-attended annual meeting in Salt Lake City. The degree and diversity of interest in nuclear plant siting was gratifying. Siting practitioners and protagonists alike recognized the rapid advance in geologic technologies evolving from the siting effort. Enthusiasm to assemble and disseminate an Engineering Geology Division handbook on reactor siting has resulted in this publication. Special recognition for this effort goes to Chairmen James Skehan, David J. Varnes, and Richard W. Galster. The volume includes 16 papers and is divided into the following parts:

Part 1, The Regulatory Process, explains how the siting and licensing process is actually conducted and deals with the siting and licensing process as specified by legal regulations.

Part 2, Seismicity, develops the background for selection of the design earthquake.

Part 3, Techniques, includes topical treatments of the most important geologic and geophysical methods employed in siting and licensing.

Part 1 opens with a paper by the editors that describes development of the regulatory process in terms of engineering-design needs and public-safety requirements. Until this time, only those people actually involved in siting had an overall concept of how the various geotechnical studies are blended into a single document: The Preliminary Safety Analysis Report. J. A. Caggiano, Jr., describes a methodology used to screen potential sites on a best-risk basis for successful plant licensing. Merlyn J. Adair's paper treats the manner in which government regulations are satisfied in the actual process of conducting a site-safety analysis. He shares his experiences as a seasoned

geologic project manager. Robert H. Morris of the U.S. Geological Survey presents insight on the magnitude of geologic licensing submissions, managerial pitfalls, and the effect of improper submittals. State geologists James F. Davis (New York), James E. Slossen (California), and associate Robert H. Fakundiny describe State participation in nuclear plant licensing. State motives, objectives, and contributions are covered in detail.

Part 2 includes papers by Otto W. Nuttli and Bruce A. Bolt. They describe state-of-the-art seismic evaluation techniques plus regionally specific seismic histories of instrumented and historic earthquakes. The seismic record—its meaning and application—is discussed for two of the three major seismic regions of the United States. James W. Dewey presents a well-received new theory of analyzing earthquake hypocentral data using velocity records and the entire near-region seismic catalog.

Part 3 opens with a paper by Roland C. McEldowney and Richard F. Pascucci describing remote sensing techniques and data treatment that are playing an increasing role in site selection technology. Robert H. Osborne and co-authors detail the importance of establishing stratigraphic continuity in sediments underlying potential reactor sites. They also describe techniques used to determine date of last movement on faults. Philip J. Murphy and co-authors also discuss age-determination techniques in fault investigations. Allen W. Hatheway and F. Beach Leighton present the rationale behind the use of exploratory trenching to examine otherwise unobservable subsurface features, how trenching has been used at 21 nuclear plant sites, and the procedures, costs, and logistics of undertaking such efforts. V. J. Murphy and co-authors review the potential uses of geophysical techniques in both regional and site-specific geologic correlations. T. L. Dobecki outlines the use of downhole geophysical velocity measurements to provide geotechnical and soil dynamics engineers with critical input toward their determination of foundation material response to earthquake ground motion. Expanding on individual techniques, James W. Crosby III and John D. Scott provide detailed guidance on borehole geophysical logging methods for proving stratigraphic continuity. And finally Clifford R. Farrell and John W. Harshbarger discuss the efforts undertaken to define the ground-water regime of a site and how radioactive spill potential is assessed; they also assess the need for expensive dewatering systems in engineered design.

We believe that there is no other single field within geology that offers so many exciting ways to use classical geologic knowledge as the realm of nuclear power plant siting and licensing. Advances have been made at frequent intervals, and this will continue. Research and academic geologists have been involved from the beginning in the application of these techniques. Astute geologic managers in siting and licensing recognize that a continued high-level involvement by geologists means a more efficient licensing process.

ACKNOWLEDGMENTS

We extend our heartfelt gratitude to the authors and sincere thanks to the numerous reviewers. We wish also to recognize Haley & Aldrich, Inc., and Bechtel Incorporated for supplying substantial clerical support, drafting services, and encouragement to us in collecting and editing these papers.

ALLEN W. HATHEWAY
Cambridge, Massachusetts

COLE R. MCCLURE, JR.
San Francisco, California

PART 1

THE REGULATORY PROCESS

Geological Society of America
Reviews in Engineering Geology, Volume IV
1979

An overview of nuclear power plant siting and licensing

COLE R. McCLURE, JR.
Bechtel Incorporated, Engineers and Constructors, 50 Beale Street (6-B7), San Francisco, California 94119

ALLEN W. HATHEWAY
Haley & Aldrich, Inc., Consulting Geotechnical Engineers and Engineering Geologists, 238 Main Street, Cambridge, Massachusetts 02142

ABSTRACT

Studies on nuclear power plant siting and licensing are expensive and complex undertakings requiring critical geologic input for the planning, design, and construction phases. Commercial production of nuclear power in the United States began in 1959, in an era when geologic hazards were seemingly not as critical as they are today to designers, constructors, and regulatory agencies. By the early 1970s, however, siting work required a more sophisticated appreciation of geologic hazards such as earthquake effects, subsidence, slope stability, and foundation integrity. These concerns were formalized by the U.S. Atomic Energy Commission (AEC) in 1971 in its "Seismic and Geologic Siting Criteria for Nuclear Power Plants" and in 1972 in the Standard Format.

The required Federal license to construct and operate nuclear power plants is awarded through a careful and demanding process. Construction permits are not granted until high levels of assurance are attained as to suitability of the site; the construction process must be observed and monitored. Electric utility applicants for construction permits and operating licenses organize large teams of scientific and technical personnel to compile the Preliminary Safety Analysis Report (PSAR) required for each nuclear power plant. Geologists constitute a key part of these teams, producing site-specific and regional assessments that are accurate enough to withstand scrutiny and timely enough to avoid costly delays in the programmed design-and-construct sequence.

Management techniques must be applied to coordinate data-collection efforts and timely release of findings. As soon as a complete set of findings is compiled to the specifications of the Standard Format, the PSAR is accepted for review by the Nuclear Regulatory Commission (NRC). These reports become complex documents and include the responses to subsequent review questions which are included as amendments. The Final Safety Analysis Report (FSAR) includes supplementary reports dealing with geologic findings revealed during construction.

Many of the key geologic issues identified in siting and licensing are often analogous to those problems that confront researchers in the geological sciences today, such as evaluation of remote imagery, proof of subsurface stratigraphic continuity, evaluation of potential fault activity, a thorough assessment of ground-water conditions at each site, and subsidence potential including evaluation of dissolution of foundation material.

The overriding goal of each applicant utility is the construction of a safe power plant; however, the future of the industry in the United States is dependent on its ability to maintain construction schedules while staying within allotted budgets. Lessons learned from previous sitings have pointed out that effective management and judgment, efficient communication, and coordination contribute to timely and cost-efficient license studies.

INTRODUCTION

The worldwide turn toward a dependence on electric energy came as a consequence of the proved advantages of steam-powered machinery—the muscle of the industrial revolution. Around the world the production and installation of steam-powered electricity-generating units grew at a quiet, yet astounding rate. Cities, towns, ports, and industrial centers in even the smallest republics came to acquire small-package electric generators. Generating plants were installed at nearly every location to which the necessary fuel, generally coal or oil, could be transported.

For 75 yr, advances toward increased efficiency and greater production were numerous and exciting. None of these advances, however, could foreshadow the harnessing of nuclear energy to produce the vast quantity of electricity required by burgeoning worldwide industrial growth.

Plutonium was first successfully produced in September 1944 at the wartime metallurgical laboratory at the University of Chicago. The heavy water moderated reactor was under development by 1945, and technological advances soon brought about the boiling water reactor. Nuclear electric power production became a reality in September 1959 with initiation of operations at the Dresden I plant of the Commonwealth Edison Company in Grundy County, Illinois. Production capacities of these early units were relatively small, 200 MW for the Dresden plant, compared to today's standard range of 900 to 1,250 MW. In the decade of the 1970s, nuclear power stands at a crossroads. Global energy crises, brought about by the growing independence and politically oriented behavior of some oil-supplying countries, have spurred public and private utilities to look increasingly toward a further dependence on nuclear energy. Early in 1978 this trend resulted in the generation by nuclear plants of more than 13% of the electricity used in the United States.

However, the overall question of nuclear electricity generation and nuclear waste storage is an issue hotly debated by environmentalists. Storage of radioactive waste in the form of spent fuel from nuclear power plants has sometimes been described as a tremendous problem requiring vast underground storage capacities. However, technically qualified specialists in waste storage as well as underground design and construction generally agree that the technical aspects of providing this storage present no major problems. Hammond (1974) advised that a single aspirin tablet represents the volume of spent fuel resulting from the production of 7,000 kW·h of nuclear power. If the entire generation capacity of the United States were through nuclear power, the resulting waste of 350 yr of sustained operation would be a cubic storage volume of 60 m per side. Added to this, the volume of uranium ore required (assuming 0.25% ore and appropriate breeding processing after 1984) would

be an additional ore-excavated space 60×60 m in section and 8 km long. The total volumetric impact of the two components (ore and waste) is about 5.8×10^6 m³. Contrast this with the volume of coal required to generate an equivalent amount of electricity: 1.37×10^{11} m³. The savings of nuclear plants compared with fossil fuel generation plants would be approximately 1.5×10^6 bbl of oil per 1-MW unit per year (Mason, 1976).

The publication of this volume comes at a time of heated debate on the issue of further construction of nuclear power plants. However, those who have made truly in-depth reviews of the energy situation (such as Rose and others, 1976) doubt that the world economy can sustain population growth without continued reliance on nuclear power generation.

As geologists, we will continue to avoid siting nuclear plants in areas where geologic hazards are present or in regions where seismic risk is unduly high. Geologists working for and with applicants and government review agencies can adequately define and design the safety requirements needed to meet geologic hazards. The geologic profession has the responsibility to assure that proper, reasonable, and conservative expertise is provided in the siting of nuclear power plants. This responsibility creates a challenge that geologists must meet by providing high standards of professionalism.

THE REACTOR AS A PHYSICAL PLANT

Nuclear power plants are designed to generate steam to spin turbines that produce electricity. Basically, there is no difference in the operating principle between nuclear and fossil fuel plants. The nuclear steam supply system and the critical nature of its connections with turbines and the outside environment are, however, complex. The nuclear steam supply system consists of the nuclear reactor vessel, steam turbines (generators), reactor coolant pumps, a pressurizer, associated piping, and a large array of auxiliary equipment and instrumentation, all located in the power block (Figs. 1, 2).

The heart of the plant is the Category I power-block structures (Tables 1, 2). The safe operation and shutdown of the plant centers around these high-temperature, high-pressure units. The containment structure is the central building, and the adjacent turbine building houses the turbine generators, condensers, condensate and feedwater pumps, low- and high-pressure feedwater heaters, and various auxiliary equipment. Auxiliary buildings house the fuel storage and handling systems, waste-management systems, most of the engineered safety-control equipment, electrical switchgear, power distribution facilities, and the master control room.

Once-through cooling-water requirements of the plant are met by large (3- to 6-m-diameter) conduits bringing water in from intake structures located at a nearby water source. Naturally, the proximity and elevation of the water supply source are important factors, when one considers the energy consumed in moving large quantities of cooling water. The cooling-water system consists of the basic water supply source or a reservoir and cooling-water tower, the intake structure, circulating and service water pumps, and transport conduits. In designing plants to be located at some distance from sea

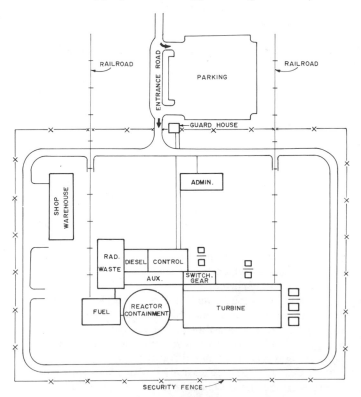

Figure 1. Typical nuclear power plant, PWR (pressurized water reactor).

coasts, large lakes, or rivers, cooling towers are generally stipulated to reduce the quantity of water required.

Reactors come in a variety of types and designs (pressurized water, boiling water, and others). Efforts to control costs and to ensure efficient and safe design have led to some degree of standardization throughout the specialized nuclear steam supply system industry. The plant is generally laid out and designed by architectural-engineering firms specializing in heavy industrial design. Because of escalating costs and long time leads in site licensing, many nuclear plants are designed for multiple units, each generally ranging from 900- to 1,250-MW peak production. The basic production ratings of the proposed units are based on demonstrated and predicted power production needs of the utility, as approved by the State public utility commission.

The process of obtaining permission to build and operate a nuclear plant is based on a successful regulatory review and approval of the License Application. When the utility commits to a nuclear construction program, it prepares documentation concerning the predicted power generation requirements and produces information relating to the relative position the utility holds in the production and sale of electric power. These data are reviewed by State regulatory bodies and, in some cases, by the Federal Power Commission. The process is in parallel with the rest of the licensing application.

Facts concerning the general physical suitability of the site are presented in the Preliminary Safety Analysis Report (PSAR), a detailed document containing a description of the site in terms of geography, demography, meteorology, hydrology, geology, seismology, geotechnical engineering, and a summary

of the design concept and physical layout of the proposed plant. Preparation of the PSAR is often managed by a separate entity within the utility, a consulting firm offering this type of service, or an architectural-engineering firm. Similar siting suitability reports are now required by several of the States (see Davis and others, this volume).

LICENSING PRACTICE IN THE UNITED STATES

Although the siting and operation of nuclear power plants are stringently regulated by the Federal Government and many of the States, there is a powerful interplay of other political and financial forces present in the free-enterprise system. Although the regulatory agencies have, in a sense, control of the speed of construction and operational qualifications, the financial resources and rationale of the utility help influence the pace of licensing. Utilities know that they can engineer and design a plant to fit almost any site, but utilities have found that they cannot predict to what extent geologic conditions will affect the licensing schedule.

In the decade of the 1960s, the utilities were enthusiastic about matching growth predictions for electric power generation demand with an ever-increasing commitment to nuclear power. The Atomic Energy Commission (AEC) became overwhelmed with license applications and, as a result, expanded its staff several fold. Geotechnical reviews, which were previously conducted on a consulting basis by the U.S. Geological Survey and the U.S. Army Corps of Engineers, became an in-house function of the AEC. The trend toward using the consulting government agencies on regional problems and special studies was established. Many of these problems and studies were deemed too extensive for any one applicant to undertake. Contracts were let to State agencies and universities in efforts to obtain much needed geologic and seismic data as rapidly as possible. Licensing has always been governed by Federal law, notably the provisions of Title 10 (Energy) of the *Code of Federal Regulations*, Part 100 (Reactor Site Criteria) (see Code of Federal Regulations, 1978). Appendix A (10 CFR 100) stipulates the studies required to be included in a PSAR. The first Standard Format for Safety Analysis Reports (SARs), which appeared in 1972 in Regulatory Guide 1.70, attempted to better define the requirements for review.

Most workers in power plant siting will agree that the terms of SAR compilation and review changed with the issuance of Regulatory Guide 1.70. For the first time, it was required that a SAR contain certain listed information before the License Application could be considered. This was an attempt to accelerate the review process, as every SAR was compiled according to a standardized format, and required topics were treated in a prescribed order.

The Standard Format brought about a significant revision in the manner in which siting studies were conducted and presented. The Nuclear Regulatory Commission's (NRC) objective was to aid the utility applicants who up to that time were having to make assumptions as to what the regulatory agency would like to have in the way of PSAR documentation. The Standard Format now delineates the requirements of each siting study.

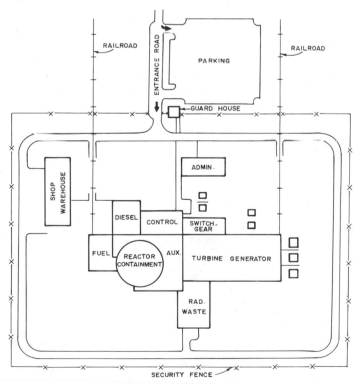

Figure 2. Typical nuclear power plant, BWR (boiling water reactor).

The Licensing Team

To present an acceptable PSAR in minimal time, a utility usually forms a license application team. Because construction of a nuclear power plant is a large and expensive undertaking, a carefully tailored organization is created. It is interesting to note, however, that the cost of modern coal-fired generating stations, complete with emission scrubbers, may equal or exceed that of comparable nuclear generating facilities. Not only must the licensing organization assess the risk associated with safety-related geologic aspects, but it must cope with interveners raising real or imagined safety concerns. Intervention often causes significant schedule delays in the form of injunctions and other legal tactics. Delays in licensing, especially those that develop during the construction stage, are costly. It is estimated that delays during the licensing stage of a two-unit nuclear power plant cost more than $7 million per month and that during the construction stage this cost increased to about $11 million per month.

Because the general undertaking is of such magnitude, a senior utility executive is usually assigned the direct management of the effort. Most of these individuals have extensive nuclear engineering experience and are generally surrounded by a staff experienced in siting, design, and operation. There has been a distinct trend in recent years to place an environmental scientist in a key position on this staff. Gone are the days of siting based solely on the economics of power transmission and distribution.

A matter of prime concern to utility management is the choice of the managing body for the PSAR and associated Environmental Reports. Some utilities prefer to staff for the in-house compilation of the wide spectrum of discipline-oriented data necessary for the NRC review. Few utilities prefer to collect the original data, and there is also a genuine interest in finding an organization to oversee and produce the PSAR and the Environmental Reports. This is currently accomplished in two ways: (1) by delegation to a consulting firm experienced in production of complicated environmentally related assessments or (2) by delegation to a large architectural-engineering firm possessing an arm of equivalent experience. There are many organizations of both types in the United States that are capable of timely and efficient compilation of necessary reports.

As with any large and relatively complicated undertaking, there are the usual problems of coordination and direction. Each of the utilities has its internal SAR management or direction team. Every unexpected action that must be completed to satisfy the NRC or State requirements has an impact on the overall licensing schedule.

Realizing that successful siting is the sum of a complicated array of constituent parts, utilities usually choose a functionally identified SAR team. To this end, the licensing arm of the utility forms a team composed of representatives of all the activities that will eventually be necessary to the siting, design, and construction of the power plant.

Early Site Qualification Studies

Soon after the formulation of a Standard Format and Standard Review Plan (SRP) by the AEC, it became apparent to all parties that acceptance of a proposed nuclear plant site was strongly influenced by geologic and environmental conditions. It had previously been the policy of utilities to begin site evaluation studies with environmental reviews. However, as the provisions of Chapter 2.5 (Geology) of the Standard Format took shape, the importance of geologic qualification became an accepted fact. A few sites in California, Puerto Rico, and New York were abandoned after substantial expenditures already had been made on licensing commitments by the applicant. The sites were abandoned because previously undetected geologic structures were noted or because geologic features were discovered that may have posed a potential licensing problem.

To avoid last-minute delays, utilities have now turned to careful preliminary geologic-geotechnical siting studies designed to ferret out the most important aspects of licensability.

TABLE 1. KEY STRUCTURAL ELEMENTS
OF A TYPICAL, TWO–UNIT NUCLEAR POWER PLANT

Element	Typical plan	Typical uniform dead load	
		(N/m^2)	(psf)
Category I elements*			
Reactor containment	45 m diam	35,900 to 38,300	7,500 to 8,000
Auxiliary building	1,500 m^2	19,100 to 33,500	4,000 to 7,000
Fuel-handling building	900 m^2	19,100 to 28,700	4,000 to 6,000
Intake screen house at cooling-water source	400 m^2	14,400 to 19,100	3,000 to 4,000
Radioactive-waste building	1,500 to 2,400 m^2	12,000 to 28,700	2,500 to 6,000
Non-Category I elements			
Turbine generator building	4,400 to 9,000 m^2	21,500 to 23,900	4,500 to 5,000
Service building	100 to 150 m^2	12,000 to 14,400	2,500 to 3,000
Turbine pedestal	800 to 1,150 m^2	26,300 to 28,700	5,500 to 6,000

*Category I elements are those designated as being critical to safe operation and shutdown of the plant.

In answer to this requirement, in 1977 the NRC instituted a formal Early Site Review (ESR) process. In this ESR process, the Site Analysis Branch (SAB) undertakes to judge the general site suitability on the basis of a report similar to a PSAR, but containing only as much preliminary information and detail as the utility is willing to provide at this stage. The burden still rests on the utility as applicant to commit itself to a level of expenditure commensurate with its assessment of the licensing risk. A favorable NRC opinion in an ESR is generally considered a satisfactory assurance that no condemning geologic or seismologic problems exist.

Some utilities conduct limited preliminary site geologic-geotechnical studies, structured along the PSAR format, but bear the responsibility of risk assessment internally, without recourse to an NRC mini-review. Studies of this nature are often made as part of a long-range generation development plan and are the basis for preselection of likely power plant sites before other uses can preempt the sites. Such sites are prequalified to the satisfaction of the utility and its consultants and may be held in waiting while the political, financial, and consumer-demand facets of new plant construction are evaluated.

The Licensing Procedure

Licensing of nuclear electricity-generation facilities is governed by a procedure specified in Title 10 of the *Code of Federal Regulations* (see Code of Federal Regulations, 1978) (Fig. 3). However, as in the case of all regulatory procedures, numerous variations are affected by the legal representatives of both the applicant and the regulatory agency. The variations do not produce shortcuts, rather they are primarily focused on the relative speed at which the application is presented and reviewed. In the eyes of the regulatory agency, the applicant must produce the evidence in support of the application in a complete, honest, and forthright manner, in terms of the PSAR or ESR packages. Much of this material is also presented in oral briefings and testimony before the NRC at meetings held at the Bethesda, Maryland, headquarters and by field visits to the proposed site. In any case, disclosures must be complete, factual, and clearly presented. Brevity and clarity of presentation should be borne in mind, for the reviewing parties have been subjected to a continual stream of such technical presentations over the years.

We recognize that there are variations in tenure and scope of licensing applications, but the theme remains the same: a structured process of review (Fig. 3). Our assessment of the process is as follows:

Decision to Commit. Utility planners, aware of capital funding and continuing cash-flow requirements, assess the generation capability on a regular basis. Utilities actively promote the conservation of electricity and endeavor to keep pace with its consumption, based on economic and social trends over which they have little control. The unusually long lead times for addition of new generation facilities weigh heavily on these planners. For instance, 10 to 13 yr are now required for addition of a functional nuclear generating station; 7 to 10 yr for a fossil fuel station. As a meeting of the minds comes from discussions between planners and managers, decisions are made as to a "mix" of generation and distribution, often considering complex arrangements of partnership in generation with adjacent utilities and "peak-load" transfer of electric power between utilities. Electric power is a unique manufactured product; it cannot be economically stored. Generation to consumption time is generally no longer than the short interval of transmission between the generator and the consumer.

Federal and State regulations require that the applicant demonstrate (1) need to generate the electric power, (2) financial solvency to complete each project so undertaken, and (3) a nonmonopolistic position in the industry. The evidence needed to substantiate favorable aspects of these requirements is comprehensive. The licensing procedure begins with the above disclosure and cannot continue without satisfactory resolution of all issues.

As the utility begins to assemble the non-geotechnical data, it has the option of beginning to search for and qualify the risk associated with final proof of its contemplated and alternative sites. Many utilities have found that a regional site-selection study is a logical first step toward identification of likely candidates for primary and alternative site studies.

A genuine need for electrical power production must be demonstrated in the Environmental Report portion of the Lincense Application. In addition, the NRC requires that the Environmental Report include an evaluation of viable site alternatives. This is, of course, in the best interest of the utility and its customers, should the primary site encounter extreme licensing difficulties. Initial site comparative studies concentrate on favorable geologic conditions and seismic risk.

When the utility begins the licensing application procedure, it implements site-specific studies designed to produce a PSAR, the large and complex document upon which the site is judged for suitability in terms of possible safety-related hazards. The scope of this engineering geology review volume is to deal with the content of Section 2.5 of the Standard Format for SARs as to geologic, seismological, and geotechnical engineering aspects.

At the time a site-specific geologic (includes all aspects of

TABLE 2. PLAN FOR A TYPICAL NUCLEAR POWER PLANT

Element	PWR	BWR
Category I elements*		
Reactor containment	42 m diam	42 m diam
Auxiliary building	2,047 m²	2,647 m²
Fuel-handling building	854 m²	881 m²
Radioactive-waste building	1,377 m²	1,587 m²
Control building	866 m²	866 m²
Diesel generator building	493 m²	875 m²
Non-Category I elements		
Turbine generator building	4,227 m²	4,142 m²
Turbine pedestal	792 m²	792 m²
Switchgear building	360 m²	360 m²

Note: PWR = pressurized water reactor; BWR = boiling water reactor.

*Category I elements are those designated as being critical to safe operation and shutdown of the plant.

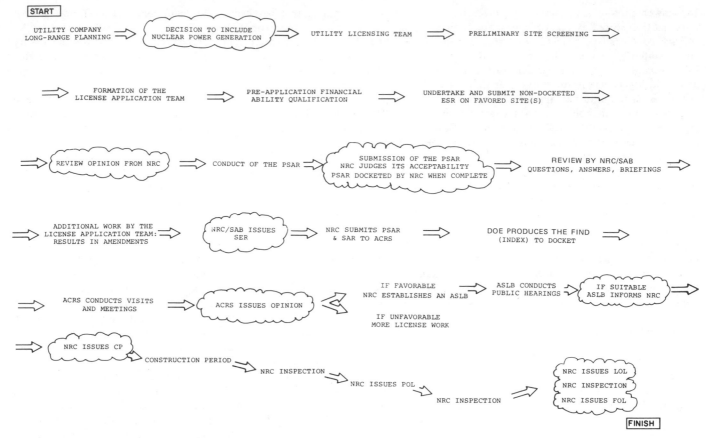

Figure 3. Conduct of licensing for a nuclear power plant.

Section 2.5) study is undertaken, be it at the PSAR, ESR, or at a more limited site-qualification level, the utility has gained options or otherwise controls parcels of land sufficient to fulfill all the physical requirements of siting. Representatives of the utility often introduce the contract investigators to the residents of the area at meetings arranged to inform them of the project and its planned activities.

Field operations in siting are often seasonal, and utilities have found that site qualification is difficult to schedule for completion within a 12-mo period. The more complex PSAR-level studies may require 24 mo or more for collection and analysis of data. Complete internal review of all data, as generated, is a must for all siting studies. Continued results are best reviewed and assimilated by other partners to the study, such as structural engineers, seismologists, and hydrologists. Draft compilations are released to all parties at phased intervals.

When the document is judged complete by the PSAR manager and the utility applicant, multiple copies are released to NRC for acceptance review prior to "docketing." As soon as the PSAR is deemed adequate, NRC officials accept and docket the document, and the formal application review process begins.

The NRC Division of Site Safety and Environmental Analysis is responsible to the Office of Nuclear Reactor Regulation for certification of site safety. Review by the several branches is coordinated through the Division of Project Management. Upon receipt of the completed and docketed PSAR, the Site

Analysis Branch (SAB) begins a thorough technical review of the contents. Review policy makes provision for an exchange of questions from NRC to the utility and a subsequent return of answers. In practice, this exchange often goes into two or more sets of questions. Replies are incorporated into the PSAR as amendments. On issues that remain unresolved, the NRC transmits a position to the applicant who then may contest or develop additional data. Morris (this volume) details the nature of the review process.

The SARs are public documents and are available through the National Technical Information Service (NTIS) of the Department of Commerce.

Frequently, issues raised during the review of the PSAR will require meetings and exchange of information on the part of the SAB team, the utility, and the geologic and seismologic consultants. Supplementary site visits are often scheduled, mainly to review questionable geologic features.

When the SAB team completes its review, it prepares a Safety Evaluation Report (SER) which states the position of the NRC staff. Unresolved safety issues, if any, remain as "open items" which will require additional study or explanation. The Environmental Reports and the PSAR are submitted to the congressionally established Advisory Committee on Reactor Safeguards (ACRS) for independent review by subcommittees of experts not in governmental service.

By this time, the amount of documentation materials associated with the PSAR is formidable. The NRC in contract with the Department of Energy (DOE) has compiled a literature index of the docketed material. This very useful summary, known as the Fiche Index to Nuclear Dockets (FIND), is produced prior to review by the ACRS and is designed to assist the ACRS in its overall assessment.

Numerous meetings and visits are held by the ACRS in conjunction with its review of each plant site. If the ACRS deems the site suitable, it sends a letter to the NRC stating its position and indicating that, in its judgment, the plant can be constructed without undue risk to the health and safety of the public. Those findings are then submitted to the Atomic Safety and Licensing Board (ASLB) which conducts public hearings and a final comprehensive review. Providing the site and plant are found suitable, the ASLB informs the NRC that a Construction Permit may be granted. In lieu of a Construction Permit, a Limited Work Authorization permit is also available from the NRC. This is a conditional permit to perform work that will not unduly disturb the environment in the event that future work stoppages are required in the course of the review procedure.

The construction license period terminates with inspection of the plant and issuance of a Possession Only License, followed by a Limiting Operating License to begin generation of electric power. As the operation is provided in stages, the authorized output is increased through successive Limiting Operating Licenses until a Full Operating License is granted to the utility. According to Morris (this volume) some 10 to 13 yr may be required to gain a Full Operating License.

NATURE OF SAR GEOLOGY

License application studies require a blend of both classical geologic principles and engineering geologic practices. For the most part, utility managers are usually engineers; the NRC project manager is likely to be an engineer; and the users of the geologic data are structural and civil engineers. What forms the difficult basis of reconciliation in this blend of classical and engineering geology is that the reviewers at the regulatory agencies are, by and large, classical geologists. However, the critical issues surrounding nuclear plant licensing are those to be solved or resolved using techniques as broad as the spectrum of geology itself.

This blend of classical and engineering geology is knit together by the thread of applicability; the presentation by the applicant and its consultants must be (1) thorough, (2) accurate, and (3) timely. If the applicant attempts to employ less than state-of-the-art techniques, the regulatory reviewers will judge the study wanting. A reaction of this sort is to be expected, as the regulatory staff has been bombarded by endless series of theories and arguments, all tested by generous allocations of applicant's funding and backed up by the best geologic minds available. Because of the demanding circumstances in which the regulatory team works, SAR submittals that are found to be less than accurate in terms of logic, interpretation of references, or in quality of field work subject the entire submittal to greater scrutiny on the part of the reviewers. Incomplete or unacceptable submittals result in costly schedule delays.

MANAGEMENT OF GEOLOGIC STUDIES

Effective management of these geologic investigations requires using the best available professional skills experienced in this type of effort to achieve valid evaluation, high production, timely response, cost effectiveness, accuracy, and communication—all basic to the conduct of geologic studies in support of the License Application. The selection of the management technical team should include careful consideration of its technical and licensing experience and ability to organize and direct various highly specialized scientific specialists.

Added to the critical procedure of selecting the best of compatible managerial and technical skills is the fact that geologic-geotechnical licensing studies must be coordinated with numerous other activities involving licensing and design. They begin as a concerted effort to define geologic conditions, but later evolve into application of those conditions to other areas such as seismology and ultimately structural engineering. After this shift in emphasis, some difficult but basic decisions must be resolved among geologists, seismologists, and the various engineering disciplines.

Communication

Communication is basic to licensing. The cost of licensing investigations by geologists and their related field operation amount to literally tens of thousands of dollars per day in expenditures. The field observations and data collected are analyzed and evaluated. Various interpretations are proposed, assessed, and revised, and an overall understanding developed among the various geologists and engineers responsible for guiding each part of a licensing study.

It is difficult for the structural engineer to provide guidelines on the location and depth of structural embedment without a specific model of dynamic properties. Through trial and error, the circle of uncertainty decreases; the geologist produces more detailed stratigraphic information; the foundation specialist provides more physical property data and dynamic moduli; the seismologist provides better estimates of ground motion for design; and, finally, the structural engineer establishes load and geometric parameters. Throughout each of the iterations, an effort must be made to develop more reliable design data based on previous findings.

Based on historical seismicity, regional geology, and site foundation conditions, the seismologist provides reasonable estimates of the magnitude, duration, frequency content, recurrence interval, and probable ground acceleration levels that may be anticipated at the site. The Safe Shutdown Earthquake is developed using these parameters which govern the seismic response of the plant and require its shutdown for inspection should such motion occur. The seismologist develops the design earthquake, its assumed epicentral location, and attenuates this energy to the site. The foundation engineer uses these data for liquefaction analysis at those sites where structures are located on soil or poorly consolidated sediments. Dynamic structural response, per se, is calculated by the structural engineer but using parameters developed by the geotechnical engineer and the seismologist.

The structural engineer cannot deliver the wave model to the base of the containment vessel without the assistance of the geologist and seismologist who developed the physical model into which the dynamic shear moduli and damping ratios are placed. The very complex questions of interaction between the model and the structure are considered in the evaluation of soil-structure interaction (including rock sites). These studies are generally the responsibility of the structural engineer.

State-of-the-Art in Licensing Studies

One aspect of siting that has resulted in considerable discussion involves the historical development of positions taken by regulatory agencies as a result of repeated exposure to various license applications. Available theory and fact are continually being judged by NRC and ACRS subcommittees, and agency position trends begin to emerge. Geologists involved in siting must be well versed on the content and substance of those cases and decisions that have influenced agency positions.

Decisions on these topics are rendered by the regulatory agencies as the result of NRC review questions, ACRS subcommittee meetings, and ASLB hearings. The results of these decisions become common knowledge throughout the siting community. Additional documentation thus becomes available to those who follow developments at nearby plants or at sites that bear some geologic or geotechnical resemblance to the site or sites of interest. Findings of the NRC are made a part of the public record. NRC policy dictates that all transactions of licensing activities are to be made available for public inspection at a designated public library near the proposed plant site. Complete files of appropriate data are available to the public at the five regional offices of the NRC. Most large, technically oriented universities maintain in the government publications section of their libraries microfiche files of SAR documents. All public meetings and the release of summary documents are announced in the *Federal Register*.

PITFALLS OF LICENSING

The scenario for conducting a geologic-geotechnical licensing study is not written, rather it unfolds. The applicant's project manager, something of a producer-director, sets the activity into motion and modulates its efforts. Also, because geologic conditions at no two sites are alike, each licensing effort must become a case-by-case exercise.

A well-planned licensing effort operates on a task and milepost-oriented schedule. The schedule is structured to provide timely data submissions to other partners in the project. What the schedule cannot manage to accommodate is the less-than-predictable variables such as geologic conditions, weather, and team productivity. Such variations may introduce serious deviations in the project scheduling.

Critical situations in terms of scheduling may come from overconfidence on the part of the geologic-geotechnical organization; more is promised in the haste of enthusiasm or in the rush to promote services than reasonably can be expected. An example is that of hedging to avoid the penalties of time and to gain a favorable review by regulatory personnel. An attempt is often made to buy both time and favorable review by overcommitting personnel and equipment to separate tasks of the study. NRC officials frequently recognize this potential "overkill," but this is not their concern. The economic impact of overkill rests entirely on the applicant.

Considerable overkill results from attempts to second-guess the regulatory agencies—a common applicant-consultant indulgence before and after briefings and hearings before the NRC.

Pitfalls are usually attributable either to errors in human judgment or to the fact that some sites are inherently unlicensable. The human errors often result from unreasonable assessments of the nature of specific tasks, from overzealous commitments, from over-reaction to regulatory assessments, from inabilities to discuss progress and goals with the utility, and from unrealistic attempts to buy time with increased resource commitments. The avoidance of pitfalls should be a major concern of the applicant during the continuing assessment of team progress and performance.

WHY SITES HAVE FAILED TO BE LICENSED

The NRC does not normally categorically reject the site proposed in the licensing application, but by refusing to accept proposed explanations for geologic findings, a rejection of the site is effectively accomplished. When geologic conditions are judged to be critical and unfavorable, they generally appear so unequivocally. Sites have been abandoned for the following reasons or combination of reasons: (1) unfavorable geologic findings, (2) unresolved geologic conditions, (3) unmanageable geotechnical conditions, (4) exhaustion of the applicant's funds, or (5) a "loss-of-heart" on the part of the applicant.

A site with a tectonic fault is an example of an unfavorable geologic finding. Unresolved geologic findings constitute the most frustrating aspects of siting. Often there seems to be ample supporting evidence that the site is suitable in terms of safety, but it cannot be proved to the satisfaction of the NRC. Federal regulations specify an arbitrary age of last activity for faulting that can be accommodated in the near-site area. What is unfortunate, however, is that the causative mechanisms are not treated separately. Nontectonic features such as growth faults and isostatic readjustments may not be subject to differentiation, but have been treated on a case-by-case basis by the NRC. Until the *Code of Federal Regulations* is amended, a small percentage of sites, particularly in the north-central, northeastern, and southwestern states, may remain unlicensable.

Unmanageable geotechnical conditions generally deal with potential or actual forms of instability in the foundation materials beneath the power block. Most of these conditions can be corrected by the application of known engineering principles. For instance, in limestone terranes, it may be that grout injection of solution cavities may totally solidify the subsurface and result in an acceptable bearing capacity; however, the geologic conditions may be so questionable that the applicant utility is unwilling to spend the funds required to completely grout, permanently dewater, or otherwise provide major corrective treatment.

If the siting effort lasts more than 3 or 4 yr, the applicant utility may find itself beyond fiscal capability to continue the project. This has been the case when the protraction of seismically related questions exceeds the patience of one or more partners in the venture, and withdrawals force a reassessment on behalf of the major owner of the plant. The plant is then normally "shelved" while the major owner applicant seeks to restructure the financial obligations of underwriting the plant licensing and construction. Meanwhile, inflation continues to raise the overall cost of the project. What were $200- to $400-million ventures of a decade ago are now (1978) costing in excess of $1 billion. Some Federal and State agencies are advising that utilities strongly consider initiation of seismic studies within their franchise or cooperative electricity pool areas for use in predicting licensability of future site selections. While the drain on resources continues, the protracted nature of siting and construction in the 1970s now approaches 11 to 13 yr from the initiation of the PSAR to the granting of the Full Operating License.

SUMMARY OF SITING

Since the time that the first commercial power reactor went on stream in 1959, tremendous strides have been made in understanding the effects of regional and local geology surrounding the more than 60 existing plants. As the regulatory process has evolved, so have the environmental and sociological problems that envelop nuclear power.

Interveners, blocked by other avenues of approach in their quest to preserve natural conditions as they are, or were, have used the regulatory process, mandated by Congress as a safety-related measure, to further their environmental goals. The licensing process of the seventies has developed into an unsettled atmosphere of legalistic uncertainty surrounding the efforts of conscientious scientists and engineers who strive to find reasonable answers to tomorrow's problems using today's technology.

A profound increase of scientific knowledge has resulted from the many geologic and geotechnical studies completed in support of nuclear power plant licensing. This volume has as its purpose a thoughtful divulgence of concepts and techniques that have been hard-won and that are presented in the hope that geologists will continue to interact with the environment without detriment to society.

ACKNOWLEDGMENTS

We sincerely thank the following people for their careful and detailed manuscript critiques: Robert H. Morris, John W. Bardgett, M. J. Ray, A. F. Zallnick, John R. Rand, Joseph D. LeBlanc, Robert H. Fakundiny, J. W. Skrove, and Peter F. Mason.

APPENDIX 1. SAFETY ANALYSIS REPORTS AND RELATED DOCUMENTS: DEFINITIONS AND SEARCH AND RETRIEVAL INFORMATION

A wealth of useful data for geologists and geotechnical engineers are contained in the SARs submitted to the NRC for the licensing of nuclear power plants in the United States. The licensing program involves a stringent review procedure as specified in the *Code of Federal Regulations*, Title 10, Part 50. As of 1978, more than 240 separate generating units are in planning, construction, or are operating. Each nuclear station is generally designed for construction of two or three separate generating units. Approval for construction and operation follows only after conduct of an extensive PSAR and a FSAR. Both SAR versions contain comprehensive compilations of existing and newly acquired geologic and geotechnical data, both regional and site-specific. The studies making up the reports are prepared for the applicant electric utility by consulting geologists, seismologists, and geotechnical engineers.

Early Site Review Report (ESRR)

An undocketed mini-PSAR delivered by the applicant utility to the NRC to gain an official position as to the licensability of the site in selected areas of geologic and seismic considerations. A provision for making these positions binding was introduced in 1977. The ESRR is not released to the public through government document distribution offices of the Department of Commerce, but is available for inspection at the NRC headquarters and regional offices.

Preliminary Safety Analysis Report (PSAR)

The document upon which the NRC and its independent, congressionally chartered review board, the ACRS, acts in review of the site for a license to construct. The PSAR must be compiled according to the NRC stipulated format. Upon initial submittal of the PSAR, the assigned NRC project manager must determine if the document is basically complete with respect to format and inclusion of all data components. If judged complete, the PSAR is docketed and officially accepted for review. The Construction Permit is issued or rejected on the basis of information contained in the PSAR. As the review is undertaken, the need for clarifications and additional work is generally sensed by the SAB, the NRC personnel who conduct the actual technical assessment of geologic, seismologic, and geotechnical data. Required changes and supplementary data consist of the following:

Questions. Questions are supplied by NRC to the applicant utility and require formal action as amendments of supplemental reports to the PSAR.

Revisions. Revisions are officially submitted changes to the PSAR text. They account for corrections of errors in the text and contain responses to official questions delivered to the utility by NRC. Revisions are contained in amendments.

Amendments. Amendments are the officially submitted package of changes to the PSAR. New and revised pages are arranged for posting in the original document (obsolete pages are removed).

Supplemental Reports. Supplemental reports are furnished as official documents, but do not result in revision pages. They are generally wide-scope answers to NRC questions. Such reports are not within the paginated body of the PSAR, rather they are separate items appearing under the docket number of the proposed nuclear power plant.

Final Safety Analysis Report (FSAR)

This is the document upon which the NRC acts in its review for the site operating license after construction is completed. The FSAR presents expanded new data in the form of geologic conditions exposed during construction, notably those in the form of face and floor maps of the excavated foundation area. The FSAR contains only a brief summary of the PSAR geologic, seismological, and geotechnical findings.

The Docket Number

Each plant is identified by its NRC docket number (for example, 50389 is the docket number assigned to the Florida Power and Light Company, St. Lucie Plant, Unit 2). To the original docket number is added a dash and an accession number, furnished by the Technical Information Center (TIC) of the DOE for specific supplementary information filed (for example, Docket 50443-7; PSAR, vol. 2, Public Service Company of New Hampshire, Seabrook Station, Units 1 and 2, June 1973, 558 p). An accession number is given to a packet of revision materials, appearing as an amendment (for example, Docket 40376-117; PSAR, Amendment No. 30, Puerto Rico Water Resources Authority, North Coast Nuclear Plant, Unit 1, December 1975, 1340 p). A supplementary report also receives a sequential accession number (for example, Docket 50466-127; PSAR; Memorandum of the Effect of Subsidence on the Safety of the Station, Houston Lighting and Power Company, Allens Creek Nuclear Generating Station, Units 1 and 2, March 1974, 10 p). The dashed number is needed to order a specific document from the library or from NTIS.

Search and Retrieval of SAR Documents. The selection process for identifying individual SAR chapters, amendments, or pages of interest should proceed as follows:

1. Choose the appropriate NRC docket number by consulting publications Nos. 3 or 5 from the list of government publications that follows, or by telephone request to the NRC Public Information Office in Washington, D.C., or the nearest regional NRC office.

2. Order or inspect the Fiche Index to Nuclear Dockets (FIND—publication No. 6 from the list that follows) for the plant site. An alternative would be to browse through the Power Reactor Docket Information (publication No. 5 following) which lists accession numbers (NTIS order numbers) for all plants, but not in as handy a form as FIND. FIND lists the microfiche or hard-copy SAR volume that contains the desired data; it identifies amendments and supplements.

3. Request a loan of the microfiche from the nearest depository library, or remit the standard microfiche packet price to the National Technical Information Service (NTIS), Springfield, Virginia 22150, for each docket requested. Prices for hard copy vary depending on the number of pages; prices are quoted in government bibliographic announcements.

4. Scan the microfiche and print the pages that you wish to keep. Most large public and university libraries have reader-printer machines that make hard copies for about ten cents per page. Small, hand-held readers may be purchased for under $50.

U.S. Government Publications to Consult in Search and Retrieval of SAR Documents

1. Code of Federal Regulations, Title 10, Energy; Parts 0-199: U.S. Nuclear Regulatory Commission, Washington, D.C.
2. Regulatory Guide 1.70, Standard Format and Content of Safety Analysis Reports for Nuclear Power Plants: U.S. Nuclear Regulatory Commission Information Office, Washington, D.C.
3. Facilities License Application Record: U.S. Nuclear Regulatory Commission Information Office, Washington, D.C.
4. Nuclear Power Reactors in the U.S.; Index map and abbreviated information: U.S. Nuclear Regulatory Commission Information Office, Washington, D.C.
5. Power Reactor Docket Information: Department of Energy, Oak Ridge, Tennessee.
6. Fiche Index to Nuclear Documents (FIND): Available for each plant having a docketed PSAR (see paragraph 3 under Search and Retrieval of SAR Documents).
7. U.S. Energy, Research and Development Administration, 1975, Nuclear Reactors, Built, Being Built, or Planned: U.S. Department of Energy, National Technical Information Service, Springfield, Virginia 22150, Report TID-8200-R31, 41 p.

REFERENCES CITED

Code of Federal Regulations, 1978, Title 10, Energy; Part 50 [10 CFR 50], Domestic licensing of production and utilization facilities; Appendix B, Quality assurance criteria for nuclear power plants and fuel processing plants: Washington, D.C., U.S. Nuclear Regulatory Commission.

Code of Federal Regulations, 1978, Title 10, Energy; Part 100 [10 CFR 100], Reactor site criteria; Appendix A, Seismic and geologic siting criteria for nuclear power plants: Washington, D.C., U.S. Nuclear Regulatory Commission.

Davis, J. F., Slosson, J. E., and Fakundiny, R. H., 1979, The State-Federal partnership in siting of nuclear power plants, in Hatheway, A. W., and McClure, C. R., Jr., eds., Geology in the siting of nuclear power plants: Geological Society of America Reviews in Engineering Geology, v. IV (this volume).

Hammond, R. P., 1974, Nuclear power risks: American Scientist, v. 62, p. 155–160.

Mason, E. A., 1977, The future of nuclear power in meeting the nation's energy needs [Address by NRC Commissioner Mason before Panel on Energy Resources for the Future, held at Massachusetts Institute of Technology, Cambridge]: U.S. Nuclear Regulatory Commission, Press Release, 4 March 1977.

Morris, R. H., 1979, Geologic reports used in evaluation of nuclear reactor sites, in Hatheway, A. W. and McClure, C. R., Jr., eds., Geology in the siting of nuclear power plants: Geological Society of America Reviews in Engineering Geology, v. IV (this volume).

Regulatory Guide 1.70, 1975, Standard Format and content of Safety Analysis Reports for nuclear power plants: Washington, D.C., U.S. Nuclear Regulatory Commission, revision 2.

Rose, D. J., Walsh, P. W., and Leskovjan, L. L., 1976, Nuclear power—Compared to what: American Scientist, v. 64, p. 291–299.

U.S. Nuclear Regulatory Commission, 1977, Early site reviews for nuclear power facilities; procedures and possible review options: Washington, D.C., U.S. Nuclear Regulatory Commission, Office of Nuclear Reactor Regulation, NUREG-0180, available from NTIS as PB 266 826.

U.S. Nuclear Regulatory Commission, 1975, Standard review plan: Washington, D.C., U.S. Nuclear Regulatory Commission, Office of Nuclear Reactor Regulation, NUREG-75/087.

Weinberg, A. M., 1976, the maturity and future of nuclear energy: American Scientist, v. 64, p. 16–21.

MANUSCRIPT RECEIVED BY THE SOCIETY JULY 13, 1978
MANUSCRIPT ACCEPTED NOVEMBER 13, 1978

Geological Society of America
Reviews in Engineering Geology, Volume IV
1979

A three-phase program of investigation for site selection and development

J. A. CAGGIANO, JR.*
D'Appolonia Consulting Engineers, Inc., 10 Duff Road, Pittsburgh, Pennsylvania 15235

ABSTRACT

The selection of a site and the development of geologic and seismic design parameters may be facilitated through the use of a three-phase program of investigation. This program is cost effective and expedites management decisions that benefit from current relevant geologic information. A resource review and regional reconnaissance during Phase I serve to eliminate areas of low potential, to focus on favorable areas, and to identify possible problems that may require further study. Preliminary estimates of certain design parameters during Phase I may be used to initiate contract negotiations with a plant supplier. Candidate sites and associated problems can then be examined through analysis of large-scale maps and imagery, preliminary geologic mapping, and subsurface investigation during Phase II. Phase II may lead to preparation of an Early Site Review Report (ESRR) for submission to the Nuclear Regulatory Commission (NRC). A Phase III investigation leading to the preparation of a Preliminary Safety Analysis Report (PSAR) can be performed concurrently or sequentially on any or all candidate sites recommended at the conclusion of Phase III.

This approach is illustrated with examples from Spain and Iran showing how such a program assists in selection and study of possible sites.

INTRODUCTION

The United States, along with many other nations, is currently facing an energy dilemma; annual energy consumption for the present and the immediate future exceeds domestic energy production (Risser, 1973). This dilemma is compounded by the increasing demand for preservation of a quality environment that has led to restrictions on production and combustion of certain fossil fuels. Nowhere is this more apparent than in

the generation of electricity. Energy to drive turbine generators has come largely from combustion of fossil fuels. Increasing demands for electricity have accentuated the need to develop nonpolluting sources of energy to drive turbines, as well as to relieve a growing dependence on imported fuels.

SPECIAL PROBLEMS IN SITING

Facilities housing nuclear reactors are unique in the number and diversity of safety-related factors that must be considered in their location and design. This concern with safety of nuclear reactors has led to a degree of sophistication in locating and designing the plants that perhaps has not been approached in any other industry. Many elements of safety are governed by the nature of the region and the site on which a reactor will be constructed. Determination of regional and site characteristics that affect the safety and design of a plant is the realm of the geologist and is of particular concern to this volume.

In addition to the safety-related aspects of siting, the National Environmental Policy Act (NEPA) of 1969 places a legal as well as a moral commitment on the owner to determine the impact of nuclear power plants and their by-products on the health and welfare of man and the environment. Any potentially adverse impact on an ecosystem through the construction, operation, or the discharges of a nuclear power plant must be assessed and satisfactorily resolved before construction may begin.

STEPS IN CONSTRUCTION

The licensing of a nuclear power plant entails three major processes: (1) selecting a site, (2) obtaining a permit to construct the plant, and (3) obtaining a permit to operate the plant. A utility or group of utilities (hereafter referred to as the applicant) selects a site and then attempts to license the site. Prime and alternate sites are commonly selected by consultants who are familiar with planning and conducting an investigation.

Once a site is chosen, the applicant prepares a Preliminary

---

*Present address: Rockwell Hanford Operations, P.O. Box 800, Richland, Washington 99352.

Safety Analysis Report (PSAR), which is then submitted to the Nuclear Regulatory Commission (NRC)[1] (see Adair, this volume). The PSAR is carefully reviewed by the NRC and its consultants to ensure that the investigation (1) has considered all pertinent data and interpretations in the published or available literature (with proper citations), (2) has employed state-of-the-art techniques for analysis and interpretation of data, (3) has satisfactorily addressed all areas of concern as specified in published criteria for siting a nuclear power plant, (4) has carefully integrated new data and interpretations with published ideas, (5) has included all required and necessary maps, plans, and cross sections for presenting regional and site characteristics, and (6) has been reported in accordance with the specified format for report preparation (see Morris, this volume). The Standard Review Plan (U.S. Nuclear Regulatory Commission, 1975) guides the review of a PSAR.

After a thorough review by the NRC and its consultants, the applicant may be (1) granted a permit to construct the facility, (2) advised of modifications or additional investigations that may be necessary before the PSAR will be reviewed again by the NRC, or (3) informed that the site is not considered acceptable for construction of the proposed plant. In the United States the evaluative process includes public hearings and a review by the Advisory Committee on Reactor Safeguards (ACRS). Sites that have been rejected and abandoned after many supplemental investigations and revisions of the initial PSAR are costly to the applicant and should be avoided whenever possible.

Upon issuance of the construction permit, the plant is completed according to the design specified in the PSAR. A Final Safety Analysis Report (FSAR) is then submitted to the NRC. The FSAR has two objectives: (1) to assure that the plant has been constructed according to the approved design, and (2) to assure that all systems have been subjected to a careful and thorough analysis and inspection to ensure safe operation. Once accepted, the plant is granted an operating license. Legislation has been enacted in several States requiring State review of power plant license applications (see Davis and others, this volume). This review may be made at the same time or after review by the NRC. As the requirements vary, the code of regulations for a particular State should be considered (Evans, 1976).

The steps outlined above are those followed in the United States. Because the United States has been building nuclear power plants for a longer period of time and has more operating plants than any other nation, the techniques and procedures used to select and determine the safety of sites for nuclear power plants have been used extensively as a model throughout the world. In many countries, the criteria used to determine site suitability and safety are those of the NRC and have been adopted verbatim. Other countries have adopted their own regulations which are patterned after those of the International Atomic Energy Agency (IAEA), as well as the NRC. Safety criteria of various areas relative to faults and earthquakes are given in Table 1. Recognition of United States expertise and

experience has led to the participation of many United States consultants in the licensing activities of many foreign utilities.

CONDUCTING AN INVESTIGATION IN PHASES

Schedule delays and costs increase with the length of the investigations and PSAR preparation; therefore, every effort should be made to minimize these tasks through the careful selection of a site. Undesirable sites usually can be eliminated quickly if money and effort are expended early in the licensing process. It is important for the applicant to be informed of the cost-benefit ratio for each candidate site in an expeditious manner; therefore, investigations should be conducted in phases. In this way, information can be quickly passed from consultant to applicant so that informed decisions can be made on whether suitable sites exist, which areas seem technically preferable, and what problems might be anticipated. A sequenced program of investigation is especially valuable in tectonically complex areas where the potential for constructing a nuclear power plant can be assessed with a minimum expenditure of time and money.

An investigation in three phases can be used to (1) expedite site selection, (2) determine site characteristics, (3) facilitate decision making, (4) initiate communication with the NRC and/or research groups, and (5) begin plant supply contract negotiations based on preliminary design estimates.

The three phases leading to selection and licensing of a site may de summarized:

1. Phase I is a regional survey designed to eliminate unsuitable or problem areas and identify potential areas for sites. Phase I consists of a review of existing literature, maps, and imagery at small scales ($\leq 1:500,000$) as well as reconnaissance-level field work.

2. Phase II consists of investigations of candidate sites through analysis and interpretation of large-scale maps and imagery, preliminary geologic mapping, and investigations of subsurface conditions.

3. Phase III consists of the preparation of a PSAR on the chosen site. Figure 1, an operational flow chart, illustrates the sequence of tasks.

PHASE I. SELECTION AND RECONNOITERING CANDIDATE AREAS

Selection of Criteria

In order to facilitate selection of good sites, criteria to be used in the selection and licensing process must first be established. Federal and State regulations provide guidelines for many of the conditions to be investigated in selecting and licensing sites. Some of these Federal guidelines are the "Seismic and Geologic Siting Criteria for Nuclear Power Plants" (Code of Federal Regulations, 1978) and various Regulatory Guides, including the "Standard Format and Content of Safety Analysis Reports for Nuclear Power Plants" (Regulatory Guide 1.70, 1975). Criteria of the various States are generally similar to those of the NRC but may have unique,

---

[1]The Nuclear Regulatory Commission (NRC) is used throughout this paper. For other countries, readers should substitute the name(s) of appropriate regulatory group(s).

geographically related aspects that affect the choice of guidelines. Criteria and design guides for siting and licensing nuclear power plants have been developed by the governments of Japan (Hisada and others, 1972), the Federal Republic of Germany, Italy, France, and Switzerland (Stevenson, 1975), as well as the IAEA (International Atomic Energy Agency, 1972). The Atomic Energy Control Board of Canada also has an unpublished draft of design guides. Criteria are under development in other countries, but use of existing criteria of other agencies may be required or recommended. As a minimum, these criteria stipulate the type of information required, some of the procedures to be employed, and the limits of the areas to be investigated. As seen in Table 1, two levels of earthquakes are generally considered in design, but the manner in which they are determined and the extent of investigation vary. In addition, other factors limiting the selection of a site may be

TABLE 1 EARTHQUAKE AND FAULT SAFETY CRITERIA FOR NUCLEAR POWER PLANTS

Country/Agency	Faults	Earthquakes
U.S.A.*	Capable 1. Movement in last 35,000 yr; more than 1 movement in last 500,000 yr 2. Connected to capable fault 3. Instrumentally recorded and located events, or creep along fault	Safe Shutdown Earthquake (SSE): Maximum potential earthquake considering regional (200 mi radius) geology and historical seismicity Operating Basis Earthquake (OBE): 1. Maximum expected during 40-yr life of plant 2. $\geq 1/2$ SSE 3. Plant to remain in operation during this event
International Atomic Energy Agency	Capable 1. Movement in late Quarternary 2. Topographic evidence of surface rupture 3. Instrumentally recorded and located events or creep along fault 4. Connected to capable fault	Regional Design Earthquake: Strongest expected earthquake in region (area unspecified) of site Site Design Earthquake (SDE): Regional design earthquake modified to take into account site features—allows unit to be safely shut down
Federal Republic of Germany	Not addressed	Safety Earthquake: Maximum expected earthquake in area (up to 200 km) based on existing knowledge Design Earthquake: Maximum event in same seismotectonic province as site and/or ≤ 50 km from site
Japan	Active[†] 1. Creep along fault 2. Movement during Quarternary 3. Expected movement in near future	Maximum Design Earthquake (MDE): 1. Considers nearby active faults and large earthquakes 2. Causes surface of base stratum to experience the most unfavorable ground motion from earthquakes expected to occur Safety Margin Check Earthquake (SMCE): 1.33 to 1.5 times the MDE Same as item 2 above for MDE except from events considered conceivable to occur
Italy	Not addressed	Reference Earthquake A (REA): Maximum possible event considering seismotectonic conditions in seismotectonic province of site and adjacent provinces Reference Earthquake B (REB): Event likely to occur during life of plant—maximum event in seismotectonic province containing site
France	Not addressed	Maximum Probable Earthquake (MPE): Defined by consideration of past historic events and geologic characteristics Maximum Expected Earthquake (MEE): 1.5 to 2.0 times the MPE
Canada	Not addressed	Design Basis Earthquake (DBE): Event producing maximum ground motion at site during plant lifetime Site Design Earthquake (SDE): Earthquake expected once in 100 yr (0.03g minimum)
Switzerland	Not addressed	Safe Shutdown Earthquake (SSE): Event with probability of 10^{-4} yr Operating Basis Earthquake (OBE): Event with low probability of occurrence during plant life (usually 0.35 to 0.5 SSE)

Note: Criteria generalized from published or draft criteria available at time of writing and intended only for comparison. Complete and current criteria should be sought for any country before beginning any investigation. Information compiled from sources given in References Cited.

*No attempt has been made to integrate any variations of these criteria as they may have been adopted for use in individual states.
[†]Graded according to amount of displacement per unit of time.

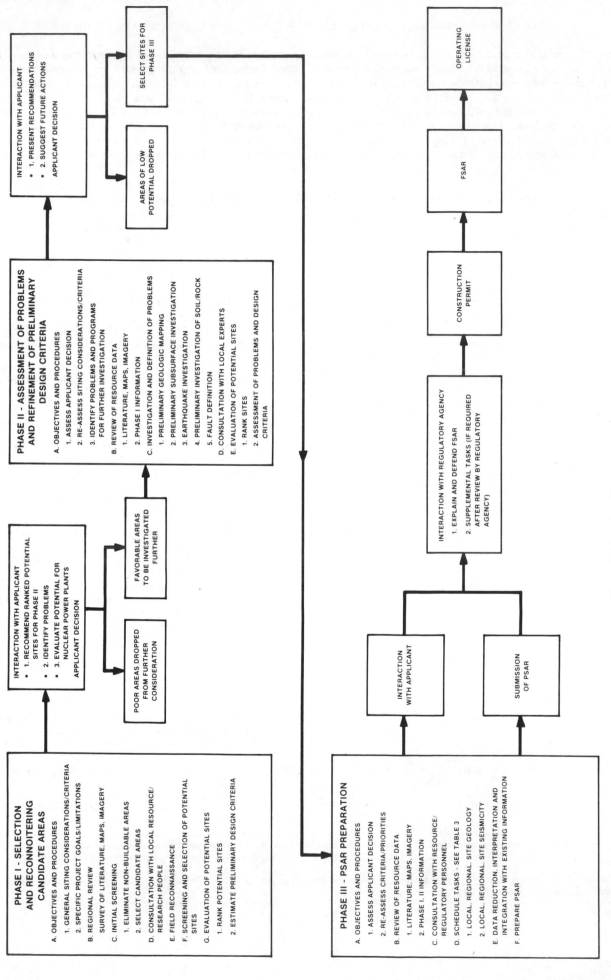

SITE SELECTION AND INVESTIGATION

PHASE I - SELECTION AND RECONNOITERING CANDIDATE AREAS

A. OBJECTIVES AND PROCEDURES
1. GENERAL SITING CONSIDERATIONS/CRITERIA
2. SPECIFIC PROJECT GOALS/LIMITATIONS
B. REGIONAL REVIEW
   SURVEY OF LITERATURE, MAPS, IMAGERY
C. INITIAL SCREENING
1. ELIMINATE NON-BUILDABLE AREAS
2. SELECT CANDIDATE AREAS
D. CONSULTATION WITH LOCAL RESOURCE/ RESEARCH PEOPLE
E. FIELD RECONNAISSANCE
F. SCREENING AND SELECTION OF POTENTIAL SITES
G. EVALUATION OF POTENTIAL SITES
1. RANK POTENTIAL SITES
2. ESTIMATE PRELIMINARY DESIGN CRITERIA

INTERACTION WITH APPLICANT
- 1. RECOMMEND RANKED POTENTIAL SITES FOR PHASE II
- 2. IDENTIFY PROBLEMS
- 3. EVALUATE POTENTIAL FOR NUCLEAR POWER PLANTS
  APPLICANT DECISION

POOR AREAS DROPPED FROM FURTHER CONSIDERATION

FAVORABLE AREAS TO BE INVESTIGATED FURTHER

PHASE II - ASSESSMENT OF PROBLEMS AND REFINEMENT OF PRELIMINARY DESIGN CRITERIA

A. OBJECTIVES AND PROCEDURES
1. ASSESS APPLICANT DECISION
2. RE-ASSESS SITING CONSIDERATIONS/CRITERIA
3. IDENTIFY PROBLEMS AND PROGRAMS FOR FURTHER INVESTIGATION
B. REVIEW OF RESOURCE DATA
1. LITERATURE, MAPS, IMAGERY
2. PHASE I INFORMATION
C. INVESTIGATION AND DEFINITION OF PROBLEMS
1. PRELIMINARY GEOLOGIC MAPPING
2. PRELIMINARY SUBSURFACE INVESTIGATION
3. EARTHQUAKE INVESTIGATION
4. PRELIMINARY INVESTIGATION OF SOIL/ROCK
5. FAULT DEFINITION
D. CONSULTATION WITH LOCAL EXPERTS
E. EVALUATION OF POTENTIAL SITES
1. RANK SITES
2. ASSESSMENT OF PROBLEMS AND DESIGN CRITERIA

INTERACTION WITH APPLICANT
- 1. PRESENT RECOMMENDATIONS
- 2. SUGGEST FUTURE ACTIONS
  APPLICANT DECISION

SELECT SITES FOR PHASE III

AREAS OF LOW POTENTIAL DROPPED

PHASE III - PSAR PREPARATION

A. OBJECTIVES AND PROCEDURES
1. ASSESS APPLICANT DECISION
B. RE-ASSESS CRITERIA/PRIORITIES
   REVIEW OF RESOURCE DATA
1. LITERATURE, MAPS, IMAGERY
2. PHASE I, II INFORMATION
C. CONSULTATION WITH RESOURCE/ REGULATORY PERSONNEL
D. SCHEDULE TASKS - SEE TABLE 3
1. LOCAL, REGIONAL, SITE GEOLOGY
2. LOCAL, REGIONAL, SITE SEISMICITY
E. DATA REDUCTION, INTERPRETATION AND INTEGRATION WITH EXISTING INFORMATION
F. PREPARE PSAR

INTERACTION WITH APPLICANT

SUBMISSION OF PSAR

INTERACTION WITH REGULATORY AGENCY
- 1. EXPLAIN AND DEFEND FSAR
- 2. SUPPLEMENTAL TASKS (IF REQUIRED AFTER REVIEW BY REGULATORY AGENCY)

CONSTRUCTION PERMIT

FSAR

OPERATING LICENSE

Figure 1. Flow chart for three-phase investigation.

imposed by the utility or the reactor supplier, such as (1) the volume of water necessary for cooling, (2) a maximum value for the largest earthquake to be considered in design, (3) centers of high demand of electricity, (4) accessibility, and (5) the number of generating units and, thus, the size of the site.

Selection of Areas

Once criteria have been established, then the order in which they are applied should be established. No two projects or areas are identical, hence the sequence of steps may vary. Safety and licensing criteria should be weighed at the onset of site-selection investigations, with project limitations applied later. If it appears that there are areas in the region in which plants cannot be built, these areas should be quickly removed from further consideration. Areas for potential sites may be ruled out because of (1) proximity to military installations, (2) economics, (3) population, (4) topography, (5) politics (close to border of unfriendly neighboring country), and (6) ecological and environmental considerations.

Once these areas are eliminated, the site-selection process can continue with the application of geologic and seismic criteria. Not all geologic and seismic design criteria are of equal importance in the selection of the site. Some conditions, such as surface faulting, cannot be accommodated in design. Other conditions, such as deep weathering, fractured rock, or swelling clays, may be accommodated if the conditions are not severe. However, accommodation is often costly. In areas where the geology is poorly understood, was mapped only at regional scales, or was mapped years ago, refinement and upgrading may be costly enough to constitute an undesirable condition. This can be especially true in areas where detailed fault investigations may be required to satisfy licensing criteria even if tectonic activity is generally considered ancient. The presence of one or more undesirable conditions may militate in favor of an alternate locality, especially if remedial measures are costly. The cost-benefit ratio of remedial measures must be carefully weighed against the choice of an alternate site.

The impact of geologic conditions varies from region to region as a function of the age and degree of the most recent tectonic and volcanic activity. Thus, the possibility that topography is affected or produced by faulting or volcanism in areas deformed during late Cenozoic time may eliminate an area, whereas similar topography will have less importance in a stable craton or pre-Cenozoic orogenic belt. As discussed later in Phase I evaluation, a weighted numerical scheme of evaluation allows direct comparison of areas and facilitates decisions.

The principal abortive factor to be ascertained during Phase I is ground stability (Table 2). Areas that have experienced or that very likely may experience surface faulting, seismically induced slope failure, liquefaction, volcanism, or rapid elevation changes resulting from active tectonic processes should be eliminated. Table 2 lists undesirable conditions that may be accommodated if remedial measures are not too expensive. The number and severity of undesirable conditions at a site should be carefully evaluated, as sites on which many costly remedial measures are necessary may be eliminated.

The distinction between conditions that are abortive and those that are undesirable is often difficult. Certain conditions such as surface faulting, liquefaction, and excessively high vibratory ground motion, either singly or in combination, are conditions that as yet cannot be accommodated in design and thus are considered abortive because they serve to eliminate any site on which they can occur with certainty. Undesirable conditions are those that can be accommodated in the design and construction of a plant, but usually at great expense. Deep weathering, potentially liquefiable soil, expansive clays, collapse or severe settlement potential, and zones where rock is extensively fractured or sheared are examples of undesirable conditions that may be accommodated in design if not too costly. Overexcavation and backfilling with structural fill or concrete may ameliorate these conditions if quantities of excavation material and backfill are acceptable. On the other hand, if such conditions are deep and widepread, remedial measures may increase costs so significantly that construction on these sites would be uneconomical or impossible. In regions where alternate acceptable sites are not available, an applicant may accept a site that in a different geologic environment would be unacceptable; that is within the region under consideration, sites with abortive factors are very common, and only areas with undesirable conditions remain from which to select a site. In such circumstances, selection of a site that is licensable can become a matter of economics. In a stable craton, such a set of circumstances would be unlikely; however, in an area of late Cenozoic tectonic and/or volcanic activity, the only available potentially licensable site may be one where development is very costly.

As shown in Table 2, Phase I consists of a careful review of existing literature, maps, and imagery followed by consultation with research authorities and brief field visits to candidate areas or sites. Regional geologic, tectonic, and geophysical anomaly maps (at scales of about 1:500,000) are reviewed to (1) identify areas where faults have been mapped or may exist, (2) ascertain the age or probable age of last movement on faults, (3) determine the nature and age of various tectonic stresses to which the area has been subjected, and (4) identify any lithospheric plate boundaries in the region of interest. Imagery is carefully examined to (1) develop specific targets for geologic field mapping and (2) identify photolinears that may represent the traces of unmapped faults. Topographic maps at several scales along with aerial photographs can be checked to determine if any other potential problems such as karst topography or slope stability may exist in the area. Observation of candidate sites from the air, especially under conditions of low sun angle, may reveal problem areas in need of further investigation on the ground and may also locate outcrops that might not otherwise be seen. Discussions with persons engaged in research should be arranged so as to acquaint the geologist with recent interpretations or unpublished information regarding the region of interest.

A preliminary Safe Shutdown Earthquake (SSE), along with estimates of possible ground shaking and ground failure, can be proposed. Maps of instrumentally recorded and historic earthquakes are compiled at the same scale as regional geologic and tectonic maps and imagery. These maps are then superimposed to determine whether any relationship exists between mapped geologic structures, photolinears, and seismicity. Alignment of reliably determined epicenters along mapped

TABLE 2. THREE PHASES OF GEOLOGIC AND SEISMIC INVESTIGATION TO SITE A NUCLEAR POWER PLANT

Phase I	Phase II	Phase III

A. Goals
  1. Eliminate
  2. Identify possible areas
  3. Recognize problems
  4. Assess preliminary design criteria
 	
B. Specific problems to identify
Abortive
  1. Ground stability
    a. Surface faulting
    b. Liquefaction
    c. Slope stability
    d. Neotectonic processes
  2. Volcanism
 	
Undesirable and/or Abortive
  1. Subsidence
    a. Karst
    b. Mining
    c. Withdrawal of fluids (oil, gas water)
  2. Bad foundation conditions
    a. Deep weathering
    b. Expansive clays or minerals
    c. Highly broken rock
    d. Potential for liquefaction
    e. Artesian aquifer at shallow depth
  3. Flooding
  4. Diapirism
  5. Induced seismicity
 	
C. Tasks
  1. Review of literature, maps, imagery
  2. Discussions with authorities
  3. Field reconnaissance
 	
D. Weighted evaluation
  1. Choose criteria for acceptance and/or rejection
  2. Choose weighting factors
  3. Assign values to candidate sites and/or areas
  4. Assess relative suitability of each site and/or area
 	
E. Interaction with client
  1. Present findings
  2. Make recommendations
  3. Decide future actions/investigations
	A. Goals
	  1. Confirm preliminary interpretations
	  2. Investigate problems
	
	B. Tasks
	  1. Detailed image interpretation
	  2. Preliminary geologic mapping
	  3. Preliminary subsurface investigations
	  4. Preliminary laboratory testing
	  5. Refinement of seismic risk evaluation
	
	C. Weighted evaluation
	  1. Choose criteria
	  2. Choose weighting factors
	  3. Assess sites
	
	D. Interaction with client
	  1. Present results
	  2. Make recommendations
	  3. Pick site(s) future action and/or investigations
		A. Goals
		  1. Detailed regional geologic and seismic investigation
		  2. Detailed local area investigation
		    a. Surface
		    b. Subsurface
		    c. Offshore
		  3. Prepare PSAR
		
		B. Tasks
		  1. Regional geology
		    a. Determine stratigraphic and structural framework
		    b. Determine geologic and tectonic history
		    c. Detailed imagery analysis
		    d. Fault investigations
		    e. Other geologic hazards
		  2. Regional seismicity
		    a. Plate boundaries
		    b. Capable faults
		    c. Relationship of structure and seismicity
		    d. Historic earthquake studies
		    e. Quaternary tectonism
		  3. Local geology (5-mi or 8-km radius)
		    a. Surface
		      (1) Detailed geologic mapping
		      (2) Detailed geologic history
		      (3) Geologic hazards
		      (4) Fault dating
		    b. Subsurface
		      (1) Drilling in problem areas
		      (2) Seismic refraction and/or reflection in problem areas
		      (3) Ground-water regimes
		      (4) Fault dating
		    c. Offshore
		      (1) Bathymetry
		      (2) Hydrography and sedimentation
		      (3) Geologic mapping
		        (a) Materials
		        (b) Structure
		        (c) Sedimentary processes
		        (d) Geologic history
		        (e) Integration with terrestrial data
		  4. Thorough analysis of all pertinent published and unpublished data
		  5. Analysis of samples
		
		C. Interpretation and analyses of field data and integration with previous work
		
		D. Preparation of PSAR
		  1. Presentation of draft to client
		    a. Client assessment of results
		    b. Discussion of results with client
		  2. Preparation of final PSAR
		
		E. Submittal of PSAR and application for Construction Permit

structures or photolinears suggests the possibility of active faults that should be further investigated. Concentrations of epicenters in zones or lines where no faults are mapped further suggest the possibility of stress relief along deeply buried or previously unsuspected structures. A comparison of epicenter maps and geophysical anomaly, structure contour, or isopach maps is then made to ascertain what relationship there may be between earthquakes and buried structures. Thus, every earthquake can be associated either with a tectonic structure or a seismotectonic province (Coulter and others, 1973), so a preliminary SSE can be arrived at either by the deterministic method of the NRC, the probabilistic method, or some combination thereof (Shukla and others, 1975). It is important in seismic risk analysis to relate earthquakes to basement structures or levels in the earth where they are generated and not to surface or near-surface physiographic units that may be unrelated to deep structures or stresses generating seismic events. Severe events not recorded on seismographs can be investigated by checking contemporary newspaper, journal, or diary accounts to determine (1) the severity of damage from ground motion and thus the intensity, (2) whether ground failure occurred, and (3) the pattern of attenuation, which may also suggest correlation of the event with geologic structure or as an indication of amplification in areas underlain by thick unconsolidated sediments.

Evaluation of Possible Sites

Phase I concludes with an assessment of the relative suitability of each possible site. As this can be a difficult task, a weighted scheme may be devised, which identifies abortive and undesirable conditions and assigns each a number, depending on the severity of each condition. A multiplier can then be assigned to each condition as a function of its importance in the selection of a site in a given area. Thus, the numerical value assigned for abortive factors (surface faulting and capable faults) will be weighted more heavily in the cumulative total than the presence of undesirable conditions (such as deeply weathered rock). The evaluation scheme is heavily dependent upon area and project limitations and should be created specifically for each project and each phase of investigation. For example, available cooling water may receive a much higher weighting factor than foundation conditions in a semiarid area, whereas the reverse might be true for a humid or temperate climate. An example of a numerically weighted scheme is given in Table 3. Geologic and seismic factors along with the weighting factor should be determined for each site investigated.

The applicant can then be provided with sufficient substantive data along with weighted evaluation to make a critical decision as quickly as possible. Phase I (1) may terminate an applicant's consideration of particular candidate sites or (2) may result in supplemental investigations to provide additional information necessary for licensing *before* proceeding to a full-scale PSAR investigation.

The amount of time required for Phase I varies with the geological complexity of the region as well as the availability, clarity, and extent of geologic mapping and research. Generally, however, a one- to two-month effort is involved. Those sites that are acceptable after Phase I can proceed to Phase II.

PHASE II. PRELIMINARY SITE INVESTIGATIONS

Phase II is a program of further refinement and confirmation of Phase I data. Attention is focused on only those areas that may contain possible sites. Geologic problem areas may be investigated in the field by preliminary or supplemental geologic mapping, drilling, trenching, and geophysical testing. Problems of fault definition, type, length, and geometry, as well as age of last movement of faults and the nature of foundation materials, can be investigated during Phase II (see Murphy and others, this volume). This can be done on one or more sites either concurrently or sequentially. Geologic and tectonic maps at scales of 1:62,500 or larger are used to further refine the data and interpretations gathered during Phase I. A more detailed interpretation of imagery may supplement map interpretation. Any residual problems connected with investigating historic earthquakes may be resolved at this time. The monitoring of microseismicity may be implemented at this time if there are problems of location, frequency, and levels of stress release in an area.

Topography and late Cenozoic deposits should be be examined carefully for evidence of Quaternary activity, which is especially significant in determining the seismic risk (Allen, 1975). Many long, major faults, such as the Median Tectonic Line in Japan and the Anatolian fault in Turkey, have gone for long periods without earthquakes in historic time. However, geomorphic and stratigraphic evidence clearly indicates movement along these faults during Quaternary time—probably accompanied by large earthquakes. During Phase II, trenching and examination of exposures to determine the relationship of bedrock structures to overlying Quaternary deposits are strongly recommended, especially in areas where evidence of Neogene tectonic activity occurs. Evidence of ground failure in Quaternary deposits that may have occurred during earthquakes should be sought (Sims, 1973; Coates, 1975). Terraces in an area should be checked to determine (1) their age and origin, (2) whether any differential tilting has occurred, and (3) whether any tectonic activity is indicated. Geodetic data should be examined carefully for any evidence of tectonic activity.

Test drilling and/or seismic reflection or refraction can be used to determine (1) thickness and nature of unconsolidated materials overlying bedrock, (2) whether bedrock or surficial units are offset, (3) topography of buried rock surface, and (4) depth to ground water. The length of a Phase II program is a function of (1) the existing knowledge of geology and seismicity in an area, (2) the complexity of local and regional geology, (3) the extent of subsurface investigations required, and (4) the number of sites being investigated. In general, a minimum of 12 weeks will be required.

With completion of Phase II, potentially licensable sites are identified and ranked using a unique weighting scheme that allows for comparison of sites. The evaluation of possible sites at the conclusion of Phase II should rank potential sites in terms of undesirable conditions (if it is assumed that obviously unsuitable sites were aborted at the conclusion of Phase I). Thus, the points awarded for the severity of each condition and the weighting factor will differ from those used in the Phase I evaluation scheme. Regional geologic setting and

TABLE 3. AN EXAMPLE OF A WEIGHTED EVALUATION

WEIGHTED EVALUATION FOR EACH SITE

CHARACTERISTICS	POINTS	WEIGHTING FACTOR	CUMULATIVE TOTAL
GEOLOGY			
A. SEISMOTECTONIC SETTING	0 TO 15	3	0 TO 45
B. REGIONAL CHARACTERISTICS	0 TO 20	2	0 TO 40
SEISMICITY	0 TO 25	3	0 TO 75
SITE FOUNDATION CONDITIONS	0 TO 20	2	0 TO 40
FLOODING POTENTIAL (STORM, DAM FAILURE TSUNAMI)	0 TO 15	2	0 TO 30
DEMOGRAPHY	0 TO 5	1	0 TO 5
METEOROLOGY	0 TO 5	1	0 TO 5
COOLING WATER POTENTIAL	0 TO 5	1	0 TO 5
GRAND TOTAL FOR SITE			0 TO 245

$\overset{*}{\vee}$ ERUPTED DURING THE QUATERNARY

$\overset{\dagger}{\vee}$ NO ERUPTIONS DURING THE QUATERNARY, BUT A FRESH PHYSIOGRAPHIC CONE OR GEOLOGICALLY YOUNG ERUPTIVE MATERIAL IF PRESENT

$\overset{\S}{\vee}$ FROM SUBSURFACE SOLUTION IN SOLUBLE ROCKS, WITHDRAWAL OF SUBSURFACE FLUIDS, MINING, OR FAILURE OF LAVA TUNNELS IN VOLCANIC ROCKS

GEOLOGY

A. SEISMOTECTONIC SETTING

DISTANCE (km)	CAPABLE FAULT PRESENT	POSSIBLE CAPABLE FAULT PRESENT
0 TO 8	0	1
8 TO 25	0 TO 1	2
25 TO 50	2	3
50 TO 100	3	4
> 100	4	5

B. REGIONAL CHARACTERISTICS

DISTANCE (km)	ACTIVE VOLCANO $\overset{*}{\vee}$	"DORMANT" VOLCANO $\overset{\dagger}{\vee}$
0 TO 8	0	2
8 TO 25	0 TO 1	3
25 TO 50	2	5
50 TO 100	3	5
> 100	4	5

	COLLAPSE $\overset{\S}{\vee}$	POSSIBLE COLLAPSE
0 TO 8	0	1
8 TO 25	1	1
25 TO 50	2	2
50 TO 100	4	5
> 100	5	5

	DIAPIRISM	POSSIBLE DIAPIRISM
0 TO 8	0	2
8 TO 25	1	3
25 TO 50	3	5
50 TO 100	4	5
> 100	5	5

	LANDSLIDE	POSSIBLE LANDSLIDE
0 TO 2	0	0 TO 1
2 TO 5	1	2
5 TO 8	2	3
8 TO 15	3	4
> 15	4	5

SITE CONDITIONS

FOUNDATION CONDITIONS	STATIC	DYNAMIC (LIQUEFACTION)
THICK UNDESIRABLE SOILS	0	0
THIN UNDESIRABLE SOILS	1	0
MODERATELY GOOD SOILS	2	1
GOOD SOILS	3	2 TO 3
DEEPLY WEATHERED OR HIGHLY FRACTURED ROCK	3	3
COMPETENT ROCK	5	5

GROUNDWATER CONDITIONS DEPTH (m) TO WATER TABLE OR POTENTIOMETRIC SURFACE	PHREATIC	ARTESIAN
0 TO 3	1	0
3 TO 6	2	0
6 TO 12	3	1
12 TO 20	4	2
> 20	5	4

SEISMICITY

DISTANCE (km)	LARGEST MODERN EARTHQUAKE M>8	M7≤8	M6≤7	M5≤6	LARGEST HISTORIC EARTHQUAKE I≥X	I IX≤X	I VIII≤IX	I VII≤VIII	I<VII
0 TO 8	0	0	1	2	0	0	0	1	3
8 TO 25	0	0 TO 1	2	3	0	1	1	2	4
25 TO 50	1	2	3	4	1	2	2	3	5
50 TO 100	2	3	4	5	2	3	4	3	5
> 100	3	4	5	5	3	4	5	5	5

	TECTONIC CREEP	INDUCED SEISMICITY	POSSIBLE INDUCED SEISMICITY
0 TO 8	0	0 TO 2	2
8 TO 25	1	2 TO 3	3
25 TO 50	2	4	4
50 TO 100	3	5	5
> 100	4	5	5

certain project considerations favor the creation of a unique Phase II evaluation scheme. Phase II may (1) eliminate some or all candidate sites, (2) identify potential sites along with suspected problems at each, and (3) facilitate the applicant's decision as to how to proceed with Phase III. At the discretion of the applicant, a full-scale investigation, as required for the preparation of a PSAR (Phase III), can be initiated simultaneously or sequentially on any chosen sites, or a more limited report similar to an Early Site Review Report (ESRR) can be prepared so as to obtain an opinion from the NRC on site suitability (Code of Federal Regulations, 1978).

PHASE III. PREPARATION OF A PSAR

Phase III is intended to complete the investigations necessary to provide the final design criteria that must be submitted with the application for Construction Permit. Any design factors not derived or determined during Phase I and Phase II must now be firmly established, especially the final details of local and regional geology and seismic design criteria, along with geologic and engineering characteristics of the site foundation materials.

Phase III tasks that are the subject of several other papers in this volume include (1) preparation or finalization of site and local geologic maps, (2) determination of detailed site stratigraphy and preparation of cross sections by means of a detailed program of subsurface drilling and geophysics, (3) in-situ geophysics and laboratory testing of materials to determine static and dynamic engineering properties of strata in the subsurface, and (4) integration of all geologic, seismic, and test data so as to provide recommendation for foundation design, excavation, backfill, and remedial measures to be employed in construction and design.

Phase III, the preparation of a PSAR, is also outlined in Table 2. Guides and requirements for the preparation of a PSAR (see Adair, this volume) may be found in publications of the NRC, the IAEA, and various States. Codes and standards

TABLE 4. PROPOSED INDUSTRY STANDARDS AND/OR GUIDELINES

ANS* identifying No.	ANSI[†] identifying No.	Proposed title
2.1	N18.4	Vibratory ground motion for the design earthquake
2.7	N180	Guidelines for assessing capability for surface faulting at nuclear power reactor sites
2.11	N174	Guidelines for determining soil and geologic characteristics at power reactor sites
2.14		Geologic design criteria

Note: Proposed standards and/or guidelines are in various stages of completion, but not yet issued.
*American Nuclear Society.
[†]American National Standards Institute.

in use by supplier and related industries may also prove useful (Table 4). Review of a recent PSAR is often very beneficial. McClure and Hatheway (this volume) explain the procedures for obtaining a PSAR.

Assessment of geology and seismicity should not terminate with the granting of a Construction Permit. Any unknown or previously unsuspected geologic structures or characteristics that are uncovered in construction must be carefully and thoroughly evaluated to determine their extent and geometry and their effect on the design and construction of the facility. Discovery of such features may warrant additional review by the applicant and the NRC.

The following examples illustrate the utility of a three-phase approach to siting and licensing a nuclear power plant.

EXAMPLES OF A THREE–PHASE PROGRAM

West-Central Spain

An area in the central Hercynian shield of the Iberian Peninsula was evaluated for possible nuclear power plant sites, as seen in Figure 2. Neogene, nonmarine, clastic sediments in basins of limited size unconformably overlie eugeosynclinal metasediments that were deformed and intruded during the late Paleozoic Hercynian orogeny (Julivert and others, 1973). Except for Quaternary alluvial terraces and floodplains and terrigenous clastics in Neogene basins, there is no cover of younger sediment overlying deformed rocks of the Hercynian shield. The several candidate areas selected by the applicant had been chosen on the basis of criteria other than geology and seismicity.

Figure 2 illustrates the numerous faults previously mapped on the basis of interpretation of aerial photographs with little subsequent field checking (Arribas and others, 1971; Instituto Geologico y Minero de Espana, 1971). Landsat imagery of the area suggests that some of these features may not be faults; other significant faults were not known. The area is one of relatively infrequent low- to intermediate-level earthquakes, none of which has produced surface faulting or is known to be associated with geologically ancient faults. None of the mapped faults was found to be capable (active) according to NRC or IAEA criteria.

Several possible sites were recommended at the conclusion of Phase I. Sites with a thin cover of Quaternary or Neogene sediments were preferred, because they provided evidence for a minimum age of last movement on any buried faults within the Hercynian shield rocks. On the basis of the recommendations, the applicant decided to proceed to Phase II at a preferred site.

Preliminary geologic mapping, test drilling, soil testing, and a seismic refraction survey were conducted during Phase II investigations to further assess potential problems and to confirm some preliminary interpretations made during Phase I. Borings indicated that 25 to 30 m of previously unmapped Neogene lacustrine clays occurred beneath 1 to 2 m of Quaternary terrace gravel. A seismic refraction survey was conducted to determine whether a buried fault might have formed an earlier border to the basin. The Paleozoic rock surface was

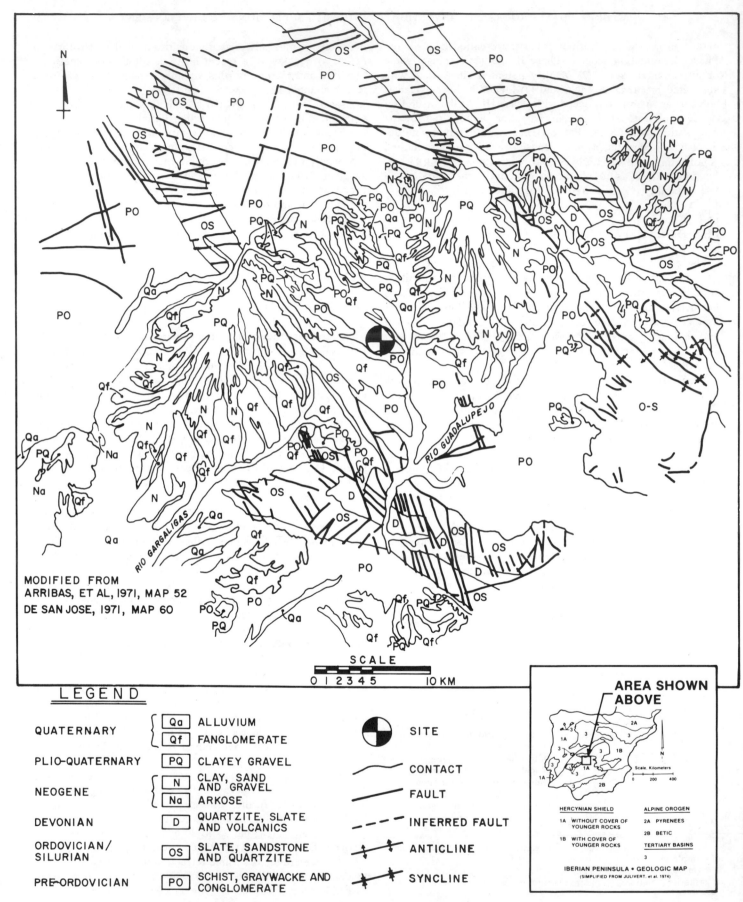

Figure 2. Geologic map of area of site investigation.

MODIFIED FROM
ARRIBAS, ET AL, 1971, MAP 52
DE SAN JOSE, 1971, MAP 60

SCALE

0 1 2 3 4 5   10 KM

LEGEND

QUATERNARY	Qa	ALLUVIUM
	Qf	FANGLOMERATE
PLIO-QUATERNARY	PQ	CLAYEY GRAVEL
NEOGENE	N	CLAY, SAND AND GRAVEL
	Na	ARKOSE
DEVONIAN	D	QUARTZITE, SLATE AND VOLCANICS
ORDOVICIAN/SILURIAN	OS	SLATE, SANDSTONE AND QUARTZITE
PRE-ORDOVICIAN	PO	SCHIST, GRAYWACKE AND CONGLOMERATE

⬤ SITE

⌇⌇ CONTACT

━━ FAULT

─ ─ INFERRED FAULT

✛━━✛ ANTICLINE

✛━━✛ SYNCLINE

AREA SHOWN ABOVE

HERCYNIAN SHIELD
1A WITHOUT COVER OF YOUNGER ROCKS
1B WITH COVER OF YOUNGER ROCKS

ALPINE OROGEN
2A PYRENEES
2B BETIC

TERTIARY BASINS
3

IBERIAN PENINSULA • GEOLOGIC MAP
(SIMPLIFIED FROM JULIVERT, et al 1974)

Scale, Kilometers
0   200   400

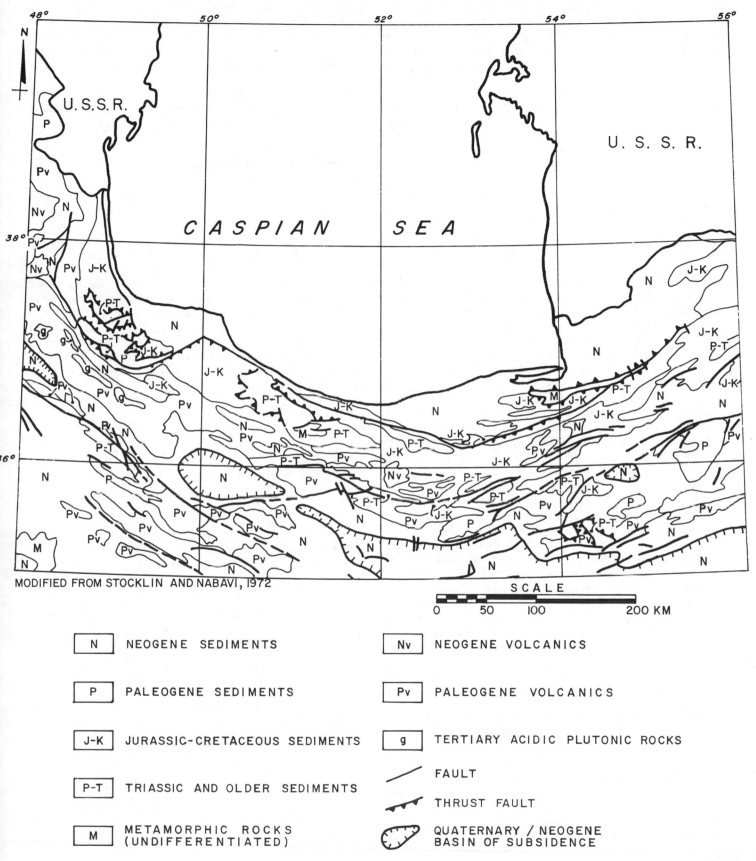

SCALE

0   50   100   200 KM

| | N | NEOGENE SEDIMENTS | | Nv | NEOGENE VOLCANICS |

| | P | PALEOGENE SEDIMENTS | | Pv | PALEOGENE VOLCANICS |

| | J-K | JURASSIC-CRETACEOUS SEDIMENTS | | g | TERTIARY ACIDIC PLUTONIC ROCKS |

| | P-T | TRIASSIC AND OLDER SEDIMENTS | | | FAULT |

| | | | | | THRUST FAULT |

| | M | METAMORPHIC ROCKS (UNDIFFERENTIATED) | | | QUATERNARY / NEOGENE BASIN OF SUBSIDENCE |

Figure 3. Geologic map of northern Iran.

found to slope continuously away from its outcrop, indicating that such a buried fault was not present. Preliminary geologic mapping revealed no suspected faults within 10 km of the proposed site. Preliminary soil testing suggested that some expansive clays were present in the Neogene sediments.

A summary of Phase II investigations and recommendations was presented to the applicant. The applicant agreed that a feasible site was present where the Neogene sediments were thin enough so that they could be removed to allow foundations to rest on competent bedrock. A site was chosen and Phase III was carried to confirmation.

Iran

A narrow coastal plain of Neogene paralic sedimentary rocks separates the Alborz Mountains of northern Iran from the Caspian Sea. Alluvial fans are common at the mouths of larger streams where they debouch from well-entrenched courses in the Alborz Mountains onto the gently sloping Caspian Coastal Plain of low relief. Complexly folded and reverse-faulted, shallow marine clastic and carbonate sediments, as well as paralic sedimentary rock of Mesozoic and early Cenozoic age, form the arcuate Alpine orogen of the Alborz (Fig. 3) (Stöcklin and Nabavi, 1972; Stöcklin, 1974). The abrupt topographic change suggests that a significant geologic structure forms the border between the front of the range and the coastal plain. A few deep wells that were drilled for oil and gas exploration confirm the difference in elevation of bedrock between the front of the range and the base of the coastal plain.

The frequency and level of earthquakes in the Alborz Mountains are much higher than in the coastal plain. The Shahrud fault, a long transcurrent fault paralleling the strike of the Alborz Mountains (Wellman, 1965), has been interpreted as the boundary between two small lithospheric plates (Nowroozi, 1971; McKenzie, 1972). The record of seismicity in the area is incomplete; data from instrumentally recorded earthquakes is sparse before 1950. Historic records of events predating the twentieth century suggest that destructive earthquakes have occurred in areas where there have been no earthquakes or only a few low-level events in the twentieth century (Ambraseys, 1963; Ambraseys and Tchalenko, 1969). However, evidence of surface faulting in the Alborz is equivocal, because slopes commonly fail thereby masking any evidence of faults that typically occur in or along valleys. Displacement along surface faults, as well as fault-plane solutions for earthquakes in northern Iran, suggests that the area is under compression. Deformation of Neogene sediments in the northern foothills of the Alborz attests to the recency of tectonic processes.

The coastal plain was investigated in search of sites for nuclear power plants where a once-through cooling system using Caspian Sea water could be utilized. Reconnaissance-level interpretation of imagery, as well as available small-scale geologic maps, suggested that the surficial Quaternary sediments were not deformed or affected by neotectonic processes. Reconnaissance-level observation of stream cuts similarly failed to disclose any tectonic deformation in the surficial Quaternary sediments. To identify areas with minimum potential for liquefaction, areas on alluvial fans were sought where gravel was assumed to be more abundant than in the generally fine-grained paralic sediments of the coastal plain. A wide, shallow shelf in the southeastern Caspian Sea limited the search to the central and western coastal plain where sufficient depth (and therefore volume) of water was present in the nearshore area to permit once-through cooling.

Several potential sites were selected and presented to the applicant in the form of a weighted evaluation. Three were chosen by the applicant on which to proceed to Phase II.

SUMMARY AND CONCLUSIONS

A three-phase program of investigation allows relatively rapid selection and determination of the technical feasibility of candidate sites. As few sites are alike, the nature, duration, and timing of a program of investigation will vary with the geologic setting and applicant preferences. A flexible three-phase investigation can quickly eliminate undesirable sites and enable preliminary assessment of design criteria. Early contract negotiations with plant vendors and realistic construction schedules can then be established. This is especially important in tectonically complex areas where potential sites may be quickly found and assessed. The ability of the applicant to make rapid, informed decisions based on technical evaluations facilitates efficient design and construction of a nuclear power plant and a smooth-flowing operation.

ACKNOWLEDGMENTS

I thank Allen Hatheway, John Gibbons, and John Briedis who offered many helpful comments during their review of the manuscript.

REFERENCES CITED

Adair, M. J., 1979, Geologic evaluation of a site for a nuclear power plant, in Hatheway, A. W., and McClure, C. R., Jr., eds., Geology in the siting of nuclear power plants: Geological Society of America Reviews in Engineering Geology, v. IV (this volume).

Allen, C. R., 1975, Geological criteria for evaluating seismicity: Geological Society of America Bulletin, v. 86, p. 1041–1057.

Ambraseys, N. N., 1963, The Buyin-Zara (Iran) earthquake of September 1962: Bulletin of the Seismological Society of America, v. 53, p. 705–740.

Ambraseys, N. N., and Tchalenko, J. S., 1969, The Dasht-e Bayaz (Iran) earthquake of August 31, 1968: A field report: Bulletin of the Seismological Society of America, v. 59, p. 1751–1792.

Arribas, A. E., Jimenez, J. M., and Fuster Casas, J. M., 1971, Talavera de la Reina: Madrid, Instituto Geologico y Minero de Espana, Hoja 52, scale 1:200,000.

Coates, D. R., 1975, Identification of late Quaternary deformation and its relation to seismicity in the St. Lawrence Lowland, New York: Binghamton, New York, Report to New York State Energy Research and Development Authority, 266 p.

Code of Federal Regulations, 1978, Title 10, Energy, Part 100 [10 CFR 100], Reactor site criteria: Appendix A, Seismic and geologic siting criteria for nuclear power plants: Washington, D.C., U.S. Nuclear Regulatory Commission.

Coulter, H. W., Waldron, H. H., and Devine, J. F., 1973, Seismic and geologic siting considerations for nuclear facilities: Rome, International Association for Earthquake Engineering, Proceedings Fifth World Conference on Earthquake Engineering, p. 2410–2419.

Davis, J. R., Slosson, J. E., and Fakundiny, R. H., 1979, The State-Federal partnership in siting of nuclear power plants, in Hatheway, A. W., and McClure, C. R., Jr., eds., Geology in the siting of nuclear power plants: Geological Society of America Reviews in Engineering Geology, v. IV (this volume).

Evans, V. A., 1976, Recent State laws regulating power facility siting: Nuclear Technology, v. 31, p. 319–325.

Hisada, T., Akino, K., Iwata, T., Kawaguchi, O., Omatsuzawa, K., Sata, H., Shibata, H., Sonobe, Y., and Tajimi, H., 1972, Philosophy and practice of the aseismic design of nuclear power plants—summary of the guidelines in Japan: Nuclear Engineering and Design, v. 20, p. 339–370.

Instituto Geologico y Minero de Espana, 1971, Villanueva de la Serena: Madrid, Hoja 60, scale 1:200,000.

International Atomic Energy Agency, 1972, Earthquake guidelines for reactor siting: International Atomic Energy Agency, Technical Report Series No. 139, 26 p.

Julivert, M., Fonbote, J. M., Riviero, A., and Conde, L., 1973, Mapa Tectonico de la Peninsula Iberica y Baleares: Madrid, Instituto Geologico y Minero de Espana, scale 1:1,000,000.

McClure, C. R., Jr., and Hatheway, A. W., 1979, An overview of nuclear power plant siting and licensing, in Hatheway, A. W., and McClure, C. R., Jr., eds., Geology in the siting of nuclear power plants: Geological Society of America Reviews in Engineering Geology, v. IV (this volume).

McKenzie, D. P., 1972, Active tectonics of the Mediterranean region: Geophysical Journal of the Royal Astronomical Society, v. 30, p. 109–185.

Morris, R. H., 1979, Geologic reports used in evaluation of nuclear reactor sites, in Hatheway, A. W., and McClure, C. R., Jr., eds., Geology in the siting of nuclear power plants: Geological Society of America Reviews in Engineering Geology, v. IV (this volume).

Murphy, P. J., Briedis, J., and Peck, J. H., 1979, Age determination

techniques in fault investigations, in Hatheway, A. W., and McClure, C. R., Jr., eds., Geology in the siting of nuclear power plants: Geological Society of America Reviews in Engineering Geology, v. IV (this volume).

Nowroozi, A. A., 1971, Seismo-tectonics of the Persian Plateau, eastern Turkey, Caucasus, and Hindu-Kush regions: Bulletin of the Seismological Society of America, v. 61, p. 317–341.

Regulatory Guide 1.70, 1975, Standard Format and Content of Safety Analysis Reports for nuclear power plants: Washington, D.C., U.S. Nuclear Regulatory Commission.

Risser, H. E., 1973, The U.S. energy dilemma: The gap between today's requirements and tomorrow's potential: Illinois State Geological Survey, Environmental geology Notes, no. 64, 64 p.

Shukla, D. K., Kissenpfennig, J. F., and Rizzo, P. C., 1975, Safe shutdown earthquake loading: Deterministic and probabilistic evaluations: London, Transactions Third International Conference on Structural Mechanics in Reactor Technology, v. 4, p. K1/3-1–K1/3-11.

Sims, J. D., 1973, Earthquake-induced structures in sediments of Van Norman Lake, San Fernando, California: Science v. 182, p. 161–163.

Stevenson, J. D., 1975, Survey of extreme load design regulatory and licensing requirements for nuclear power plants: Amsterdam, North Holland Publishing Company, Proceedings International Association of Structural Mechanics in Reactor Technology Conference, 32 p.

Stöcklin, J., 1974, Northern Iran–Alborz Mountains in Spencer, A. M., ed., Mesozoic-Cenozoic orogenic belts—data for orogenic studies: Edinburgh, Scottish Academic Press, Geological Society of London Special Publication 4, p. 213–234.

Stöcklin, J., and Nabavi, M. H., 1972, Tectonic map of Iran: Tehran, Geological Survey of Iran, scale 1:2,500,000.

U.S. Nuclear Regulatory Commission, 1975, Standard review plan: Washington, D.C., Office of Nuclear Reactor Regulation, Sections 2.5.1, 2.5.2, 15 p.

Wellman, H. W., 1965, Active wrench faults of Iran, Afghanistan and Pakistan: Geologisches Rundschau, v. 55, p. 716–735.

MANUSCRIPT RECEIVED BY THE SOCIETY JULY 13, 1978
MANUSCRIPT ACCEPTED NOVEMBER 13, 1978

Geological Society of America
Reviews in Engineering Geology, Volume IV
1979

Geologic evaluation of a site for a nuclear power plant

MERLYN J. ADAIR

Bechtel Inc., 50 Beale Street, San Francisco, California 94119

ABSTRACT

The scope and detail of geologic studies made for a nuclear power plant site far exceed those made for any other type of engineering structure. The regional and local physiography, geomorphology, geologic history, lithology, stratigraphy, and structural geology must be studied through (1) reviewing the literature, (2) discussions with local, academic, State and Federal geologists, geophysicists, and seismologists, and (3) original geologic mapping, geophysical studies, and subsurface investigations. Reviews of previous studies in the region are an important part of the evaluation of any site; they help to identify, and form the basis for, additional detailed studies of particular geologic conditions and features which may be significant to that site.

All historical earthquakes that could have been felt at a proposed site should be identified. All historical earthquakes of modified Mercalli (MM) intensity greater than IV or magnitude greater than 3 which have been reported within 200 mi (320 km) of a site are listed and shown on epicenter maps that also show significant tectonic structures within 200 mi of the site. The maximum potential earthquake for the site is evaluated from a consideration of the regional and local geologic setting and the historical seismicity. The maximum vibratory ground motion that safety-related plant structures and equipment are designed to withstand is defined on the basis of an evaluation of the maximum potential earthquake and the assumed location of the earthquake that will produce the maximum vibratory ground motion.

Geologic, seismic, and man-made hazards significant to the site are identified and evaluated. The soils and rock underlying a site are investigated to determine their characteristics and behavior under static and dynamic loads. Safety Analysis Reports (SARs) for the site are prepared. They document the studies which were made by the applicant; they also document that pertinent reports and studies by others were considered. The SARs provide the basis for the conclusions as to the geologic suitability of the site and the basis for the parameters selected for engineering design.

INTRODUCTION

In this paper I describe geologic hazards or potential hazards that, in my opinion, must be considered and evaluated in order to provide reasonable assurance that a site is geologically suitable for a nuclear power plant. I also discuss methods of evaluating these potential hazards. Criteria prepared by the Nuclear Regulatory Commission (NRC) define specific seismic and geologic investigations and analyses required in order to demonstrate the acceptability of a proposed site; some of these are summarized and discussed. Some suggestions are made herein for improving and clarifying parts of the NRC criteria. The role of geologists in providing information to be used for design of the plant structures and the interface between the geologists and other scientists and engineers who contribute to the plant design are described. A flow chart (Fig. 1) outlines typical geologic investigations required for most sites and the approximate sequence of these investigations.

This paper is largely a compilation and summary of information that has already been published. Some subjects that I treat only briefly are described in detail in other papers in this volume. Additionally, I express some of my personal opinions, but they are not all original with me. Many, and perhaps most, have developed from discussions with others.

FEDERAL AND STATE REGULATORY GUIDELINES

Documents issued by the NRC identify the geologic and seismic factors that must be considered in evaluating all nuclear plant sites. These documents serve as an excellent check list of factors to be considered, and geotechnical personnel investigating sites should be thoroughly familiar with them.

Appendix A, "Seismic and Geologic Siting Criteria for Nuclear Power Plants" (see Code of Federal Regulations, 1978), was first issued in November 1973. Appendix A, as it will be called herein, sets forth the principal seismic and geologic considerations that guide the NRC in its evaluation of the suitability of proposed sites.

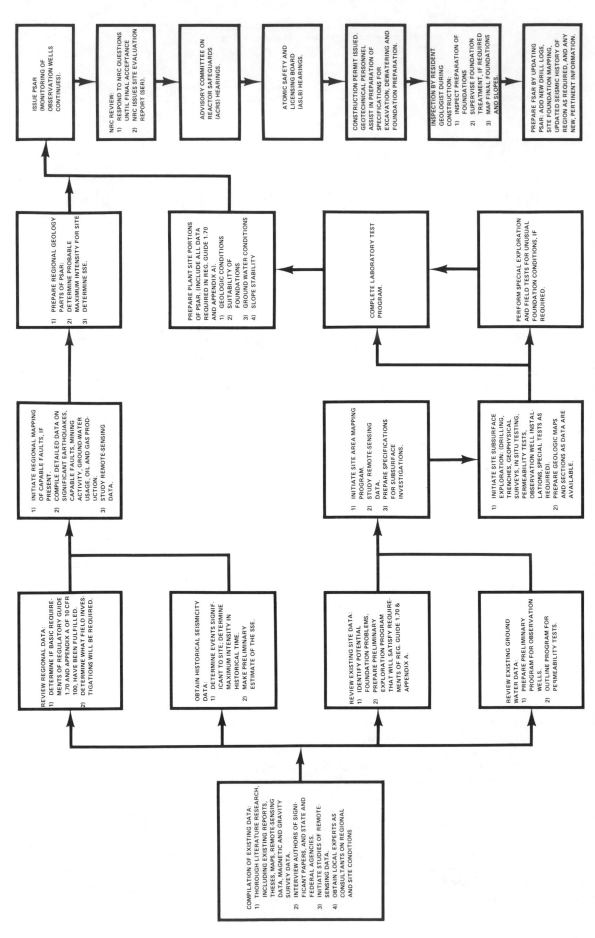

Figure 1. The typical sequence of investigations for the geologic evaluation of a nuclear power plant site.

Regulatory Guide 1.70 (1975), "Standard Format and Content of Safety Analysis Reports for Nuclear Power Plants" (hereafter referred to as Standard Format), lists information to be provided by the applicant in Preliminary Safety Analysis Reports (PSARs) and Final Safety Analysis Reports (FSARs); the Standard Format also establishes a uniform format for presenting the information.

Standard Review Plans (SRPs; U.S. Nuclear Regulatory Commission, 1975a, 1975b, 1975c, 1975d, 1975e) have been prepared by the NRC for the guidance of the NRC personnel who perform safety reviews of the geologic parts of PSARs. The SRPs list geologic and seismic information to be provided.

Some States also have guidelines and requirements for geologic and seismic investigations of nuclear power plants sites (see Davis and others, this volume). Many States have an agency or council that must be satisfied as to the adequacy of the investigations before the State will grant permits to proceed with a nuclear power plant.

GEOLOGIC HAZARDS

Evaluation of geologic hazards is extremely important to determining that a site is safe for a nuclear power plant. Approval for construction and operation of plants is not granted by the NRC until the applicant has demonstrated that the site is geologically suitable and that seismic conditions have been adequately evaluated and accounted for in the plant design. Table 1 lists potential geologic hazards that should be considered for all nuclear power plant sites. Some are applicable to all sites; others are not pertinent to some sites. Significant advances have been made since the late 1960s in techniques of evaluating potential hazards; many of these advances have resulted from, and have been stimulated by, investigations of nuclear power plant sites.

Geologic investigations for a site should be performed while keeping in mind the ultimate objective of the particular study—that is, to determine if, or to what extent, the geologic conditions being investigated would or may present a hazard to a power

TABLE 1. POTENTIAL GEOLOGIC HAZARDS TO BE CONSIDERED IN EVALUATING ALL SITES

Faults
Vibratory ground motion from earthquakes
Stability of foundation materials
   Strength of foundation materials
   Loss of strength or stability during life of plant
   Existing or potential subsurface cavities
   Differential settlement
   Subsidence from mining or from withdrawal of fluids
Landslides
Regional warping or tilting
In situ stresses
Tsunamis or seiches
Flooding related to dams upstream from a site
   Failure of dams
   Failure of slopes above reservoirs
Volcanic hazards
Ground water (in relation to uplift on structures and liquefaction of
   soils)

plant at the site. For the work to be done efficiently, the geologists making the investigations should be made aware that a particular study is made for a specific purpose, not just to accumulate scientific data. Geologic investigations must consider all the available, pertinent geologic information, but the resulting SAR need not contain all the supporting geologic data; if it does, it will become voluminous and unwieldy. A SAR should contain the information necessary to demonstrate that the data pertinent to the safety of a site have been evaluated; inclusion of purely scientific information that does not contribute to the conclusions of the study should be avoided. A SAR should include concise summaries, conclusions, and documentation giving the bases for the conclusions. The Standard Format (section 2.5.1.1) succinctly summarizes the types of geologic information required for all SARs:

Discuss all geologic, seismic, and man-made hazards within the site region and relate them to the regional physiography, tectonic structures and tectonic provinces, geomorphology, stratigraphy, lithology, and geologic and structural history, and geochronology. The above information should be discussed, documented by appropriate references, and illustrated by a regional physiographic map, surface and subsurface geologic maps, isopach maps, regional gravity and magnetic maps, stratigraphic sections, tectonic and structure maps, fault maps, a site topographic map, a map showing areas of mineral and hydrocarbon extraction, boring logs, aerial photographs, and any maps needed to illustrate such hazards as subsidence, cavernous or karst terrain, irregular weathering conditions, and landslide potential.

FAULT INVESTIGATIONS

Investigations for faulting are required at all sites for at least three basic purposes: (1) to evaluate the potential for surface-fault displacement at the site, (2) to determine the potential for earthquakes that could generate significant vibratory ground motion at the site, and (3) to aid in defining the stratigraphic relationships, structure, and tectonics of the region around the site.

Numerous textbooks on structural geology, field geology, and geomorphology describe criteria for recognition of faults (see Table 2). However, not all of the features suggestive of faults are caused by faulting, nor are all faults of tectonic origin, nor are all tectonic faults significant. This is not generally emphasized either in textbooks or in most university training. One textbook definition of a "fault" is that it is "a fracture across which there has been some displacement." Some geologists use the term without any connotation of tectonic activity having been involved; they refer to offsets in soils as faults even when the offsets are due to slumping or to compaction or shoving by a glacier. Thus, by this definition, faults may be caused by glacial activity, gravity sliding, deformation of sediments prior to lithification, compaction of sediments, and other nontectonic causes. Some old faults or fault zones are mineralized and actually stronger than the adjacent rock; other faults contain clayey, very weak material. Faults may be either conduits for or barriers to movement of ground water. Hence, the cause of a fault, its age (or minimum age), and the condition of the material in and adjacent to it must be determined in order to assess its significance to a site.

TABLE 2. SOME FEATURES THAT MAY
INDICATE FAULTING

Juxtaposition of dissimilar materials
Missing or repeated strata
Truncation of strata or structures
Slickensides, gouge, or fault breccia
Offset drainage
Sag ponds or linear depressions
Topographic scarps or triangular facets on ridges
Tilting or changes in elevation of terraces or shorelines
Anomalous stream gradients
Lineaments on remote-sensing imagery
   Topographic
   Vegetation
   Tonal contrasts
Abrupt changes in ground-water levels, gradients, chemical composition
Alignment of springs or volcanic vents
Hot springs
Geophysical data
   Steep, linear gravity or magnetic gradients
   Differences in seismic velocities
   Offset of seismic reflection horizons
Historical seismicity
   Alignment of epicenters
   Planar distribution of hypocenters
Movements measured by surveying techniques
   Tilting
   Change in distance between fixed points
Disruptions of ground surface

The most significant indicators of faults are direct evidence of recent tectonic movement and large earthquakes related to a fault, because such data indicate that the faults are "capable." Appendix A defines a "capable fault"; stated simply, if a fault is judged to be "capable," it is assumed that it will experience tectonic displacement during the life of the plant.[1] A fault that is not capable is not significant to a site in terms of potential surface displacement or seismicity, but it may be significant because of the engineering characteristics of the material in the fault zone or because of the effect it may have on interpretations of geologic structures. All tectonic faults near a site need to be thoroughly evaluated. Faults at considerable distances from a site need to be evaluated in terms of their potential for generating earthquakes and as part of the study of the structural geology of the region.

Investigations for the existence of faults and for dating the most recent displacements along them (see Table 3) should include review of all pertinent geologic data, studies of remote-sensing imagery and geophysical data, and detailed geologic mapping along and across the structure. Drilling, trenching,

and geophysical surveys may subsequently be required to prove or disprove faulting and/or to establish its age. Microseismic surveys have been used in evaluating whether a fault is capable; they have also been the source of inconclusive and controversial data, the significance of which will likely be endlessly debated.

Bolt and others (1975) noted that geologic criteria indicating fault movement in Holocene time are of particular importance in assessment of seismic risk at a site. Allen (1975) argued that the late Quaternary history is a far more valuable tool in estimating seismicity and associated seismic risk than has generally been appreciated:

The geologic history of late Quaternary faulting is the most promising source of statistics on frequencies and locations of large shocks [p. 1041]. . . . [In California,] virtually all large earthquakes (those exceeding magnitude 6.0) have occurred . . . on faults that *had* been recognized, *could* have been recognized, or *should* have been recognized by field geologists prior to the events. . . . All of these faults have been characterized by a history of earlier Quaternary (and possibly Holocene) displacements [p. 1043; Allen's italics].

He stated that large earthquakes apparently did not occur on the North Anatolian fault zone in Turkey for 100 to 200 yr before 1939, although the fault has been the source of many destructive earthquakes since then. However, he noted that physiographic features of Quaternary displacement on that fault are so spectacular that they would surely be noticed on aerial photographs. Allen concluded (p. 1056),

The most important single contribution to gaining a better understanding of long-term seismicity . . . is to learn more, region by region, of the late Quaternary history of deformation, and particularly that of the Holocene Epoch.

The importance of the above statements is that faults likely to be surface-rupture hazards should be detected in any site survey made by a competent team of engineering geologists. Likewise, faults likely to be sources of large shallow earthquakes (focal depth less than about 15 km) are likely to be detected by the same survey. (Deep earthquakes not related to surface faults would be exceptions.) Negative evidence—that is, delineation of areas where capable faults do not exist and where historical earthquakes have not occurred—obtained during site investigations is also important in evaluating a site. Careful site surveys should detect the features described above according to Bolt and others (1975) and Allen (1975).

The results of a fault study should include the following, as a minimum:

1. A comprehensive study of any fault in close proximity to the site, to demonstrate whether or not it is capable.

2. A map showing the location, length, continuity, and sense of motion of capable faults that may be significant to determining the Safe Shutdown Earthquake (SSE; see the section entitled Vibratory Ground Motion) for the site.

3. A tectonic map covering a radius of 200 mi (320 km) of the site and showing the locations of all faults or other tectonic structures that may be significant to a site, with a superimposed plot of historical epicenters. An exception to the 200-mi radius would be where it is obvious that the most likely source of large earthquakes is closer. For example, if

---

[1] Because of the imprecise meaning of the term "active fault," the NRC replaced it with the term "capable fault" and defined in Appendix A the characteristics of a "capable fault" [paragraph III(g)]. As defined, a capable fault is a fault that has exhibited one or more of the following characteristics: (1) movement at or near the ground surface at least once within the past 35,000 yr or movement of a recurring nature within the past 500,00 yr; (2) macroseismicity instrumentally determined with records of sufficient precision to demonstrate a direct relationship with the fault; or (3) a structural relationship to a capable fault according to characteristics (1) or (2) above, such that movement on one could be reasonably expected to be accompanied by movement on the other.

a site were located within 20 mi (32 km) of the San Andreas fault, it would not be necessary to evaluate faults or historical earthquakes 200 mi (320 km) from the site, because they would not be significant in comparison to events that would be assumed to occur on the San Andreas fault at its closest approach to the site. Special attention should be given to the accuracy of location of epicenters of larger earthquakes and of earthquakes near the site (see Dewey, this volume).

4. A report relating faulting to the geologic history, structural geology, and tectonics of the region around the site.

Design for Surface Faulting

Appendix A [paragraph V(b)] defines investigations required for capable faults near a site in order to determine whether or not plant structures must be designed for surface faulting. At the present time, no nuclear plant in the United States has been constructed on a capable fault; several sites have been abandoned because of nearby, possibly capable faults. SRP subsection 2.5.3.8 (U.S. Nuclear Regulatory Commission, 1975c) states,

It is an open question as to whether it is possible to design for surface or near-surface displacement with confidence that the integrity of the safety-related features of the plant would remain intact should displacement occur. It is therefore [NRC] staff policy to recommend relocation of plant sites found to be located on capable faults as determined by the detailed faulting investigation.

The same section acknowledges that it may become possible in the future to design for surface faulting. This policy is considered to be entirely reasonable. It is my opinion that unless special design procedures are taken to negate the effects of surface faulting under structures (such as floating the structures on water so that ground displacement cannot be transmitted directly to them), plant structures should not be placed on a capable fault.

Vibratory Ground Motion

Selection of the ground acceleration for which the plant structures are to be designed and obtaining the necessary approval commonly require the greatest expenditure of time and effort in the licensing process. Some vibratory ground motion must be considered possible during the life of a plant at any site; the amount of potential motion obviously varies with the location of the plant site and depends on the tectonic and seismic settings.

Certain structures, systems, and components of a nuclear power plant must be designed to remain functional after experiencing two different hypothetical earthquakes, (1) the Safe Shutdown Earthquake (SSE) and (2) the Operating Basis Earthquake (OBE). Appendix A [paragraph III(c)] defines the SSE as that earthquake which is based on an evaluation of the maximum earthquake potential, considering the regional and local geologic setting, historical seismicity, and specific characteristics of the local subsurface material. Those systems necessary to assure (1) the integrity of the reactor coolant pressure boundary, (2) the safe shutdown of the plant, and

TABLE 3. SOME METHODS OF DATING THE MINIMUM AGE OF LAST DISPLACEMENT ON FAULTS

Determining the age of undisplaced strata overlying the fault through the use of fossils, radiometric dating, or paleomagnetic studies

Determining the age of crosscutting undisturbed dikes, sills, or other intrusions

Determining the rate of development of undisturbed soil profiles across a fault

Radiometric dating of minerals caused by the fault movement or of undeformed minerals in a fault zone

Relating the age of the fault movement to the age of associated, dated geologic structures

Dating of geomorphic features along or across the fault

(3) the capability to mitigate the offsite consequences of certain accidents must be designed to remain functional after experiencing the SSE. The OBE is that earthquake which could reasonably be expected to affect the plant site during the operating life of the plant. Those features of the plant necessary for continued operation without undue risk to the health and safety of the public are designed to remain functional after experiencing the OBE. These earthquakes, or the ground motion resulting from them, are defined by horizontal ground accelerations, in terms of percent or fractional amounts of the acceleration due to gravity (g), in conjunction with horizontal and vertical design spectra that relate acceleration, particle velocity, and displacement to frequency of the seismic waves causing the vibratory motion. Regulatory Guide 1.60 (1973) defines horizontal and vertical design spectra that are acceptable for nuclear plants founded on either rock or firm soil. Appendix A [paragraph V(1)(v)] requires that the minimum SSE for any nuclear plant site shall be $0.10g$ and that the OBE shall be at least one-half the SSE. However, in 1978 some plants were licensed with the OBE less than one-half the SSE.

Before the methods of determining the SSE and OBE are described, it may be of interest to discuss the evolution of the present criteria for selecting the SSE and OBE. The SSE was at one time termed the "Maximum Credible Earthquake" and the "Design Basis Earthquake." The OBE was first determined; it commonly approximated the maximum historical intensity or acceleration experienced in the region near the site. The "Maximum Credible Earthquake" was then often obtained by designing for one intensity unit higher than the maximum historical intensity experienced near the site, or by doubling the maximum historical ground acceleration experienced near the site. It was recognized that the maximum historical intensity in the region usually occurred on poorer foundation materials than those on which the plant structures would be founded and that this maximum historical intensity had affected structures which were either not designed at all for vibratory ground motion or were less carefully designed and constructed than nuclear power plants. Hence, this method was assumed to assure a large factor of safety in designing the plant to survive earthquakes and be able to be shut down safely.

The present criteria require that the SSE be determined first and that the OBE be at least one-half the SSE. With this method, the OBE for some plant sites exceeds the maximum historical ground acceleration experienced near the site by a factor of four or more. This appears to be inconsistent with the concept that the OBE "could reasonably be expected to affect the plant site" [Appendix A, paragraph III(d)]. Additionally, the OBE rather than the SSE controls the design of many of the plant structures, because different allowable stresses and damping values are used in designing for the two earthquakes. Thus, use of an OBE less than one-half the SSE is logical for many sites.

From the preceding, it is apparent that nuclear power plants are now required to withstand higher levels of ground motion than plants licensed previously, even though the earlier, lower levels of ground motion were considered by many experts to be amply conservative. Nuclear power plants are such important structures that they obviously must be conservatively designed. However, the effects of, and necessity for, designing for ever-increasing levels of vibratory ground motions need to be carefully considered. Many applicants have designed for SSE values that they and their experts believed to be unnecessarily conservative, because this was less costly than the cost of delays entailed by prolonged hearings. Opponents to the construction of nuclear power plants are well aware of how much delays cost an applicant.

The scientists and engineers who are most knowledgeable of seismology and engineering design must collectively develop a suitably conservative but also realistic design for each site. Demands for *unrealistic* conservatism should not be permitted to delay licensing.

Selection of the SSE is a team effort requiring input from geologists, geophysicists, and seismologists. Some teams include the structural design engineers so that a group discussion of the overall factor of safety built into the plant is possible. However, with the existing "compartmentalized" approach to the complete seismic design, geologists and seismologists select the SSE in accordance with Appendix A, the Standard Format, and the SRP (U.S. Nuclear Regulatory Commission, 1975b).

The SSE for a site is determined after evaluating regional historical seismicity and capable geologic structures with which earthquake activity in the region can be associated. This requires a listing of historically reported earthquakes of MM intensity greater than IV or Richter magnitude greater than 3.0 that have been reported within at least 200 mi (320 km) of the site. The epicenter or regions of highest intensity are then correlated either with geologic structures or with tectonic provinces; the maximum potential earthquake associated with either, or both if applicable, is then assessed. This maximum earthquake is assumed to recur on the structure, or on the boundary of the tectonic province, at its closest approach to the site. The resulting horizontal ground acceleration at the site is then conservatively estimated, after giving due consideration to (1) attenuation of ground motion from the energy source to the site and (2) any amplification of ground motion that might be peculiar to the site. Both methods of defining the SSE will be briefly discussed.

Capable Faults

Appendix A [paragraph IV(a)(7)] requires that within 200 mi of a site all faults that may be of significance in establishing the SSE shall be evaluated. (An important point here is that if the SSE is associated with a fault closer than 200 mi from the site, this need not be carried out.) Where a specific fault may be reasonably expected to cause the maximum ground motion that could affect a site, the maximum potential earthquake for that fault should be determined on the basis of the nature of the fault, its length, its displacement and earthquake history, and any other relevant geologic information; that earthquake is then assumed to occur on that fault at its closest approach to the site. At some sites, this has required that the maximum potential earthquake from more than one fault be considered. If different maximum potential earthquakes are estimated to produce the maximum ground motion in different frequency bands, the conditions describing all such earthquakes should be specified.

Determining whether or not a structure is capable may be a difficult problem, and applicants have spent enormous amounts of time and money studying such situations. As a generality, if a long fault exists near a site (such as in the western United States), it is conservative (although not necessarily correct) to assume that the fault is capable and that it can generate a large earthquake. Conversely, it is conservative to assume that a distant fault is not capable—then, large historical earthquakes that might have been related to that fault would not necessarily be assumed to only recur on it; they may be assumed to recur adjacent to a site. Taking the "conservative" approach is often tempting and more expedient when there is controversy or uncertainty; however, geologists have the professional obligation of clearly expressing their opinions on the basis of what the scientific evidence indicates and on what they believe to be the facts, not just on what is conservative. Subsequently, they may choose to add conservatism for one or more reasons.

Several investigators have published data on the relationship between type of faulting, observed fault-rupture length and fault displacement, and magnitude of the resulting earthquake (Tocher, 1958; Ida, 1965; Wyss and Brune, 1968; Housner, 1969; Bonilla, 1967; Bonilla and Buchanan, 1970; Slemmons, 1977; and others). These reports show considerable variation in the relationship between rupture length of the fault and magnitude of the earthquake. The portion of the fault assumed to rupture in any one earthquake has varied from one-third to about one-half of the total fault length.

It is apparent that widely varying acceleration values can be "computed" at a site depending on the combination of assumptions and formulas used. It is a simple task to make the computations, but sound judgment must be used in applying them, in order to arrive at a conservative yet reasonable design value.

A capable fault as defined by Appendix A is one which has exhibited one or more of several characteristics, including "movement at or near the ground surface at least once within the past 35,000 years or movement of a recurring nature within the past 500,000 years." The latter portion of this criterion has caused some controversy. It should be emphasized that the criterion uses the terminology *has exhibited movement of a recurring nature*. In some cases, however, even where it can be shown that a fault has not moved in the past 35,000 yr, it has been assumed that the fault is capable because it has experienced enough total movement that the movement must have been recurrent, although the fault may not actually *exhibit any evidence of movement* within the past 500,000 yr. If it can be shown that a fault has not moved in the past 35,000 yr and if the fault has none of the other defined characteristics of a capable fault, my opinion is that it should be adequately conservative to assume that the fault will not move within the next 40 yr (approximate life of the plant). Exceptions might be in regions where known Holocene faulting exists in close proximity to the fault in question. In my opinion, this part of Appendix A has been misinterpreted, and it should be rewritten so that it cannot be misunderstood.

Tectonic Provinces and Seismotectonic Provinces

In most of the United States, and particularly east of the Rocky Mountains, the SSE is usually determined on a so-called tectonic province approach, because historical earthquakes are relatively infrequent and few can be clearly correlated with geologic structures. Appendix A defines a tectonic province as "a region of the North American continent characterized by a relative consistency of the geologic structural features contained therein." It would be beneficial to replace the term "tectonic province" with the term "seismotectonic province" for two reasons. First, it would eliminate confusion by disassociating the term and concept from that of "tectonic province," which has been defined in the literature without considering seismicity (King, 1951, 1969; Eardley, 1951; Cohee, 1962; Rodgers, 1970). (The term "active fault" was replaced with "capable fault" in Appendix A for this reason.) Second, because the seismic characteristics of the province are important in the SSE evaluation, the term selected to define the province should reflect this. Therefore, the term "seismotectonic province" will be used in this paper. The reader is referred to Davis and others (this volume) for a more complete discussion of the alternative bases for determining seismic risk as a function of regional tectonics.

Hadley and Devine (1974) described the purpose of a seismotectonic map: "to describe the distribution of historic seismic activity in relation to geologic structures and tectonic provinces and to identify structures or regions that are characterized by consistent relations between seismic activity and structural features." In my opinion, a reasonable definition of a seismotectonic province is "a region characterized by a relative consistency of historical seismicity and of structural and other geologic features contained therein."

Where earthquakes cannot be reasonably related to a geologic structure, they are associated with seismotectonic provinces, and the accelerations at the site are determined by assuming that the largest historical earthquake will occur on the boundary of the seismotectonic province at its closest point to the site. Those historical earthquakes within the province in which the site is located are assumed to occur adjacent to the site. They should be assumed to occur at a depth that is consistent with focal depths for historical events in the region. This, of course, assumes that the seismic risk, or potential for seismic activity within the life of the plant, is the same anywhere within a seismotectonic province.

With the present state of knowledge (or lack of precise knowledge) of the relationship of earthquakes and geologic structures in much of the United States, an approach of this type is necessary to assure adequately conservative seismic design. However, the limits of seismotectonic provinces must be reasonably defined in order to avoid gross overdesign. Seismotectonic provinces should be delineated on the basis of the geologic conditions in the region and after consideration of the spatial locations of historical seismic events; also, a seismotectonic province should be reasonably limited in its areal extent. For example, the central stable region of the United States is too large, in my opinion, to assume that it is one seismotectonic province.

SRP subsection 2.5.2.3 (U.S. Nuclear Regulatory Commission, 1975b) is superior to Appendix A in methods used to define the extent of seismotectonic provinces, because it requires consideration of detailed seismicity studies, contrasting structural fabric, geologic history, and differences in stress regime. It would be beneficial to revise Appendix A so that it more closely corresponds to SRP subsection 2.5.2.3 and the Standard Format.

Some additional comments are offered regarding the conservatism inherent in the assumption that seismic risk is equal throughout a large seismotectonic province. It is currently accepted by most seismologists and geologists that nearly all earthquakes of significance to engineering structures result from strain release along faults—that is, stress builds up until the strength of the rock and/or the frictional resistance between the rocks on each side of the fault is exceeded, whereupon the fault ruptures and seismic waves are released. It is important to remember therefore, that *the fault controlled the location* of the earthquake, that is, the location of the release of energy. It is unlikely that the earthquake, particularly if it was a large one, occurred on a fault formed at the time of the earthquake; it almost certainly occurred on or adjacent to a well-developed fault zone that had experienced many previous displacements (Louderback, 1942; Allen, 1975). It seems logical, then, to expect that future rupture and release of energy will occur along or close to the existing faults that caused the historical events, because these faults contain crushed and fractured rock that is weaker than the adjacent rock and is more likely to break and relieve renewed stresses. It is also logical to expect that historical seismicity, especially the larger events, provides an indication of the location of these weaker zones or faults. Consequently, future large earthquakes should be expected to occur preferentially on the same fault zones where they have occurred in the past, even if the associated fault is not visible at the ground surface. Large earthquakes should not be expected to occur randomly. A minimum SSE of $0.10g$ implies the reasonable assumption that small earthquakes may occur randomly, since small earthquakes need not be generated by large stresses nor be associated with long faults. Conversely, large earthquakes release large stresses and are usually associated with long faults.

It is interesting to note that clusters of earthquakes have in fact occurred in rather close proximity in many areas of the eastern United States, including Anna, Ohio; Cape Anne, Massachusetts; and Charleston, South Carolina. Is it geologically reasonable to assume that within the next 50 yr or so, these or similar earthquakes will recur anywhere within large regions because the faults along which they occurred are not visible at the ground surface? I doubt it. Although the earthquake history of the United States is relatively short, it deserves much more consideration in delineating seismotectonic provinces than it usually receives. Such consideration is consistent with the concept of seismotectonic provinces.

Probability analyses (that is, attempting to define the probability that a certain intensity or acceleration will not be exceeded at a site within a given time period) are often used to evaluate seismic risk, and it has been proposed that probability analyses be used to define the SSE for nuclear power plants. Appendix A does not require such analyses, but they are frequently discussed at length in licensing proceedings.

In my opinion, there are several basic problems with any attempt to use a probability analysis to determine the SSE for a site: (1) The historical data base on which the estimate depends is small and usually reflects excessive spatial and temporal scatter. (2) To estimate the probability of the SSE occurring or being exceeded at a site, it is necessary to estimate the probability of occurrence of something that has not occurred previously, at least in historical time. (3) The estimate is always based on several assumptions, one of which is usually that large earthquakes can occur randomly within a given area. Yet in areas where active faults are visible at ground surface, there is good evidence that large earthquakes do not occur randomly; the earthquakes occur on the faults. (4) When it is necessary to make several assumptions from a small data base in order to compute a number, what is the validity of the number computed? (5) What is the probability that a fault which last experienced movement as much as 30,000 yr ago will move and generate a large earthquake in the next 40 yr? Remote certainly, but the siting criteria of Appendix A requires the conservative assumption that it will happen. Who can "compute" the probability of this happening, and what is the accuracy of the computation? (6) What is the probability of a large earthquake occurring in an area (such as adjacent to a site) where studies have demonstrated with near certainty that no structure exists that is capable of generating such an earthquake?

Probabilistic methods have not been and may never be developed to the degree where they should be used as the basis for specifying the SSE for nuclear power plants, in my opinion. The SSE should continue to be defined in accordance with Appendix A, the Standard Format, and the Standard Review Plans (U.S. Nuclear Regulatory Commission, 1975b).

INVESTIGATION OF PLANT FOUNDATION MATERIALS

Foundation materials for plant structures must be studied and evaluated, both under the proposed sites for the structures and in the areas near enough to possibly affect them. In areas with soil foundations, the investigations must reveal the types of soils that are present, their geologic origin and history, and the thickness, extent, and correlation of the several strata. For areas with rock foundations, the types of rocks that are present, their stratigraphic and detailed structural relationships, the presence of any zones of weakness (as from alteration, deep weathering, or shearing) or any mineral concentrations

that are potentially unstable, and the geologic history must be determined. Engineering geologists, soil engineers, and geophysicists must sample, examine, and test the foundation materials to define their static and dynamic properties for the civil and structural engineers who design the plant structures.

Foundation investigations for plant structures are made for the following basic reasons: (1) to demonstrate lack of faulting in the foundation materials or to define minimum age of movement on existing faults; (2) to determine that the foundation materials have adequate strength to support the plant structures and that settlements will be within tolerable limits; (3) to demonstrate that the foundation materials will remain stable throughout the life of the plant; potential causes of long-term instability are large natural cavities that may exist in limestone, dolomite, salt beds, gypsum, anhydrite, or lava flows; man-made cavities caused by mining activities; subsidence due to withdrawal of fluids, including oil, gas, and ground water; sliding of the foundation materials (vibratory ground motion or changes in ground-water conditions may trigger such slides); liquefaction of soils during vibratory ground motion; and chemical or physical changes of foundation materials; (4) to identify weak zones that may require remedial treatment; (5) to determine ground-water conditions; and (6) to define the dynamic characteristics of the foundation materials.

Subsurface exploration techniques are defined in numerous textbooks and publications. Hall and others (1974) prepared for the U.S. Atomic Energy Commission a description of methods of exploring soils and rock. Continuous deep trenches across entire foundations are currently used at most nuclear power plant sites, principally because they provide the best view of the foundation materials and because of the difficulty of detecting small fault offsets with only drill holes. Excavations at several nuclear power plant sites have disclosed unsuspected shears and faults, although the sites were explored extensively with drill holes. Such trenches provide information that is usually not otherwise available until the foundations are exposed. The use of trenches for exploratory purposes is discussed in detail by Hatheway and Leighton (this volume).

Cavities in Soluble Materials

Where limestone, dolomite, gypsum, and anhydrite occur at a plant site, the possibility of the existence of cavities in these materials should be considered and investigated. Numerous important structures, including nuclear power plants, have been constructed on cavernous limestone. The Tennessee Valley Authority has constructed and successfully operated many large dams founded on highly cavernous limestone, but only after proper treatment. The condition can be successfully treated, if the extent of the problem is properly defined.

Perhaps the most common method of detecting and treating cavities in foundations for nuclear plants is by drilling closely spaced probe holes and some core holes, cleaning and filling with concrete or grout any large cavities encountered, and pressure-grouting the holes. When used in conjunction with dental treatment of shallow cavities (removal of weak materials and replacement with concrete), this is an effective method and has been used successfully at several nuclear plant sites, but it is expensive and time-consuming.

Numerous techniques have been used to detect subsurface cavities. Bates (1973) provided a comprehensive discussion and evaluation of various methods of cavity detection. He grouped these methods into three classes: remote-sensing, ground-surface, and direct-contact. He concluded that remote-sensing methods are limited to general reconnaissance, because they are not now capable of delineating a specific cavity or set of cavities. Surface geophysical methods (including seismic, electrical resistivity, self-potential, acoustic, subbottom profiling, and gravity surveying) vary greatly in their ability to reveal specific subsurface cavities. Bates stated that the modified Bristow method of electrical resistivity is capable of detecting small cavities and concluded that, of all the remote-sensing methods of cavity detection that were analyzed and tested, this appeared to be the most promising for development. He noted that direct-contact methods, especially exploratory drilling, are the only methods of definitely establishing the existence of a cavity.

D. C. Moorehouse and R. A. Millet (1972, written commun.) described three geophysical methods—seismic-velocity, resistivity and gravity studies—that were used together with direct exploratory methods to examine the bedrock at a site in Ohio for solution cavities. All methods were successful to some extent, but the microgravity method was the best, because of its ability to directly measure mass deficiencies (cavities) in the rock. Moorehouse and Millet stressed that all geophysical methods require direct corroborating data obtained by boreholes, probes, or other methods; geophysical methods should not be relied upon without such data.

Acoustic surveys in drill holes have been used successfully in some cases to locate cavities. However, the success of this method is influenced by the density of the rock (penetration in poorly cemented rock is poor), the filling in the cavities, and the presence of joints of small vugs that sometimes obscure the larger, significant cavities. In order to delineate the dimensions of a cavity by the acoustic method, surveys in drill holes around the cavity are required.

Anhydrite and gypsum are much more soluble than limestone, and cavities are commonly associated with them. Whenever they occur near the ground surface, the possibility of cavities and sinkholes being associated with them should be investigated. Where either gypsum or anhydrite occur under sites of proposed structures, it is important that the ground-water conditions at the level of the gypsum or anhydrite not be significantly altered. Canals and reservoirs constructed in gypsum-bearing areas have experienced severe subsidence failures within a few years after their construction because the impounded water dissolved the underlying rocks.

Subsidence Caused by Mining or Withdrawal of Fluids

Subsidence of the ground surface has been known to occur above relatively shallow cavities formed by mining activities (particularly coal mines) and where large quantities of salt, oil, gas, or ground water have been extracted. Where these conditions exist near a site, consideration must be given to the possibility that surface subsidence will occur.

The amount of subsidence that may occur over an underground opening is dependent on the width of the opening, its height, its depth below ground surface, and the characteristics of the strata overlying it. Much valuable data have been obtained from direct observations of actual cases. The National Coal Board (1963, 1966) in England has published much useful data on the rate, amount, and lateral extent of surface subsidence that has occurred and can be expected to occur above coal mines.

Brauner (1973) presented data based mainly on conditions in European coal fields. He noted that the limit angle (the angle of the sides of the cone within which any subsidence will take place) usually ranges between 45° and 65° measured from the horizontal, but maximum angles of 35° and 40° have been reported in single cases. The limit angle is affected by the competency of the strata overlying the opening and the inhomogeneities in these strata. Structures located within the limit angle determined for a particular area could be affected by subsidence. Mineral rights should be obtained to ensure that possible future mining activities near a site can be controlled.

Extraction of fluids has caused severe subsidence problems in some areas. Such subsidence often occurs principally as a broad warping, but the resulting flexing and tensions have caused cracking and offsets at ground surface. The amount and character of expected subsidence due to withdrawal of fluids is best indicated by records of what has occurred under similar geologic conditions in the past. Precise leveling surveys taken at frequent intervals are important to evaluating the effects at ground surface of fluid withdrawal.

Landslides

Landslides occur when the downslope component of the forces acting on the material in a slope exceeds the shearing strength of the material. Consequently, landslides often occur as the result of earthquakes or saturation of the material (which reduces its shear strength and increases the driving force). Slides may also be triggered by erosion and man's activities.

Investigations for landslide potential should include geologic mapping to delineate areas of old sliding, because such areas are highly susceptible to future instability. Aerial photographs are especially useful for this purpose. Rock slopes should be mapped carefully to determine if planes of weakness, such as bedding planes or fractures, occur either nearly parallel to the slope or dip out of the slope. Slides in rock almost always occur along pre-existing weak planes; intact rock usually has enough inherent strength that slide planes do not cut across it. Excavated soil slopes should be mapped geologically, but they must be analyzed by soil engineers to evaluate their stability. Both rock and soil slopes should be evaluated with due consideration given to potential earthquake forces.

Landslides have caused large waves in lakes and bays and flooding downstream due to failure or overtopping of dams. Thus, landslides at considerable distances from a plant site might, in some cases, affect plant structures.

Chemical or Physical Changes of Foundation Materials

Some clay minerals, particularly those in the montmorillonite group, expand considerably when water comes in contact with them. This expansion has caused heaving and tilting of structures where this possibility was not recognized and considered in the design. Some shales are well known for their expansive properties, which are due to the montmorillonite they contain. Bentonite is composed principally of montmorillonite and is formed by decomposition of volcanic ash; hence, rocks containing volcanic ash should be suspect.

Anhydrite may be converted to gypsum with the addition of water; in this process it expands in volume by about 40% and may exert pressures up to several thousand pounds per square inch (several hundred kilograms per square centimetre). Billings (1942) described this volume increase as a source of compressive stresses that can cause folding. Violent explosions and uplifts have been related to hydration of anhydrite to form gypsum, as the result of construction of reservoirs above anhydrite. Brune (1975) described such phenomena in Texas, accompanied by uplifts of the ground surface by as much as 20 ft (6 m). Anhydrite usually does not occur within several hundred feet of the ground surface, because at these shallow depths it has already been converted to gypsum, but exceptions do occur, particularly in arid climates.

Where rocks bearing these minerals underlie a site, it is important to assess existing conditions, evaluate possible changes, and then determine whether foundation problems could occur.

Rock foundations have sufficient strength that consolidation and settlement under structures present no problems provided that imposed unit loads are kept at reasonable levels. Soil foundations must of course be analyzed differently, but description of such analyses is outside the scope of this paper. Liquefaction potential of granular soils during vibratory ground motions is routinely analyzed during foundation investigations.

Weak Zones in Foundation Materials

Weak zones may be due to one or more of several causes, including sheared or crushed zones (which increase permeability and permit deeper than usual weathering), weak strata, irregular weathering, and cavities. Site investigations should be designed to detect such zones.

Treatment of weak zones that do not dip steeply usually consists of (1) removal of the zone and backfilling with suitable compacted fill or concrete or (2) extending foundation systems (such as piles or caissons) below it. Steeply dipping weak zones in rock are usually treated by "dental excavation," which consists of removing the soft material to a specified depth below foundation grade, shaping the sides of this excavation so that it becomes narrower downward (to transfer vertical loads to the sides of the excavation), and backfilling with concrete. The depth of excavation into the weak zone is directly related to the width of the zone; depths of one to two times the width are usually adequate. Treatment of cavities in foundation materials was discussed in a previous section.

Ground Water

Investigation of ground-water conditions is an important part of the geologic evaluation of a site. Ground water may exert hydrostatic uplift on plant structures, and it can affect the

strength and compressibility of some foundation materials. Some shales and clays expand when water is brought into contact with them. Liquefaction potential of granular soils is dependent on ground-water levels. The possible effects on gypsum and anhydrite of a change in ground-water conditions must be considered.

Details of ground-water investigations are described by Farrell and Harshbarger (this volume), but some points will be discussed briefly here. It is important that observation wells be installed early in the site investigation and that periodic measurements be made for as long as practicable so that the seasonal effects on ground-water levels can be determined. More importantly, the measured water levels should be related to levels that can be expected during a long-range period of maximum precipitation, because prolonged wet periods can cause a significant rise above the normal ground-water level. The maximum level of ground water during the life of the plant must be conservatively determined, and its effect on foundations, structures, and slopes evaluated.

Dynamic Characteristics

The dynamic characteristics of the materials underlying a site are evaluated by measuring the following properties of each stratum (down to rock or to a depth of several hundred feet) under the site (SRP subsection 2.5.2.5, U.S. Nuclear Regulatory Commission, 1975b): seismic compressional and shear wave velocities on in situ materials, bulk densities, soil properties and classification, shear modulus and its variation with strain level, and ground-water level and its variation. Determination of these properties is most important for soils. Some of the dynamic properties are determined by soil engineers in the laboratory; others are determined during site investigations. Engineering geologists relate the results of the seismic surveys to the various geologic strata, their geologic history, and their other properties to evaluate the significance and cause of variations in velocities and other geophysical properties.

Cross-hole surveys need to be made in drill holes on-site to measure directly the velocities of the individual strata. Holes need to be close enough together to avoid refraction of waves to higher-velocity layers, which can result in masking of low-velocity layers. However, the holes also need to be far enough apart to avoid velocities being significantly affected by disturbance caused by drilling and to measure velocities over distances long enough for the velocities to be representative of the overall foundation materials. Generating seismic waves in one hole while recording simultaneously in several other holes at varying distances from the energy source is a common technique. Uphole or downhole measurements should also be made to help evaluate the extent of possible refraction to higher-velocity layers.

REGIONAL WARPING OR TILTING

Regional warping or tilting due to such phenomena as melting of Pleistocene glaciers or sedimentation usually occurs over such broad areas and at such slow rates that it has little significance to structures.

Evidence of local tilting or warping because of tectonic activity is much more significant. Accurate maps with contours showing amount and rate of historical changes in land levels contain valuable information, and they should be carefully evaluated when they are available. Closely spaced contours can indicate areas of active or potentially active faulting. Unfortunately, maps sufficiently accurate for this purpose are not available for much of the United States.

Bostrom and others (1968) prepared a map for the Puget Sound area in western Washington showing contours of rate-of-level-change per year and compared it to the incidence of seismicity. The areas of sharpest temporal elevation change occur in southern Puget Sound, where the largest historical earthquakes in that region have also occurred.

The National Geodetic Survey has a large amount of data available on change in elevations of ground surface in many areas in the United States. Such information can be obtained from their Vertical Division Network in Rockville, Maryland.

IN SITU STRESSES

Evidence of unusual in situ stresses in the rock at or near a site should be evaluated. Knowledge of the orientation and magnitude of in situ stresses may be useful in evaluating the tectonics of a region. Sbar and Sykes (1973) presented data on stresses in eastern North America and concluded that the results of their study (which considers fault-plane solutions of earthquakes, in situ stress measurements, and geologic observations) demonstrate that a significant increase in our knowledge of the driving mechanism of plate tectonics and intraplate tectonics can be obtained by mapping stress distributions within plates. However, they noted that many more stress measurements are needed to fill in the gaps in North America and to determine the effect of remnant stress or structure (inhomogeneities in the rocks) on these measurements.

If the shearing resistance along a fault and the magnitude and direction of in situ stresses adjacent to the fault are known, theoretically the possibility of incipient movement of the fault can be evaluated, although it is doubtful that one can determine whether the movement would be by creep or abrupt displacement. Practically, it has not as yet been demonstrated that these factors can be accurately determined; therefore, the relationship of existing in situ stresses to seismicity is not clear. It is quite clear, however, that stress measurements made at shallow depths should be used with caution, because they are clearly affected by local inhomogeneities such as fractures, bedding planes, and changes in rock type. In situ stress measurements for underground excavations in rock commonly show wide variations in stress levels even at adjacent locations. Nevertheless, efforts should be made to determine whether or not unusual in situ stress exists in the area around a site. Sbar and Sykes (1973) described pop-ups of rock at ground surface in the northeastern United States. Operators of quarries and mines and personnel who have been involved in underground excavations in a given region will have information on the existence of in situ stresses, although they may not be aware of it until they are asked the proper questions. It is important to distinguish between true indications of in situ tectonic stresses and such phenomena as "squeezing ground" that may be due to the presence of certain minerals, the condition of the materials, or the lithostatic load over the underground opening. In rare cases, it may be desirable to make in situ measurements of stresses at a site or adjacent to a fault. Various methods of making these measurements are described in books on rock mechanics.

VOLCANIC HAZARDS

Potential hazards from volcanoes are insignificant in most of the world. They may be significant, however, in some of the western states, Alaska, and Hawaii. The U.S. Geological Survey has published a map showing volcanic hazards in the United States (Mullineaux, 1976); it shows no hazard areas east of New Mexico.

Volcanic hazards can be separated into two categories on the basis of distance from the volcano. For sites close to volcanoes, the principal potential hazards are or may be debris flows or mudflows, ash falls, lava flows, nuées ardentes or hot ash flows, and poison gases. For sites distant from volcanoes, the only direct significant hazard may be ash falls resulting from major explosions. Secondary effects may include volcano-induced tsunamis and floods caused either by melting of ice on the volcanic cones or failure of dams in valleys draining the slopes of a volcano. Debris flows or lava flows into a nearly full reservoir could cause its dam to fail.

McDonald (in Bolt and others, 1975) vividly described numerous volcanic events throughout the world. He included a section on "Evaluation of Volcanic Risk" and noted that with due allowances for change in behavior resulting from evolutionary changes in the magma in the underlying reservoir, a volcano is most apt to do in the future much the same as it has done in the past. This concept seems to offer the most valid approach to an assessment of volcanic hazards at any site.

TSUNAMIS

Tsunamis are long-wavelength water-waves with wave periods of from 5 to 60 min or longer. Sites located adjacent to an ocean and, in some cases, to lakes should be evaluated for safety against tsunamis. Most tsunamis are caused by large earthquakes that result in displacements on the sea bottom, but they can also be caused by volcanoes and submarine landslides. One of the most destructive tsunamis in terms of loss of life was caused by the violent eruption of the volcano Krakatoa in 1883. In a few cases, such as at Lituya Bay in Alaska, and at the Vaiont dam in Italy, large waves have been caused by surface landslides.

Most of the historical tsunamis have occurred in the Pacific Ocean as the result of fault displacement, almost exclusively of the dip-slip type. Strike-slip faulting seldom causes tsunamis; none was caused by the 1906 San Francisco earthquake along the San Andreas fault, although strike-slip displacement amounted to about 20 ft (6 m). Tsunamis have also occurred in the Atlantic Ocean. One of the most devastating tsunamis in recorded history was caused by the Lisbon earthquake in 1755. In evaluation of sites along the southeastern coast of the United States and in the Caribbean area, this tsunami is generally considered as a model.

Tsunamis have been assigned a magnitude scale ranging from slight up to a maximum of 3. A tsunami of magnitude 3 may have a run-up as great as 12 m. Coastal topography and nearshore bathymetry greatly affect the waves and their extent of run-up.

R. L. Wiegel (1970) has a chapter titled "Earthquake Engineering" devoted exclusively to tsunamis. Bolt and others (1975) discussed tsunamis and included a list of great historical tsunamis of the world. The 1976 tsunami in the Philippine Islands can be added to that list.

PITFALLS IN SITE INVESTIGATIONS

It is beneficial to be aware of geologic problems that have been discovered at various sites at a late date in spite of extensive investigations and to consider what could have been done to define those problems earlier. The following are some exploratory techniques and practices that could have prevented surprises at particular sites.

Inclined Core Holes. Vertical or steeply dipping faults or shear zones can be missed during site subsurface exploration by vertical core holes.

Deep Trenches across Foundations. Extensive core drilling may not detect small fault offsets, particularly in igneous and metamorphic rocks where marker beds or horizons are lacking. Deep trenches provide information that is otherwise not available until excavation starts.

Offshore Exploration for Coastal or Lake-side Sites. Sites adjacent to bodies of water may require geophysical surveys and other offshore studies to evaluate geologic conditions underwater. The type of investigations and the area to be covered should be determined on the basis of what conditions might reasonably be anticipated from the knowledge of the regional geology.

Resident Engineering Geologist on Site. The excavation for plant structures provides the best information available on geologic and foundation conditions at a site. An experienced engineering geologist should be on site essentially continuously from the start of excavation until the foundation materials are covered. The geologist should assure that significant geologic features are identified as soon as possible and must have the authority to stop construction activities in a specific area if necessary to prevent significant features from being covered or obliterated before they are adequately evaluated. This geologist should prepare geologic maps of the foundations, examine all other excavations, and map any significant geologic features exposed therein.

Consultation with Local Geologists. Experts on the geology of the site area and region around it should be retained for consultation and review of geologic evaluations and reports. These consultants should preferably be retained before the site is selected. Contact with the appropriate State geological survey should be considered a must (see Davis and others, this volume).

QUALITY ASSURANCE

A quality assurance program is a necessary part of the complete geologic evaluation of a site. However, it should be recognized that quality assurance is really nothing more than following good geologic and engineering practices. For geologic investigations, this requires (1) that the studies be made by personnel competent to do the work assigned to them, (2) that the conditions encountered be accurately identified and adequately investigated, and (3) that the data obtained, tests performed, judgments made, and design parameters selected be reviewed and approved by experienced, competent professionals. All the above should be documented to the degree deemed adequate. It should be recognized by quality assurance inspectors that many geologic decisions must be based in large part on judgment and experience, because geologic conditions are extremely variable compared to, say, concrete or steel. It is not practicable to attempt to prepare a "cookbook" sort of quality assurance document that tells how to make geologic investigations. Thousands of existing publications relative to this subject apparently are not adequate for that purpose, because new ones are being published each year.

I have noted a tendency for some quality assurance programs to be unnecessarily complicated and cumbersome, especially when they are not prepared by professionals in the discipline that the work entails. One example was a requirement that drill-hole locations could not be adjusted unless approved beforehand by several levels of reviewers. Such a requirement does not belong in a quality assurance program for geologic investigations, although a similar requirement for no deviation without prior approval would be entirely appropriate for placing concrete or structural steel. The reason for the different approaches is that drill holes should be located in large part on the basis of what was encountered in adjacent holes—not on what a drawing indicates. The field geologist in charge of the exploration, and his direct supervisor, should be experienced enough to make such judgments. Relocation of a drill hole should be no concern of quality assurance personnel, because all completed drill holes will be accurately located. The subsequent reviews by experienced personnel should determine if and where additional drill holes are required. It serves no useful purpose for quality assurance to hold up drilling a hole because someone has not approved a revised location; it can do no harm to drill the hole. This may seem to be a minor point, but it is intended to illustrate what should be, and what need not be, included in a quality assurance program.

As a generality, quality assurance programs should be as uncomplicated as possible, consistent with their being adequate. It is my firm opinion that quality assurance programs for geologic or other geotechnical investigations should be prepared by the technical experts in the discipline that is involved in the work. They are most knowledgeable of what is necessary to ensure a workable, adequate program.

REFERENCES CITED

Allen, C. R., 1975, Geological criteria for evaluating seismicity: Geological Society of America Bulletin, v. 86, p. 1040–1057.

Bates, E. R., 1973, Detection of subsurface cavities: U.S. Army Corps of Engineers, Waterways Experiment Station, Miscellaneous Paper S-73-40, 63 p.

Billings, M. P., 1942, Structural geology: New York, Prentice-Hall, Inc., 473 p.

Bolt, B. A., and others, 1975, Geological hazards: New York, Springer-Verlag, 328 p.

Bonilla, M. G., 1967, Historic surface faulting in continental United States and adjacent parts of Mexico: U.S. Geological Survey Open-File Report, 36 p.

Bonilla, M. G., and Buchanan, J. M., 1970, Interim report on worldwide historic surface faulting: U.S. Geological Survey Open-File Report, no. 70-34, 32 p.

Bostrom, R.C., Couch, R. W., Rasmussen, N. H., and Sherif, M., 1968, An observation program of level changes and the incidence of seismicity in the Puget Sound area: The Trend in Engineering; p. 18–20.

Brauner, G., 1973, Subsidence due to underground mining: U.S. Bureau of Mines Information Circular no. 8571, 56 p.; no. 8572, 53 p.

Brune, G., 1975, Anhydrite and gypsum problems in engineering geology: Association of Engineering Geologists Bulletin, v. 2, p. 26–37.

Code of Federal Regulations, 1978, Title 10, Energy; Part 100 [10 CFR 100], Reactor site criteria; Appendix A, Seismic and geologic siting criteria for nuclear power plants: Washington, D.C., U.S. Nuclear Regulatory Commission.

Cohee, G. V., 1962, Tectonic map of the United States: U.S. Geological Survey.

Davis, J. F., Slosson, J. E., and Fakundiny, R. H., 1979, The State-Federal partnership in siting of nuclear power plants, in Hatheway, A. W., and McClure, C. R., Jr., eds., Geology in the siting of nuclear power plants: Geological Society of America Reviews in Engineering Geology, v. IV (this volume).

Dewey, J. W., 1979, A consumer's guide to instrumental methods for determination of hypocenters, in Hatheway, A. W., and McClure, C. R., Jr., eds., Geology in the siting of nuclear power plants: Geological Society of America Reviews in Engineering Geology, v. IV (this volume).

Eardley, A. J., 1951, Tectonic divisions of North America: American Association of Petroleum Geologists Bulletin, v. 35, p. 2229–2237.

Farrell, C. R., and Harshbarger, J. W., 1979, Ground-water studies for nuclear power plant siting, in Hatheway, A. W., and McClure, C. R., Jr., eds., Geology in the siting of nuclear power plants: Geological Society of America Reviews in Engineering Geology, v. IV (this volume).

Hadley, J. G., and Devine, J. F., 1974, Seismotectonic map of the eastern United States: U.S. Geological Survey Miscellaneous Field Studies, MF-620.

Hall, W. J., Newmark, N. M., and Hendron, A. J., Jr., 1974, Classification, engineering properties and field exploration of soils, intact rock and in situ rock masses: U.S. Atomic Energy Commission Report WASH-1301, 197 p.

Hatheway, A. W., and Leighton, F. B., 1979, Trenching as an exploratory tool, in Hatheway, A. W., and McClure, C. R., Jr., eds., Geology in the siting of nuclear power plants: Geological Society of America Reviews in Engineering Geology, v. IV (this volume).

Housner, G. W., 1969, Engineering estimates of ground shaking and maximum earthquake magnitude: 4th World Conference of Earthquake Engineering, Proceedings, p. 1–13.

Ida, K., 1965, Earthquake magnitude, earthquake fault, and source dimensions: Nagoya University, Journal of Earth Sciences, p. 115–132.

King, P. B., 1951, The tectonics of middle North America: New Jersey, Princeton University Press, 203 p.

——1969, The tectonics of North America—A discussion to accompany the tectonic map of North America, scale 1:5,000,000: U.S. Geological Survey Professional Paper 628, 94 p.

Louderback, G. D., 1942, Faults and earthquakes: Seismological Society of America Bulletin, v. 32, p. 305–330.

Mullineaux, D. R., 1976, Preliminary map of volcanic hazards in the 48 conterminous United States: U.S. Geological Survey Miscellaneous Field Investigations Map MF-786, scale 1:7,500,000.

National Coal Board, 1963, Principles of subsidence engineering: London, National Coal Board Information Bulletin 63/240.

——1966, Subsidence engineers handbook: London, National Coal Board.

Regulatory Guide 1.60, 1973, Design response spectra for seismic design of nuclear power plants, Revision 1: Washington, D.C., U.S. Nuclear Regulatory Commission.

Regulatory Guide 1.70, 1975, Standard Format and content of Safety Analysis Reports for nuclear power plants, Revision 2: Washington, D.C., U.S. Nuclear Regulatory Commission.

Rodgers, J., 1970, The tectonics of the Appalachians: New York, Interscience, 270 p.

Sbar, M. L., and Sykes, L. R., 1973, Contemporary compressive stress and seismicity in eastern North America: An example of intra-plate tectonics: Geological Society of America Bulletin, v. 84, p. 1861–1882.

Slemmons, D. B., 1977, State-of-the-art for assessing earthquake hazards in the United States: Report 6—Faults and earthquake magnitude: U.S. Army Corps of Engineers, Waterways Experiment Station, Miscellaneous Paper S-73-1, 166 p.

Tocher, D., 1958, Earthquake energy and ground breakage: Seismological Society of America Bulletin, v. 48, p. 147–153.

U.S. Nuclear Regulatory Commission, 1975a, Standard Review Plan 2.5.1, Basic geologic and seismic information: Washington, D.C., U.S. Nuclear Regulatory Commission, Office of Nuclear Reactor Regulation, 5 p.

——1975b, Standard Review Plan 2.5.2, Vibratory ground motion: Washington, D.C., U.S. Nuclear Regulatory Commission, Office of Nuclear Reactor Regulation, 10 p.

——1975c, Standard Review Plan 2.5.3, Surface faulting: Washington, D.C., U.S. Nuclear Regulatory Commission, Office of Nuclear Reactor Regulation, 5 p.

——1975d, Standard Review Plan 2.5.4, Stability of subsurface materials and foundations: Washington, D.C., U.S. Nuclear Regulatory Commission, Office of Nuclear Reactor Regulation, 14 p.

——1975e, Standard Review Plan 2.5.5, Slope stability: Washington, D.C., U.S. Nuclear Regulatory Commission, Office of Nuclear Reactor Regulation, 8 p.

Wiegel, R. L., 1970, Tsunamis, in Wiegel, R. L., ed., Earthquake Engineering: Englewood Cliffs, N.J., Prentice-Hall, p. 257–306.

Wyss, M., and Brune, J. N., 1968, Seismic moment, stress and source dimensions for earthquakes in the California-Nevada region: Journal of Geophysical Research, v. 73, p. 4681–4694.

MANUSCRIPT RECEIVED BY THE SOCIETY JULY 13, 1978
MANUSCRIPT ACCEPTED NOVEMBER 13, 1978

Geological Society of America
Reviews in Engineering Geology, Volume IV
1979

Geologic reports used in evaluation of nuclear reactor sites

ROBERT H. MORRIS

U.S. Geological Survey, National Center, Reston, Virginia 22092

ABSTRACT

More than a decade has passed since the earliest geologic reports relating to proposed nuclear reactor sites were completed. Then, guidelines were few, and the safety analysis was brief and general. Today, the geologic portions of Preliminary Safety Analysis Reports (PSARs) and Final Safety Analysis Reports (FSARs) are by requirement more complex. Through the cooperative efforts of the Nuclear Regulatory Commission (NRC; formerly the Atomic Energy Commission) and the American Nuclear Society, specific seismic and geologic criteria for nuclear plant sites and a standard format for the presentation of data have been developed. These standards and requirements have shifted the emphasis of power plant siting from one that considered mainly the economics of the site and its proximity to the service area, as in the case of fossil fuel plants, to one that gives important consideration to the geologic suitability of the site.

Geologic studies of nuclear plant sites require a comprehensive exposition of the areal and structural geology, hydrology, and seismicity in addition to site exploration of engineering-geology and foundation characteristics, which are the major concerns in geologic studies for fossil fuel plants. For each site a design acceleration (g) value must be derived from studies of local and regional geology and seismicity. In recent years these studies have resulted in more comprehensive as well as more voluminous reports. Such an evolution has its problems. Reports commonly lack coherence and integration of subsurface and surface geology, particularly in the case of geophysical data. Cross reference is hampered when illustrations differ in scale. The geologic safety analysis should include more basic, original field investigations of the areal geology of the site and the surrounding area.

INTRODUCTION

Electricity-generating plants using fossil fuels have been traditionally constructed close to the market area, with little regard for geologic conditions other than soil foundation characteristics and availability of fuel and water. If earthquakes or some other geologic hazard caused plant failure, the plant could be repaired and put back on line without concern for long-lasting detrimental effects to the adjacent area or populace. The advent of nuclear power required that plants be sited in areas relatively free of geologic hazards and generally distant from the energy market and population centers. In the early years of nuclear plant construction, few formal guidelines or regulations restrained utilities as to site criteria, particularly regarding geology and seismology. In the decade beginning in 1960, geologic and seismologic reports generally were authored by one or two consultants. The reports were brief and lacked definitive analyses of regional geology, tectonics, and seismicity. As industry's desire to increase utilization of nuclear plants grew, specific guidelines and regulations concerning geologic and seismic hazards had to be developed. In December of 1970 the Standards Committee of the American Nuclear Society issued the "Guidelines for seismic and geologic investigations to determine an operating base earthquake and associated ground motion." In November 1971, for comment and interim guidance, the Atomic Energy Commission (AEC) published in the *Federal Register* (36 FR 228) Appendix A, "Seismic and Geologic Siting Criteria for Nuclear Power Plants," to *Code of Federal Regulations,* Title 10, Part 100, "Reactor Site Criteria." This was followed in 1972 by AEC's release of the document "Standard Format and Content of Safety Analysis Reports for Nuclear Power Plants" (see Regulatory Guide 1.70, 1975, for updated version). In November 1973, an amended version of Appendix A (10 CFR 100) was published in the *Federal Register* (38 FR 218) (see Code of Federal Regulations, 1978, for updated version). All geologic and seismologic reports concerning proposed nuclear power plants are now subject to these regulations and guidelines. These reports are commonly known as the Preliminary Safety Analysis Report (PSAR). After the geologic and seismologic studies have been completed and all data presented in the PSAR have been reviewed and accepted, the revised and updated PSAR is issued as the Final Safety Analysis Report (FSAR).

The adoption of these requirements has produced some rather interesting changes. Utilities have had to change their concept of site selection from one formerly based upon non–earth-science parameters to one concerned with all environmental parameters. This broader scope of required investigations has necessitated a change in consulting services from the use of individual consultants to the use of large geotechnical corporations capable of multidisciplinary investigations. This transition has involved problems in some instances. Proposed sites near or on active or capable faults [according to Appendix A (10 CFR 100), a capable fault has exhibited movement at or near the ground surface within the past 35,000 yr or movement of a recurring nature within the past 500,000 yr] have been abandoned after considerable investment in time and money, because the sites were selected before appropriate evaluation of regional tectonics and geologic structure.

Most consultants now go through some form of candidate-site screening after conducting a preliminary geologic reconnaissance, and then concentrate on the most viable site for formal presentation and docketing to the Nuclear Regulatory Commission (NRC). Availability of adequate cooling water has become a major problem. Several proposed plants are being designed to utilize low-grade agricultural or waste-treatment effluent.

Of all the changes brought about by the more stringent requirements for geologic and seismic studies, perhaps the biggest change is the resultant documentation, the PSAR. Gone are the sketchy geologic summaries of about 20 pages. Today the PSAR may contain seven or more book-sized volumes entirely devoted to geology and seismology. A comprehensive exposition of hydrology, areal and structural geology, and seismicity, in addition to engineering-geology and foundation characteristics of the site, is required by the Standard Format and Appendix A (10 CFR 100). The PSAR must be lucid and well organized so that its subsequent review can be performed in a timely yet thorough manner. The NRC now employs a staff of geologists, hydrologists, and seismologists to meet the increased demands of the review process. The U.S. Geological Survey (USGS) assists, under contract to NRC, in review of geologic and seismologic sections of some PSARs. In addition, other agencies or individual consultants, as may be needed, assist NRC in review of specific parts of the PSAR. The NRC has established a review schedule and guide, as given in Table 1.

As a participant in the review process for several years, I have become aware of many of the problems in the compilation of a PSAR and of the efforts by industry and the NRC to maintain the review schedule. The following comments are intended to provide a constructive critique.

CRITIQUE

Once the PSAR is accepted by the NRC for review, the PSAR is docketed and the schedule begins. As may be seen in Table 1, there are normally two rounds of review questions and subsequent replies. Meetings involving NRC and USGS reviewers and applicants are held as part of the two rounds. The applicant frequently makes oral presentations of appropriate data at such meetings, and the reviewer questions are discussed in order to ensure that the applicant understands the basis for the request for additional data. Yet, because of inadequacies in the PSAR or responses, there are frequent slips in schedule. If new or additional data are required, each additional round of questions and replies could add as much as several months to the review. If the applicant fails to meet a response date, the remainder of the schedule is delayed

TABLE 1. SAFETY–REVIEW SCHEDULE AND GUIDE FOR CONSTRUCTION PERMIT

Stage	Interval (in weeks)	Total elapsed time (in weeks)
Docketed date	0	0
Draft review questions (Q-1*)	6	6
Site examination	1	7
Initial questions (Q-1) to LPM[†]	1	8
Applicant's response to Q-1	9	17
Draft Q-2*	6	23
Formal Q-2 to LPM	2	25
Applicant's response to Q-2	9	34
Draft SER§ to LPM	7	41
Hydrology input	5	46
SER issued	2	48
ACRS[#] meeting	6	54
SER supplement to LPM	4	58

*Q-1, Q-2 = Questions from reviewers to applicant.
[†]LPM = Licensing Project Manager, NRC staff.
§SER = Safety Evaluation Report, the NRC formal statement on suitability of the site, includes USGS review comments.
[#]ACRS = Advisory Committee Reactor Safeguards, a civilian advisory group to NRC.

accordingly. The acquisition of additional data is the most frequent cause for delays, which are often caused not by an intentional avoidance or delay of response by the applicant, but by the very nature of the geologic data that the applicant needs to prove a point. For instance, using radiometric age-date samples, an applicant must spend considerable time to establish datable stratigraphic horizons by geologic mapping, to collect adequate datable material, and to make sample analyses. Or an applicant may decide to conduct additional geophysical surveys, seismic reflection or refraction surveys, or magnetic or gravity surveys. These generally require more time for mobilization, actual surveying, computer processing, and analysis than is allowed in the schedule. Many other steps involved in data collection and analysis may result in schedule delays.

As stated earlier, the PSAR should be a lucid, comprehensive, geologic and seismologic document. Many PSARs fail to meet this objective for various reasons: The applicant may try to economize by doing as little as possible in the way of original geologic mapping and hope to get by. Research funds that have been budgeted may be inadequate, or the schedule allowed by the applicant may be unrealistic and may limit the scope of investigations. In either case, the geologic analysis in the resulting PSAR lacks depth, and more adequate data usually are required to assure a reasonable level of conservatism in the safety interpretations. In addition to the add-on costs for these data, the overall costs due to delay may well offset the original "economic saving." Utilities willing to invest about $800 million (U.S. Atomic Energy Commission, 1974) for a nuclear plant should underwrite that investment with provisions for more adequate geologic investigations.

A major factor in timely review progress is the consultant's concept of the geologic report and how the various parts of the report are integrated. A typical procedure for site selection begins with a literature search and acquisition of readily available geologic data. Both State and Federal agencies may be contacted for preliminary geologic data regarding candidate areas. This step generally is followed by photogeologic evaluation and limited field reconnaissance leading to selection of a specific site. More detailed geologic investigations follow to ascertain that no capable faults, landslides, potential subsidences, or other geologic hazards are present at or near the site. Trenches and necessary drill holes are completed in the site area. Laboratory analyses of field and drill-hole rock samples are performed. Refraction, velocity, and any other geophysical surveys are conducted.

By this time a large volume of data has been acquired, and it is the responsibility of the geologist-authors and of the consultant's project manager to synthesize the data and prepare an integrated report. This type of integration is often lacking in PSARs. The local-site geology is not well integrated with regional geology, stratigraphy, and tectonics; the subsurface geology, as interpreted through drill holes, is not adequately related to local-site or regional geology. The geophysical surveys appear to be independent entities; lacking is a correlation or interpretation of geophysical data with either surface or subsurface geologic units. In one case a hole used to determine the seismic velocities of stratigraphic units beneath the site was located only several hundred feet from a stratigraphic test hole, yet the report failed to present a cross correlation or interpretation of the two. It is not surprising that the two presented conflicting interpretations. In other cases test holes in the site area have been drilled at various stages throughout the investigation. As many as three or more series of test holes may have been drilled, and each series is illustrated independently of the others, often by diagrams differing in scale and in reference of drill-hole depths to surface elevation or sea level. All such data should be integrated on one diagram, with a common reference depth and a coherent interpretation.

What would be useful, if not already in use by the consultants, is a technical editor to review the document in-house and to assure that all data are properly integrated and that the report has continuity prior to its submittal for formal docketing. It is not the NRC reviewer's responsibility to examine the PSAR for such inadequacies and lack of continuity prior to acceptance for docketing.

Some consultants, particularly in the eastern half of the country, either by policy or for economic reasons, do not appear to expend a real effort in original field mapping as part of the areal geologic investigations. In these investigations the consultants rely heavily on published literature or theses, either published or on record. As a consequence the consultant's geologist does not have the depth of insight that would be a product of original field mapping. Maps required in the PSAR include one of the site vicinity [5-mi (8-km) radius] and one of the site region [20-mi (32-km) radius]; it is the latter that generally is inadequate. Frequently, all that is presented is an enlargement or generalized redrafting of a State 1:500,000-scale geologic map, which, having been prepared for other purposes, does not provide the detail or completeness in stratigraphic and structural definition that is required to identify structures potentially critical to site safety. Occasionally a larger portion of the same State map appears as the illustration for the geology of the broader region [200-mi (320-km) radius] in which the site is located; this use is probably appropriate.

In many areas of the eastern United States, the NRC has had to apply very conservative assumptions because of the uncertainties associated with earthquake areas. Among many of these for which the NRC has funded research are two major problem areas—the New Madrid, Missouri, earthquake area and the Charleston, South Carolina, earthquake area. Although research on these two areas has been in progress for over a year, much still remains to be done before valid conclusions can be published. These two research projects are significant in that design earthquakes for many of the nuclear plants in the eastern half of the United States are based upon these two earthquake areas. Other important areas include Attica, New York; Anna, Ohio; Cape Ann, Massachusetts; and the St. Lawrence Valley, New York and Canada. Although research presently is being conducted by several utilities and State agencies on some of these, evidence of structures likely to be the earthquake generators is not entirely conclusive at this time. The map (Fig. 1) shows the generalized locations of nuclear plants built, under construction, or planned and the locations of several of these important earthquake areas. As may be seen, the seismic design parameters of more than three-fourths of the nuclear plants in the United States are controlled by one or more of these earthquake areas. Until all of these areas and their relations to geologic structures are understood, the industry must continue with a conservative evaluation of each.

As geologic investigations have become more varied and comprehensive, geophysical exploration has been increasingly used. Both marine and terrestrial seismic reflection surveys, gravity and magnetic surveys, and geophysical logs of drill holes are now common. Of particular concern in the application of these techniques is the system resolution. For instance, the optimum resolution for standard terrestrial seismic reflection surveys varies from about 50 ft (15 m) under ideal conditions to 100 ft (30 m) under poorer conditions. Furthermore, standard reflection surveys are best for strata 1,000 ft (300 m) or more in depth. Two major limitations are imposed by these two characteristics: (1) resolution to 50 ft (15 m) at best precludes recognition of faults having less than 50 ft (15 m) of vertical displacement, and (2) the shallow subsurface [from ground level to 1,000 ft (300 m) of depth] is blanked out, and projection of deeper faults upward into the shallow subsurface is not possible. Yet this could be the most critical zone beneath the site, thus requiring structural interpretation. However, a recently developed system using modified reflection survey techniques appears to be capable of obtaining resolution of several feet and reflection response within the shallow subsurface. A system of such capabilities promises to be adaptable to surveys of the site area and to studies of faults suspected to be capable that are concealed by a thin veneer of alluvium.

Another problem that involves a different scheduling need is the determination of the seismic design parameters—the acceleration or g value and the response spectra. Engineers need to know these parameters as early as is feasible, so that they can order nuclear plant components that require extensive lead time. If geologists and seismologists are pressured by engineers or management into making preliminary estimates of the seismic parameters, the estimates must be extremely conservative. A misjudgment could result in review-schedule

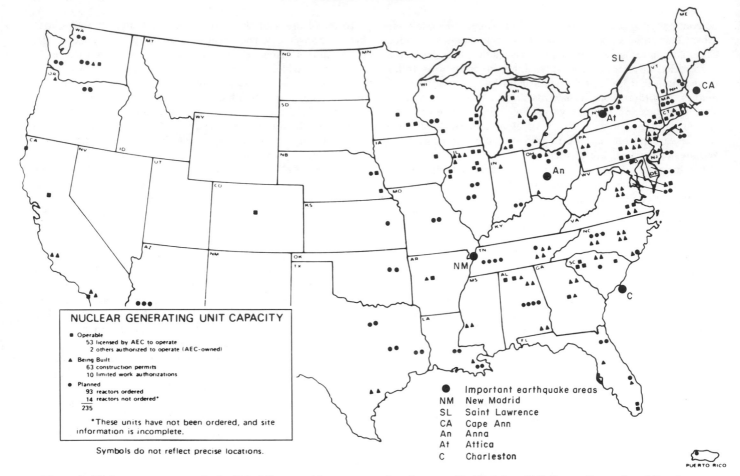

Figure 1. Nuclear power reactors in the United States and important earthquake areas. Modified from U.S. Energy Research and Development Administration (1975).

delays as well as costly redesigning. One approach that could avoid this conflict would be for the utility to submit an Early Site Review Report (ESRR). In this case the geologic and seismologic data are reviewed in a manner similar to that used for the PSAR, except that there is no actual plant design. When the review of the ESRR is concluded, the design-earthquake and seismic-design parameters for that site are established, and the plant engineering design can then be implemented using the accepted seismic-design values.

Documentation for data that are presented in the PSARs and ESRRs is another area of concern. Frequently a statement based on an incomplete evaluation of a feature is made. For example, take the statement "the Alma fault is 10 km long." This statement does not adequately describe the fault unless it is followed by descriptions of how the fault is terminated at each extremity. Often the obvious alternative interpretation is not discussed or illustrated. This lack is particularly evident in cross sections where only a broad monoclinal warp is shown and the alternate fault interpretation of the same data is omitted. This problem also occurs in the use of qualifying rather than quantifying phrases in descriptions of faults, such as "virtually no" or "only minor" movement along the fault has occurred in the Holocene. Neither of these phrases is acceptable because it has no clear quantitative significance. Would one consider the San Andreas fault to be "less capable" because at the

place examined it shows "only minor" movement, such as 150-mm offset of a curbstone? Any amount of displacement is significant and should be so stated, and qualifying phrases should be omitted.

ALTERNATIVES

Because utilities and the NRC desire to maintain the review schedule, or even shorten it, some means of accomplishing this must be considered. One suggestion that has been proposed for sites east of the Rocky Mountains would be to adopt a specific universal acceleration value for all locations except those near certain earthquake areas, such as New Madrid or Charleston (Fig. 1). The use of determined acceleration values from 90 sites gives an average acceleration value of $0.16g$. Within this grouping, however, five plants have values between $0.20g$ and $0.25g$. If $0.25g$ were established as a universal acceleration value east of the Rocky Mountains, it would be too conservative compared to the overall average of $0.16g$. Furthermore, if an applicant wanted to justify a lesser value, it would have to make the same geologic and seismologic investigations as under the present regulation, and there would be no savings in time or research expenses. Even if the applicant accepted the conservative $0.25g$, it would need to make the necessary geologic and seismologic investigations to assure that no nearby fault exists that might generate a larger acceleration and that the plant site will not be subjected to ground displacement. Despite recent intensive research at New Madrid, Charleston, and other areas, knowledge of specific earthquake-generating structures east of the Rocky Mountains is too meager to provide an understanding of the seismicity of these areas. Consequently, the adoption of a universal acceleration value does not appear to offer a viable solution to apparent schedule problems.

Another possibility that might help alleviate the problems of individual site approval would be to establish nuclear power parks. After appropriate geologic and seismologic evaluation, each park would be assigned specific seismic-design parameters. Clusters of reactors could then be built within the park as energy needs demanded. Such parks could also provide fuel fabrication and recycling facilities. However, the advantages of centralized energy parks must be measured against other concerns such as security, the environment, and accidents. Would it be wise to centralize nuclear plants in several regional parks, or should the plants be dispersed throughout the country? What problems would the distribution of electricity from centralized energy parks entail? A careful analysis of alternatives should be made before nuclear parks can be accepted as the plan for the future. For a more comprehensive discussion of the nuclear energy–park concept, refer to a report by Cope (1975).

CONCLUSIONS

To the present, no shortcuts to nuclear plant siting have emerged. Utilities may assure closer adherence to review schedules by adequately funding the geologic and seismologic investigations and, in turn, demanding more adequate docu-

mentation from the consulting firms. The perfect PSAR may be only an illusion, but the closer a PSAR is to perfection the better its chances of prompt, timely review.

ACKNOWLEDGMENTS

The author greatly appreciates the critical review of this paper by James Devine and Frederick Houser.

REFERENCES CITED

Code of Federal Regulations, 1978, Title 10, Energy; Part 100 [10 CFR 100], Reactor site criteria; Appendix A, Seismic and geologic siting criteria for nuclear power plants: Washington, D.C., U.S. Nuclear Regulatory Commission.

Cope, D. F., 1975, Nuclear energy centers—A prime element in reactor siting, in Nuclear safety: Oak Ridge, Tennessee, U.S. Nuclear Regulatory Commission, v. 16, no. 3, p. 282.

Regulatory Guide 1.70, 1975, Standard Format and content of Safety Analysis Reports for nuclear power plants: Washington, D.C., U.S. Nuclear Regulatory Commission.

U.S. Atomic Energy Commission, 1974, Power plant capital costs—Current trends and sensitivity to economic parameters: Washington, D.C., U.S. Atomic Energy Commission, Division of Reactor Research and Development, WASH-1345, 76, p.

U.S. Energy Research and Development Administration, 1975, Nuclear reactors built, being built, or planned in the United States as of December 31, 1974: Available only from U.S. Department of Commerce, National Technical Information Service, Springfield, Virginia 22161, as Report. TID-8200-R31, 41 p.

MANUSCRIPT RECEIVED BY THE SOCIETY JULY 13, 1978
MANUSCRIPT ACCEPTED NOVEMBER 13, 1978

Geological Society of America
Reviews in Engineering Geology, Volume IV
1979

The State-Federal partnership in the siting of nuclear power plants

JAMES F. DAVIS*

State Geologist, Geological Survey–New York State Museum, New York State Education Department, Room 973, State Education Building, Albany, New York, 12234

JAMES E. SLOSSON

Slosson and Associates, Consulting Geologists, 14054 Victory Boulevard, Van Nuys, California 91401 (Former State Geologist of California)

ROBERT H. FAKUNDINY

Environmental Geologist, Geological Survey, New York State Museum and Science Service, Room 973, State Education Building, Albany, New York 12234

ABSTRACT

Geology and seismology studies are becoming increasingly important in nuclear power plant siting decisions. Earthquake hazard assessment is perhaps the most challenging application of these disciplines to siting. Techniques for determination of the probabilities of damaging earthquakes and forecasting of seismic events need further development before they can be routinely applied as prescribed standards to power plant siting. Although the plate-tectonics model provides a functional explanation for the loci of earthquake activity along plate boundaries, the genesis of seismicity within lithospheric plates is less well understood. The seismic potential of numerous mapped, geologic structures in many portions of the North American continent are still matters of conjecture and disagreement.

The current siting criteria provide a normative procedure for establishing seismic design bases using the regional earthquake history and structural geology, together with detailed observations at the site. This process of prescribed analysis can, and has, led different investigators to contrasting conclusions.

States review the seismic design conclusions of the applicant utility and the safety evaluations of the Nuclear Regulatory Commission (NRC). Outside of the utilities and the NRC, the States are virtually the only other entities with scientific expertise that regularly participate in the siting process. The State role is usually advisory and nonregulatory. States contribute extensive knowledge of regional geology and seismicity to the decision-making process. Increasingly, the State geological surveys provide comments and suggestions to the Federal government and to utilities at an early enough stage so that an extensive and helpful dialogue precedes the State's ultimate, formal review of siting reports.

In this discussion, we examine the State roles in determining the site-specific seismic-design bases for nuclear power plants. We consider the roles and perspectives of other parties as well. The scientific and procedural limitations that affect the siting process are analyzed. Finally, recommendations are made to improve the manner in which conclusions about seismic hazards at nuclear power plant sites are presented.

OBJECTIVES OF THE SITING PROCEDURES

The desired results of the regulatory process include (1) development of decisions in a fair manner that provides judicial "due process" to all participating parties and (2) attainment of safe, economically desirable decisions from the vantage of both the consumer and the utility. Costs should not result from unnecessary overdesign. Adequate design based on good scientific data helps to assure that no future retrofitting, loss of life, or power outages will result from the original siting decisions.

---

*Present address: State Geologist of California, Room 1341, 1416 9th Street, Sacramento, California 95814.

THE LICENSING PROCESS

Approximately 67 reactors have been licensed using the general procedures outlined below. The Congress established a Federal regulatory agency with the Atomic Energy Act of 1954 and its amendments. The Energy Reorganization Act of 1974 abolished the original Atomic Energy Commission (AEC) and created the Nuclear Regulatory Commission (NRC), giving it the licensing and related regulatory functions of the original AEC.[1]

Licensing a reactor is achieved in two stages. The NRC issues a Construction Permit after the NRC has decided that a site is generally satisfactory and that the proposed construction plans developed by the utility are adequate. Following construction, the NRC must issue a Full Operating License before the reactor can be placed in service.

The regulations require that the applicant prepare a Preliminary Safety Analysis Report (PSAR), which includes the determination of the seismic design (Code of Federal Regulations, 1978). Staff members of the NRC Site Analysis Branch (SAB) conduct an extensive review of the document and make at least one field trip to the proposed reactor location. The NRC staff then prepares a Safety Evaluation Report (SER) that presents conclusions regarding the seismic and other safety-related considerations. A public hearing is held before an Atomic Safety and Licensing Board (ASLB), constituted separately for each nuclear plant under consideration. If, in the opinion of this quasijudicial panel, the applicant's design conclusions and construction plans are satisfactory, a Construction Permit will be issued.

A Final Safety Analysis Report (FSAR) is prepared by the applicant as construction continues. A NRC staff review of the FSAR is intended to assure that all newly available data that have appeared since the PSAR was submitted have been identified and interpreted by the applicant.[2]

Finally, after an additional set of hearings before the ASLB, the Operating License is granted with or without conditions (stipulations), which may require further investigations or limit operating conditions for the reactor.

In order to guide the applicant in the preparation of adequate SARs, the NRC has issued the "Standard Format and Content of Safety Analysis Reports for Nuclear Power Plants" (Regulatory Guide 1.70, 1975).

The NRC Office of Nuclear Reactor Regulation also issues Standard Review Plans to guide the NRC technical staff responsible for the review of the applicant's SARs. These plans are keyed to the Standard Format for SARs and provide NRC staff guidelines for acceptance criteria, review steps, methods of evaluating applicant's conclusions, and procedures to be employed during staff on-site visits.

The specific procedures by which the applicant must reach the seismic design conclusions are set forth in the regulations of Appendix A (Code of Federal Regulations, 1978).[3] Since 1973, when this regulation was promulgated, applicants have

---

[1] In this paper the abbreviation NRC will refer to both the Atomic Energy Commission and its successor.

[2] Subsequently in this report, PSARs and FSARs when referred to in a general sense will be designated as "SAR."

[3] Appendix A in this paper refers to this citation.

been required to establish the seismic design bases for critical structures using the vibratory ground motion associated with the Safe Shutdown Earthquake (SSE) or events along any "capable faults" that could affect the proposed reactor site.

The licensing process and plant construction commonly takes more than 10 yr to complete. As this long and expensive undertaking goes forward, the commitment of the applicant utility to the specific site in question becomes very great. Recently, provisions for an early NRC review of site suitability have been established in Appendix Q to 10 CFR part 50. Together, these modifications establish procedures for the early NRC review of issues of site suitability and rendering of "partial site suitability decisions." Under these new rules, the NRC may deny requests for an early review on sufficient grounds including objections from State or local government or the likelihood that the preliminary findings would not retain their validity as the licensing process continues. As in the regular process, the staff must prepare a SER stating its conclusions. Although issuance of a staff report does not constitute a commitment to issue a permit or license, the partial decision will remain in effect for a period of 5 yr, or until a PSAR is docketed and the Construction Permit proceedings are concluded, if accomplished in less than that time.

These latter rules are too new for us to precisely evaluate their influence on safety siting decisions. A recommendation regarding their probable effect is discussed later in this report.

After the ASLB issues a license, parties that participated in the licensing hearing may petition the NRC Atomic Safety Licensing Appeals Board (ASLAB) for a hearing in order to appeal the decision. If a hearing is granted before the ASLAB and that board's ruling is also unsatisfactory in the view of a party, further review can be sought from the commissioners of the NRC acting as a panel and, ultimately, relief can be sought in the Federal courts.

In discharging its regulatory responsibilities, the NRC receives independent geological and seismological advice from several agencies and groups. The Advisory Committee on Reactor Safeguards (ACRS) was established in 1957 by an amendment to the Atomic Energy Act of 1954 (Public Law 85-256, Section 29). ACRS has up to 15 members who are appointed by the NRC. This panel routinely reviews the findings of the applicant and the NRC staff concerning the safety of each reactor before the Construction Permit and the Operating License are granted by the ASLB. The committee also provides comments or recommendations on any matter referred to it by the commission.

There has never been an earth scientist member of the ACRS. Present membership comprises environmental health scientists, and nuclear, civil, metallurgical, and materials engineers. However, earth scientists of national reputation do serve regularly as consultants to the ACRS.

The United States Geological Survey (USGS) and the National Oceanic and Atmospheric Administration (NOAA) have assisted the NRC in developing the geologic and seismologic criteria for nuclear plant siting (Appendix A, 10 CFR 100) that were promulgated in draft form for comment in 1971 and were revised and adopted in 1973. In addition, a memorandum of agreement provides for USGS review of technical matters on request. On occasion, these reviews will include commentary on specific portions of an applicant's SAR (see Morris, this volume).

As the licensing process goes forward, the NRC technical staff is expected to carry on a dialogue with the geological and geotechnical consultants of the applicant utilities in order to assure that important items are being considered in a timely manner. In those cases where the State technical agencies are actively participating in the earth science review, State scientists may also be requested to make comments while sections of the SARs are being prepared. Both of these procedures expedite getting the applicant oriented for addressing the major geological and seismological considerations as early as possible.

THE APPROACH IN THE GEOLOGIC AND SEISMIC SITING CRITERIA

Appendix A is generally regarded as a significant improvement over the preceding regulation, because it specifies the manner in which a conclusion is to be derived concerning the faults in the neighborhood of the site and the manner in which these structures are to be regarded in reference to the seismicity of the region. These data are employed to document a design basis for maximum vibratory ground motion (peak acceleration).

On November 25, 1971, the first draft of Appendix A was published in the *Federal Register*. The regulation was presented for comment, and no effective date for its application was provided. However, between this time and the December 13, 1973, effective date, applicants generally sought to conduct only such investigations as required by the interim version of Appendix A.

The Inherent Conservatism of Appendix A

Appendix A was issued by the NRC as a tentative document. As stated in section I, Purpose (second paragraph),

These criteria are based on the limited geophysical and geological information available to date concerning faults and earthquake occurrence and effect. They will be revised as necessary when more complete information becomes available.

Appendix A is flexible regarding the extent of studies that may be adequate for specific sites. The third paragraph of section II, Scope, reads:

Each applicant for a construction permit shall investigate all seismic and geologic factors that may affect the design and operation of the proposed nuclear power plant irrespective of whether such factors are explicitly included in these criteria. Additional investigations and/or more conservative determination than those included in these criteria may be required for sites located in areas having complex geology or in areas of high seismicity. If an applicant believes that the particular seismology and geology of a site indicate that some of these criteria or portions thereof need not be satisfied, the specific sections of these criteria should be identified in the license application and supporting data to justify clearly such departures should be presented.

Appendix A recognizes that geologic and seismologic conditions may differ across the country. Three specific characteristics of capable faults are set forth in the definition of the term in section III, Definitions (g). These characteristics are discussed later in this paper. The definition is followed by the following statement:

Notwithstanding the foregoing paragraphs III(g) (1), (2), and (3), structural associations of a fault with geologic structural features which are geologically old (at least pre-Quaternary) such as many of those found in the Eastern region of the United States shall, in the absence of conflicting evidence, demonstrate that the fault is not a capable fault within this definition.

The problems in applying the siting criteria with an incomplete understanding of site geology and seismicity are recognized in Appendix A. In section V, Seismic and Geologic Design Bases, (a) Determination of Design Basis for Vibratory Ground Motion, (1) Determination of Safe Shutdown Earthquake, paragraph (iv), the following statement is made: "in order to compensate for the limited data, the procedures in paragraphs (a)(1)(i) through (iii) of this section shall be applied in a conservative manner." Additional conservatism is applied in paragraph (v) which reads:

Where the maximum vibratory accelerations of the Safe Shutdown Earthquake at the foundations of the nuclear power structures are determined to be less than one-tenth the acceleration of gravity (0.1 g) as a result of the steps required in paragraphs (a)(1)(i) through (iv) of this section, it shall be assumed that the maximum vibratory accelerations of the Safe Shutdown Earthquake at these foundations are at least 0.1 g.

To summarize: Appendix A was intended to be open to incorporation of new technical developments, flexible in regard to the characteristics of specific sites, cognizant of variations in geology and seismicity throughout the country, and conservative in its approach. The challenge to all parties is to make wise judgments in these regards while using the results of the specific investigations required by Appendix A to derive design conclusions concerning vibratory ground motion.

Two recent developments further emphasize the conservatism required in applying Appendix A. In 1977, the NRC ruled that the SSE can exceed the maximum historical event in the regional seismic history, if such a conclusion is warranted by existing information. In January 1977, the ACRS advised the NRC that in the eastern United States new plants should be designed for at least 0.2g acceleration, because there is a general lack of understanding of earthquake genesis in this region. We shall comment on the significance of these decisions later.

Investigations Required by the Siting Criteria of Appendix A

Appendix A prescribes a means of determining design accelerations associated with vibratory ground motion either by identification of a SSE or by establishing the presence of a *capable* fault sufficiently close to affect the proposed plant to a greater degree than the SSE.

Design for the SSE acceleration seeks to protect the plant

against occurrence of a "maximum probable earthquake" during the lifetime of the proposed nuclear facility. A plant with such a design would be so constructed that if an event equivalent to the SSE were to occur, the utility would be able to shut down the reactor under conditions of adequate cooling capability and structural integrity for a necessary shutdown period. Appendix A, section III, Definitions, paragraph (c) specifies that the SSE is "that earthquake which is based upon the evaluation of the maximum earthquake potential considering the regional and local geology and seismology and specific characteristics of the local subsurface material."

We believe the concept of the SSE to be valid. The greatest limitation of the SSE is that the magnitude and frequency characteristics of this hypothetical seismic event cannot be calculated in a straightforward, deterministic way that is premised on an understanding of earthquake-generating mechanisms with equivalent confidence in all parts of the United States. The procedure for establishing the SSE is prescribed in section IV of Appendix A, Required Investigations and section V, Seismic and Geologic Design Bases.

Determination of the SSE requires preparation of a list of all of the historically reported earthquake epicenters that could have affected or could reasonably have been expected to have affected the site. These are to be noted by location, magnitude or felt intensity, and any other characteristics that may be available.

Tectonic provinces within a 322-km (200-mi) radius of the proposed site are to be identified. These provinces are defined in section III, paragraph (h) as regions "of the North American continent characterized by relative consistency of geologic structural features contained therein." *No maps are provided of these provinces in the Appendix, nor have any been supplied in the Regulatory Guide or even informally proposed by the NRC Staff.* As a result, each applicant can and must propose his own.

Appendix A specifies that the earthquake epicenters compiled in the historical earthquake listing shall be correlated "where possible, with tectonic structures any part of which is located within 200 miles of the site." These tectonic structures are defined in section III, paragraph (i) as "A large scale dislocation or distortion within the earth's crust. Its extent is measured in miles." Presumably, this dislocation is most generally a fault or break in the Earth's crust along which offset has taken place. The term "dislocation" broadens this definition presumably to include certain types of folds that, where observed in three dimensions, pass vertically downward into faults. Section V (a)(1)(i) of Appendix A provides that "The accelerations at the site shall be determined assuming that the epicenters of greatest magnitude or locations of highest intensity [felt events, not instrumentally monitored] related to the tectonic structures are situated at the point on the structures closest to the site." For the purpose of determining the SSE, if the largest event can be associated with a structure, the earthquake is hypothetically assumed to occur at the location where this structure is closest to the site, and the vibratory ground motion affecting the facility then is calculated.

Section V(a)(1)(ii) states:

Where epicenters or locations of highest intensity of historically reported earthquakes cannot be reasonably related to tectonic structures but are identified . . . with tectonic provinces in which the site is located, the accelerations of the site shall be determined assuming that these earthquakes occur at the site.

Similarly, those highest intensity events that are not associated with tectonic structures in the tectonic provinces adjacent to the site will be considered to take place hypothetically at the closest position of the province to the site for purposes of calculating vibratory ground motion effects at the facility [section V(a)(1)(iii)]. For the rest of this paper we will refer to these "highest intensity events" as the "controlling earthquakes."

Alternatively, under appropriate geologic conditions the seismic design bases can be established by the presence of a "capable" fault in the vicinity of a nuclear facility. Section III(g) of Appendix A defines a capable fault as

a fault which has exhibited one or more of the following characteristics:

(1) Movement at or near the ground surface at least once within the past 35,000 years or movement of a recurring nature within the past 500,000 years.

(2) Macro-seismicity instrumentally determined with records of sufficient precision to demonstrate a direct relationship with the fault.

(3) A structural relationship to a capable fault according to characteristics 1 and 2 of this paragraph such that movement on one could be reasonably expected to be accompanied by movement on the other.

The stipulation is also made as follows:

Notwithstanding the foregoing paragraphs III(g)(1), (2) and (3), structural association of a fault with geologic structural features which are geologically old (at least pre-Quaternary) such as many of those found in the Eastern region of the United States shall, in the absence of conflicting evidence, demonstrate that the fault is not a capable fault within this definition.

Section IV(a)(8) provides that the length, structural relationships, and offset characteristics of capable faults must be presented in the applicant's SAR. Section V(b) sets forth the scope of the mapping of capable faults.

One difficulty immediately arises in applying the criterion of movement during the past 35,000 yr or recurrent movement during the past 500,000 yr in many parts of the northern United States. Glaciation has produced a sequence of unconsolidated materials (sand, gravel, clay, and so forth) that lies upon the much older bedrock which exceeds 500,000 yr in age. In many places, these materials are considerably less than 35,000 yr old and provide a very short time during which movements might have been recorded. A sedimentary section spanning the past 500,000 yr is not common in the East.

Another serious difficulty in applying the criteria of Appendix A relative to capable faulting is in the ambiguity of the terms "macroseismicity" and "records of sufficient precision to demonstrate a direct relationship with a fault."

LIMITATIONS IN APPLYING THE CRITERIA OF APPENDIX A

The status of geologic and seismologic understanding imposes limitations upon the rigor with which Appendix A can be applied to determination of SSE and capable faults. These circumstances exist in both the eastern and western United States.

Eastern United States

Difficulties in using the present status of understanding of earthquake activity in the eastern United States arise from the following: (1) limited perception of the modern seismogenic significance of ancient tectonic structures that were formed under Paleozoic and Mesozoic deformational conditions that no longer exist; (2) lack of understanding of the earthquake-generating mechanisms in the eastern United States and, therefore, an inability to definitively explain the historical pattern of earthquake distribution; and (3) uncertainty concerning the recurrence rate for large, damaging earthquakes in any part of the East (a number of damaging earthquakes have occurred in historical time near such locations as Cape Ann, Massachussetts, Fig. 1).

In the absence of rigor, it is best to be at least moderately conservative, so that siting decisions will not be premised upon optimistic hypotheses that may soon fade away. The intensity of studying earthquakes in the East is increasing, and this rapid development has led to the demise of some of the more traditional, earlier speculations and concommittantly has spawned a newer round of hypotheses. Such is the manner in which science progresses. Unfortunately, in the absence of more conclusive facts, both the defunct and the newer, untested conjectures are being seized upon by some parties as geologic determinations worthy of use in seismic design-basis conclusions.

Until about 15 yr ago, earth scientists regarded the eastern United States as a region in which the significant events occurred comparatively deep within the Earth's crust and bore no causal relationship to structures that are observable at the surface. This is the conception presented by Richter (1958). A much more complicated picture is now emerging. Parts of these new insights can be attributed to the closer collaboration between geologists and seismologists in recent years and to improved knowledge of regional structural geology and seismicity.

Development of the plate-tectonics theory, which attempts to explain geologic and geophysical phenomena on a planetary scale, has also provided a context for understanding depositional and deformational events in time and space during the geologic past in regions such as the Appalachian fold belt. A great deal of new geologic mapping is in progress throughout the eastern United States. Expanded coverage of aeromagnetic and gravity surveys (see V. J. Murphy and others, this volume) is providing geophysical evidence of intermediate and very large-scale features that are not identifiable when conventional mapping techniques are used at the surface. Since the early 1960s, radiometric age determination of rocks throughout the metamorphic and igneous terranes of the East have contributed to significant revision in the "classical" geologic history for that region (see P. J. Murphy and others, this volume). Interpretation of satellite imagery (see McEldowney and Pascucci, this volume) is providing an expanded knowledge of brittle structures in the region. These new data, together with plate-tectonics concepts, are beginning to provide a greatly improved understanding of the sequences of deformation and metamorphism that took place within the Appalachian fold belt during the Paleozoic Era and the subsequent overprint of Mesozoic tensional structural events.

On a smaller scale, insights into tectonic styles such as gravity sliding of soft, unindurated sediment and formation of gneiss domes have assisted in resolving persistent enigmas such as the Taconic geology of western New England and the Baltimore gneiss domes of the central Appalachians. Vibratory-source, seismic reflection interpretations that were formerly confidential have fortunately been released by oil companies during the past seven or eight years. These deep-penetration seismic profiles have modified the understanding of structural characteristics of parts of the Appalachian fold belt and the adjacent plateau. New seismic, gravity, reflection, and aeromagnetic surveys off the Atlantic Coast have extended our knowledge of the structural geology in those areas. The USGS has undertaken intensive geological and geophysical investigations of the Charleston, South Carolina, area and the Mississippi Embayment (see Nuttli, this volume), where very severe, damaging earthquakes occurred during the 19th century. Some new perspectives on the relationship of seismicity and faulting are in the process of development.

Since the late 1950s, a number of earthquake catalogs have synthesized the seismic history of the eastern United States (Coffman and von Hake, 1973; Heck and Eppley, 1958; Smith, 1962). Network monitoring has demonstrated the geographic correlation of instrumentally located events and the epicenters of much older "felt" events in the seismic history of the region. In contrast to earlier thought, most events are comparatively shallow (10 km or less). The epicentral pattern of events is complicated and nonrandom. Hypotheses explaining these distributions in relation to geologic structure have been developed but do not provide a rigorous basis for applying Appendix A. Limitations in correlating seismic events and known geologic structures are apparent in the work of Hadley and Devine (1974).

It has recently been proposed that some earthquakes may result from stress releases near the boundaries of massive igneous intrusive bodies (Kane, 1977). Details of the mechanisms remain obscure, however, and it is not yet clear whether there is a spatial correlation of earthquakes with some mafic plutons.

The maximum possible earthquake at any location in the eastern United States cannot be well established by the short seismic history of the region according to McGuire (1977). More work is needed on geologic and tectonic evidence that might contribute to increased understanding. In situ stress and strain measurements may ultimately be helpful in such assessments.

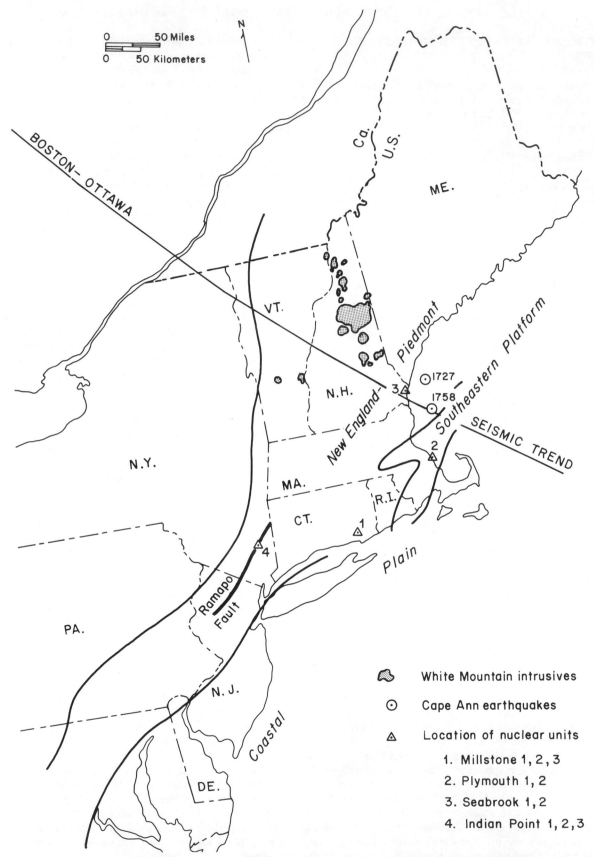

Figure 1. Selected nuclear power stations and pertinent geologic features. Heavy lines indicate boundaries of the New England–Piedmont, Southeastern Platform, and Coastal Plain tectonic provinces advocated by NRC testimony in Indian Point Appeals Board Proceeding.

Improved understanding of the attenuation of earthquake waves in the East is necessary to seismic hazard analysis. Better understanding of this phenomenon will improve intensity estimates of historical events, interpretation of magnitudes of instrumentally recorded earthquakes, and calculation of on-site accelerations from off-site hypothetical events.

To summarize, we are just beginning to critically examine the structure and seismicity of the East. Multiple hypotheses are available to explain the same phenomena. Of really critical significance is the possible role of reactivated Precambrian, Paleozoic, and Mesozoic structures in the generation of earthquakes under modern stress conditions. These relationships must be more fully understood. In the meantime, Appendix A must be conservatively, but realistically, applied to seismic design decisions.

Western United States

Although the relationships of earthquakes to faulting are more substantially correlated in the western United States (particularly on the coast), there are, nevertheless, significant uncertainties in applying earth science to siting decisions (see Bolt, this volume). During the 1970s the approaches recommended by Allen (1975) which have included emphasis on geological observations, particularly measurements of sequences of displacements along faults during the Quaternary, have proven to be useful in seismic hazard analysis. The recent results of Sieh (1977) are a notable example of success in expanding the knowledge of large earthquake recurrence rates on important faults.

An example of recently developed insights between earthquake activity and structure is provided by the Ferndale earthquakes of 1975 which were located and the fault mechanism determined in part as a result of data from the State of California Strong Motion Program that was initiated soon after the 1971 San Fernando earthquake. The location of the strong motion instruments at selected sites throughout the State of California has added greatly to the seismic data bank. As of January 1978, 325 instruments (or stations) have been placed by the California Division of Mines and Geology in compliance with the Strong Motion Program.

The state of California in another program to better delineate fault zones and improve the understanding of the ages of movement along them has enacted the Alquist-Priolo Special Studies Act, which was passed in 1972 and is directed to identification and mapping of active faults (Docket 50–286, 1976). The Alquist-Priolo Act has provided some new input but of only limited extent and limited value. The Alquist-Priolo Act requires that the State Geologist delineate a zone 180 m (600 ft) wide on each side of the apparent or most recent trace of the San Andreas, Hayward, Calaveras, and San Jacinto faults and other faults that can be proven to have suffered Holocene fault displacement (Fig. 2). Thus, the effect of the act is to alert planners, government officials, land owners, or purchasers that an active fault exists in a given geographical area. The requirements for the geologic investigations is placed upon the land user or seller, and local government is responsible for the review of the reports. Because most local government entities do not have geologic expertise on their staffs, the review process and, in turn, the quality of the reports have ranged from good where the review capability exists to very poor and, in some cases, substandard or subprofessional where ineptness exists with regard to review. Thus, even though the intent of the act is exemplary, the products have often been very questionable and, in some cases, of little value.

Monitoring with strong-motion instruments during the past 10 yr has also provided a greater reason for conservatism, because some very localized vibratory ground-motion accelerations have been recorded that exceeded levels commonly thought possible by seismologists a few years earlier. Accelograms of the San Fernando event of February 1971 clearly underscore this point. Some geologists and seismologists correctly argued for higher acceleration values prior to 1971, and the instrument data from the 1971 quake seem to support their contentions. The earlier siting decisions should not influence our application of the siting criteria at the present time.

Additional insights are required to better understand the significance of microearthquakes. In this paper, the term "microearthquake" refers to events of less than modified Mercali (MM) intensity III or about Richter magnitude 3. Microearthquake studies throughout the United States have added to our knowledge of motions on active faults and to the limits of seismically active regions. Yet, the relationship between microearthquake activity and the potential for damaging earthquakes to occur is not clearly understood. Nevertheless, the expanding data base, derived from the existing seismic networks and from those being planned, still holds much promise for eventually producing the information necessary to determine the variable nature of earthquake-generating mechanisms.

The need for conservatism is underscored by the circumstances at Humboldt Bay (Humboldt County, California) where the nuclear plant was designed for less than the magnitude 5.2 Ferndale earthquake of June 1975. This event, located about 16.5 km (35 mi) from the site, created a ground acceleration at the plant that exceeded a design basis for the SSE. The Corral Canyon site in Malibu and the Diablo Canyon site are examples of locations that were discovered to have previously unappreciated seismic potentials after new, detailed information was acquired (Fig. 2).

SEISMIC DESIGN SITING DECISIONS PRIOR TO APPENDIX A

The siting criteria which are employed for seismic design have an obvious effect upon the values for which the plant is designed. We shall examine the regulatory procedures and an example of the nuclear plant design requirement outcomes before adoption of Appendix A and how the Appendix has been applied in several siting cases.

Prior to the development of Appendix A and the Standard Format and Standard Review Plan, geologic and seismologic sections of SARs were quite informal. The PSARs and FSARs of Indian Point reactors 1 and 2 in New York State can serve as cases in point, although other examples exist. Documents for reactor Unit 1 predate 1958; the plant was given a Provisional Operating License in 1962. The SAR geologic discussion was primarily a regional review that provided the type of information commonly incorporated in accounts of regional geologic history (Docket 50-2, 1962). A very generalized map was presented that illustrated the distribution of rock types in the immediate vicinity of the plant. No attention was drawn to the Triassic Ramapo border fault that passes within a few kilometres of the site. As subsequent, detailed mapping has revealed, this original map did not identify certain faults in the immediate vicinity of the reactor locations. Rather, the map is the type that is commonly part of a static-type foundation-design report for routine construction. The seismology section is a short, incomplete list of significant earthquakes in the eastern United States. The August 10, 1884, event in southeastern New York is presented as MM VI. There is no evaluation of the relationship between the faults and regional seismicity. An acceleration of only 0.03g was concluded to be adequate for design.

When filing for unit 2 in the late 1960s, the applicant largely represented the same geology and seismology reports from the earlier SARs for unit 1 (Docket 50-2, 1962). This neglected the newly developed catalog of eastern North American earthquakes of the U.S. Coast and Geodetic Survey (Heck and others, 1958) and that for eastern Canada and adjacent areas, developed by the Ottawa Observatory (Smith, 1962, 1966). These standard references classify the August 10, 1884, event as MM VII. The applicant did not take note of any of these publications nor was a rationale proposed for an intensity figure lower than presented in these documents.

Prior to the implementation of Appendix A, Federal seismic design review of the SARs for the period are essentially presented in one-page letters provided by the U.S. Coast and Geodetic Survey, which had earthquake cataloging responsibilities. Officers of the Coast and Geodetic Survey simply stated in such letters that the applicant's information on the earthquake history was essentially correct. In the review of the Indian Point unit 2 PSAR, the NRC staff also failed to mention that the SAR earthquake list was in disagreement with the standard catalog references. Neither the staff persons responsible for the conclusions nor the essence of their deliberations were identified. This suggests the nature of the generally low-key approach applied to satisfying seismic criteria prior to the appearance of Appendix A.

The practical result of this early approach to regulatory decision-making was a comparatively low acceleration design basis for plants sited during this period. Probing questions were not posed by any party to licensing, the NRC, or its advisors. The fact that some newer plants in the same regions or later units at the same sites are licensed for higher acceleration designs than their predecessors bears tacit witness to the increased scrutiny of geologic and seismologic factors in recent years.

About the same time as Appendix A became effective, the NRC acquired a technical staff of geologists and seismologists to conduct the reviews of the SARs. It should be noted that this technical group is quite small in relation to its responsibility. It is recognized throughout the siting community that this group is performing a heroic task, given its small resources.

In the succeeding section, we will examine some of the more recent seismic design conclusions.

SEISMIC DESIGN SITING CONCLUSIONS DEVELOPED UNDER CRITERIA OF APPENDIX A

The promulgation of Appendix A by the NRC has improved the application of geology and seismology to nuclear plant design. Nevertheless, there is need for clarification and standardization of the means by which the design conclusions are reached. The following discussion highlights this need using general examples.

The Safe Shutdown Earthquake

Separate parties determining the seismic design basis for a single site may reach different conclusions concerning the number and areal extent of tectonic provinces, the relationship of seismicity to specific tectonic structures, or the existence of capable faults. Some divergences derive from the ambiguous definitions of these terms in Appendix A. Other disagreements result from different interpretations of geology and seismicity. Typical uncertainties regarding terminology include the following questions: (1) How much structural contrast should exist within a tectonic province? (2) Considering the objective of the siting criteria, should a tectonic province comprise an area of uniform seismic potential even though seismicity is not part of the province definition? (3) What criteria should be employed for associating 18th and 19th century earthquakes with mapped tectonic structures as required in the determination of the SSE? (4) When, if ever, should a pluton or stock be considered a tectonic structure capable of generating earthquakes? In the face of such uncertainties, the NRC has the very difficult responsibility to make decisions affecting public safety that are correct for specific locations and to set satisfactory precedents for future regulatory positions. The States can make important contributions to this process by constructively and objectively conducting independent reviews of the applicant's SARs and the NRC's SERs.

Several examples of the ambiguities and uncertainties of the siting process should illustrate the difficulties in reaching decisions and demonstrate the type of contributions that States can provide.

Several past inconsistencies in administering Appendix A can be demonstrated by comparison of the regulatory decisions for Millstone unit 3 in Connecticut and Indian Point units 2 and 3 in New York.

The Millstone Case of SSE Determination

In 1727 and 1755, MM VIII events occurred near Cape Ann in eastern Massachusetts. The standard earthquake catalogs are agreed that the intensities are at least VIII, but the catalogs are not in complete agreement on precise location (Heck and Eppley, 1958; Smith, 1962; Coffman and von Hake, 1973). Other events such as the Woburn, Massachusetts, event of 1817 and the East Hadden, Connecticut, event of 1719 (Heck and Eppley, 1958; Coffman and von Hake, 1973) have been termed MM VIII by some investigators, although lower intensities are suggested by others (for example, Smith, 1962, 1966). The Cape Ann events have considerable significance for siting decisions in the East, but there is wide divergence of opinion about the geographic extent to which they should be considered as the SSE (Fig. 1).

In the FSAR for Millstone, Connecticut, unit 3 (Docket 50-423, 1973), the applicant presented six tectonic provinces located within 322 km (200 mi) of the site. Five of these provinces were accepted by the NRC staff in the SER issued concerning this reactor (Docket 50-423, 1974, p. 2–31).

> For purposes of seismicity consideration the Staff accepts the applicant's division of the New England Appalachian Mountain system into five tectonic provinces. From west to east there are the Berkshire–Green Mountains highlands, the Bronson Hill anticlinorium, the Merrimack synclinorium, the Narragansett Basin and, trending transverse to these, the Cape Ann–White Mountains intrusive zone.

Locations of the Cape Ann earthquakes were herein confined to the "White Mountain intrusive zone," Although the Berkshire–Green Mountains, the Bronson Hill anticlinorium, the Merrimack synclinorium, and the Narragansett basin were established designations in the geological literature, they have never before been presented as tectonic provinces. No evidence was submitted by either the applicant or the NRC staff to suggest that seismic potential within these areas is uniform or that their potentials contrast with each other. The NRC acceptance of the White Mountain structural province was based exclusively on the presence of Mesozoic plutons and is also without precedent in the literature, although there had been some speculation that the seismicity and the presence of plutons might somehow be related (Fig. 1).

Rodgers (1970) and King (1969) have presented structural subdivisions of the eastern United States to aid in their text discussions. Although their provinces encompass areas with "relative consistency of geologic structure," the categories were not developed with Appendix A in mind. On the other hand, the tectonic province map of Hadley and Devine (1974) was developed specifically for use with Appendix A. Hadley and Devine developed province subdivisions that are generally similar to those of Rodgers. These three publications are currently among the most widely cited eastern regional structural analyses. The provinces proposed by the Millstone 3 applicant and accepted by the NRC staff do not correspond to the structural subdivisions discussed by these authors. The provinces proposed by the Millstone 3 applicant are much smaller in size and with the exception of the "White Mountain intrusive zone" are discrete regional structures.

The Indian Point Case

In April 1974, the New York State Geological Survey pointed out (J. F. Davis and others, April 19, 1974, written commun.) to the NRC that the applicant's FSAR for Indian Point unit 3 (Docket 50-286, 1972) contained an incomplete and inaccurate earthquake catalog and lacked a tectonic province analysis. Following this communication in January 1976, although the applicant was not required to provide any new information prior to the April 1975 Operating License Hearing, the NRC staff issued Supplement 1 to its SER for unit 3 (Docket 50-286, 1976). The staff derived an SSE with ground-motion acceleration equivalent to the design specifications already established by the applicant for the almost completed reactor. The analysis for Indian Point addressed the same terrain lying within a

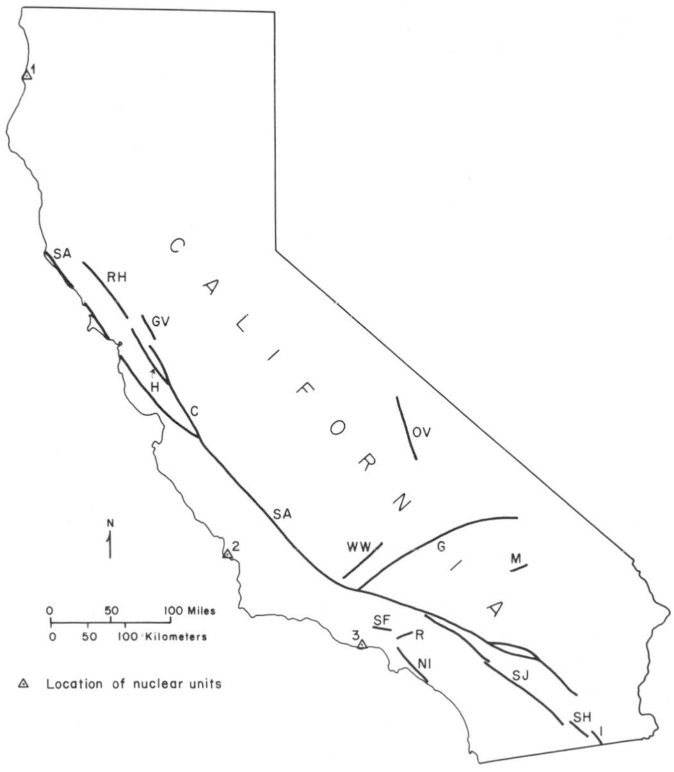
CALIFORNIA
1
2
3
SA
RH
GV
H
C
OV
WW
G
M
SF
R
NI
SJ
SH
I
N
0 50 100 Miles
0 50 100 Kilometers
Location of nuclear units
FAULT ZONES
C Calaveras
G Garlock
GV Green Valley & Concord
H Hayward
I Imperial
M Manix
NI Newport-Inglewood
OV Owens Valley
R Raymond Hill
RH Raymond Creek-Healdsburg
SA San Andreas
SF San Fernando
SH Superstition Hills
SJ San Jacinto
WW White Wolf

Figure 2. Special studies zones as delineated by the Alquist-Priolo Act of 1972 and selected nuclear power stations. Nuclear units are as follows: 1, Humboldt Bay; 2, Diablo Canyon; 3, Corral Canyon (proposed).

320-km radius of the plant that was also the subject of the SER for Millstone unit 3. Where the Millstone 3 SER specified there were five tectonic provinces, the NRC now concluded there was only one, the New England–Piedmont province, which is similar to the Piedmont province of Rodgers, including all of New England and the deformed Precambrian and Paleozoic rocks of eastern New York and adjacent New Jersey. The southern terminus of the province was not discussed. No map was presented, but rather simply a list of provinces considered by the staff to be within 322 km of the site. In such an arrangement, Cape Ann and Indian Point are in the same tectonic province. Without evidence of the 18th century Cape Ann events being associated with some tectonic structure, Appendix A requires that the SSE be derived assuming that equivalent earthquakes could occur on the Indian Point site. This would require a SSE of MM VIII rather than MM VII for which the plant is designed. The staff contended that a belt of seismicity known as the Boston-Ottawa seismic trend extends in a discontinuous fashion between the two metropolitan areas for which it is named, and it represents a tectonic structure with which the Cape Ann events can be associated. The NRC staff was cross-examined on this interpretation by the New York officials at the Indian Point unit 3 Operating License hearing. The State subsequently petitioned the NRC for a special seismic hearing to clarify the matter and was granted this request. Late in 1975, in answer to State interrogatories preparing for the seismic hearing on Indian Point, the NRC staff proposed a second province newly termed the "Southeast Platform province." It is a very small province that generally includes the Boston basin and the adjacent Cape Ann area.

The NRC thus contended that either the Cape Ann events were restricted to the Southeast Platform province or they were associated with the Boston-Ottawa seismic trend, which the staff interpreted to be a tectonic structure. None of the standard structural references considers the Southeast Platform province to exist as a discrete province of equal rank to the Piedmont. The Boston-Ottawa seismic trend has been described previously in the literature. On the basis of seismicity patterns, Diment and others (1972) made passing reference to a number of possible crustal structures that might exist in the eastern United States. One of these inferred structures extends across the main trends of the Appalachian Mountain system from the Boston area northwestward into adjacent Canada. Sbar and Sykes (1973) hypothesized that the patterns of seismicity in the Ottawa environs and in eastern Massachusetts may be related to an unobserved, deep-crustal "paleofracture" that may have been formed during the separation of the North American and African tectonic plates in the early Mesozoic. They also pointed out that this thesis is further supported by the positions of the Kelvin Seamounts off the coast of Massachusetts, the locations of the plutons of the White Mountain magma series in northern New England, and the Monteregion Hills intrusive series of Quebec Province. They identified anomalously fast traveltimes that may imply contrasts in crustal character of this seismically active zone. Obviously, there is merit in presenting such proposals before the profession. However, since the very existence of such a structure was presented as conjectural, it is patently premature to associate the regionally controlling Cape Ann earthquakes with an inferred feature and thus avoid dealing with MM intensity VIII SSEs that otherwise would have to be considered.

In a seismic hearing before the ASLAB, the state of New York rejected this approach as speculative and supported its position by the appearances of both L. R. Sykes and W. H. Diment as witnesses who testified that the NRC SSE conclusions based on their hypotheses were not warranted applications of Appendix A. In their testimony at this hearing, the NRC staff subsequently emphasized that the White Mountain plutons, taken as a group, constitute a tectonic structure with which the Cape Ann events may be associated. Yet there is no simple and direct relationship between the distribution of these intrusive units and the seismicity of the region. This is certainly not proposed in the work of Hadley and Devine (1974), who sought to explore relationships between structure and seismicity in their study.

Thus, the NRC staff has associated the Cape Ann events with the "White Mountain intrusive zone" as a tectonic province in the Millstone unit 3 licensing. But, in the Indian Point proceeding, the same events have been associated with the Boston-Ottawa seismic trend and with the White Mountain intrusive series as tectonic structures. The staff has further proposed that the events may be located in the small, little-known Southeast Platform province.

The Seabrook Case

In the Seabrook SER for units 1 and 2 (Docket 50443, 1975), which are situated along the New Hampshire coast just north of Cape Ann, the NRC staff proposed that the reactor sites and the Cape Ann earthquakes lie within the New England–Piedmont province. Later, in the licensing proceeding for Seabrook units 1 and 2, the NRC staff testified that the events might be located within the adjacent Southeast Platform tectonic province (Docket 50-443, 1976, p. 11908–11909). This province was unmentioned in the SER. In the same testimony, the NRC staff asserted that the Cape Ann events are also associated with the Boston-Ottawa seismic trend (Docket 50-443, 1976, p. 11888). The staff further subdivided the trend into two "zones" so that the MM IX 1732 event near Montreal would be in one zone and the MM VIII Cape Ann events near Boston in another.

The Consequences

The consequences of the above siting decisions basically determine that the SSEs at the Indian Point, New York, Millstone, Connecticut, and Pilgrim, Massachusetts, sites are considered to be MM VII rather than MM VIII, because of the NRC staff interpretations which at various times proposed existence of the Southeast Platform tectonic province, a "White Mountain intrusive zone province" and a White Mountain tectonic structure and/or a Boston-Ottawa seismic trend that is considered to be a tectonic structure. However, the SSE at the Seabrook, New Hampshire, site is a MM VIII rather than a MM IX because of subdivision of the Boston-Ottawa seismic trend into two zones in a HRC conclusion which is unique to this proceeding. It is not our intention to argue the merits of these alternatives in this paper but, rather, we wish to point out the difficulties in applying Appendix A. The NRC staff, nevertheless, has been inconsistent in its designation of provinces and structures within the same region with both the established literature, its own SERs, and its testimony provided on various occasions. The critical question is, of course, whether the public safety is significantly affected by this situation. The answer to this question, like the seismic potential of structures and the provinces in the eastern United States, cannot be rigorously and unequivocably assessed. This uncertainty goes back to the lack of definitive understanding of the causes of earthquakes in the region. The ACRS (Myron Bender, 1977, written commun.) recognized this situation in the recommendations that accompanied its advice in a letter to NRC Chairman Marcus A. Rowden of the NRC regarding units 1 and 2, North Anna stations, in Virginia. An excerpt from this letter states:

Consultants to the ACRS concur with this interpretation that the faulting near the reactors at North Anna is not capable. While they generally find the current design bases acceptable for the already constructed North Anna plants, they have recommended that, in view of the uncertainty of knowledge concerning the sources of earthquakes in the eastern United States, a minimum safe shutdown earthquake (SSE) of 0.2g acceleration should be utilized for which construction permit applications are submitted in the future.

This recommendation is significant because it proposes a defacto tectonic province with a minimum 0.2g acceleration (twice the country-wide Appendix A requirement), and it further underscores the need for a conservative approach in employing Appendix A. When the generalized curve (Trifunac and Brady, 1975) relating intensity to acceleration is used, the acceleration within a MM VII isoseismal area is 0.15g and within a MM VIII isoseismal area is approximately 0.25g. Thus the ACRS recommendation of 0.20g suggests that a minimum acceleration be generally applied in future siting in the East which would be greater than the 0.15g acceleration specified in the NRC staff SSE decisions in the licensing of the units previously discussed.

The ASLAB members in the Indian Point seismic hearing questioned the NRC staff about why they had not put out a siting tectonic province map. In its response (Dockets 50-3, 50-247, 50-286, 1976, p. 3743) the NRC staff testified that the Standard Review Plan suggests that tectonic provinces should be patterned after the Hadley-Devine map and the works of King and Rodgers, but that the NRC staff advisory committee (not to be confused with the ACRS) made up of USGS staff members had recommended against putting out a map during a three-year period during which the NRC Staff had repeatedly raised the question (p. 3745). The NRC staff stated (p. 3750) that the staff could produce such a map. The advisory committee had advised against issuing such a map because "it would only result in confusion" (lines 7 and 8, p. 3754).

When members of the ASLAB questioned the NRC staff concerning the inconsistencies between the SERs for Millstone unit 3 and Indian Point unit 3 (Dockets 50-3, 50-247, 50-286, 1976, p. 3481–3494), the staff testified that the staff had accepted the Millstone unit 3 applicant's tectonic provinces

because the resulting SSE, so derived, was generally compatible with the staff's intuitive judgment of the seismic potential in the area. Thus, the staff conceded that it had accepted certain tectonic province determinations of applicants which were inconsistent with other NRC staff positons in other licensing proceedings and were not rigorously derived in accordance with the requirements of Appendix A. The staff positon in the Millstone unit 3 licensing hearing was based primarily on its own general judgment of seismic potential and not on the applicant's analysis employing Appendix A. Our observations are that the failure to issue an official NRC map causes confusion, not avoids it. Furthermore, if the staff's opinion of seismic potential, exclusive of Appendix A, prevails in their decisions, Appendix A should be set aside and the SERs should contain whatever evidence the staff can provide as to how it has really reached its conclusions. The States are potentially the only technical parties outside of the NRC and its Federal advisers who can regularly review all applicants' SARs, and the States can provide a positive service to all parties and the public by surveying the decision-making scene for consistency and by asking probing questions about the rationales for specific applications of Appendix A.

Probably no one would object to a rigorous and consistent application of Appendix A such as that outlined in the NRC Standard Review Plan (U.S. Nuclear Regulatory Commission) for vibratory ground motion. It reads as follows (section 2.5.2–2, item 4, and continues onto the succeeding page, paragraph 2.5.2–3):

Subsection 2.5.2.3 (Correlation of Earthquake Activity with Geologic Structure or Tectonic Provinces); Acceptance is based on the development of the relationship between the relatively short history of earthquake activity and the geologic strucutres or tectonic provinces of a region. The applicant's presentation is accepted when the earthquakes discussed in Subsection 2.5.2.1 of the SAR are shown to be associated with either geologic structure or a tectonic province. Whenever an earthquake epicenter or concentration of earthquake epicenters can be reasonably correlated with geologic structure, the rationale for the association should be developed considering the properties of the geologic structure and the regional tectonic model. The discussion should include identification of the methods used to locate the earthquake epicenter, an estimate of their accuracy, and a detailed account which compares and contrasts the geologic structure involved in the earthquake activity with other areas within the tectonic province. Particular attention should be given to determining the capability of faults with which instrumentally-located earthquake epicenters are associated.

The applicant may choose to define tectonic provinces to correspond to subdivisions generally accepted in the literature. A subdivision of a tectonic province is accepted if it can be corroborated on the basis of detailed seismicity studies, tectonic flux measurements, contrasting structural fabric, different geologic history, differences in stress regime, etc. If detailed investigations reveal no significant differences between areas within a tectonic province, the areas should be considered to compose a single tectonic province. The presentation should be augmented by a regional-scale map showing the tectonic provinces, the earthquake epicenters, and the locations of geologic structures and measurements used to define provinces. Acceptance of the proposed tectonic provinces is based on the staff's independent review of the seismicity, tectonic flux, *geologic structure* and *stress regime* in the region of the site.

It must be pointed out that for the eastern United States, there is no established *regional tectonic model* of modern intraplate stress and stress release. Functionally usable information on relationships between modern *stress regimes, older geologic structures, newer geologic structures,* and *regional seismicity* are just beginning to be developed. In the absence of such rigor, it does not appear to be very conservative to employ hypothetical structures and tectonic province subdivisions based on structural nuances in applying Appendix A.

The SSE determination procedure was modified, effective January 10, 1977, to make certain that the intensity or magnitude of the SSE for a particular nuclear facility need not be limited to the maximum earthquake previously recorded (U.S. Nuclear Regulatory Commission). The following statement was added to section V(a)(1)(iv) of Appendix A:

The determinations carried out in accordance with paragraphs (a)(1)(ii) and (a)(1)(iii) shall assure that the Safe Shutdown Earthquake intensity is, as a minimum, equal to the maximum historic earthquake intensity experienced within the tectonic province in which the site is located. In the event that geological and seismological data warrant, the Safe Shutdown Earthquake shall be larger than that derived by use of the procedures set forth in Section IV and V of the Appendix.

Capable Faults

As in determination of the SSE, different conclusions relating to capable faults are often based either on ambiguities in the definition of terms in Appendix A or on different interpretations of geologic and seismologic information.

In the formerly glaciated, northern area of the United States, it is often difficult to find a well-stratified sedimentary section that is older than 35,000 yr. Thus, demonstrable evidence of fault movement at or near the ground surface during the past 35,000 yr is extremely difficult to document. Where fault movement has occurred in such glaciated terrane, it is not certain that the evidence of the displacement would be readily discernible. Similar difficulties are associated with the criterion of recurrent movement during the past 500,000 yr, because in many parts of the country there is no record of sediment deposition during this period and, therefore, no means of preserving a record of movement.

Where bedrock faults do not offset unconsolidated sediments, some applicants have sought to demonstrate the antiquity of the latest movement along the structures by attempting to date the age of mineral materials that have been deposited by ground water as coatings upon the surfaces of the fracture (see P. J. Murphy and others, this volume). If the mineral coatings are interpreted to be uncrushed, some investigators think that movement could not have occurred along any part of the fault since the mineral was deposited. In some situations where appropriate isotopes are present, the age of the mineral coating is established using radiometric methods. In other instances, the dating has been quite tenuous and based upon the assumed temperature of crystal formation (using liquid inclusion methods) and the time elapsed since this crystallization (at a depth inferred from the temperature) for erosion to have exposed the rock at the surface. An appropriate North American regional denudation rate is usually taken from the literature.

Such reasoning requires the assumption that collecting and dating mineral material from several places along a fault zone can prove that no movement could have taken place anywhere along the structure, including its concealed extent. Acknowledgment of the lack of rigor of this approach is usually not pointed out by the applicant in its SAR or the NRC in its SER.

The definition of capable fault is ambiguous because the meaning of the term "macroseismicity" is not presented in Appendix A.

Case of the Ramapo Fault

We are going to examine the case of the definitions of "macroseimicity" as employed by NRC and how it has changed from time to time. We will recommend employment of a standardized definition.

On March 9, 1976, the State of New York took a deposition of the NRC staff concerning the presumed capability of the Ramapo fault in southeastern New York. The fault extends within a few thousand metres of the Indian Point plant. At that time, re-evaluation of seismograph records at Lamont Doherty Geological Observatory had recently indicated that a 1951 seismic event, exceeding MM IV, was instrumentally located at or very near to the Ramapo fault. The NRC staff indicated that, in order to achieve the status of *capability*, the Appendix A definition of *macroseismicity* would require the existence of at least two events of MM intensity III or greater which were instrumentally determined to have occurred along the Ramapo fault. At the time of the deposition only the 1951 event seemed to satisfy the criteria of instrumental association.

Neither the Standard Review Plan nor the Standard Format provide any specific guidance for interpreting macroseismicity vis-a-vis capability. It might be inferred from the Standard Format that MM intensity III events or larger constitute macroseismicity because they are included in the required inventory of regional seismicity. Section 2.5.2.1, Seismicity, of the Standard Format describes the process of assessing the regional seismic activity in the following manner:

A complete list of all historically reported earthquakes that could have affected the region surrounding the site should be provided. The listing should include all earthquakes of MM Intensity greater than III or Magnitude greater than 3.0 that have been reported in all the tectonic provinces, any part of which is within 200 miles of the site.

Section 2.5.3.3, Earthquakes Associated with Capable Faults, states the following:

List all historically reported earthquakes that can be reasonably associated with faults, any part of which is within five miles of the site. A plot of the earthquake epicenters superimposed on a map showing the local tectonic structures should be provided.

Although *no* guidelines or even a passing mention of the use of instrumentally monitored events to identify capable faults are to be found in the Standard Format, one might naturally presume that events of MM intensity III or greater were included in the pertinent data used in analysis.

One might also surmise that, although the NRC staff did not state it explicitly on March 9, 1976, the Standard Format was the basis for their definition of a macroseismic MM intensity III or greater. The real problem of having no formal regulatory definition soon became apparent.

On March 11, 1977, two days following the deposition, a second event exceeding MM III took place in northern New Jersey and was instrumentally determined to have a probable hypocenter along the Ramapo fault. The NRC staff definition of macroseismicity changed in fact and in essence! This change is documented in their subsequent testimony at the Indian Point seismic hearing.

This paper does not undertake to address the capability of the Ramapo fault. It is very important, however, to establish an explicit interpretation of how the term "macroseismicity" should be applied in the texts of both Appendix A and the Regulatory Guides. Further precision is needed in the criteria for *instrumentally determined records of sufficient precision to demonstrate a direct relationship with the fault*. This should be prescribed rather than administered or litigated on an ad hoc basis. Appendix A must be made explicit enough to serve its intended purpose. It is not presently precise enough to be uniformly applied.

Regional Stress Anomalies

Recently, another type of uncertainty in the application of the Appendix A to capable faults has developed around the phenomena of pop-ups. These are small movements along joints or new breaks in bedrock. In formerly glaciated regions, some of these are definitely the result of postglacial stresses, because some of these features offset glacially grooved bedrock surfaces or mildly deform the overlying Pleistocene sediments of glacial deposits (see Hatheway and Leighton, this volume). Some of these phenomena may indicate comparatively high, horizontal, compressive stresses (Sbar and Sykes, 1973). The significance of these structures relative to capable faulting needs local investigation.

West Coast Implications

In the western United States, particularly in California, the principal challenge is to identify the existence of any capable faults which may exist in the neighborhood of a proposed reactor site as early as possible. The Corral Canyon (Fig. 2) (never constructed) and Diablo Canyon sites, where additional mapping revealed new evidence of capability of faults, have already been mentioned. In addition to the magnitude 5.2 Ferndale earthquakes of June 1975, which caused vibratory accelerations at the Humboldt nuclear station exceeding the design basis, additional field studies resulted in the location of a previously unidentified fault within 1,200 m of the power-block. Preliminary evidence raises the question of the possible capability of the fault.

Although the Alquist-Priolo Special Studies Act of 1972 was directed toward general hazards and not nuclear power plant siting per se, the results of the studies required by this legislation may enhance the background information available for power plant siting in some areas.

THE STATE ROLE IN ASSESSING SEISMIC DESIGN BASES

The States are the only non-Federal entities that regularly review applicant SARs on a scientific and technical basis. The States are the only parties that routinely examine the internally prepared NRC SERs. State staffs conduct field visits, often with personnel who have had field mapping experience in the vicinity of the site. This State review responsibility is derived from the traditional State roles of insuring public safety, regulating land use, and the regulation of public service utilities.

States are given a special status in the Federal licensing hearing. Under the Rules of Practice, [10 CFR Part 2.715 Section (c)], a presiding officer will afford a representative of an interested State (when not a party to operation of the nuclear power station) a reasonable opportunity to participate. This privilege includes introducing evidence, interrogating witnesses, and providing advice to the NRC without necessarily having to take a positon with respect to the issues. States may, of course, take positions if their responsible officials so wish.

In those States that require State siting permits for electric generating facilities or water impoundment projects, geological and seismological criteria may exist as State regulation. In some States the State geological survey works closely with State regulatory bodies such as the Public Service or Public Utility Commission, in order to evaluate applicant compliance with State law. Some coordination of State hearings with Federal proceedings is being explored at this time.

The question is sometimes raised as to whether a State can refuse to issue a permit for a nuclear power plant because of a State position that the applicant's seismic design basis is inadequate. Attorneys familiar with this part of law are generally of the opinion that a State could refuse to issue a siting permit on a seismic safety basis, if the justification covered water impoundments or other threats to public safety not narrowly related to radiation. Radiation is considered to be exclusively within Federal jurisdiction. Furthermore, some attorneys conclude that an adverse State ruling could be made on a utility site application, not on a safety-related basis, but on the contention that the seismic design bases were not adequate to insure sustained and uninterrupted power output throughout the projected lifetime of the plant. Such a decision would rest on social and economic criteria that are well within the scope of State jurisdiction. We are not presently aware of any State rulings of this kind nor litigation of any such cases in court.

New York State Participation

Since 1971, the New York State Geological Survey has reviewed applicant SARs and NRC SERs on plants sited within the State. This review is also supplemented by reviews in other disciplines within the State Department of Environmental Conservation and the Public Service Commission. Formal commentaries from these agencies are collected by the State Energy Office and submitted to the NRC. Beginning in 1973, informal discussions have taken place between the NRC staff and the New York State Geological Survey. Both staffs coordinate their field visits to examine geologic evidence in exploratory trenches and foundation excavations at power plant sites. Thus, comparison of opinion can take place early and provide a maximum opportunity for the Federal technical staff to benefit from the observations of the New York State Geological Survey. Not the least value of these discussions is the valuable and timely input to the applicant, to whom delays may cost many tens of thousands of dollars per day.

During 1972, the New York State Geological Survey assisted in drafting Part 76, Geology and Seismology, of the Rules of Procedure of Article VIII of the Public Service Law, 16 NYCRR, Chapter 1, of the regulations covering the siting of all types of power plants in New York under Article VIII of the Public Service Law.[4] Article VIII requires utilities to demonstrate a genuine need for the electrical generation capacity of the proposed facility and to make application for two alternative sites. The hearing process on nuclear plants for construction permits and operating licenses have been separate for the most part from those of the NRC. The geological survey advises the Public Service Commission concerning New York testimony and cross-examination of the applicant's and the NRC's hearing participants. This approach assures that both the State agencies and the NRC get the same insights from the geological survey and presents the opportunity for the Federal regulatory program to assimilate the State perspective before final conclusions have been developed.

The New York State Geological Survey has compiled a computerized catalog of all historical earthquakes that have affected the State. Retrieval is possible for events within a specified radius of a site, as a chronological list and as a printout map. A number of special regional background investigations have also been conducted to provide a good point of departure for evaluations of individual candidate plant sites. These include a gravity map of the entire state, a set of State-wide bedrock maps, a series of State-wide brittle structure maps, a seismicity map of the State and an aeromagnetic map. Special studies have been undertaken on faults that show evidence of being seismically active. The results of these investigations and many others are made available together with advisory services to consultants preparing SARs for nuclear power plants.

California State Participation

In California, the Division of Mines and Geology (State geological survey) first became involved with nuclear power plant siting in a very indirect manner in the 1960s when the State Department of Fish and Game became concerned about possible damaging effects of excavation and sediment transport associated with nuclear power plants in coastal areas. The Division of Mines and Geology reviewed the proposed site and construction plans in terms of these effects on marine life. Subsequent to these activities, local "interested parties" requested the State Geologist to review the geologic and seismic conditions at the proposed Corral Canyon site in Malibu, California (Fig. 2).

---

[4] Copies of this legislation are available, gratis, from the New York State Public Service Commission, Empire State Plaza, Agency Building 3, Albany, New York 12223.

The California Environmental Quality Act (CEQA) was passed by the State Legislature in 1970, requiring Environmental Impact Reports (EIR) for all major construction. These reports are submitted to a State Clearing House which in turn distributes copies to interested State agencies for review and comments. Thus, EIRs have been required for design of nuclear power facilities in California for some time. The comments of the Division of Mines and Geology are included in the final Clearing House reviews, which are prepared and issued by the Resources Agency of the State of California.

The Division of Mines and Geology continued this limited advisory and review involvement until issuance of a 1973 administrative order by then State Geologist, James E. Slosson. The division was therein directed to prepare thorough and indepth reviews of all EIRs.

The State Participation Movement

Active participation by State geological surveys in nuclear power plant siting has been sought by most states. In May 1975, at the annual meeting of the Association of American State Geologists (AASG), the California State Geologist proposed a resolution that would seek to develop a working arrangement between NRC and each appropriate State Geologist wherever a new facility or additional unit was proposed. This motion was seconded by the State Geologists of New York, Delaware, Colorado, and Montana. Following considerable discussion the motion was passed unanimously and adopted by the fifty states that form the AASG. The resolution is as follows:

A Resolution stressing concern for Geological and Seismic information at proposed nuclear power sites and urging closer and more timely communication with the State Geologists in the Respective States.

Whereas, one of the important and continuing concerns of the NRC must be with the geology and seismicity of sites proposed for nuclear plants; and

Whereas, NRC will be developing additional information and reports on the proposed sites;

Now, therefore be it resolved that in the interests of NRC, the State Geological Surveys and of the Public, the NRC provide early advice to the State Geologists of each state in which a site is under consideration, in order to obtain available geologic and seismic information; and

Be it further resolved that as a matter of policy for the purpose of receiving review and comment, the NRC should supply in a timely fashion, copies of its reports on the geology and seismicity of such sites to the State Geologist in the concerned states.

The NRC immediately complied with the intent of the resolution and an excellent working relationship and cooperation have been developed with many State governments. The end product of involvement of State governments should be a more thorough analysis of all pertinent data prior to decision-making.

Roles of Local Government

Practically all State governments delegate specific land use decisions to local regulatory bodies; therefore, land use is the principal power plant siting concern of local government. Representatives of the local government often make limited appearances at State and Federal hearings. They are sometimes parties to State, and more rarely, to Federal proceedings. Local governments are not provided any special status under the siting regulations, and because these bodies do not normally employ the services of professional earth scientists, it may be inconsistent to involve such entities to a further degree in site analysis.

Position of Utilities

Utility financing and insurance do not usually involve safety review or evaluation of seismic design on the part of either the lending institution or the private insurer. These parties are content to accept the assurance of the NRC that the seismic design basis for a proposed plant is adequate. NRC has imposed a stringent program of qualities assurance on all parties to the utility's siting and design team (see McClure and Hatheway, this volume). These internal checks and balances attempt to detect nonconformances and to review all newly obtained data at each stage. There are, however, commonly no checks and balances to the applicant's licensing team that influence seismic design conclusions before they are submitted to the NRC and undergo the question-and-answer routine of regulatory review (see Morris, this volume). The entire weight of evaluating the safety of the applicant's proposals currently rests upon the Federal review process.

Utility financing of power plants is undertaken by issues of bonds and common and preferred stocks. These are credits against the total assets of the corporation and are not specifically related to the fate of any plan for which funding is sought. The sale of such issues is often undertaken by a firm that locates buyers throughout the country. Thus, a large stock or bond issue can usually be dispersed among a substantial number of purchasers. These issues commonly follow granting of the Permit to Construct by the NRC ASLB. Usually no special attention is given to the seismic safety of the contemplated plant by financial institutions providing the capital, because the bonds are issued against the entire assets of the utility.

In 1957, the Atomic Energy Law of 1954 was amended to include Section 170 (PL 35-256) which provides for Federal indemnification and limitation for nuclear reactors including utility power plants. Insurance for liability arising from "nuclear incidents" is obtainable from the Federal government up to a limit of $500,000,000. No safety review is provided in this process, either.

The siting process is initiated by the utility when it perceives that a need exists for increased generating capacity. The utility quite understandably wishes to acquire the new generating capacity with as little expenditures of time and money as possible. Corporate management is sensitive to both the ratepayers and the investors in all monetary matters involving plant construction. In general, utilities have accepted the geologic and seismologic criteria for design bases that have been prescribed by the NRC. However, much discontent has been expressed by individual utilities and geological/seismological consultants over the wording of Appendix A as it relates to capable faulting. Late in 1977, formal efforts were made by the Central Maine Power Company to amend and clarify the wording of Appendix A as it pertains to nonseismic faults.

Utilities cannot undertake to develop their own geologic and seismologic siting criteria, but they may request to have certain required investigations waived if they do not feel those specified in Appendix A are necessary. Most utilities do not have their own geologists and seismologists but rather rely upon consultants. When the consultants propose additional comprehensive field investigations to the utilities, the power companies tend to ask the NRC about the need for these prior to deciding whether or not to undertake them. Some utilities propose seismic-design-basis conclusions with the same philosophy that some governmental agencies present budgets, that is, they go for the most desirable ground acceleration values and anticipate a regulatory upward adjustment. Other utilities, realizing that the most favorable price package from the Nuclear Steam Supply System (NSSS) vendor comes from early negotiation, will opt to purchase a system designed for slightly higher levels of ground motion, with the hope of not having to renegotiate with the NSSS vendor at a later date.

Roles of Participating Earth Scientists

Some scientists have a tendency to operate on the intuitive belief that "there cannot be more than a magnitude 'x' or an intensity 'y' event in this area." This approach stems from the difficulty of making rigorous design acceleration decisions in the context of the current state of the science. The principal problem with this sort of approach is that it limits the probing questions that the individual should pose to himself during the safety analysis and, in extreme cases, can reduce the intellectual effort in the geologic and seismologic investigations to merely going-through-the-motions effort.

RECOMMENDATIONS FROM THE STATE PERSPECTIVE

In order to avoid unacceptable public risk and retrofitting costs, it is firmly recommended that some modifications be made in the licensing process. The recommendations proposed here are intended to mitigate the specific license process difficulties that we have identified in the previous section.

Analysis of Design Acceleration Value Versus Cost

Many of the problems discussed above stem from the commonly stated position that to increase the magnitude of the SSE (and thus the related vibratory ground acceleration at the site) would increase the cost of the plant prohibitively. There are no readily available figures that purport to show the relative cost increase of plant designs incorporating incremental increases in acceleration values.

A panel of consultants should be charged by the NRC with

determining the feasibility of this analysis and developing a study design, if such is practical. The insights from the acceleration-versus-cost analysis are extremely important and should be used in quantifying the balance between cost and public safety in the development of seismic designs.

Improvement in the Content and Application of Appendix A

Reasonable modification of the content and wording of Appendix A constitutes the most reasonable and effective method of improving the nuclear plant licensing process. Specifically, as present and former State officials, we recommend the following changes to Appendix A:

1. Designation of tectonic provinces and association of tectonic structures for purposes of identifying the SSE
   (a) The definition of tectonic provinces should be clarified to incorporate map scales and to require the determination of seismic characteristics of areas of contrasting seismic potential within 322 km (200 mi) of proposed plant sites. This might best be done by a panel of outside experts working in concert with the NRC staff and their advisory committee.
   (b) The letter of ACRS Chairman Myron Bender, January 17, 1977, to NRC Chairman Marcus Rowden proposed that 0.2g be considered as the minimum design-basis ground acceleration for the East, since the causes of earthquakes are poorly understood. This is a defacto tectonic map of the region. An expert panel should be requested to prepare a tectonic (seismotectonic variety) map for the East. Perhaps there are regions of significant size in the East where a minimum design should be above 0.2g and, conversely, there may be regions where the acceleration designations could be less. We suggest that such a map would be extremely useful to applicants in initial site selection and might serve to shorten this phase of the Construction Permit and Operating License procedure. If the map were issued as a Regulatory Guide, it could be amended and updated periodically. The recognition of possible map revision would serve to set the proper approach of conservatism in the decisions for which it was employed. It should be drafted in such a manner that it is conservative in a balanced fashion with the objective that, in the future, new scientific information would only confirm the seismic designs established using the map and *no retrofitting would thus have to be considered*. This is the greatest assurance that the science can provide an applicant today that his plant will not have to undergo substantial retrofitting for seismic design purposes.
   (c) A higher and more explicit degree of proof needs to be proposed for associating epicenters of "controlling earthquakes" with tectonic structures (see Dewey, this volume). Speculative associations of higher impact should not be acceptable. Perhaps some generalized criteria could be provided in the Regulatory Guide.
   (d) One of the objectives of the new Federal 1977 Earthquake Legislation should be to initiate a country-wide study of the highest intensity "controlling earth-

quakes" in the historical record. An overview committee should design the approach and contract for studies of these events to upgrade information on intensity and location. All unpublished contemporary records of the events should be included. This will reduce the time and money expenditures of applicants in evaluating earthquake history and improve the confidence of all parties in the catalog data available on this relatively small number of controlling earthquakes.

2. Capable Faults
   (a) The term "macroseismicity" should be defined. We suggest the lower threshold be MM III or magnitude 3.
   (b) Criteria should be set forth to describe the manner in which the applicant is to assess macroseismicity that has been determined with "records of sufficient precision to demonstrate a direct relationship with the fault."
   (c) Guidelines should be established for rigorous determination of the age of most recent movement along faults where future displacement could affect the proposed reactor.

3. General
   (a) A commitment should be made by the NRC to engage an outside panel to review the adequacy of Appendix A, the Standard Review Plan, and the Standard Format every five years in order to determine whether these documents should be revised on the basis of new scientific insights and, if so, which parts would require attention.

Recommendation Based on the Incomplete Understanding of Earthquake Causes in the East

A panel of NRC, USGS, university and State scientists, and independent constituents should be requested to recommend a program of geologic mapping, seismic monitoring, in situ stress measurements, and regional geophysical studies directed toward providing an expanded body knowledge for future applicants to employ in seismic design basis conclusions. The resulting studies should be funded by the new Federal earthquake legislation. The results will be beneficial for all types of regional earthquake hazard assessment as well as nuclear plants.

Monitoring networks and stress measurements are particularly important because these undertakings should provide much of the needed basic information for developing a regional intraplate tectonic model of stress release and earthquake genesis.

The NRC should immediately establish an outside study group to investigate the best means of determining any seismic potential associated with pop-up type features on both a site-specific and a regional basis, as the tectonic significance of these features is poorly understood. Recommendations by this group should include both an approach to making contemporary siting decisions and identifications of directions for future research in order to assure improving capacity to evaluate these structures.

Topical studies should be undertaken to improve our understanding of earthquake wave-form attenuation in the East; none now exist. This can be expedited by assuring accurate timing and precise calibration of instrumentation employed in regional monitoring networks.

Improvement of Seismic-Design Decision-Making in the Licensing Procedure

The size of the technical staff of the NRC Site Analysis Branch should be increased so that more intensive assimilation of the local and regional geology pertinent to proposed plants is feasible.

The scope of the USGS advice to NRC on nuclear plant SARs should include all proposed units. Perhaps this advisory relationship should be made more formalized and structured than it is at present.

Earth scientists should be appointed to ASLABS and to the ACRS as soon as feasible. Assignments of earth science members of the ASLABS to proceedings where geology and seismology were expected to be especially important would then be possible. This would save a great deal of time, because a geologist on the board could provide background perspective to his two colleagues rather than parties having to "educate" all three panelists during the hearing.

A study group should be established to evaluate means by which State participation in the review of geologic and seismic siting criteria can be enhanced. In many States, much expertise and data are available, but provision for their inclusion is not formally assured. Since there is no other scientific commentary outside of the Federal agencies, this increased participation can assure the benefit of the State's science perspectives in the decision-making process. The result may lend greater credibility to the resulting decisions.

The new "partial review" procedure should be examined to assure that an NRC hearing will take up geologic and seismic design decisions thoroughly at an appropriate stage before granting the Construction Permit.

A study group should be set up by the NRC to determine whether *seismic risk* as well as seismic potential and seismic hazard should be considered in the seismic design basis conclusions for nuclear plant sites.

ACKNOWLEDGMENTS

We acknowledge the critical reviews of this manuscript furnished by William H. Diment and James F. Devine of the U.S. Geological Survey, Lynn R. Sykes of Lamont-Doherty Geological Observatory, and Allen W. Hatheway of Haley & Aldrich, Inc. Interpretations presented herein, however, remain our responsibility.

REFERENCES CITED

Allen, C. R., 1975, Geologic criteria for evaluating seismicity: Geological Society of America, v. 86, p. 1041–1057.

Bolt, B. A., 1979, Seismicity of the western United States, *in* Hatheway, A. W., and McClure, C. R., Jr., eds., Geology in the siting of nuclear power plants: Geological Society of America Reviews in Engineering Geology, v. IV (this volume).

Code of Federal Regulations, 1978, Title 10, Energy; Part 100 [10 CFR 100], Reactor site criteria; Appendix A, Seismic and geologic siting criteria for nuclear power plants: Washington, D.C., U.S. Nuclear Regulatory Commission.

Coffman, J. L., and von Hake, C. A., 1973, Earthquake history of the United States: Washington, D.C., U.S. Government Printing Office, U.S. Department of Commerce, Publication No. 41-1, revised edition (through 1970).

Dewey, J. W., 1979, A consumer's guide to instrumental methods for determination of hypocenters, *in* Hatheway, A. W., and McClure, C. R., Jr., eds., Geology in the siting of nuclear power plants: Geological Society of America Reviews in Engineering Geology, v. IV (this volume).

Diment, W. H., Urban, T. C., and Revetta, F. A., 1973, Some geophysical anomalies in the eastern United States, *in* Robertson, E. C., ed., The solid Earth: New York, McGraw-Hill Book Co., p. 544–572.

Docket 50-3, 1962, FSAR, Indian Point NPS (Unit 1), Westchester County, New York: New York City, Consolidated Edison Company of New York.

Dockets 50-3, 50-247, and 50-286, 1976, Transcript of the Indian Point ASLAB Seismic Hearing: Washington, D.C., U.S. Nuclear Regulatory Commission, p. 3646–3794, June 11, 1976.

Docket 50-423, 1973, FSAR, Millstone NPS (Unit 3), New London County, Connecticut: Hartford, Connecticut, Northeast Nuclear Energy Company.

Docket 50-423, 1974, SER, Millstone NPS (Unit 3), New London County, Connecticut: Washington, D.C., U.S. Nuclear Regulatory Commission.

Dockets 50-443 and 50-444, 1975, SER, Seabrook NPS (Units 1 and 2), Rockingham County, New Hampshire: Washington, D.C., U.S. Nuclear Regulatory Commission.

Dockets 50-443 and 50-444, 1976, Testimony, Seabrook generating stations (Units 1 and 2): Washington, D.C., U.S. Nuclear Regulatory Commission.

Docket 50-286, 1972, FSAR, Indian Point NPS (Unit 3), Westchester County, New York: New York City, Consolidated Edison Company of New York.

Docket 50-286, 1976, SER, Indian Point NPS (Unit 3), Westchester County, New York, Supplement No. 1: Washington, D.C., U.S. Nuclear Regulatory Commission.

Hadley, J. F., and Devine, J. F., 1974, Seismotectonic map of the eastern United States: U.S. Geological Survey Miscellaneous Field Study, MF-620.

Hart, Earl W., 1977, Fault hazard zones in zones in California: California Division of Mines and Geology, Special Publication 42.

Hatheway, A. W., and Leighton, F. B., 1979, Trenching as an exploratory method, *in* Hatheway, A. W., and McClure, C. R., Jr., eds., Geology in the siting of nuclear power plants: Geological Society of America Reviews in Engineering Geology, v. IV (this volume).

Heck, M. H., and Eppley, R. A., 1958, Earthquake history of the United States, Part 1, Continental United States (exclusive of California and western Nevada): Washington, D.C., U.S. Government Printing Office, U.S. Department of Commerce, No. 41-1, revised edition (through 1956).

Kane, M. F., 1977, Correlation of major eastern epicenters with mafic/ultramafic basement masses, *in* Studies related to the Charleston, South Carolina, earthquake of 1886—A preliminary report: United States Geological Survey Professional Paper 1028-05, p. 199–204.

King, Philip B., 1969, The tectonics of North America—A discussion to accompany the tectonic map of North America, scale 1:5,000,000: U.S. Geological Survey Professional Paper 628, 95 p.

McClure, C. R., Jr., and Hatheway, A, W., 1979, An overview of nuclear power plant siting and licensing, *in* Hatheway, A. W., and McClure, C. R., Jr., eds., Geology in the siting of nuclear power plants: Geological Society of America Reviews in Engineering Geology, v. IV (this volume).

McEldowney, R. C., and Pascucci, R. F., 1979, Application of remote-sensing data to nuclear power plant site investigations, *in* Hatheway, A. W., and McClure, C, R., Jr., eds., Geology in the siting of nuclear power plants: Geological Society of America Reviews in Engineering Geology, v. IV (this volume).

McGuire, R. K., 1977, Effects of uncertainty in seismicity on estimates of seismic hazard for the East Coast of the United States: Seismological Society of America Bulletin, v. 67, no. 3, p. 827–848.

Morris, R. H., 1979, Geologic reports used in evaluation of nuclear reactor sites, *in* Hatheway, A. W., and McClure, C. R., Jr., eds., 1979, Geology in the siting of nuclear power plants: Geological Society of America Reviews in Engineering Geology, v. IV (this volume).

Murphy, P. J., Briedis, J., and Peck, J. H., 1979, Age determination techniques in fault investigations, *in* Hatheway, A. W., and McClure, C. R., Jr., eds., Geology in the siting of nuclear power plants: Geological Society of America Reviews in Engineering Geology, v. IV (this volume).

Murphy, V. J., Secton, T. F., and Levine, E. N., 1979, Geophysics as related to siting of nuclear power plants, *in* Hatheway, A. W., and McClure, C. R., Jr., eds., Geology in the siting of nuclear power plants: Geological Society of America Reviews in Engineering Geology, v. IV (this volume).

Nuttli, O. W., 1979, Seismicity of the central United States, *in* Hatheway, A. W., and McClure, C. R., Jr., eds., Geology in the siting of nuclear power plants: Geological Society of America Reviews in Engineering Geology, v. IV (this volume).

Regulatory Guide 1.70, 1975, Standard Format and content of Safety Analysis Reports for nuclear power plants: Washington, D.C., U.S. Nuclear Regulatory Commission.

Richter, Charles F., 1958, Elementary seismology: San Francisco, California, W. H. Freeman and Co., 768 p.

Rodgers, John, 1970, The tectonics of the Appalachians: New York, Interscience, 270 p.

Sbar, M. L., and Sykes, L. R., 1973, Contemporary stress and seismicity in eastern North America, An example of intra-plate tectonics: Geological Society of America Bulletin, v. 84, no. 6, p. 1861–1882.

Sieh, K. E., 1977, Prehistoric large earthquakes produced by slip on the San Andreas fault at Pallet Creek, California: Journal of Geophysical Research, v. 82, no. 88, p. 3907–3939.

Smith, W.E.T., 1962, Earthquakes of eastern Canada and adjacent areas, 1534 to 1927: Publications of the Dominion Observatory, Ottawa, v. 26, no. 5, p. 271–301.

——1966, Earthquakes of eastern Canada and adjacent areas, 1928 to 1959: Publications of the Dominion Observatory, Ottawa, v. 26, no. 3.

Trifunac, M. D., and Brady, A. G., 1975, On the correlation of seismic intensity scales with the peaks of recorded strong ground motion: Seismological Society of America Bulletin, v. 65, no. 1, p. 139–162.

U.S. Nuclear Regulatory Commission, standard review plan: Washington, D.C., U.S. Nuclear Regulatory Commission, Office of Nuclear Reactor Regulation.

U.S. Nuclear Regulatory Commission, 1977, Regulations: A summary, *in* Nuclear Regulation Reports: Chicago, Illinois, Commerce Clearing House Inc., no. 78.

Manuscript Received by the Society July 13, 1978
Manuscript Accepted November 13, 1978
Published with Permission of Director, State Museum, New York State Education Department. Journal Series No. 251

PART 2

SEISMICITY

Geological Society of America
Reviews in Engineering Geology, Volume IV
1979

Seismicity of the central United States

OTTO W. NUTTLI

Department of Earth and Atmospheric Sciences, St. Louis University, St. Louis, Missouri 63156

ABSTRACT

The combination of moderate seismic activity, sparsity of seismograph stations and relatively low density of population makes it difficult to assign quantitative seismicity values to most of the central United States. In the New Madrid seismic zone, where the level of seismic activity is higher and the number of seismograph stations is more adequate, one can delineate the active fault zone and determine a magnitude-recurrence relation. These capabilities will be extended to other seismic zones as arrays of seismographs are installed for recording microearthquakes, which will give information on fault delineation, focal mechanism, and magnitude frequency. Only after such information is available will we be able to make positive statements relating seismic activity to specific geologic features.

The seismicity data suggest that earthquakes that occur outside the recognized seismic zones or major structural features will have a maximum body-wave magnitude m_b of 5.5 and that this maximum value will occur only infrequently. Experience shows that if these relatively minor earthquakes are only a few kilometres deep they may have an epicentral intensity at least as large as VII (observed for an earthquake of $m_b = 3.8$), but their magnitude and area of perceptibility will be small. With the exception of the New Madrid seismic zone and possibly the Wabash Valley seismic zone, a conservatively reasonable value for the maximum body-wave magnitude to be expected in the major seismic and structural zones of the central United States is 6.5. For the New Madrid seismic zone an earthquake of body-wave magnitude equivalent to that of a great earthquake ($m_b = 7.5$) can be expected, on the basis of what has already been experienced in 1811–1812.

Because of low anelastic attenuation, the earthquakes in the central United States are felt and cause damage over much wider areas than earthquakes of comparable magnitude in the western United States. Further consequences are that the ground shaking has a longer duration and that the ground-motion spectrum shifts at the larger distances to lower frequencies, which results in relatively low ground acceleration for relatively large ground displacements and a greater effect on high-rise than low-rise structures.

INTRODUCTION

In general, most of our information about the seismicity of the central United States is derived from intensity reports, rather than instrumental observations. The central United States, defined here as the area bordered by the states of Texas, Oklahoma, Kansas, Nebraska, South Dakota, and North Dakota on the west and the Appalachian front and the states of Ohio and Michigan on the east, is with few exceptions an area deficient in seismographic stations. Because even at the present time there is a low instrumental density and low population density, particularly in the western portion, it is possible that some earthquakes with a body-wave magnitude m_b as large as 3.5 are escaping detection.

Intensity data in the central United States vary in completeness. Parts of the eastern section were settled in the mid–eighteenth century but in much of the western section not until the late nineteenth century. As a consequence there are approximately two centuries of intensity data in the eastern section compared to only one century in the western section. Even for these time periods the intensity data are not complete. However, because of the unusually large felt areas that are associated with central United States earthquakes (Mitchell, 1973; Nuttli, 1973a), except for very shallow ones, it is fairly certain that no earthquake with epicentral intensity VI or larger has escaped notice if it occurred after the region was populated. An exception to this statement, as shall be discussed later, is the very shallow earthquake which, for an epicentral intensity as high as VII, for example, is not felt 25 km away. The southern Illinois earthquakes of August 1965 were of this type.

SEISMICITY MAP

It is obvious that there is no one-to-one relationship between earthquake risk and density of earthquake epicenters as seen on a seismicity map of the central United States when the above mentioned limitations are considered. Furthermore, and more importantly, even 200 yr is far too limited a time to present information on large earthquakes that may have a return period of as much as 10,000 yr.

In gathering data for the seismicity map I have attempted to include all known earthquakes of $m_b \geq 3.0$. In practice this means all known felt earthquakes prior to 1960, for until instrumental magnitudes are available it is assumed that all felt earthquakes had an m_b of at least 3.0. Recent seismographic data indicate that the assumption is sometimes violated, that is, felt earthquakes of normal focal depth may have m_b values as small as about 2.5 (Nuttli and Zollweg, 1974). This points out just one inadequacy of the map. Another and more serious one is that there must have been many earthquakes of $m_b \geq 3.0$ that were neither reported as being felt nor detected instrumentally and as a consequence do not appear on the map. Thus, although I have attempted to make the map as complete as possible considering the data sources and the time available to me, I recognize and acknowledge its incompleteness.

Data sources consulted include Coffman and von Hake (1973), U.S. Department of Commerce (1928–1972), U.S. Geological Survey (1972–1974), Docekal (1970), Heinrich (1941), Seismological Society of America (1911–1975), Stauder and others (1974–1976), J. E. Zollweg (St. Louis University, unpub. data), M. M. Varma and R. F. Blakely (Indiana University, unpub. data), and the Preliminary Safety Analysis Reports for proposed nuclear power plant sites at Marble Hill (Jefferson County, Indiana), Calloway (Calloway County, Missouri), Koshkonong (Jefferson County, Wisconsin), Hartsville (Trousdale-Smith Counties, Tennessee), Perry (Lake County, Ohio), and Sterling (Cayuga County, New York).

For some earthquakes there is a difference in the epicentral coordinates contained in the various data sources. This particularly is true of the older earthquakes, for which only intensity data are available. In such cases, I examined the intensity data and any other information that was available and selected the epicentral coordinates that I believed best conformed to the data.

Table 1 lists the date, latitude, longitude, origin time, epicentral intensity, felt area, and body-wave magnitude of central United States earthquakes. This table is not to be considered as a complete seismicity record; it can, however, serve as a check on the accuracy of the plotting of the epicenters on the seismicity map (Fig. 1).

In Figure 1 the size of the symbol used in plotting the epicenters is proportional to the body-wave magnitude. For the majority of cases where seismographic data were unavailable, I estimated the magnitude from the intensity map or the epicentral intensity in the manner described by me (Nuttli, 1974). If an isoseismal map was available, the magnitude was determined from the fall-off of intensity with distance, such as was done for the December 16, 1811, earthquake (Nuttli, 1973b). If no isoseismal map were available, the magnitude was estimated to be the larger of the two values obtained from the felt area (Nuttli and Zollweg, 1974) or from the epicentral intensity (Nuttli, 1974). Omitted from the map are the thousands of aftershocks of the three major New Madrid 1811–1812 earthquakes. In cases where several earthquakes had the same epicenter, they were plotted adjacent to each other in an area of 0.1° × 0.1°, which is smaller than the area of uncertainty of location of most events. In cases where the 0.1° × 0.1° area became filled, the remaining epicenters were not plotted. This happened most frequently in the New Madrid seismic zone.

NEW MADRID SEISMIC ZONE

From Figures 1 and 2 it can be seen that the New Madrid seismic zone (an area about 50 km wide roughly parallel to the Mississippi River that extends from about lat 35° to 37°N) has been by far the most active seismic region in the central United States during the past 200 yr. It is the only place where earthquakes of intensity greater than VIII or body-wave magnitude greater than 5.7 have occurred. Furthermore, the New Madrid seismic zone accounts for more than one-third of the felt earthquakes in the central United States.

The seismicity of the central United States is dominated by a series of strong earthquakes that began on December 16, 1811, and continued for about three months, followed by lesser aftershocks that lasted until at least 1817. Extensive discussions of these so-called New Madrid earthquakes have been given by Fuller (1912) and by me (Nuttli, 1973b). The earthquakes were remarkable for the large amount of uplift and subsidence that they produced, for their very large areas of damage and perceptibility, and for the size and number of aftershocks. There were three principal shocks that occurred on December 16, 1811, January 23, 1812, and February 7, 1812. Their body-wave magnitudes m_b were estimated by me (Nuttli, 1973b) to be 7.2, 7.1, and 7.4, respectively. To estimate their surface-wave magnitudes M_S one must know the fault rupture length and rupture time. If the rupture lengths are less than those of typical plate-margin earthquakes, as suggested by Everden (1975), their M_S values would be smaller than 8.0, 7.8, and 8.2, respectively, which one would obtain from $m_b - M_S$ relations for typical plate-margin earthquakes.

Figure 3 compares the number and magnitude of these three principal earthquakes and three months of their aftershocks with the seismic activity in the southern half of California for the period 1932 through 1971, as given by Hileman and others (1973). Figure 3 demonstrates the remarkable fact that the number and size of earthquakes that occurred in a 40-yr period throughout southern California, including the large Kern County earthquake of 1952 and its aftershocks, were equaled by just 3 mo of activity in the New Madrid seismic zone in the winter of 1811 and 1812.

In the New Madrid seismic zone, there is no surface evidence of faulting, because the whole region is underlain by a thick sequence of recent alluvial deposits. Therefore, microearthquake data must serve to delineate the extent and scope of this seismic zone. Figure 4, which is taken from Stauder and others (1976), shows the New Madrid faulted zone to consist of a linear southern segment about 100 km long and a linear northern segment at least 40 km long, the two segments offset by a central region of greater-than-average microearthquake activity. Focal mechanism solutions of Herrmann (1974) and many of those of Street and others (1974) gave fault planes whose strike direction agrees with that determined from the trend of the microearthquakes along the southern and northern branches. It is interesting to note that the two largest earthquakes to occur in the New Madrid seismic zone since 1812

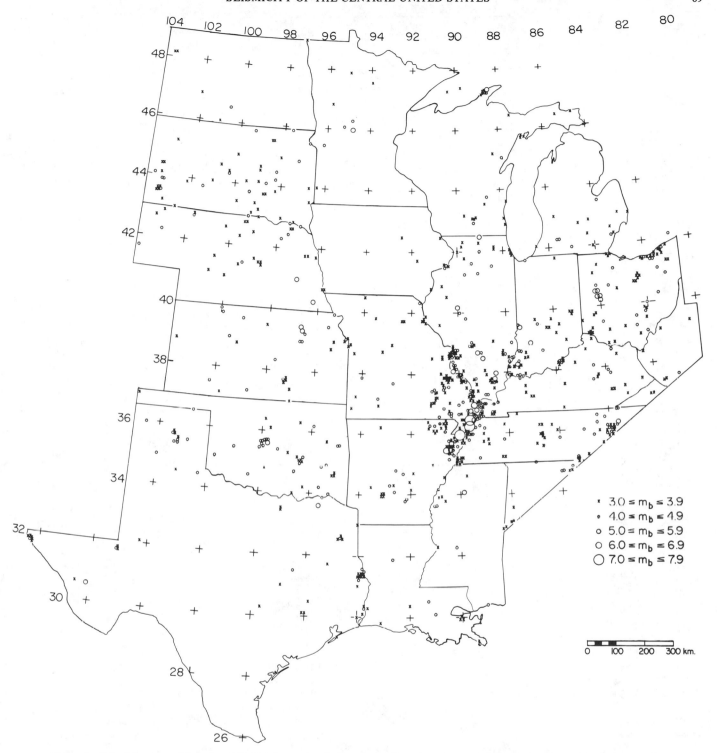

Figure 1. Seismicity map of the central United States showing known earthquakes of $m_b \geq 3.0$ that have occurred in historic times.

were the January 4, 1843, event of $m_b = 6.0$ near the southern terminus of the seismic zone and the October 31, 1895, event of $m_b = 6.2$ near the northern terminus of the seismic zone.

Although there is no surface evidence of faulting in the New Madrid seismic zone, the distribution of microearthquakes together with the focal mechanism solutions presents a strong argument for the existence of a faulted zone. From focal depth

determinations of recent earthquakes it appears that the faulted zone extends from about 5 to 20 km in depth.

By use of the historic data plotted in Figure 1 and the microearthquake data shown in Figure 4, one can determine a magnitude-recurrence curve for the New Madrid seismic zone. In order to make the two data sets compatible, each is reduced to the number of earthquakes of a given magnitude or greater

TABLE 1. EARTHQUAKES IN THE CENTRAL UNITED STATES OF $m_b \geq 3.0$

Date	Origin time (GMT)	Lat (°N)	Long (°W)	Felt area (km²)	I_o	m_b	M_S
Dec 25, 1699		35.2	90.5	6,000	IV-V	4.0	
Summer, 1776	14^h	40.0	82.0		VI	4.7	
1779		northern Kentucky				3.0	
Apr 1791	13	north. & east. Kentucky			IV-V	4.0	
Jan 08, 1795	09	37.9	89.9	12,000	IV-V	4.0	
*Aug 20, 1804	20 10^m	42	89	80,000	V-VI	4.5	
*Dec 16, 1811	08 15	36	90	5,000,000	XI	7.2	8.0
*Jan 23, 1812	15	36.3	89.6	5,000,000	X-XI	7.1	7.8
Feb 07, 1812	09 45	36.5	89.6	5,000,000	XI-XII	7.4	8.2
Jul 25, 1816	15	36.5	89.5		III-IV	3.6	
Jul 25, 1816	21	36.5	89.5		III-IV	3.6	
Dec 12, 1817		Kentucky				3.0	
Mar 1818		36.2	89.7		III	3.4	
Apr 11, 1818	20	38.6	90.2		III-IV	3.6	
Sep 02, 1819	08	37.7	89.7		V	4.2	
Sep 17, 1819	04	38.1	89.8		IV	3.8	
Sep 17, 1819		38.1	89.8		III-IV	3.6	
Nov 09, 1820	22	37.3	89.5		V	4.2	
1820		36.6	89.5		III-IV	3.6	
May 30, 1823		41.5	81.0		IV	3.8	
Jul 05, 1827	11 30	38.3	85.8	430,000	IV	4.8	
Aug 07, 1827	04 30	38.3	85.8		VI	4.7	
Aug 07, 1827	07	38.3	85.8		VI	4.7	
Aug 14, 1827		38.6	90.2		III	3.4	
Mar 10, 1828	03	38.7	83.8	550,000	V	4.8	
May 1829		35.6	88.8			3.0	
Feb 04, 1833		42.3	85.6	20,000	VI	4.7	
Nov 20, 1834	19 40	northern Kentucky			V	4.2	
Jul 08, 1836		41.5	81.7		IV	3.8	
Jun 09, 1838	14 45	38.5	89	500,000	VII-VIII	5.7	
Sep 05, 1839		36.7	88.6		IV	3.8	
Dec 28, 1841	05 50	36.6	89.2		V	4.2	
May 28, 1842	05	36.6	89.2		IV	3.8	
Nov 04, 1842	06 30	36.6	89.2		V	4.2	
Nov 04, 1842	08 30	36.6	89.2		V	4.2	
Jan 05, 1843	02 45	35.5	90.5	1,500,000	VIII	6.0	
Feb 14, 1843		29.9	90.1			3.0	
Feb 17, 1843	05	35.5	90.5	250,000	V	4.8	
Jun 13, 1843	15	36.6	89.2		III	3.4	
Aug 09, 1843		35.6	87.1	40,000	III-IV	4.2	
Nov 28, 1844	13	36.0	83.9		VI	4.7	
1845		41.1	84.2		II	3.0	
Mar 26, 1846	17 25	36.6	89.6		III	3.4	
Jan 24, 1848		36.6	89.2		V	4.2	
Apr 05, 1850	02 05	38.3	85.8		V	4.2	
Oct 01, 1850		41.4	82.3		IV	3.8	
Aug 28, 1853		36.6	89.2		III	3.4	
Dec 12, 1853		36.6	89.2	100,000	IV-V	4.5	
Feb 12, 1854		37.2	83.8		III-IV	3.6	
Feb 13, 1854		37.2	83.8		III-IV	3.6	
Feb 28, 1854		37.6	84.5	20,000	IV-V	4.2	
Mar 08, 1854		38.2	85.2		IV	3.8	
May 03, 1855	03 33	37.0	89.2		IV	3.8	
May 03, 1855	10	37.0	89.2		III	3.4	
Nov 09, 1856		36.6	89.5	80,000	IV	4.4	
Feb 1857		36.6	89.5		IV	3.8	
Mar 01, 1857	a.m.	41.7	81.2		IV-V	4.0	
Oct 08, 1857	10	38.7	89.2	200,000	VII	5.3	
Apr 16, 1858	12	41.7	81.3		IV	3.8	
Sep 21, 1858		36.5	89.2		VI	4.7	
1860		46.0	94.8		VI-VII	5.0	
Aug 07, 1860	15 30	37.8	87.5	80,000	V	4.4	

TABLE 1. *(Continued)*

Date	Origin time (GMT)	Lat (°N)	Long (°W)	Felt area (km^2)	I_o	m_b	M_S
Aug 17, 1865	15	36.5	89.5	250,000	VII	5.3	
Sep 07, 1865	14 15	36.6	89.5		III-IV	3.6	
Jan 13, 1867		41.5	81.7		III	3.4	
Apr 24, 1867	20 22	39.5	96.7	800,000	VII	5.3	
Apr 28, 1867		40.7	95.8		IV	3.8	
Nov 21, 1868		36.6	89.2		III	3.4	
Feb 20, 1869		38.1	84.5		V	4.2	
Apr 09, 1869		42.7	80.8		III	3.4	
Dec 14, 1870		36.6	89.2		III-IV	3.6	
Jul 24, 1871		37.0	89.2		III	3.4	
Jul 25, 1871	06 40	38.5	90.0	2,500	III	3.6	
Feb 06, 1872	14	43.5	83.8		V	4.2	
Feb 08, 1872	11	37.0	89.2		III-IV	3.6	
Feb 09, 1872		44.6	100.7		III	3.4	
Mar 26, 1872		37.1	88.6		III	3.4	
Apr 20, 1872	07	35.1	90.0		III	3.4	
Jul 09, 1872	02 30	39.8	93.5		IV	3.8	
Jul 23, 1872		41.4	82.1		IV	3.8	
Aug 20, 1872		35.1	90.0		II-III	3.2	
Oct 09, 1872	16	42.7	97.0	8,000	V	4.2	
Apr 23, 1873	04 14	39.7	84.2		III-IV	3.6	
May 01, 1873	04 30	30.2	97.7		III-IV	3.6	
May 03, 1873	21	36.0	89.6	30,000	IV	4.2	
Aug 22, 1873	19	35.1	90.0		II-III	3.2	
Jul 09, 1874	22	37.0	89.2		III-IV	3.6	
Jul 23, 1874		Camp Russell, Nebr.			III	3.4	
Jun 18, 1875	13 43	40.2	84.0	100,000	VII	5.3	
Oct 07, 1875		36.1	89.6	50,000	III-IV	4.3	
Oct 28, 1875	03	35.1	90.0		IV	3.8	
Nov 08, 1875	10 40	39.3	95.5	22,000	V	4.2	
Dec 09, 1875	09	40.7	95.8		III	3.4	
Jan 27, 1876		41.9	84.0			3.0	
Feb 27, 1876		42.4	83.2			3.0	
Jun 1876		40.4	84.2			4.2	
Aug 17, 1876	05 25	44.1	99.6		IV	3.8	
Sep 25, 1876	06 00	38.5	87.8		VI	4.7	
Sep 25, 1876	06 15	38.5	87.8	150,000	VI	4.7	
Sep 26, 1876		38.5	87.8		III	3.4	
Jan 23, 1877	21	38.8	83.5	2,500	III	3.4	
May 26, 1877	21	38.2	87.9		III-IV	3.6	
Jun 03, 1877		37.5	85.7		III	3.4	
Jul 15, 1877	00 40	36.8	89.7	65,000	III-IV	4.3	
Aug 17, 1877	16 50	42.3	83.3	500	IV-V	4.0	
Nov 15, 1877	17 45	41	97	450,000	VII	5.3	
Nov 16, 1877	07 38	35.5	84.0		V	4.2	
Nov 19, 1877	11 10	37.0	89.2		III-IV	3.6	
Jan 09, 1878	04 30	37.0	89.2		III-IV	3.6	
Mar 12, 1878	10	36.8	89.1	40,000	V	4.2	
Nov 19, 1878	05 52	36.7	89.3	350,000	VI	4.9	
Mar 1879		39.6	99.1		IV-V	4.0	
Jul 26, 1879	17 45	37.0	89.2		II-III	3.4	
Sep 26, 1879	03 10	35.3	90.3	10,000	III-IV	3.9	
Dec 29, 1879	06 30	42.9	97.3		V	4.0	
Jul 14, 1880	02 30	35.3	90.3	25,000	IV	4.1	
Nov 13, 1880	20	35.6	87.3		III	3.4	
Dec 28, 1880	07 15	49.0	97.2		III-IV	3.6	
Apr 20, 1881		41.6	85.8		IV	3.8	
May 19, 1881	15	38.9	95.2		III	3.4	
May 27, 1881	a.m.	41.3	89.1		VI	4.7	
Aug 30, 1881	05	39.2	83.7		III	3.4	
Oct 07, 1881	16 52	35.1	90.0		IV	3.8	
Feb 09, 1882	20	40.4	84.2	250	V	4.2	

Continued on next page

TABLE 1. *(Continued)*

Date	Origin time (GMT)	Lat (°N)	Long (°W)	Felt area (km^2)	I_o	m_b	M_S
Apr 12, 1882	05	29.9	90.1		III	3.4	
Jul 20, 1882	10	36.9	89.2		V	4.2	
Jul 28, 1882		37.6	90.6	25,000	III-IV	4.1	
Sep 27, 1882	10 20	39	89.5	100,000	VI	4.7	
Oct 15, 1882	05 50	39	89.5	20,000	V	4.2	
Oct 15, 1882	10 35	39	89.5	20,000	V	4.2	
Oct 22, 1882	06 10	38.9	89.4		III	3.4	
Oct 22, 1882	22 15	33.6	95.6	500,000	VIII	5.5	
Nov 16, 1882	03 15	38.6	90.2		III	3.6	
Jan 06, 1883	08	northern Ohio				3.0	
Jan 10, 1883	20 25	37.4	89.3		III	3.4	
Jan 11, 1883	07 12	37.0	89.2	200,000	V-VI	4.6	
Feb 04, 1883	11	42.3	85.6	400,000	VI	4.7	
Apr 12, 1883	08 30	37.0	89.2		VI-VII	4.0	
May 23, 1883	04 30	38.4	82.6		IV	3.8	
Jun 11, 1883	18 16	35.1	90.0		VI	4.7	
Jul 06, 1883	17 15	37.0	89.2		III	3.4	
Jul 14, 1883	07 30	37.0	89.1	25,000	IV-V	4.1	
Nov 15, 1883	03 14	38.7	90.2		IV	3.8	
Dec 05, 1883	15 20	36.3	91.2	250,000	V	4.2	
Feb 14, 1884	12	37.7	90.7		III	3.4	
Mar 17, 1884	20	41.1	100.7		IV	3.8	
Mar 31, 1884	19	39.5	84.7		II	3.0	
Sep 19, 1884	20 14	40.7	84.1	320,000	VI	4.7	
Nov 30, 1884	05	35.5	89.7	12,000	IV	4.0	
Dec 23, 1884	23	40.4	84.2		III	3.4	
Jan 18, 1885	11 30	41.3	81.1		III	3.4	
Feb 21, 1885		37.2	94.3		III	3.4	
Aug 15, 1885	05 05	41.3	81.1		II-III	3.2	
Dec 27, 1885	01 05	40.4	89.0		III	3.4	
Jan 22, 1886	16 38	30.4	92.0			3.0	
Mar 01, 1886	16	39.0	85.5		III-IV	3.6	
Mar 18, 1886	05 59	37.0	89.2	45,000	VI	4.7	
May 03, 1886	03	39.5	82.1	1,000	III-IV	3.6	
Aug 14, 1886		39.7	86.1		III-IV	3.6	
Feb 06, 1887	22 15	38.7	87.5	170,000	V-VI	4.7	
Aug 02, 1887	18 36	37.0	89.2	170,000	V	4.7	
Nov 03, 1888		35.4	90.4		IV	3.8	
Jun 06, 1889	04 28	35.1	90.0		III	3.4	
Jun 06, 1889	16 25	35.9	88.1	10,000	III-IV	3.9	
Jul 20, 1889	01 32	35.2	90.0		VI	3.8	
Sep 1889		40.4	84.2		III	3.4	
Jan 08, 1891	06	31.7	95.2		VII	3.8	
Jan 14, 1891		35.1	90.0		III-IV	3.6	
Jul 27, 1891	02 28	37.9	87.5		VI	4.5	
Sep 27, 1891	04 55	37.0	89.2		V	4.2	
Jan 14, 1892	09 05	35.1	90.0		III	3.4	
Summer, 1892		40.4	84.2			3.0	
Jul 18, 1894		35.0	90.0		III	3.4	
Jul 27, 1895		35.2	88.3		III-IV	3.6	
Oct 03, 1895		35.2	90.0		III	3.4	
Oct 11, 1895	23 55	43.9	103.3	4,000	V	4.2	
Oct 12, 1895	01 25	43.9	103.3	4,000	V	4.2	
Oct 18, 1895	03	36.6	89.5		III	3.4	
Oct 18, 1895	06 10	36.6	89.5		III	3.4	
Oct 30, 1895	14 30	36.4	90.6		III	3.4	
Oct 30, 1895	20	36.4	90.6		III	3.4	
Oct 30, 1895	22 30	36.4	90.6		III	3.4	
Oct 31, 1895	11 08	37.0	89.4	2,500,000	IX	6.2	
Nov 02, 1895	04 16	37.0	89.4		IV	3.8	
Nov 02, 1895	08	37.0	89.4		III-IV	3.6	
Nov 02, 1895	17	37.0	89.4		III-IV	3.6	

TABLE 1. (Continued)

Date	Origin time (GMT)	Lat (°N)	Long (°W)	Felt area (km²)	I_o	m_b	M_S
Nov 17, 1895		37.0	89.4		III-IV	3.6	
Feb 04, 1896	11 45	42.6	97.3		III	3.4	
Mar 15, 1896	07	40.3	84.2		IV	3.8	
Apr 26, 1897	04	35.8	89.6	20,000	IV-V	4.1	
May 01, 1897	04	37	89		IV-V	4.0	
Dec 02, 1897	07 10	east. Kans. or east. Okla.		120,000	IV	4.5	
Jan 27, 1898	01 35	34.6	90.6		IV	3.8	
Mar 30, 1898	01 30	36.8	85.8		III	3.4	
Apr 15, 1898	03 20	36.4	90.6			3.0	
Jun 06, 1898	08 30	37.7	84.3		III	3.4	
Jun 14, 1898	15 20	36.0	89.4	120,000	IV	4.5	
Jun 26, 1898	08 30	37.7	84.3		III	3.4	
Sep 16, 1898	09 59	42.6	97.3		IV	3.8	
Oct 24, 1898	a.m.	41.5	81.7		III-IV	3.6	
Feb 09, 1899		41.9	87.6			3.0	
Apr 30, 1899	02 05	38.8	87.0	100,000	VI-VII	5.0	
Oct 11, 1899	04	42.1	86.5	1,700	IV	3.8	
Nov 12, 1899	14	39.3	83.0		IV	3.8	
Nov 13, 1899		Tennessee				3.0	
Dec 01, 1899	18 50	36.8	94.4		IV	3.8	
Dec 06, 1899	12	44.5	99.0	10,000	IV	3.8	
Mar 14, 1900	03	45.5	98.5		III-IV	3.6	
Mar 14, 1900	05	45.5	98.5		III-IV	3.6	
Apr 09, 1900	14	41.4	81.8		VI	4.7	
Jan 04, 1901	03 12	37.8	94.0	5,000	V	4.2	
Feb 15, 1901	00 15	36.0	90.0	30,000	IV	4.2	
May 17, 1901	07	39.3	82.5	25,000	V	4.2	
Sep 14, 1901		35.1	90.0		III	3.4	
Jan 24, 1902	10 48	38.6	90.2	130,000	VI	4.7	
Mar 10, 1902	06	39.9	85.2		III-IV	3.6	
Mar 12, 1902	11 30	39.9	85.2		III-IV	3.6	
May 29, 1902	07 30	35.1	85.3		V	4.2	
Jun 14, 1902	07	40.3	81.4		IV-V	4.0	
Jul 28, 1902	18	42.5	97.5	90,000	V-VI	4.5	
Oct 18, 1902	22	35.0	85.3		V	4.2	
Jan 01, 1903	18 30	39.9	85.2		II-III	3.2	
Jan 01, 1903	23 45	39.9	85.2		II-III	3.2	
Jan 13, 1903	14 53	38.8	95.3		II	3.0	
Feb 09, 1903	00 21	37.8	89.3	180,000	VI	4.8	
Mar 17, 1903	11 50	39.1	89.5		III-IV	3.6	
Sep 20, 1903		39.4	86.3		IV	3.8	
Sep 21, 1903		38.7	88.1		IV	3.8	
Oct 05, 1903	02 56	37	90	120,000	V-VI	4.6	
Nov 03, 1903	18	37.8	89.3		III-IV	3.6	
Nov 04, 1903	18 18	36.9	89.3	340,000	VII	5.3	
Nov 04, 1903	19 14	36.9	89.3		VI	4.7	
Nov 20, 1903		39.4	86.3		III	3.4	
Nov 24, 1903	15 20	36.6	89.5		III	3.4	
Nov 25, 1903		36.6	89.5		II-III	3.2	
Nov 27, 1903	07	36.5	89.5	30,000	V	4.2	
Nov 27, 1903	09 20	36.5	89.5	180,000	V	4.2	
Dec 11, 1903		39.1	88.5		II	3.0	
Oct 28, 1904	a.m.	37.5	100.2	7,000	V	4.2	
Dec 01, 1904	09	41.8	96.7		III	3.4	
Mar 13, 1905	16 30	45.1	87.7		V	3.8	
Apr 13, 1905	16 30	40.4	91.6	13,000	IV-V	4.0	
Jul 27, 1905	00 20	47.3	88.4	40,000	VII	5.0	
Aug 22, 1905	05 08	36.8	89.6	325,000	VI-VII	5.0	
Aug 22, 1905	10 45	39.9	91.4		II-III	3.2	
Jan 08, 1906	00 15	39.3	96.6	95,000	VII-VIII	5.5	
Jan 08, 1906	00 38	39.3	96.6			3.0	
Jan 08, 1906	04 30	39.3	96.6			3.0	

Continued on next page

TABLE 1. *(Continued)*

Date	Origin time (GMT)	Lat (°N)	Long (°W)	Felt area (km^2)	I_o	m_b	M_S
Jan 08, 1906	07	39.3	96.6		II-III	3.2	
Jan 08, 1906	08	39.3	96.6		II-III	3.2	
Jan 14, 1906	15	39.3	96.6		II-III	3.2	
Jan 16, 1906	02 40	39.3	96.6	40,000	IV	3.8	
Jan 20, 1906	05 30	39.3	96.6		III	3.4	
Jan 23, 1906	13 40	39.3	96.6		III	3.4	
Jan 23, 1906	14 25	39.3	96.6		III	3.4	
Feb 24, 1906	05 15	39.7	92.3		III	3.4	
Mar 06, 1906		39.7	91.4		IV	3.8	
Apr 20, 1906	18 30	41.5	81.7		IV	3.8	
Apr 22, 1906		43.0	87.9			3.0	
Apr 23, 1906	07 12	40.7	83.6		V	4.2	
May 08, 1906	06 58	39.5	85.8	6,000	III-IV	3.6	
May 09, 1906	06 38	39.2	85.9		IV	3.8	
May 10, 1906	00 27	43.0	101.3	45,000	VI	4.7	
May 11, 1906	06 15	38.5	87.2	3,200	IV	3.8	
May 19, 1906	09 20	42.9	85.7			3.0	
May 21, 1906	19	38.7	88.4		V	4.2	
Jun 27, 1906	12 10	41.4	81.6	1,000	V	4.2	
Aug 08, 1906		47.3	88.4	30,000		3.8	
Aug 13, 1906	13 19	39.7	86.8		IV	3.8	
Sep 07, 1906	16 33	38.2	87.7	1,500	IV	3.8	
Nov 09, 1906		47.1	88.6			3.0	
Nov 24, 1906	05 15	39.7	92.3		III	3.4	
Jan 11, 1907	07 45	37.1	97.0		IV	3.8	
Jan 30, 1907	05 30	39.5	86.6		V	4.2	
Jan 30, 1907		38.9	89.5	3,000	V	4.2	
Apr 12, 1907		41.5	81.7		II	3.0	
Apr 1907		35.5	101.2			3.0	
Jul 04, 1907	09	37.8	90.4	1,000	IV-V	3.8	
Nov 28, 1907	16 30	42.3	89.8	250	IV	3.8	
Dec 11, 1907	04 32	38.6	90.2		IV	3.8	
Jul 19, 1908		35.7	97.7		III	3.4	
Sep 28, 1908	19 34	36.6	89.6	13,000	IV	4.0	
Oct 28, 1908	00 27	37.0	89.2	13,000	IV-V	4.0	
Nov 12, 1908		38.7	93.2	1,800	IV	3.8	
Nov 28, 1908		42.2	89.8		IV	3.8	
Dec 27, 1908	21 15	37.0	89.0	80,000	IV	4.4	
Dec 31, 1908		37.0	88.9		III	3.4	
Jan 23, 1909	03 15	47.2	88.6		V	3.4	
Jan 26, 1909	20 15	42.3	97.8	2,500	IV-V	4.0	
May 26, 1909	14 42	42.5	89.0	800,000	VII	5.3	
Jul 19, 1909	04 34	40.2	90.0	100,000	VII	5.3	
Aug 16, 1909	22 45	38.3	90.1	45,000	IV	4.3	
Sep 22, 1909		38.7	86.5	10,000	V	4.2	
Sep 27, 1909	09 45	39.5	87.4	250,000	VII	5.3	
Oct 22, 1909	22	37.6	90.6		IV	3.8	
Oct 22, 1909	22 30	41.8	89.7		IV-V	4.0	
Oct 22, 1909		38.9	84.5			3.0	
Oct 23, 1909	07 10	37.0	89.5	125,000	V-VI	4.6	
Oct 23, 1909	09 47	39.0	87.8	35,000	V	4.2	
Feb 26, 1910	08	41.4	97.4		IV-V	4.0	
May 08, 1910	17 30	30.1	96.0		IV	3.8	
May 12, 1910	a.m.	30.1	96.0	2,500	IV	3.8	
Feb 28, 1911	09	38.7	90.3		IV	3.8	
Mar 31, 1911	16 57	33.8	92.2	50,000	VI	4.7	
Mar 31, 1911	18 10	33.8	92.2	6,500	IV-V	4.0	
Jun 02, 1911	22 34	44.2	98.2	100,000	V	4.5	
Jul 29, 1911		41.8	87.6		IV-V	3.2	
Jan 02, 1912	16 21	41.5	88.5	150,000	VI	4.7	
Sep 25, 1912		42.3	89.1		III-IV	3.6	
Mar 28, 1913	21 50	36.2	83.7	7,000	VII	5.3	

TABLE 1. (Continued)

Date	Origin time (GMT)	Lat (°N)	Long (°W)	Felt area (km²)	I_0	m_b	M_S
Jun 09, 1913	15 30	35.8	88.9	10,000	III	3.9	
Oct 17, 1913	02 15	41.8	89.7	10,000	III-IV	3.6	
Nov 11, 1913	14	38.2	85.8		IV	3.8	
Jan 24, 1914	03 24	35.6	84.5		V	4.2	
Oct 07, 1914	21	43.1	89.4		IV	3.8	
Dec 30, 1914	01	30.5	95.9		IV-V	3.5	
1914		40.4	84.2		III	3.4	
Feb 05, 1915	06 55	37.7	88.6	1,000	IV	3.8	
Feb 19, 1915	04 35	37.1	89.2	900	IV	3.8	
Mar 03, 1915	07 45	47.3	88.4		III-IV	3.6	
Apr 15, 1915	13 20	38.7	88.1	8,000	II-III	3.8	
Apr 28, 1915	23 40	36.5	89.5	500	IV-V	4.0	
Aug 08, 1915	15 15	48.1	103.6		IV	3.8	
Sep 16, 1915	19	42.8	99.3		III-IV	3.6	
Oct 04, 1915	14 02	47.3	88.4		IV-V	4.0	
Oct 08, 1915	16 50	35.7	95.3	8,000	III	3.4	
Oct 23, 1915	06 05	43.8	101.5		V	4.2	
Oct 26, 1915	07 40	36.7	88.6		V	4.2	
Dec 07, 1915	18 40	36.7	89.1	120,000	V-VI	4.6	
Jan 07, 1916	19 45	39.1	87.0	8,000	III	3.8	
Feb 18, 1916	01 27	37.6	88.8		III	3.4	
Feb 24, 1916	04 30	43.0	102.5		III	3.4	
May 21, 1916	18 24	36.6	89.5	20,000	IV	4.1	
May 31, 1916	22 45	43.1	89.3		II	3.0	
Jun 29, 1916	07 45	43.4	99.9		III	3.4	
Aug 24, 1916	09	37.0	89.2	10,000	IV	3.8	
Oct 19, 1916	08	36.7	88.6		III	3.4	
Dec 19, 1916	05 42	36.6	89.2		V-VI	4.5	
Dec 1916		41.5	100.5		II-III	3.2	
Jan 25, 1917	22 15	35.9	86.8		II-III	3.2	
Jan 26, 1917	13 15	35.9	86.8		II-III	3.2	
Jan 27, 1917	21	35.9	86.8		II-III	3.2	
Jan 28, 1917		35.4	101.3		II-III	3.2	
Feb 06, 1917	17 26	47.9	95.0		IV	3.8	
Mar 24, 1917		35.3	101.2		V	4.2	
Mar 27, 1917	19 56	35.3	101.3	5,000	VI	4.7	
Mar 27, 1917	23 38	35.3	101.3			3.0	
Apr 09, 1917	20 52	38.1	90.2	550,000	VI	5.0	
Apr 09, 1917	23 38	38.1	90.2		IV	3.8	
May 08, 1917	09	36.8	90.4	10,000	III-IV	3.9	
May 08, 1917	15	36.8	90.4		III	3.4	
Jun 09, 1917	13 14	36.8	90.4	45,000	IV	4.3	
Sep 03, 1917	21 30	46.3	94.8	48,000	VI	4.7	
Jan 16, 1918	15 45	35.9	83.9		V	4.2	
Feb 17, 1918	08 10	37.0	89.2	8,000	III	3.8	
Feb 22, 1918		42.8	84.2		IV	3.8	
Jun 22, 1918	01	36.1	84.1	8,000	V	4.2	
Jul 01, 1918	19 02	39.7	91.4		IV	3.8	
Sep 10, 1918	16 30	35.5	98.0	1,000	V-VI	4.5	
Sep 11, 1918	06 30	35.5	97.9	1,000	V-VI	4.5	
Sep 11, 1918	09	35.5	97.9		II-III	3.2	
Oct 01, 1918	07 38	47.3	88.4		III	3.4	
Oct 04, 1918	09 21	34.7	91.7	80,000	V	4.4	
Oct 13, 1918	09 30	36.1	91.0	4,500	V	4.2	
Oct 16, 1918	02 15	36	89.2	100,000	V	4.5	
1918		35.5	97.7		III-IV	3.6	
Feb 11, 1919	03 37	37.8	87.5	5,000	III-IV	3.8	
Apr 08, 1919	12 30	36.2	91.3		III-IV	3.6	
May 23, 1919	12 30	36.6	89.2	8,000	III	3.9	
May 24, 1919	13 30	36.6	89.2	8,000	III	3.9	
May 25, 1919	09 45	38.4	87.5	65,000	V	4.4	
May 26, 1919	13 25	36.6	89.2	8,000	III	3.8	

Continued on next page

TABLE 1. *(Continued)*

Date	Origin time (GMT)	Lat (°N)	Long (°W)	Felt area (km²)	I_o	m_b	M_S
May 27, 1919	03 06	37.7	97.3	25,000	IV	4.2	
May 28, 1919	11 30	36.6	89.2	8,000	III	3.8	
May 28, 1919	13 45	36.4	89.5	8,000	III	3.8	
Jul 26, 1919	10	37.7	97.3		III	3.4	
Jul 26, 1919	12 55	37.7	97.3	10,000	IV	3.8	
Nov 03, 1919	20 40	36.3	91.0		IV-V	4.0	
Feb 29, 1920	03 05	37.2	93.3	80,000	IV	4.3	
Apr 07, 1920	20 45	36.3	88.2	8,000	II	3.8	
Apr 30, 1920	15 12	38.6	89.1	10,000	IV	4.0	
May 01, 1920	15 15	38.5	89.5	60,000	IV-V	4.3	
May 01, 1920	16 09	38.5	89.5			3.0	
Jul 14, 1920	23	43.2	103.2	4,000	III	3.7	
Oct 03, 1920	14 15	38.6	94.3	8,000	III	3.8	
Dec 24, 1920	07 30	36.0	85.0		V	4.2	
Jan 09, 1921	21 54	36.4	89.5	5,000	IV	3.8	
Feb 27, 1921	22 16	37.0	89.2	8,000	III	3.8	
Mar 14, 1921	12 15	39.5	87.5	65,000	IV	4.4	
Mar 16, 1921	23 45	43.5	96.7		III-IV	3.6	
Mar 31, 1921	20 03	37.9	87.8		IV	3.8	
Sep 02, 1921	14	36.2	86.3		III	3.4	
Sep 09, 1921	03	38.3	90.1	10,000	IV	4.0	
Sep 09, 1921	05 45	38.3	90.1			3.0	
Sep 21, 1921		36.0	86.1		III	3.4	
Sep 24, 1921	00 30	43.7	98.7		IV	3.8	
Oct 01, 1921	09	37.7	88.6	10,000	IV	4.0	
Oct 09, 1921	07 50	38.3	90.1	8,000	III	3.8	
Oct 09, 1921	11 50	38.3	90.1		III	3.4	
Dec 15, 1921	13 20	35.8	84.6		V	4.2	
Jan 02, 1922	14 50	43.8	99.3		VI	4.7	
Jan 11, 1922	03 42	37.9	87.8	25,000	IV-V	4.2	
Mar 16, 1922	09 30	43.0	82.5		III	3.4	
Mar 22, 1922	22 30	37.3	88.9	150,000	V	4.6	
Mar 23, 1922	04 30	37.3	88.9		V	4.2	
Mar 23, 1922	21 45	37.0	88.9	50,000	IV	4.3	
Mar 28, 1922	16 42	36.7	90.4	6,000	III	4.0	
Mar 30, 1922	04 20	35.5	86.7		IV	3.8	
Mar 30, 1922	16 53	36.1	89.6	40,000	IV-V	4.2	
Apr 11, 1922	05	40.9	90.6		II	3.0	
Jul 07, 1922		43.8	88.5		V	4.2	
Nov 27, 1922	03 31	37.8	88.5	130,000	VI-VII	5.0	
Mar 07, 1923	05 03	31.7	106.5	50,000	IV-V	4.3	
Mar 09, 1923	04 45	38.9	89.4	10,000	III-IV	3.9	
Mar 27, 1923	08	34.6	89.7	10,000	III-IV	3.9	
May 06, 1923	07 50	37.0	89.2	10,000	III-IV	3.9	
May 15, 1923	23 42	37.0	89.2	8,000	III-IV	3.8	
Sep 10, 1923	06 30	41.7	96.2		III-IV	3.6	
Oct 28, 1923	17 10	35.5	90.4	120,000	VII	5.3	
Nov 10, 1923	04	40.0	89.9	1,600	V	4.2	
Nov 26, 1923	23 25	35.5	90.4	23,000	IV	4.1	
Nov 28, 1926	12 30	37.5	87.3		III	3.4	
Nov 29, 1926	23 20	37.0	89.2		IV	3.8	
Jan 01, 1924	03 05	35.4	90.3	150,000	V	4.6	
Mar 02, 1924	11 18	37.0	89.1	80,000	V	4.4	
Apr 02, 1924	11 15	37.1	88.6		IV	3.8	
Jun 03, 1924	00 40	36.3	96.5		III	3.4	
Jun 07, 1924	05 42	36.4	89.5	25,000	IV-V	4.2	
Sep 24, 1924	11	40.9	100.1		IV	3.8	
Dec 30, 1924	22 10	43.5	103.5	18,000	IV	3.8	
Jan 26, 1925	08 34	42.5	92.4	500	II	3.2	
Jan 27, 1925	22 42	36.2	91.7	6,000	III	3.8	
Mar 03, 1925	16	42.1	87.7		II-III	3.2	
Mar 27, 1925	04 06	39.5	83.9		V	4.2	
Apr 04, 1925		39.1	84.5			3.0	

TABLE 1. *(Continued)*

Date	Origin time (GMT)	Lat (°N)	Long (°W)	Felt area (km²)	I_0	m_b	M_S
Apr 27, 1925	04 05	38.3	87.6	250,000	VI-VII	5.0	
May 13, 1925	12	36.7	88.6	10,000	IV-V	3.8	
Jul 08, 1925	16	36.2	93.2	10,000	IV	3.8	
Jul 13, 1925		38.8	90.0		V	4.2	
Jul 29, 1925	11 30	34.5	101.2		IV	3.8	
Jul 30, 1925	08	34.5	100.3		V	4.2	
Jul 30, 1925	12 17	35.4	101.3	500,000	VI	4.8	
Aug 25, 1925	06 27	42.8	97.4		IV	3.8	
Sep 02, 1925	11 55	37.8	87.5	200,000	VI	4.8	
Sep 20, 1925	09	37.8	87.5	25,000	IV	4.1	
Oct 1925		40.4	84.2		III	3.4	
Jan 20, 1926		35.6	94.9	47,000	V	4.2	
Mar 10, 1926		38.8	101.7			3.0	
Mar 22, 1926	14 30	37.8	88.6	10,000	IV	4.0	
Apr 28, 1926	04 16	36.2	89.6	10,000	IV	4.0	
Jun 20, 1926	14 20	35.6	94.9	47,000	V	4.2	
Oct 04, 1926	04 20	38.3	87.6		III	3.4	
Oct 27, 1926	04 20	38.3	87.6	10,000	IV	4.0	
Oct 28, 1926	08 42	41.7	83.6		III	3.4	
Oct 28, 1926	11 00	41.7	83.6		IV	3.8	
Nov 05, 1926	15 53	39.1	82.1	900	VI-VII	4.0	
Dec 13, 1926	23 03	36.7	89.4	8,000	III	3.8	
Dec 17, 1926		36.4	89.5	10,000	IV	4.0	
Jan 07, 1927	09 30	38.3	97.7	10,000	V	4.2	
Feb 01, 1927	01 30	37.4	89.7	10,000	IV	4.0	
Feb 03, 1927	08	36.7	90.4	8,000	IV	3.8	
Feb 17, 1927	05 30	40.7	82.5		IV	3.8	
Feb 17, 1927	06 00	40.7	82.5		II	3.0	
Mar 18, 1927	17 25	39.9	95.3	800	V	4.2	
Apr 18, 1927	10 30	36.3	89.5	10,000	IV	4.0	
Apr 30, 1927	04 15	46.9	102.1		II	3.2	
May 07, 1927	08 28	35.7	90.6	300,000	VII	5.3	
Jun 16, 1927	12	34.7	86.0	6,500	V	4.2	
Jul 20, 1927		35.8	86.0	180,000	VI	4.7	
Aug 13, 1927	16 10	36.4	89.5	65,000	V	4.4	
Oct 08, 1927	12 56	35.0	85.3		V	4.2	
Oct 14, 1927	16 10	41.6	98.9	1,000	IV	3.8	
Oct 29, 1927		40.9	81.2		V	4.2	
Nov 13, 1927	16 21	32.3	90.2	8,000	IV	4.2	
Dec 15, 1927	04 30	28.9	89.4	10,000	IV	4.2	
Jan 23, 1928	09 19	42.0	90.0	1,000	IV	3.8	
Mar 07, 1928	02 45	35.6	87.0	5,000	II-III	3.4	
Mar 17, 1928	21 15	38.6	90.2	1,200	II	3.3	
Apr 15, 1928	11	36.6	89.5		IV	3.8	
Apr 15, 1928	15 05	37.3	89.5		IV	3.8	
Apr 23, 1928	11	36.5	89.2		IV	3.8	
May 31, 1928	22 40	36.6	89.5		IV	3.8	
Sep 09, 1928	21	41.5	82.0	4,000	V	4.2	
Oct 27, 1928		40.4	84.1	250	III	3.4	
Nov 08, 1928	14 15	39.5	98.1		IV	3.8	
Nov 10, 1928	06 20	36.1	91.1		IV	3.8	
Nov 16, 1928	13 45	44.1	103.7	5,000	V	4.2	
Dec 23, 1928	06 10	47.6	93.9		IV	3.8	
Dec 26, 1928	03 25	36.1	91.1		IV	3.8	
Feb 14, 1929	20 12	38.3	87.6	2,500	IV	3.8	
Feb 26, 1929	08 15	37.6	90.6		IV	3.8	
Mar 08, 1929	09 06	40.4	84.2	13,000	V	4.2	
May 13, 1929	03 50	36.4	89.5	5,000	III	3.8	
Jun 10, 1929		41.5	81.7		III	3.4	
Jul 28, 1929	17	28.9	89.4	8,000	IV	3.8	
Sep 17, 1929	19 19	41.5	81.5		III	3.0	
Sep 23, 1929	10	39.0	96.6		V	4.0	
Sep 23, 1929	11	39.0	96.6	40,000	V	4.2	

Continued on next page

TABLE 1. *(Continued)*

Date	Origin time (GMT)	Lat (°N)	Long (°W)	Felt area (km²)	I_o	m_b	M_S
Oct 06, 1929	12 30	42.8	97.4	1,800	V	4.2	
Oct 21, 1929	21 30	39.2	96.5	20,000	V	4.2	
Oct 23, 1929		39.0	96.8		II-III	3.2	
Nov 27, 1929	04 20	37.2	99.8		IV	3.8	
Dec 07, 1929	08 02	39.2	96.6	2,500	V	4.2	
Dec 28, 1929	00 30	35.5	97.9	17,000	VI	4.7	
Jan 02, 1930	16 30	35.7	89.5		II	3.0	
Jan 24, 1930	03 45	46.5	84.4		III	3.4	
Jan 26, 1930	21	36.1	91.1		IV	3.8	
Feb 18, 1930	17	35.5	90.4		III	3.4	
Feb 25, 1930	12 45	37.0	90.2		III-IV	3.6	
Mar 27, 1930	08 56	35.1	90.1	1,000	IV	3.8	
Apr 02, 1930	09 39	36.1	89.7		IV	3.8	
May 28, 1930	17 30	39.7	91.4		III	3.4	
Jun 26, 1930	21 45	40.5	84.0		IV	3.8	
Jun 27, 1930	07 23	40.5	84.0		IV	3.8	
Jul 11, 1930	00 15	40.6	83.2		IV	3.8	
Aug 08, 1930	18 31	39.7	91.4		IV	3.8	
Aug 13, 1930	19 59 52	36.6	89.5		II	3.0	
Aug 29, 1930	06 26 54	37.0	89.1	10,000	IV	4.0	
Aug 30, 1930	09 28	35.9	84.4			3.0	
Sep 01, 1930	20 27 28	36.6	89.4	10,000	V	4.2	
Sep 03, 1930	12	37.0	88.9		III	3.4	
Sep 04, 1930	05 30	37.0	88.9		III	3.4	
Sep 29, 1930	21 15	40.4	84.2		III	3.4	
Sep 30, 1930	20 40	40.3	84.3		VII	5.3	
Oct 1930		40.4	84.2		III-IV	3.6	
Oct 16, 1930	12 30	34.3	92.7			3.0	
Oct 16, 1930		36.0	83.9		V	4.2	
Oct 19, 1930	12 12	30.1	91.0	50,000	VI	4.7	
Nov 16, 1930	12 30	34.3	92.8	900	V	4.2	
Nov 20, 1930		42.6	83.4		III	3.4	
Dec 23, 1930	14 44	38.5	90.7	2,500	IV	3.8	
Jan 06, 1931	04 51	39.0	87.0	1,300	V	4.2	
Jan 17, 1931	18 45	43.7	98.7		IV	3.8	
Mar 21, 1931	15 48	40.4	84.2		III	3.4	
Apr 01, 1931	00 15	40.4	84.0		III	3.4	
Apr 01, 1931	23 20 09	36.9	88.3	5,000	III	3.8	
Apr 06, 1931	15 37 03	36.8	89.0	1,200	IV	3.8	
Jun 10, 1931	08 30	41.3	84.0	4,000	V	4.2	
Jul 18, 1931	14 52	36.6	89.5	5,000	IV	3.8	
Aug 09, 1931	06 18 37	39.1	94.7	800	IV-V	4.0	
Aug 09, 1931	07 07	39.1	94.7			3.0	
Aug 09, 1931	07 15	39.1	94.7			3.0	
Aug 16, 1931	11 40 21	30.6	104.1	1,400,000	VIII	5.6	
Aug 16, 1931	19 33	30.6	104.1			3.0	
Aug 19, 1931	02 36	30.6	104.1		V	4.2	
Aug 26, 1931		30.6	104.1		III	3.4	
Sep 20, 1931	23 04 54	40.4	84.2	120,000	VII	5.3	
Oct 02, 1931		31.7	106.5		II-III	3.2	
Oct 08, 1931	14 30	40.4	84.2		III	3.4	
Oct 18, 1931	21 12	43.1	89.4		III	3.4	
Nov 03, 1931	15 50	29.9	104.2		II	3.2	
Nov 27, 1931	09 23	36.2	86.8		III	3.4	
Dec 10, 1931	08 11 36	35.9	89.9		IV	3.8	
Dec 17, 1931	03 36	34.1	89.8	5,000	VI-VII	5.0	
Dec 17, 1931	21 08 19	38.6	90.2	220,000	II	3.0	
Dec 31, 1931		38.5	87.2		II	3.0	
Jan 22, 1932	a.m.	41.1	81.5		V	4.2	
Jan 29, 1932	00 15	39.0	99.6	5,000	V	4.2	
Apr 09, 1922	10 15	31.5	96.0	2,500	V-VI	4.0	
Nov 22, 1932	07 56 42	36.0	90.2	2,500	III	3.6	
Jan 29, 1933	11	46.4	85.5		II	3.0	

TABLE 1. *(Continued)*

Date	Origin time (GMT)	Lat (°N)	Long (°W)	Felt area (km²)	I_o	m_b	M_S
Feb 20, 1933	17	39.8	99.9	15,000	V	4.2	
Feb 23, 1933	03 20	40.3	84.2	5,000	IV	3.8	
Mar 11, 1933	12 48	36.7	90.4		IV	3.8	
Mar 11, 1933	13 04	36.7	90.4		IV	3.8	
May 28, 1933	15 10	38.6	83.7	1,800	V	4.2	
Jul 13, 1933	14 42 39	37.9	89.9		III	3.4	
Aug 04, 1933	04 34 15	37.9	89.9	1,200	IV	3.8	
Aug 08, 1933		41.9	103.7		IV-V	4.0	
Aug 19, 1933	19 30	35.5	98.0	500	VI	4.7	
Oct 24, 1933		37.3	89.5		III	3.4	
Nov 16, 1933	09 29 01	38.6	90.6	4,000	IV	3.8	
Dec 07, 1933	05 55	42.9	89.2	1,200	IV	4.2	
Dec 09, 1933	08 50	35.8	90.2	250	VI	4.2	
Jan 29, 1934	12 30	45.9	97.7		IV	4.2	
Apr 11, 1934	17 40	33.9	95.5	8,000	V	4.2	
Apr 17, 1934	13 53	37.9	89.9		III	3.4	
May 11, 1934	10 40	41.5	98.7	2,500	IV	3.8	
May 15, 1934	14 28	37.9	89.9		III-IV	3.6	
Jul 02, 1934	15 10 41	35.2	90.0		IV	3.8	
Jul 03, 1934		36.2	89.7		II	3.0	
Jul 30, 1934	07 20	42.2	103.0	60,000	VI	4.7	
Aug 20, 1934	00 47 27	36.9	89.2	85,000	VI	4.7	
Aug 20, 1934	03 37 25	37.0	89.2		II-III	3.2	
Aug 30, 1934	03 50	43.4	99.1		IV	3.6	
Oct 30, 1934	02 25 47	37.5	88.5	4,000	IV	3.8	
Nov 08, 1934	04 45	42.6	100.2	3,000	III	3.4	
Nov 12, 1934	14 45	41.5	90.5	13,000	VI	4.7	
Jan 05, 1935	18 40	41.5	90.6	500	IV	4.2	
Jan 05, 1935	18 45	41.5	90.6		III	3.4	
Jan 30, 1935	22	40.5	94.0		III	3.4	
Feb 26, 1935	14 15	40.8	91.1		III	3.4	
Mar 01, 1935	10 59 44	40.3	96.2	210,000	VII	5.3	
Mar 01, 1935	11 04	40.3	96.2			3.0	
Mar 22, 1935	22 45	40.3	96.1		IV	3.8	
Jul 24, 1935	01 38	36.4	89.5		IV	3.8	
Oct 1935	17 15	46.5	87.6		II-III	3.2	
Oct 29, 1935		39.6	90.8			3.0	
Nov 01, 1935	10	44.0	96.6		III	3.4	
Jan 31, 1936	19 30	41.2	83.2		IV	3.8	
Jan 31, 1936	20	41.2	83.2		II	3.0	
Feb 17, 1936	05 05 08	36.2	89.7		IV	3.8	
Mar 14, 1936	17 20	34.0	95.2	2,300	V	4.2	
Jun 20, 1936	03 13	35.7	101.4			3.0	
Jun 20, 1936	03 18	35.7	101.4			3.0	
Jun 20, 1936	03 24 06	35.7	101.4	110,000	VI	4.7	
Jul 12, 1936	00 23	36.9	102.9	500	III-IV	3.6	
Aug 02, 1936	22 16 25	36.7	89.0	20,000	III	3.8	
Aug 08, 1936	01 40	31.7	106.5		III	3.4	
Oct 08, 1936	16 30	39.3	84.4	1,800	III	3.4	
Oct 15, 1936	17 50	31.7	106.5		IV	3.8	
Oct 20, 1936	21 17	36.6	89.6		II	3.0	
Oct 30, 1936	10 30	43.5	103.5		IV	3.8	
Oct 31, 1936	16 11 38	36.6	89.6		II	3.0	
Nov 23, 1936	09 38 40	36.6	90.6		II	3.0	
Nov 25, 1936	17 42 35	36.6	90.6		II	3.0	
Dec 20, 1936	22 41 12	37.3	89.5		II	3.0	
Dec 26, 1936	01 15	39.1	84.5		III	3.4	
Dec 26, 1936	02 05	39.1	84.5		III	3.4	
Jan 30, 1937	08 57 09	36.2	89.7	5,000	IV	3.8	
Mar 02, 1937	14 47 36	40.4	84.2	280,000	VII	5.3	
Mar 03, 1937	09 50	40.7	84.0	500	V	4.2	
Mar 03, 1937	09 55	40.7	84.0		III	3.4	
Mar 09, 1937	05 44 33	40.4	84.2	500,000	VII-VIII	5.3	

Continued on next page

TABLE 1. *(Continued)*

Date	Origin time (GMT)	Lat (°N)	Long (°W)	Felt area (km²)	I_0	m_b	M_S
Mar 18, 1937	11 58	37.7	89.9		II-III	3.2	
Mar 30, 1937	22 45	31.7	106.4		III	3.4	
Apr 23, 1937	17 15	40.7	84.0	650	III	3.4	
Apr 27, 1937	17	40.7	84.0	650	III	3.4	
May 02, 1937	17 05	40.7	84.0		IV	3.8	
May 17, 1937	00 49 46	36.1	90.6	65,000	IV-V	4.4	
Jun 08, 1937	14 26	35.3	96.9	2,500	IV	3.8	
Jun 23, 1937	15 28	36.4	89.5		III	3.4	
Jun 29, 1937	21 45	40.7	89.6		II	3.0	
Aug 05, 1937	23 12	38.7	90.1		III	3.4	
Aug 08, 1937	01 40	31.7	106.5		III	3.4	
Oct 05, 1937	22 58	36.6	89.5		III	3.4	
Oct 17, 1937	04 25	39.1	84.5		III	3.4	
Nov 17, 1937	17 04	38.6	89.1	50,000	V	4.4	
Jan 02, 1938	17 05	44.5	98.2	8,000	IV-V	4.0	
Jan 17, 1938	04 18	37.7	89.9		III	3.4	
Feb 12, 1938	06 27	41.6	87.0	17,000	V	4.2	
Mar 13, 1938	16 10	42.4	83.2		IV	3.8	
Mar 16, 1938	10 12	36.6	89.6		II	3.0	
Mar 24, 1938	13 11	42.7	103.4	5,000	IV	3.8	
Apr 26, 1938	05 42	34.2	93.5		IV	3.8	
Jun 17, 1938		35.8	89.9		III	3.4	
Sep 17, 1938	01 57	35.5	90.3			3.0	
Sep 17, 1938	03 34 24	35.5	90.3	250,000	IV-V	4.8	
Sep 17, 1938	07 20	35.5	90.3		II-III	3.2	
Sep 28, 1938	11 32	36.5	89.9		III	3.4	
Oct 01, 1938	22 15	43.8	99.3	23,000	V	4.2	
Oct 11, 1938	09 37	43.5	96.7	20,000	V	4.2	
Nov 04, 1938	22 10	43.2	98.9	5,000	IV	3.8	
Nov 08, 1938	05 30	42.5	90.7			3.0	
Nov 08, 1938	07 15	42.5	90.7			3.0	
Nov 08, 1938	09 30	42.5	90.7			3.0	
Jan 28, 1939	17 55	46.8	95.8	20,000	IV	3.8	
Mar 18, 1939		40.4	84.0		II	3.0	
Mar 18, 1939	14 03	40.4	84.0	1,400	III-IV	3.6	
Apr 15, 1939	17 25	36.8	89.4	1,000	III	3.4	
Jun 01, 1939	07 30	35.0	96.4	65,000	IV	4.3	
Jun 10, 1939	18 30	43.0	98.9		IV	3.8	
Jun 18, 1939	03 20	40.3	84.0	1,000	IV	3.8	
Jun 19, 1939	21 43 12	34.1	92.6	65,000	V	4.3	
Jun 24, 1939	09 00	34.7	86.6			3.0	
Jun 24, 1939	10 27	34.7	86.6	1,300	IV	3.8	
Jun 24, 1939	11 45	34.7	86.6			3.0	
Jul 09, 1939	12 50	40.3	84.0		II	3.0	
Jul 18, 1939		45.7	87.1			3.0	
Aug 01, 1939		45.7	87.1			3.0	
Sep 19, 1939		36.4	89.5		III	3.4	
Nov 07, 1939	10	45.7	87.1		II-III	3.2	
Nov 23, 1939	15 14 53	38.2	90.1	400,000	V	4.9	
Nov 24, 1939	19 45	41.6	90.6		II-III	3.2	
Jan 08, 1940	20 05	38.3	85.8		III	3.4	
Feb 04, 1940	17 33	37.2	89.5		III	3.4	
Feb 14, 1940	11 10	35.9	89.8		III	3.4	
May 27, 1940	08 30	38.2	85.8		II-III	3.2	
May 31, 1940	17	41.1	81.5		II	3.0	
May 31, 1940	19 03	37.1	88.6	2,500	V	4.2	
Jun 16, 1940	04 30	40.9	82.3		IV	3.8	
Jul 28, 1940	09 30	40.9	82.3		III	3.4	
Aug 15, 1940	10 35	40.9	82.3		III	3.4	
Aug 20, 1940	03 30	40.9	82.3		III	3.4	
Sep 19, 1940	23 43	36.5	89.6		II-III	3.2	
Oct 10, 1940	19 34	36.8	89.2		II-III	3.2	
Dec 02, 1940	16 16	33.0	94.0		IV	3.8	

TABLE 1. *(Continued)*

Date	Origin time (GMT)	Lat (°N)	Long (°W)	Felt area (km²)	I_o	m_b	M_S
Dec 29, 1940	04 30	37.9	87.3	1,800	III	3.6	
Mar 04, 1941		36.0	83.9		II-III	3.2	
May 25, 1941	06 25	43.5	103.5	20,000	IV-V	4.0	
Jun 28, 1941	18 30	32.3	90.8		III-IV	3.6	
Sep 08, 1941	09 45	35.0	85.3	250	IV	3.8	
Oct 08, 1941	07 51	36.2	89.7	3,000	IV-V	4.0	
Oct 18, 1941	07 48	35.4	99.0	250	V	4.2	
Oct 21, 1941	16 53	37.0	89.1	3,000	IV	3.8	
Oct 27, 1941	03 59	36.7	89.7		III	3.4	
Nov 15, 1941	03 07	35.1	90.0		IV	3.8	
Nov 15, 1941	20 04	38.3	90.2		III	3.4	
Nov 17, 1941	03 08	35.5	89.7	50,000	VI	4.7	
Nov 22, 1941	21 55	37.3	89.5		II-III	3.2	
Jan 14, 1942	18 05	38.4	90.3	1,500	III	3.4	
Jan 23, 1942	16 00	38.6	90.4		II	3.0	
Jan 29, 1942	22 12	38.3	90.4			3.0	
Jan 30, 1942	15	38.7	90.3			3.0	
Mar 01, 1942	14 43 10	41.2	89.7	10,000	IV-V	4.0	
Mar 11, 1942	16 55	44.4	103.5		III-IV	3.6	
Mar 29, 1942	12 43	37.7	88.6	500	IV	3.8	
Jun 12, 1942	04 50	36.4	97.9	4,000	III	3.4	
Aug 31, 1942	10 28	37.0	89.2		IV	3.8	
Sep 10, 1942	09	38.8	99.3		IV	3.8	
Nov 17, 1942	18 18	38.6	90.2	500	IV	3.8	
Nov 18, 1942	00 10	38.6	90.2			3.0	
Nov 30, 1942	16 53	36.8	89.7		III	3.4	
Dec 27, 1942	20 40	38.6	90.3		II-III	3.2	
Feb 09, 1943	23 21	45.2	88.2		II-III	3.2	
Feb 15, 1943	12	45.7	87.1			3.0	
Mar 09, 1943	03 25 24	42.2	80.9	220,000	V	4.7	
Apr 13, 1943	17	38.3	85.8		IV	3.8	
May 16, 1943	19 40	43.5	103.5		IV	3.8	
May 20, 1943	20 05	38.9	90.2		II	3.0	
May 24, 1943	20 33	38.9	90.2		II	3.0	
Jun 08, 1943	19 50	38.6	90.4		III-IV	3.6	
Jul 25, 1943	06 49 10	38.1	91.3		IV-V	4.0	
Jan 07, 1944	05 18	37.5	89.7	2,300	IV	3.8	
Mar 16, 1944		42.0	88.3		IV	3.4	
Sep 25, 1944	11 37 23	37.9	90.0	65,000	IV	4.4	
Nov 13, 1944	11 52	40.4	84.4	45,000	III	4.3	
Nov 16, 1944	19 35	45.7	87.1		II-III	3.2	
Dec 10, 1944	11	45.7	87.1		IV	3.8	
Dec 23, 1944	07 23	36.2	89.7		IV	3.8	
Jan 16, 1945	04	37.8	90.2	1,800	IV	3.8	
Mar 28, 1945	01 45 58	38.6	90.2	8,000	III	3.4	
May 02, 1945	11 22	36.5	89.7	5,000	IV	3.8	
May 18, 1945	14 26	45.7	87.1		II	3.0	
May 21, 1945	07 51	38.6	90.2		IV	3.8	
Aug 06, 1945	23 52	36.1	89.7		III	3.4	
Aug 07, 1945	04 05	36.1	89.7		III	3.4	
Sep 23, 1945	06 22	37.0	89.8		IV	3.8	
Oct 27, 1945	10 42	36.5	89.5		III	3.4	
Nov 10, 1945	09	43.0	97.9		IV	3.8	
Nov 13, 1945	08 21	37.0	89.2	28,000	IV	4.1	
Feb 25, 1946	00 52	38.6	89.1	4,000	IV	3.8	
Apr 06, 1946		35.2	84.9		IV	3.8	
May 15, 1946	06 10	36.6	90.8	32,000	III-IV	4.2	
Jul 23, 1946	06 45	44.1	98.6	22,000	VI	4.7	
Oct 08, 1946	01 12 02	37.5	90.6	80,000	IV-V	4.4	
Oct 26, 1946	20 37	48.1	103.6		IV	3.8	
Nov 07, 1946	20 43 20	38.0	90.7		II-III	3.2	
Jan 16, 1947	16 23	37.0	89.2		II-III	3.2	
Mar 16, 1947	15 30	42.1	88.3		IV	3.8	

Continued on next page

TABLE 1. *(Continued)*

Date	Origin time (GMT)	Lat (°N)	Long (°W)	Felt area (km^2)	I_o	m_b	M_S
Mar 26, 1947		37.0	88.4		VI	4.0	
May 06, 1947	21 27	43.0	87.9	8,000	IV-V	4.0	
May 14, 1947	05 02	46.0	100.9		IV	3.8	
May 16, 1947	05 45	44.4	100.3		III-IV	3.6	
Jun 30, 1947	04 23 53	38.4	90.2	40,000	VI	4.7	
Aug 10, 1947	01 46 48	42.0	85.0	180,000	VI	4.7	
Aug 25, 1947	14	43.1	98.9		IV	3.8	
Sep 20, 1947	21 30	31.9	92.6		IV-V	4.0	
Dec 01, 1947	07 47 33	36.7	90.6	27,000	IV	4.2	
Dec 15, 1947	03 27	35.6	90.1	15,000	V	4.2	
Jan 06, 1948	01 34	38.6	89.1	800	IV-V	4.0	
Jan 15, 1948	17 40	43.1	89.7		IV	3.9	
Jan 18, 1948		41.7	83.6		III	3.4	
Feb 09, 1948		36.4	84.1		III	3.4	
Feb 10, 1948	00 04	36.4	84.1		V-VI	4.5	
Mar 12, 1948	04 29	36.0	102.5	300,000	VI	4.7	
Apr 03, 1948	03	37.7	97.3		IV	3.8	
Apr 07, 1948		41.4	99.6		II-III	3.2	
Apr 20, 1948	14 17	41.7	91.8		IV	3.8	
Jan 14, 1949	03 49	36.4	89.7	4,000	V	4.2	
Jan 31, 1949		36.3	89.7	4,000	V	4.2	
May 07, 1949	14 54 10	44.5	99.0		III	3.4	
May 13, 1949	04 15	42.5	99.0	3,000	IV	3.8	
Jun 03, 1949		45	100		IV	3.8	
Jun 08, 1949	19 51 36	38.1	90.3	800	III	3.4	
Aug 11, 1949	16 32	38.6	90.3		II-III	3.2	
Aug 13, 1949	21 45	36.1	89.7		III	3.4	
Aug 26, 1949		38.6	90.7		III	3.4	
Dec 14, 1949	03 15	43.2	99.4		III	3.4	
Feb 08, 1950	10 37	37.7	92.7	14,000	V	4.2	
Feb 15, 1950	10 05	46.1	95.2	3,000	IV-V	4.0	
Mar 20, 1950	13 24	33.5	97.1		IV	3.8	
Apr 20, 1950		39.8	84.2		IV	3.8	
May 01, 1950	15 30	36.5	89.9		II-III	3.2	
Jun 18, 1950		35.8	84.0		IV	3.8	
Sep 17, 1950	05 48	35.7	89.9		III-IV	3.8	
Jun 20, 1951	19 37 10	35	102	65,000	VI	4.7	
Sep 20, 1951	02 38	38.7	89.9	3,000	IV	3.8	
Dec 03, 1951	08 02	41.6	81.4	250	IV	3.8	
Dec 07, 1951		41.6	81.4		II	3.0	
Dec 18, 1951	02 02	35.6	90.3		III	3.4	
Dec 18, 1951	08	35.6	90.3		II-III	3.2	
Dec 22, 1951	04	41.6	81.4		II	3.0	
Jan 07, 1952	22 21	40.2	88.5		III	3.4	
Feb 20, 1952	22 34 39	36.4	89.5	34,000	V	4.2	
Mar 17, 1952	01 30	36.2	89.6		IV	3.8	
Apr 09, 1952	16 29 29	35.4	97.8	640,000	VII	5.5	
Apr 11, 1952	18 30	35.4	97.8		II-III	3.2	
Apr 11, 1952	20 30	35.4	97.8	8,000	IV	3.8	
Apr 16, 1952	05 58	35.4	97.8	8,000	II-III	3.2	
Apr 16, 1952	06 05	35.4	97.8	8,000	V	4.2	
May 28, 1952	09 54 14	36.6	89.7	3,000	IV	3.8	
Jun 20, 1952	09 38 06	39.7	82.1	13,000	VI	4.7	
Jul 16, 1952	23 48 10	36.2	89.6		VI	4.7	
Jul 17, 1952	00 09	36.2	89.6		IV	3.8	
Jul 17, 1952	00 30	35.4	97.8		III-IV	3.6	
Jul 17, 1952	02	35.4	97.8		III-IV	3.6	
Aug 14, 1952	21 40	35.4	97.8		IV	3.8	
Oct 08, 1952	04 15	35.1	96.5		IV	3.8	
Oct 17, 1952	04 16	36.2	89.6	1,000	IV	3.8	
Oct 17, 1952	04 30	36.2	89.6		II-III	3.2	
Oct 17, 1952	04 35	36.2	89.6		II-III	3.2	
Oct 17, 1952	04 46	36.2	89.6		II-III	3.2	

TABLE 1. *(Continued)*

Date	Origin time (GMT)	Lat (°N)	Long (°W)	Felt area (km²)	I_0	m_b	M_S
Oct 17, 1952	15 48	30.1	93.7		IV	3.8	
Nov 15, 1952	a.m.	44.1	103.5		IV	3.8	
Dec 25, 1952	04 23 24	35.9	89.8	23,000	IV	4.1	
Dec 25, 1952		35.9	89.8		II	3.0	
Dec 25, 1952		43.8	81.0		IV	3.8	
Dec 28, 1952	16 59	36.7	89.6		III	3.4	
Jan 26, 1953	23 18	36.0	89.5		IV	3.8	
Jan 27, 1953	06 48	36.0	89.5		IV	3.8	
Jan 27, 1953	07 48	36.0	89.5		II	3.0	
Feb 11, 1953	10 50 54	36.5	89.5	3,000	IV	3.8	
Feb 17, 1953	11 05	36.5	89.5		IV	3.8	
Feb 18, 1953	00 17	36.5	89.5		III	3.4	
Feb 19, 1953	05 05	36.0	89.5		III	3.4	
Mar 16, 1953	12 50	35.4	97.9		III	3.4	
Mar 17, 1953	13 12	35.6	98.0	7,000	V	4.2	
Mar 17, 1953	14 25	35.6	98.0		VI	4.7	
May 06, 1953	07 50	37.0	89.2		III	3.4	
May 07, 1953	23 32	39.7	82.1		IV	3.8	
May 12, 1953	18 50	35.6	90.3		IV	3.8	
May 15, 1953	23 42	37.0	89.2		III	3.4	
Jun 06, 1953	17 40	34.7	96.7		IV	3.8	
Jun 12, 1953	a.m.	41.7	83.6		IV	3.8	
Sep 11, 1953	18 26 28	38.8	90.1	15,000	VI	4.7	
Nov 10, 1953	15 45	36.0	83.9		IV	3.8	
Dec 21, 1953	22 43	45.2	102.9		III-IV	3.6	
Dec 30, 1953	22	38.6	89.1	3,000	IV	3.8	
Dec 31, 1953	20 30	43.1	99.3		IV	3.8	
Dec 31, 1953		37.3	83.2		IV	3.8	
Jan 02, 1954	03 25	36.6	83.7		VI	4.7	
Jan 17, 1954	07 15	36.0	89.4	1,000	IV	3.8	
Feb 02, 1954	16 53	36.7	90.3	80,000	VI	4.4	
Apr 11, 1954		35.0	96.4		IV	3.8	
Apr 12, 1954	23 05	35.0	96.4		IV	3.8	
Apr 13, 1954	18 48	35.1	96.4		IV	3.8	
Apr 27, 1954	04 09	35.1	90.0	40,000	V	4.4	
Aug 09, 1954		38.5	87.3		IV	3.8	
Jan 05, 1955	20	47.3	88.4		IV	3.8	
Jan 05, 1955	21	47.3	88.4		IV	3.8	
Jan 07, 1955	05	47.1	88.6		V	4.2	
Jan 07, 1955	06	47.1	88.6		V	4.2	
Jan 12, 1955	06 25	35.8	84.0		IV	3.8	
Jan 25, 1955	07 24 30	36.0	89.5	90,000	VI	4.7	
Jan 25, 1955	20 34	36.0	83.9		IV	3.8	
Jan 27, 1955	00 37	30.6	104.5		IV	3.8	
Feb 01, 1955	14 45	30.4	89.1		V	4.2	
Feb 25, 1955	01 45	41.3	98.6	3,000	IV	3.8	
Mar 29, 1955	09 03	36.0	89.5	10,000	VI	4.7	
Apr 09, 1955	13 01 24	38.1	89.9	50,000	V-VI	4.5	
Apr 11, 1955	10 50	37.7	88.6		II	3.0	
May 26, 1955	18 09	41.5	81.7		V	3.8	
May 30, 1955	a.m.	38.1	88.9		III	3.4	
Jun 29, 1955	01 16	41.5	81.7		V	3.8	
Sep 06, 1955	01 45	36.0	89.5		V	4.2	
Sep 06, 1955		36.0	89.5		III	3.4	
Sep 24, 1955	18 45	36.4	89.5		IV	3.8	
Dec 13, 1955	07 43	36.0	89.5		V	4.2	
Dec 13, 1955	07 56	36.0	89.5		III	3.4	
Jan 06, 1956	11 57 59	37.3	98.7	60,000	VI	4.7	
Jan 08, 1956	00 35	29.3	94.8		IV	3.8	
Jan 24, 1956	05 00	36.1	89.7		II-III	3.2	
Jan 27, 1956	12 03	40.4	84.2	5,000	V	4.2	
Jan 29, 1956	04 44 15	35.6	89.6	13,000	VI	4.7	
Feb 16, 1956	23 30	35.4	97.3	13,000	VI	4.7	

Continued on next page

TABLE 1. *(Continued)*

Date	Origin time (GMT)	Lat (°N)	Long (°W)	Felt area (km²)	I_0	m_b	M_S
Mar 13, 1956	15 15	40.5	90.4	5,000	IV	3.8	
Apr 02, 1956	16 03	34.2	95.6	5,000	V	4.2	
Jul 18, 1956	21 30	43.6	87.7		IV	3.8	
Jul 18, 1956	23	43.6	87.7		IV	3.8	
Sep 09, 1956	22 45	35.8	86.7	400	IV	3.8	
Oct 13, 1956		42.9	87.9		IV	3.8	
Oct 29, 1956	09 23 44	36.1	89.7		V	4.2	
Oct 30, 1956	10 36	36.2	95.9	25,000	VII	4.7	
Nov 26, 1956	04 12 44	37.1	90.6	70,000	VI	4.7	
Jan 08, 1957	16	43.5	88.8		III-IV	3.6	
Jan 25, 1957	18 15	36.6	83.7		VI	4.0	
Mar 19, 1957	16 38	32.6	94.7	47,000	V	4.3	
Mar 19, 1957	17 41	32.6	94.7			3.0	
Mar 19, 1957	22 36	32.6	94.7			3.0	
Mar 19, 1957	22 45	32.6	94.7			3.0	
Mar 26, 1957	08 27 06	37.0	88.4	800	IV	3.8	
Jun 23, 1957	06 34 18	36.5	84.5		V	4.2	
Jun 29, 1957		42.9	81.3		IV	3.8	
Jul 23, 1957	13 03	38.7	83.8		III	3.4	
Aug 17, 1957	23 00	36.2	89.5		IV	3.8	
Dec 03, 1957	07 30	43.8	98.2	250	IV	3.8	
Jan 26, 1958	16 55 37	36.1	89.7	17,000	V	4.2	
Jan 28, 1958	05 56 40	37.1	89.2	40,000	V	4.2	
Apr 08, 1958	22 25 33	36.3	89.2	2,000	V	4.2	
Apr 26, 1958	07 30	36.4	89.5	1,800	IV.	4.2	
May 01, 1958	22 47	41.5	81.7		IV-V	4.0	
May 20, 1958	01 25	35.5	90.4		IV	3.8	
Oct 23, 1958	02 29 47	37.5	82.5			3.0	
Nov 06, 1958	23 08	29.9	90.1		IV	3.8	
Nov 08, 1958	04 41 43	38.4	87.9	85,000	VI	4.7	
Nov 19, 1958	18 15	30.5	91.2	800	V	4.2	
Jan 06, 1959	15 07	38.7	90.3		III	3.4	
Jan 12, 1959	13	44.9	98.1		IV	3.8	
Jan 21, 1959	15 35	36.3	89.5		IV	3.8	
Feb 10, 1959	20 05	35.5	100.9	120,000	V	4.5	
Feb 13, 1959	08 37	36.1	89.5	450	V	4.2	
Jun 13, 1959	01	35.4	84.3		IV	3.8	
Jun 15, 1959	12 45	34.7	96.7	13,000	V	4.2	
Jun 17, 1959	10 27 07	34.6	98.4	37,000	VI	4.7	
Jul 20, 1959	08 15 26	35.9	89.8		III	3.4	
Aug 12, 1959	18 06 07	35.0	87.0	7,000	VI	4.7	
Oct 15, 1959	15 45	29.8	93.1	6,500	IV	3.8	
Dec 21, 1959	16 25	36.0	89.5	1,000	V	4.2	
Jan 28, 1960	21 38	36.0	89.5	800	V	4.2	
Apr 15, 1960	10 10 10	35.8	84.0	3,400	V	4.2	
Apr 21, 1960	10 45	36.3	89.5		V	4.2	
May 04, 1960	16 31 32	34.2	92.0		IV	3.8	
Jan 11, 1961	01 40	34.9	95.5	6,500	V	4.2	
Feb 22, 1961	09 45	41.2	83.3	13,000	V	4.2	
Apr 13, 1961	21 14 57	39.9	100.0	3,600	V	4.2	
Apr 26, 1961	07 05	34.6	95.0	6,500	III	3.8	
Apr 27, 1961	03	34.6	95.0			3.0	
Apr 27, 1961	05	34.6	95.0			3.0	
Apr 27, 1961	07 30	34.9	95.3	20,000	V	4.2	
Sep 09, 1961	22 43 02	36.4	91.3		IV	3.8	
Dec 25, 1961	12 20 03	39.1	94.6		IV	3.6	
Dec 25, 1961	12 58 21	39.1	94.6	40,000	V	3.8	
Dec 31, 1961	16 35 59	44.4	100.3	34,000	V-VI	4.5	
Feb 02, 1962	06 43 29	36.5	89.6	90,000	VI	4.3	3.5
Jun 01, 1962	11 23 41	36.0	90.2			3.2	
Jun 27, 1962	01 28 56	37.7	88.5	45,000	V	4.4	
Jul 14, 1962	02 23 46	36.9	90.0		II-III	3.2	
Jul 23, 1962	06 05 18	36.1	89.8	10,000	VI	3.6	

TABLE 1. *(Continued)*

Date	Origin time (GMT)	Lat (°N)	Long (°W)	Felt area (km²)	I_o	m_b	M_S
Feb 07, 1963	21 18 36	34.4	92.1			3.4	
Mar 03, 1963	17 30 11	36.7	90.0	280,000	VI	4.7	4.1
Mar 09, 1963	15 25	42.8	103.0		II-III	3.2	
Mar 31, 1963	13 31 04	36.5	89.5			3.0	
Apr 06, 1963	08 12 24	36.4	89.8			3.1	
Apr 19, 1963	14 31 55	36.7	90.1			3.5	
May 02, 1963	01 09 22	36.7	89.4			3.1	
Jul 08, 1963	23 51 43	37.0	90.5			3.1	
Aug 03, 1963	00 37 50	37.0	88.8	6,500	V	4.4	
Dec 05, 1963	06 51 02	37.2	87.0		II-III	3.2	
Dec 15, 1963	05 32	37.2	87.1		III	3.4	
Jan 16, 1964	05 09 57	36.8	89.5			3.2	
Jan 25, 1964	19 54 10	36.5	89.5			3.0	
Feb 02, 1964	08 23	35.1	99.7		V	4.2	
Feb 18, 1964	09 31 10	34.8	85.5		V	4.2	
Mar 17, 1964	02 16 06	36.2	89.6			3.5	
Mar 24, 1964	06 12	43.5	103.5	4,000	V	4.2	
Mar 28, 1964	10 08 45	42.8	101.7	270,000	VII	4.7	
Mar 28, 1964	10 24 50	42.8	101.7			3.6	
Apr 24, 1964	01 24 55	31.5	93.8		IV	3.8	
Apr 24, 1964	07 33 53	31.6	93.8		IV	4.0	
Apr 24, 1964	07 47 18	31.3	93.8			3.3	
Apr 24, 1964	12 07 07	31.3	93.8			3.2	
Apr 24, 1964	12 54 17	31.3	93.8			3.0	
Apr 26, 1964	03 24 50	31.3	93.8			3.3	
Apr 27, 1964	21 50 27	31.3	93.8			3.2	
Apr 28, 1964	00 24 07	31.5	93.8			3.1	
Apr 28, 1964	00 30 46	31.5	93.8	800	IV	4.0	
Apr 28, 1964	21 18 35	31.2	93.9		V	4.0	
Apr 30, 1964	21 30	31.2	94.0			3.0	
May 02, 1964	06 34 54	31.3	93.8			3.2	
May 03, 1964	03 24 12	31.3	93.8			3.0	
May 07, 1964	20 01 39	31.2	94.0		VI	3.2	
May 23, 1964	11 25 34	36.5	89.9			3.9	
May 23, 1964	15 00 35	36.5	90.0			3.6	
Jun 03, 1964	02 27 24	31.5	93.9		IV	3.1	
Jun 03, 1964	09 37	31.0	94.0		III-IV	3.6	
Jul 28, 1964		36.0	83.9		II	3.0	
Aug 16, 1964	11 35 31	31.4	93.8		V	3.0	
Aug 26, 1964	16 58 52	43.8	102.2		IV	3.8	
Sep 24, 1964	08 09 34	37.1	91.1			3.0	
Sep 28, 1964	15 41	44.0	96.4			3.4	
Oct 10, 1964	08 30	47.4	89.8			3.0	
Oct 10, 1964	11 30	47.3	90.3			3.0	
Oct 13, 1964	16 30	36.0	83.9		II-III	3.2	
Feb 11, 1965	03 40 24	36.4	89.7		III	3.3	
Feb 14, 1965	20 03 20	36.9	93.3			3.0	
Mar 06, 1965	21 08 50	37.4	91.1		III	4.1	
Mar 25, 1965	12 59 28	36.4	89.5			3.7	
May 25, 1965	07 15 43	36.1	89.9			3.3	
Jun 01, 1965	07 24 57	36.5	89.5			3.0	
Jul 08, 1965	07 03 50	36.5	89.5			3.3	
Aug 14, 1965	05 04 30	37.1	89.3			3.0	
Aug 14, 1965	05 46 17	37.3	89.5	200	IV	3.2	
Aug 14, 1965	13 13 54	37.1	89.2	700	VII	3.8	
Aug 15, 1965	04 19 01	37.4	89.5		V	3.4	
Aug 15, 1965	06 07 25	37.4	89.5		V	3.4	
Aug 30, 1965	05 17 38	32.1	102.3		IV	3.5	
Oct 10, 1965	23 51 33	36.1	97.7			3.1	
Oct 21, 1965	02 04 38	37.5	91.0	420,000	VI	4.9	4.1
Nov 03, 1965	12 33 22	37.1	91.1			3.0	
Nov 04, 1965	07 43 39	37.1	91.1			3.5	
Dec 09, 1965	22 04 51	37.4	91.1			3.5	

Continued on next page

TABLE 1. *(Continued)*

Date	Origin time (GMT)	Lat (°N)	Long (°W)	Felt area (km²)	I_o	m_b	M_S
Dec 19, 1965	22 19 10	35.9	89.9			3.6	
Feb 12, 1966	04 32 15	35.9	90.0	2,500	IV	3.6	
Feb 13, 1966	23 19 37	37.1	91.0		IV	3.6	
Feb 14, 1966	00 08 56	37.2	90.9			3.1	
Feb 26, 1966	08 10 20	37.2	91.0			3.7	
Mar 13, 1966	14 24 42	36.2	90.0			3.0	
Mar 24, 1966	23 45	30.0	94.0			3.0	
Jun 22, 1966	11 27 53	38.6	88.2			3.1	
Jun 26, 1966	11 59 44	44.3	104.3	3,000	VI	3.1	
Jul 20, 1966	09 04 59	35.6	101.4	30,000	IV-V	3.8	
Aug 14, 1966	15 25 52	31.7	103.1	50,000	VI	4.3	
Aug 24, 1966		35.8	84.0		IV	3.8	
Sep 09, 1966	09 50 31	41.4	98.6			3.5	
Sep 28, 1966		39.3	80.3		IV	3.8	
Dec 06, 1966	08 00 47	38.9	92.8			3.0	
Feb 02, 1967	06 30	42.7	84.6		IV	3.8	
Apr 08, 1967	05 40 32	39.6	82.5	10,000	V	4.2	
Apr 11, 1967	23 44 45	36.1	89.7			3.0	
Jun 04, 1967	16 14 14	33.6	90.9	54,000	VI	4.5	3.0
Jun 29, 1967	13 57 07	33.6	90.9		V	4.0	
Jul 06, 1967	16 43 51	35.8	90.4			3.4	
Jul 21, 1967	09 14 49	37.5	90.4	53,000	VI	4.3	2.8
Aug 25, 1967	19 15 18	37.1	91.1			3.1	
Oct 18, 1967	05 08 36	36.5	89.5			3.0	
Nov 23, 1967	06 23 39	43.7	99.4		V	3.8	
Jan 04, 1968		34.9	95.5		IV	3.8	
Jan 23, 1968	16 16 00	36.5	89.5			3.3	
Feb 10, 1968	01 34 32	36.5	89.9		III	3.5	
May 30, 1968	01 59 33	36.5	89.5			3.5	
Jul 08, 1968	16 50 12	46.5	100.6	25,000	IV	4.4	
Jul 15, 1968	04 21 25	36.5	89.5			3.0	
Oct 14, 1968	14 42 54	34.0	96.8		VI	3.5	
Oct 31, 1968		43.0	83.0		III-IV	3.6	
Nov 09, 1968	17 01 41	38.0	88.5	1,600,000	VII	5.5	5.2
Nov 09, 1968	17 08 17	38.0	88.5		IV	3.8	
Dec 11, 1968	16	38.3	85.8		V	3.0	
Jan 01, 1969	23 35 36	34.8	92.6	62,000	VI	4.5	3.3
Jan 20, 1969	19 25	37.8	90.4		III	3.4	
Feb 28, 1969	13 10 13	37.9	88.9			3.2	
Apr 13, 1969	06 27 51	34.2	96.3			3.5	
May 02, 1969	11 33 20	35.2	96.3		V	4.0	
May 30, 1969	14 08 05	34.8	97.8			3.0	
Jul 01, 1969	03 36 58	37.4	97.0			3.0	
Jul 13, 1969	21 51 09	36.1	83.7	50,000	V	4.3	
Jul 14, 1969	11 15	36.0	83.9		II	3.0	
Jul 24, 1969	18 10	36.0	83.9		III	3.4	
Nov 20, 1969	01 00 09	37.4	81.0	250,000	VI	4.7	
Jan 07, 1970	17 45	35.2	89.9		IV	3.8	
Feb 03, 1970		31	97		IV	3.8	
Feb 06, 1970	04 22	37.9	90.6		II	3.0	
Feb 06, 1970	04 28	37.9	90.6		II	3.2	
Feb 06, 1970	04 53 02	37.9	90.6		II	3.4	
Mar 27, 1970	03 44 29	36.5	89.7		III	3.3	
Jul 06, 1970	09 39 11	37.9	90.6		II	3.0	
Jul 30, 1970	08 48 51	37.0	82.2			3.0	
Aug 11, 1970	06 14 25	38.4	82.3		IV	3.8	
Nov 05, 1970	10 25 35	36.0	90.0			4.4	2.9
Nov 17, 1970	02 13 55	35.9	90.1	92,000	VI	3.0	
Nov 30, 1970	04 46 53	36.3	89.5	10	III-IV	3.0	
Dec 08, 1970	23 16	38	89			3.0	
Dec 14, 1970	12 41	35.7	90.0				
Dec 24, 1970	10 17 57	36.7	89.5	4,000	IV	3.6	
Feb 12, 1971	12 44 27	38.5	87.9	10,000	IV	3.3	

TABLE 1. *(Continued)*

Date	Origin time (GMT)	Lat (°N)	Long (°W)	Felt area (km²)	I_o	m_b	M_S
Feb 19, 1971	23 11 42	37.1	83.2			3.0	
Mar 14, 1971	17 27 51	33.1	87.9			3.9	
Mar 15, 1971	14 53 22	32.8	88.3			3.5	
Mar 16, 1971	02 37 28	32.8	88.3			3.7	
Mar 17, 1971	05 04 29	33.1	88.1			3.0	
Apr 01, 1971	05 05 11	37.4	81.6			3.0	
Apr 13, 1971	14 00 51	35.8	90.1			3.0	
Jul 30, 1971	01 45 51	31.7	103.1		III	3.0	
Jul 31, 1971	14 53 49	31.7	103.1		IV	3.4	
Oct 01, 1971	18 49 39	35.8	90.4	62,000	V-VI	4.1	2.9
Oct 18, 1971	06 39 31	36.7	89.6			3.0	
Oct 19, 1971	21 07 31	44.0	101.0			3.0	
Jan 09, 1972	23 24 29	37.4	81.6			3.0	
Feb 01, 1972	05 42 10	36.4	90.8	27,000	V-VI	4.2	2.8
Mar 29, 1972	20 38 32	36.2	89.6		V	3.7	
May 07, 1972	02 12 08	35.9	90.0		IV	3.4	
May 20, 1972	19 39 06	37.0	82.2			3.0	
Jun 09, 1972	19 15 19	37.7	90.4	350	III-IV	3.1	
Jun 19, 1972	05 46 15	37.0	89.1	600	III	3.2	
Sep 15, 1972	05 22 16	41.6	89.4	200,000	VI	4.4	3.3
Oct 16, 1972	05 47 33	42.3	99.6			3.7	
Jan 07, 1973	22 56 01	37.4	87.3			3.2	
Jan 08, 1973	09 11 37	33.8	90.6		III	3.5	
Jan 12, 1973	11 56 56	37.9	90.5		IV	3.2	
May 25, 1973	14 40 14	33.9	90.8		III	3.4	
May 25, 1973	14 42 32	33.9	90.8			3.2	
Oct 03, 1973	03 50 20	35.9	90.0		IV	3.4	
Oct 09, 1973	20 15 27	36.5	89.6		IV	3.7	
Oct 30, 1973	22 58 39	35.7	83.9		V	3.4	
Nov 30, 1973	07 48 41	35.8	84.0		VI	4.6	
Dec 20, 1973	10 45 00	36.2	89.6		IV	3.4	
Jan 08, 1974	01 12 37	36.2	89.4		V	4.3	
Feb 15, 1974	13 33 49	36.5	100.7		V	4.6	
Feb 15, 1974	22 32 35	33.9	93.1		III	3.6	
Feb 15, 1974	22 35 45	34.0	93.1		III	3.6	
Feb 15, 1974	22 49 02	34.0	93.0		V	4.0	
Feb 24, 1974	07 53 45	35.8	90.4			3.2	
Mar 04, 1974	14 24 28	35.7	90.3			3.0	
Mar 12, 1974	12 30 29	35.7	89.8			3.2	
Apr 03, 1974	23 05 02	38.6	88.1		VI	4.7	
May 13, 1974	06 52 19	36.7	89.4		VI	4.1	
Jun 05, 1974	00 16 40	38.6	84.8		VI	3.6	
Jun 05, 1974	08 06 11	38.6	89.9		V	3.6	
Aug 11, 1974	14 29 45	36.9	91.2		V	3.6	
Sep 29, 1974	02 26 17	41.2	83.4		II	3.0	
Oct 20, 1974	15 13 55	39.1	81.6		V	3.4	
Dec 13, 1974	05 03 58	34.7	91.9		V	3.4	
Jan 02, 1975	09 19 00	34.9	90.9		II-III	3.0	
Feb 13, 1975	19 43 58	36.5	89.6		V	3.3	
Feb 16, 1975	23 21 31	39.0	82.4			3.3	
Mar 01, 1975	11 50 00	33.5	88.0		III	3.2	
May 13, 1975	07 53 38	42.1	98.4		VI	3.5	
Jun 13, 1975	22 40 27	36.5	89.7		V	4.3	
Jun 24, 1975	11 11 36	33.7	87.8		IV	4.5	
Jul 09, 1975	14 54 15	45.5	96.1	82,000	VI	4.8	
Aug 25, 1975	07 11 08	36.0	89.8			3.0	
Sep 09, 1975	11 52 44	30.7	89.3		IV	2.9	
Sep 13, 1975	01 25 03	34.1	97.4		IV	3.8	
Nov 29, 1975	14 29 41	34.5	97.4		IV	3.5	
Dec 03, 1975	03 06 33	36.5	89.6		VI	2.8	

* The aftershocks of the three major earthquakes of the 1811-1812 series are not listed in this table.

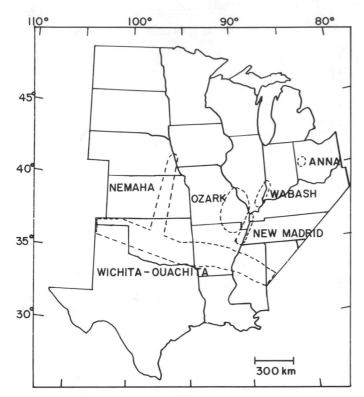

Figure 2. Map showing seismic zones as defined on the basis of earthquake activity. The boundaries of the zones (indicated by dashed lines) are not precisely known.

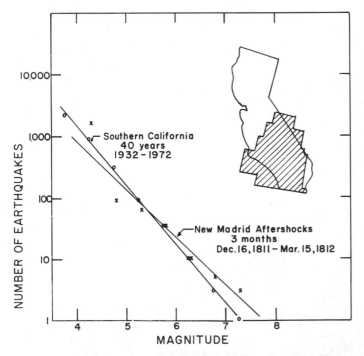

Figure 3. Magnitude-recurrence curves for the portion of southern California shown in the shaded area for the 40-yr period 1932-1972 and for the New Madrid seismic zone for the 3-mo period December 16, 1811, through March 15, 1812. Although the curves are not identical, they indicate that about as many earthquakes of similar magnitude occurred in 3 mo in New Madrid as in 40 yr in southern California.

that occurred per year in a 15,000-km^2 area. Aftershocks are not included in the data set. The three major earthquakes of 1811-1812 are treated as a single earthquake of $m_b = 7.5$ on the basis of energy considerations, so as not to have them unduly weight the large magnitude end of the curve. The magnitude-recurrence curve is shown in Figure 5. Its slope, or b value, is 0.75 ± 0.04, which can be compared with a value of 0.92 ± 0.08 found by me (Nuttli, 1974) for the period 1833 through 1972 for a larger area of the central United States, including the New Madrid seismic zone, and with values of 0.80 to 1.01 that Hileman and others (1973) found for different areas of southern California.

The magnitude interval used in plotting Figure 5 was selected as 1 unit. Thus the interpretation to be given to the figure is that on the average in the New Madrid seismic zone there will be N earthquakes of magnitude in the range $m_b \pm 0.5$ or larger in one year. For example, it is shown in Figure 5 that on the average there will be 300 earthquakes of m_b 1 ± 0.5 or greater in one year and 1.5 earthquakes of m_b 4 ± 0.5 or greater occurring annually.

WABASH VALLEY SEISMIC ZONE

The Wabash Valley seismic zone is an area of southeastern Illinois and southwestern Indiana (see Fig. 2), which is characterized by approximately north-striking faults (King, 1969). The distribution of earthquake epicenters in Figure 1 indicates that this seismic zone is about 200 km long, but the data are too sparse to determine whether it is one continuous zone or rather a series of shorter discontinuous ones. There also is some question as to whether the Wabash Valley seismic zone might be continuous with the New Madrid seismic zone. Although there are no data relating fault length to earthquake magnitude for the interior of North America, we know that the New Madrid zone of about 200 km overall length has generated earthquakes of $m_b > 7$. Except for the length of the zone of epicenters, however, there is no reason to expect that future earthquakes in the Wabash Valley seismic zone will exceed $m_b = 6.5$, which is one unit greater than that of the largest historic ones. If we do consider such an earthquake to be the maximum possible one that can occur in the Wabash Valley, we would have to conclude that the zone consists of a series of disconnected faults. Microearthquake data, when they become available, will help in determining the length of the fault segments and thus possibly assist us in estimating the potential of the seismic zone.

There are insufficient data to establish a magnitude-recurrence relation for the Wabash Valley seismic zone or, as a matter of fact, for any seismic zone in the central United States with the exception of the New Madrid seismic zone. This is due both to the relative infrequency of occurrence of earthquakes and to the limited range of magnitudes for which complete data are available. A microearthquake seismograph network in the Wabash Valley recently installed and operated by St. Louis University should extend the data at least down to $m_b = 2$, which will be adequate for recurrence studies.

Focal mechanism studies are available for only four earthquakes in this region (Street and others, 1974; Herrmann, 1974; Stauder and Nuttli, 1970; Nuttli and Zollweg, 1975). Three indicate reverse faulting on north-striking fault planes, and the fourth indicates right-lateral strike-slip faulting with the fault plane striking parallel to the Wabash Valley.

Five earthquakes with m_b values ≥ 5 have occurred in the Wabash Valley seismic zone. They are the events of April 29, 1899 ($m_b = 5.0$), September 27, 1909 ($m_b = 5.3$), November 26, 1922 ($m_b = 5.0$), April 26, 1925 ($m_b = 5.0$), and November 9, 1968 ($m_b = 5.5$). The November 9, 1968, event, which was felt over 23 states as well as parts of Canada, caused only moderate damage in the epicentral area, probably because its focal depth was about 20 km (Stauder and Nuttli, 1970). It resulted in minor damage in the nearest metropolitan centers, namely Evansville (80 km to the east), St. Louis (175 km to the northwest), and Chicago (430 km to the north). It was felt in tall buildings as far away as Mobile, Alabama, southern Ontario, and Boston, Massachusetts.

OUACHITA-WICHITA MOUNTAINS SEISMIC ZONE

The Ouachita-Wichita Mountains seismic zone is a region about 150 km wide extending over 1,000 km in length from the Texas panhandle through southern Oklahoma and central Arkansas into northern Mississippi (see Fig. 2). Earthquakes in this zone for which focal mechanism solutions could be obtained occurred in central Arkansas and western Mississippi (Street and others, 1974) and in northern Texas, central Arkansas, and western Alabama (Nuttli and Zollweg, 1975). The solutions indicate that the fault planes strike along the direction of the mountain front. These focal-mechanism studies lend support to the notion that the epicenters define a long seismic zone. The present data, however, are inadequate to establish that this long seismic zone is a continuous fault zone.

From Figure 1 it can be seen that there is a clustering of epicenters in Oklahoma near lat 35.5°N, long 98°W, including that of the damaging earthquake of April 9, 1952. Except for this one cluster, the epicenters are fairly evenly distributed along the entire mountain front. The fact that all the reported earthquakes in this zone occurred during the past 100 yr is probably the result of the area being almost unpopulated prior to that time. Although the data are much too sparse to determine a magnitude-recurrence curve, the occurrence of three earthquakes in the m_b range 5.0 to 5.5 and of 30 in the range 4.0 to 4.9 for the 100-yr interval gives some idea of the level of seismic activity.

NEMAHA UPLIFT SEISMIC ZONE

The Nemaha uplift seismic zone is a north-northeast–striking zone about 50 to 100 km wide extending 600 km in length from central Oklahoma to southeastern Nebraska (see Fig. 2). As there are no microearthquake studies or focal-mechanism solutions for earthquakes occurring in this zone, we do not have a strong argument for associating the earthquakes with particular geologic structures. The epicenters, in fact, are not uniformly distributed along the uplift region but rather cluster

near Manhattan, Kansas (lat 39.3°N, long 96.5°W), and near El Reno, Oklahoma (lat 35.5°N, long 98°W). The latter point is at the intersection of the Ouachita-Wichita Mountains seismic zone and the Nemaha uplift seismic zone. The level of present-day seismicity appears to be minor to moderate.

ST. FRANCOIS MOUNTAIN SEISMIC ZONE

The St. Francois Mountain seismic zone is a region of southeastern Missouri and northeastern Arkansas that lies to the northwest of the New Madrid seismic zone (see Fig. 2). Focal-mechanism solutions obtained by Mitchell (1973), Street and others (1974), and Herrmann (1974) indicate normal or tensional faulting, the type to be expected in an area of uplift.

An explanation of the relatively large number of epicenters lying in this area may be that the area has been populated since the late eighteenth century and that St. Louis University has had seismograph stations in operation since 1909, which has resulted in a more complete catalog of earthquake activity. The largest earthquake in the region occurred on April 9, 1917, near the town of Ste. Genevieve, Missouri. The proximity of the epicenter of this earthquake with the fault of the same name does not mean that one necessarily is associated with

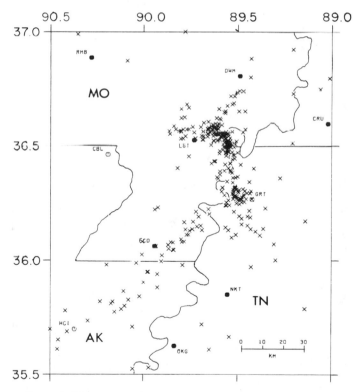

Figure 4. Microearthquakes in the New Madrid seismic zone, indicated by Xs, for the interval June 29, 1974, through March 31, 1976. The map is almost complete for earthquakes of $m_b > 1.0$. Stations of the St. Louis University microearthquake array are indicated by octagons and 3-letter code names. Stations HCI and CBL were not yet operating as of July 1, 1976. The New Madrid fault zone extends northeastward from the lower left-hand corner to about the location of station GRT, where it is offset to the north and west, and then from the location of the station LST northeastward to about lat 37.0°N, long 89.2°W.

the other. In fact, the eastward extension of the Ste. Genevieve fault, namely the Cottage Grove–Shawneetown–Rough Creek fault system of southern Illinois and Kentucky, which is a major fault system, is noteworthy for the lack of epicenters that can be associated with it in historic times.

ANNA, OHIO, SEISMIC REGION

The Anna, Ohio, seismic region is a relatively small area of western Ohio (see Fig. 2) that has been subjected to a number of earthquakes that produced moderate damage (Bradley and Bennett, 1965). These include the earthquakes of June 18, 1875 ($m_b = 5.3$), September 19, 1884 ($m_b = 4.7$), September 30, 1930 ($m_b = 5.3$), September 20, 1931 ($m_b = 5.3$), March 2, 1937 ($m_b = 5.3$), and March 9, 1937 ($m_b = 5.3$).

Although the seismic region lies near the bifurcation of the north-trending Cincinnati arch into the Findlay and Kankakee arches, no definite correlation between the structural features and the earthquake activity has been established. It does seem reasonable, though, that the arches could be responsible for locally modifying the uniform compressive stress field expected from plate tectonic theory, so as to cause strain concentrations

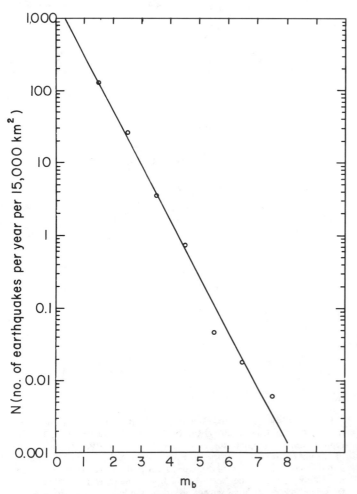

Figure 5. Cumulative magnitude-recurrence curve for the New Madrid seismic zone, plotted at an interval of 1 m_b unit.

and subsequently earthquakes. Our understanding of the seismicity and tectonics of the Anna region will be improved by the data being gathered by a microearthquake array recently installed in the area by the University of Michigan.

OTHER EARTHQUAKES

Even if the above-mentioned seismic zones can account for the majority of earthquakes in the central United States, particularly the larger ones, they do not account for all. Some of the remaining earthquakes may be associated with structural features such as the Illinois and Michigan basins and the Findlay and Wisconsin arches, although existing evidence is insufficient to allow one to place much weight on such a speculation. But even supposing such an association, there are a sizable number of earthquakes remaining that occurred in places where there are no major geologic structures. How are we to explain these earthquakes?

If it is assumed that the Minnesota earthquakes of 1860 ($m_b = 5.0$) and September 3, 1917 ($m_b = 4.7$), are not related to a major structural feature, the largest magnitude for historical events of this type is $m_b = 5.0$. To be conservative we might assume the maximum possible m_b to be 5.5. The widespread distribution of these small-magnitude earthquakes, apparently unrelated to major structural features, suggests that they might occur almost anywhere in the central United States. They will occur wherever there is some local distortion of the more-or-less uniform compressive stress field postulated by Sbar and Sykes (1973) in the interior of the North American plate.

MAXIMUM-MAGNITUDE EARTHQUAKE

For design purposes there are four kinds of seismicity information that are of particular importance. They are (1) the locations of active seismic zones, (2) the magnitude-recurrence relation for each zone, (3) the maximum-magnitude earthquake associated with each zone, and (4) the rate of attenuation of seismic energy. We have discussed the location of seismic zones in the central United States and have noted that there are inadequate data to determine magnitude-recurrence relations except for the New Madrid seismic zone. A similar lack of adequate data hinders us in estimating the maximum magnitude of future earthquakes. In this paper we define the maximum-magnitude earthquake to be the largest earthquake that can be expected to occur in a 10,000-yr period, having in mind the design of nuclear power plants. For structures of a less critical nature, the design earthquake would be of smaller magnitude.

There is no problem for the New Madrid seismic zone, because the energy equivalent of the three principal shocks of the 1811–1812 sequence is an earthquake with $m_b = 7.5$ (the February 7, 1812, earthquake had $m_b = 7.4$). Therefore, we know from direct experience that we should assign an m_b value of about 7.5 to the maximum earthquake, a value which is near the observed upper limit of earthquake size. We should note, as mentioned earlier, that the overall length of the New Madrid faulted zone is about 200 km and that it is segmented, the maximum length of an individual segment being about 100 km.

Of the other seismic zones in the central United States, the Wabash Valley seismic zone probably has the greatest potential for a large magnitude earthquake. Before any quantitative estimate can be assigned to the maximum magnitude, however, it is necessary to know if the seismic zone consists of one long fault or a series of short, interrupted segments. The seismic history of the last two centuries would suggest the latter, but two centuries of historical data by themselves are insufficient to resolve the question. The microearthquake network recently installed in the Wabash Valley by St. Louis University should provide information on the continuity of the fault system, as well as a magnitude-recurrence relation.

There is also no reliable way at present of estimating the maximum length of fault segments and thus the maximum-magnitude earthquake in the Ouachita-Wichita Mountains seismic zone and the Nemaha uplift seismic zone. All we can state is that if earthquakes of m_b equal to 6.5 or greater can occur, their recurrence rate will be measured in terms of thousands of years if the seismic activity of the last century is representative. From our present state of knowledge, a maximum-magnitude earthquake of $m_b = 6.5$ appears to be a conservative estimate.

The Anna, Ohio, seismic zone presents an interesting case, when one considers its fairly small extent and the fact that it has had five earthquakes in the m_b range of 5.0 to 5.3 since 1875 (1875, 1930, 1931, and two in 1937). That four could occur so close together in the 1930s suggests that the stress build-up cannot exceed that which results in an $m_b = 5.5$ earthquake (as obtained by summing energies of the four earthquakes in the 1930s), which may be the maximum-magnitude earthquake for the region. Conservatively, we may take the maximum-magnitude earthquake for this area to be 6.0.

The St. Francois Mountain zone is a minor seismic zone, with most of the larger earthquakes in it confined to the southeast quadrant. The largest earthquake to have occurred in the region in historic times was the April 9, 1917, earthquake of $m_b = 5.0$. An m_b of 6.0 is a conservative estimate of the maximum-magnitude earthquake for the southeast portion of the region. A value of 5.5 may be appropriate for the other three quadrants.

For the remainder of the central United States, the majority of the earthquakes in Figure 1 are in the m_b range of 3.0 to 4.9, with two isolated cases of $m_b = 5.0$. We can take 5.5 to be the maximum magnitude and note in addition that at any particular place we should expect a very low frequency of occurrence of an earthquake of such magnitude. Perhaps further study will show that all the earthquakes of $m_b > 4.0$ or perhaps 4.5 can be associated with geologic structures that are active but not presently identified as such. If that is the case, the maximum-magnitude earthquake for regions that are not part of such minor seismic zones may be reduced to 4.5.

It should be emphasized that the maximum-magnitude earthquake will be an extremely rare phenomenon, whose probability of occurrence at a given place, for example, a specific nuclear reactor site, will be very low.

The approach taken in the present study is to define seismogenic zones principally on the basis of minor seismic activity and its spatial relation to geologic structures and to assign a maximum-magnitude earthquake to each such zone. The question arises as to whether the maximum-magnitude earthquake can occur anywhere in the zone (the most conservative viewpoint from an earthquake design standpoint) or whether it will be restricted to a certain part or parts of the zone. The latter viewpoint is implicitly contained in the approaches by Algermissen and Perkins (1976) and to a lesser extent by Hadley and Devine (1974), who use the seismicity of the past few hundred years to assess what can be expected in the future. More specifically, we might ask if we should assign a maximum magnitude of 6.5 throughout the Nemaha zone or only in the neighborhood of Manhattan, Kansas, where the larger earthquakes of the nineteenth and twentieth centuries have occurred. The former approach is the more cautious and safe, although it may be considered by some to be unrealistic. If that approach is adopted, it must be recognized that the maximum-magnitude earthquake will have an extremely low probability of occurrence at a specific place, so that it need not necessarily be the design earthquake. To be more definite, the design earthquake would probably not be as large as magnitude 6.5 throughout the Nemaha and Wichita-Ouachita zones, nor as large as magnitude 6.0 throughout the St. Francois zone. It would be of magnitude 7.5 throughout the New Madrid zone, 6.0 in the Anna, Ohio, area, and probably 6.5 throughout the Wabash zone.

ATTENUATION

One of the most remarkable ways in which earthquakes east of the Rocky Mountains differ from their western counterparts is in their comparatively large areas of damage and perceptibility, which can be as much as 100 times greater. Early attempts at explaining this phenomenon called for greater than normal focal depths (Gutenberg and Richter, 1949). Later studies, however, showed that nearly all the eastern earthquakes were shallow and occurred in the crust at depths of 1 to 20 km. The proper explanation of the large perceptibility and damage areas was found to be low attenuation of the short-period surface wave energy (Mitchell, 1973; Nuttli, 1973a; Necioglu and Nuttli, 1974). For example, at periods of about 1 s the coefficient of anelastic attenuation in the central United States is 6×10^{-4} km^{-1}, whereas for southern California the corresponding value is 5×10^{-3} km^{-1} (Nuttli, 1973a).

Figure 6 compares the damage areas for two pairs of earthquakes. The first pair is the April 18, 1906, San Francisco and the December 16, 1811, New Madrid earthquakes. The second is the February 9, 1971, San Fernando and the August 31, 1886, Charleston earthquakes, the latter having a somewhat larger body-wave magnitude. Intensities of VI to VII correspond to minor damage, and of greater than VII to major damage. The western half of the damage areas of the New Madrid earthquakes is shown by dashed lines to indicate that it is inferred on the basis of symmetry, because the area west of the Mississippi River was unpopulated at the time of the earthquake. In justification of the assumption, an intensity map for a more recent large New Madrid earthquake, that of October 31, 1895, shows this symmetry (Nuttli, 1974). The

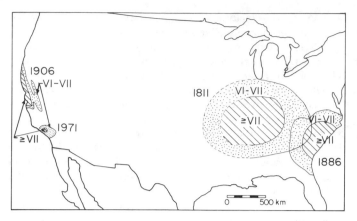

Figure 6. Comparison of areas of minor (I = VI–VII) and major (I > VII) damage for the 1906 San Francisco earthquake (M_s = 8.3) and the 1811 New Madrid earthquake (m_b = 7.2) and for the 1971 San Fernando earthquake (m_b = 6.2) and 1886 Charleston earthquake (m_b ≃ 7). The damage area for the western half of the 1811 New Madrid earthquake (outlined by dashed lines) is inferred, because there were no settlements in the area at that time.

relatively small damage area of the 1906 San Francisco earthquake may result in part from its shallow focal depth, although differences in anelastic attenuation between western and eastern North America are also of importance.

There are a number of consequences of the relatively low attenuation of wave energy in the central United States. The first is the obvious one that the amplitude of the ground motion does not decrease so rapidly with epicentral distance. The second follows from the fact that surface waves become dominant over body waves at distances of the order of 25 to 100 km and the fact that surface waves are dispersed and scattered (Aki, 1969; Herrmann, 1975). As a result the ground shaking has a larger duration at distant points. Finally, as anelastic attenuation is lower for low-frequency than high-frequency waves, the spectrum of the ground motion is shifted to the lower frequencies at the larger distances. This explains why occupants of high-rise structures of lower resonant frequencies sense earthquakes at greater distances than those dwelling in low-rise structures. It also results in relatively small ground accelerations for large ground displacements at large distances.

There is one class of central United States earthquakes for which the attenuation of intensities is as severe as it is in the West. A well-documented case of this type is the August 14, 1965, earthquake at 13^h 14^m GMT which occurred in southeastern Illinois near Cairo. It was the largest of a group of seven earthquakes that occurred in a two-day period. Although its epicentral intensity was VII, it was not felt across the Mississippi River at Cape Girardeau, Missouri, at a distance of only 25 km. Its body-wave magnitude, determined independently from both P_n waves and from the higher-mode surface L_g waves, was merely 3.8 (Nuttli, 1973a). The clue to the large epicentral intensity and the rapid fall-off of intensity with distance is the extremely shallow focal depth, determined by Herrmann (1974) to be about 1 km. For such a focal depth the excitation of the short-period fundamental-mode Rayleigh and Love waves is one or more orders of magnitude greater

than that of the higher-mode waves (Herrmann and Nuttli, 1975). The dispersion and attenuation of these short-period fundamental-mode waves is controlled by the physical properties of the outer few kilometres of the crust, a part of the crust that is of low rigidity and highly attenuating. The higher-mode surface waves, on the other hand, because of their higher velocities possess longer wavelengths, and thus their attenuation at the short periods is determined by the physical properties of the deeper parts of the crust. Furthermore, as has been shown by Herrmann and Nuttli (1975), the higher-mode wave excitation shows little variation with focal depth as long as the focus is in the crust. For this reason and because they have such low attenuation, they are well suited for determinations of body-wave magnitudes of small earthquakes from observations at regional distances, where the P waves may be too small to be seen.

Although we have no instrumental data to support the conclusion, it appears likely that the Rusk, Texas, earthquake of January 8, 1891, is another example of a shallow earthquake with an epicentral intensity of VII that was not felt in the neighboring towns. For this reason I have assigned to it an m_b value of only 3.8. Even though the evidence is not so conclusive, it is likely that most of the central United States earthquakes listed by Coffman and von Hake (1973) as having an epicentral intensity of V or greater and being felt only locally had a focal depth of less than 5 km.

DISCUSSION

Earthquakes in the central United States differ principally from their western counterparts by their less frequent occurrence, by the fact that in historic times none produced surface ground breakage, and by the much smaller anelastic attenuation of the seismic wave energy. For the first two reasons, they have received less attention than that given western earthquakes, with the result that less is known about them. Only in the New Madrid seismic zone, as a result of microearthquake and focal mechanism studies, are we presently able to delineate an active fault system. Similar studies in other areas, some of which have already begun, should enable us to outline other active faults. Once the active faults are identified, we should be able to get on with efforts such as magnitude-recurrence estimates, hazard assessment, and earthquake prediction.

Although the connection between geologic structures and earthquakes in the central United States is presently somewhat tenuous, there are places such as the Wabash Valley faulted zone and the Ouachita-Wichita Mountains front where the relation appears direct. All earthquakes must ultimately have a geologic explanation. Our understanding will be improved when we learn how some structural features, including minor ones, distort the regional compressive stress field and how others, such as the Cottage Grove–Shawneetown–Rough Creek fault system in southern Illinois and Kentucky and the Cap-au-Gres fault system in west central Illinois apparently do not. Possibly there is some explanation to be found in that the latter strike east-west, in the same direction as the maximum compressive stresses.

ACKNOWLEDGMENTS

One of the major efforts associated with this paper was the compiling of the earthquake list, which is plotted in Figure 1. For their generous assistance in supplying data, I am indebted to Carl A. von Hake, J. Carl Stepp, Robert F. Blakely, and James E. Zollweg. I also thank Bruce A. Bolt, Robert B. Herrmann, Leon Reiter, and James E. Zollweg for their critical reading of the manuscript and for helpful comments. Gabriel Leblanc, David Leeds, Richard Stearns, and James Zollweg kindly provided corrections to the list of earthquakes.

This research was supported by grant DES 74-22852 A01 from the Earth Sciences Division, National Science Foundation and by grant ENV 76-20875 from the Division of Advanced Environmental Research and Technology.

REFERENCES CITED

Aki, K., 1969, Analysis of the seismic coda of local earthquakes as scattered waves: Journal of Geophysical Research, v. 74, p. 615–631.

Algermissen, S. T., and Perkins, D. M., 1976, A probabilistic estimate of maximum acceleration in rock in the contiguous United States: U.S. Geological Survey Open-File Report 76-416.

Bradley, E. A., and Bennett, T. J., 1965, Earthquake history of Ohio: Seismological Society of America Bulletin, v. 55, p. 745–752.

Coffman, J. L., and von Hake, C. A., 1973, Earthquake history of the United States: Washington, D.C., U.S. Department of Commerce Publication 41-1, 208 p.

Docekal, J., 1970, Earthquakes of the stable interior, with emphasis on the midcontinent [Ph.D. dissert.]: Lincoln, University of Nebraska, v. 1, 169 p., v. 2, 332 p.

Evernden, J. F., 1975, Seismic intensities, "size" of earthquakes and related parameters: Seismological Society of America Bulletin, v. 65, p. 1287–1313.

Fuller, M. L., 1912, The New Madrid earthquake: U.S. Geological Survey Bulletin 494, 119 p.

Gutenberg, B., and Richter, C. F., 1949, Seismicity of the Earth and associated phenomena: Princeton, N.J., Princeton University Press, 273 p.

Hadley, J. B., and Devine, J. F., 1974, Seismotectonic map of the eastern United States: U.S. Geological Survey Miscellaneous Field Studies Map MF-620, scale 1:5,000,000, 3 sheets.

Heinrich, R. R., 1941, A contribution to the seismic history of Missouri: Seismological Society of America Bulletin, v. 31, p. 187–224.

Herrmann, R. B., 1974, Surface wave generation by central United States earthquakes [Ph.D. dissert.]: St. Louis, Mo., St. Louis University, 263 p.

——1975, The use of duration as a measure of seismic moment and magnitude: Seismological Society of America Bulletin, v. 65, p. 899–913.

Herrmann, R. B., and Nuttli, O. W., 1975, Ground-motion modeling at regional distances for earthquakes in continental interior. II. Effect of focal depth, azimuth and attenuation: Earthquake Engineering and Structural Dynamics, v. 4, p. 59–72.

Hileman, J. A., Allen, C. A., and Nordquist, J. M., 1973, Seismicity of the southern California region, 1 January 1932 to 31 December 1972: Pasadena, California Institute of Technology, Seismological Laboratory, 482 p.

King, P. B., compiler, 1969, Tectonic map of North America: U.S. Geological Survey, scale 1:5,000,000.

Mitchell, B. J., 1973, Radiation and attenuation of Rayleigh waves from the southeastern Missouri earthquake of October 21, 1965: Journal of Geophysical Research, v. 78, p. 886–899.

Necioglu, A., and Nuttli, O. W., 1974, Some ground motion and intensity relations for the central United States: Earthquake Engineering and Structural Dynamics, v. 3, p. 111–119.

Nuttli, O. W., 1973a, Seismic wave attenuation and magnitude relations for eastern North America: Journal of Geophysical Research, v. 78, p. 876–885.

——1973b, The Mississippi valley earthquakes of 1811 and 1812: Intensities, ground motion and magnitudes: Seismological Society of America Bulletin, v. 63, p. 227–248.

——1974, Magnitude-recurrence relation for central Mississippi valley earthquakes: Seismological Society of America Bulletin, v. 64, p. 1189–1207.

——1976, Seismicity of the Mississippi embayment: Proceedings, Advisory Committee on Reactor Safeguards, U.S. Nuclear Regulatory Commission Meeting Los Angeles, California, March 22–23, 1976.

Nuttli, O. W., and Zollweg, J. E., 1974, The relation between felt area and magnitude for central United States earthquakes: Seismological Society of America Bulletin, v. 64, p. 73–85.

——1975, Seismicity and tectonics of the central United States [abs.]: Earthquake Notes, v. 46, p. 54.

Sbar, M. L., and Sykes, L. R., 1973, Contemporary compressive stress and seismicity in eastern North America: An example of intra-plate tectonics: Geological Society of America Bulletin, v. 84, p. 1861–1882.

Seismological Society of America, 1911–1975 (published continuously), Seismological notes: Seismological Society of America Bulletin.

Stauder, W., and Nuttli, O. W., 1970, Seismic studies: South central Illinois earthquake of November 9, 1968: Seismological Society of America Bulletin, v. 60, p. 973–981.

Stauder, W., Best, J., Cheng, S. H., Fischer, G., Kramer, M., Morrissey, S. T., Schaefer, S., and Zollweg, J., 1974–1976, Southeast Missouri regional seismic network quarterly bulletins: St. Louis, Mo., St. Louis University, nos. 1–7.

Street, R. L., Herrmann, R. B., and Nuttli, O. W., 1974, Earthquake mechanics in the central United States: Science, v. 184, p. 1285–1287.

U.S. Department of Commerce, 1928–1972 (published annually), United States earthquakes: U.S. Coast and Geodetic Survey and the National Oceanic and Atmospheric Administration.

U.S. Geological Survey, 1972–1974 (published annually), Preliminary determination of epicenters: Denver, Colorado, National Earthquake Information Service.

MANUSCRIPT RECEIVED BY THE SOCIETY JULY 13, 1978
MANUSCRIPT ACCEPTED NOVEMBER 13, 1978

Geological Society of America
Reviews in Engineering Geology, Volume IV
1979

Seismicity of the western United States

BRUCE A. BOLT
Seismographic Station, Department of Geology and Geophysics, University of California, Berkeley, California 94720

ABSTRACT

A critical review is given of the present status of the record of earthquakes in the western United States. Special field studies for siting of nuclear reactors and other major structures have brought to light major modifications and revisions of some earlier inferences on the intensity and fault location of historical earthquakes. For example, the hypocenters of the Washington State earthquake of December 14, 1872, and the Lompoc, California, earthquake of November 4, 1927, have recently been redetermined. Presentation and retrieval of both modern and historical seismicity records are still not optimum, with various errors and inconsistencies—some introduced by computer processing.

Increased density of seismographic networks is providing sharper resolution in seismicity mapping. In northern California the pattern of widespread minor seismicity has been defined for the first time; earthquake foci in the Humboldt County region are concentrated in two crustal levels, 0 to 10 km and 18 to 20 km. Use of ocean-bottom seismographs is improving knowledge of the offshore seismicity pattern. Seismotectonic properties of northwestern California, Puget Sound (Washington), and the intermountain seismic belt are now emerging.

THE EVOLUTIONARY SAMPLE OF EARTHQUAKE STATISTICS

The objective of this study is to define the changing observational base of earthquake statistics in the western United States. Only the contiguous states west of the Rocky Mountains are considered, with attention concentrated on California and Washington where most special studies have been made.

A major part of geologic hazard investigations for proposed nuclear reactor sites and, indeed, sites for all large engineered structures nowadays, is a consideration of the earthquake risk. These evaluations rely almost entirely on structural geology and seismology. The less stringent inquiries of a decade ago did not usually require special geologic maps showing Quaternary fault movement or rigorously complete seismicity lists. This is certainly no longer the case. The hard and penetrating questions now posed (sometimes unanswerable as formulated)

on probability of occurrence and strong motion parameters have led to revolutionary rethinking of the homogeneity, reliability, and meaning of the earthquake record. The monumental catalogues of Pacific Coast earthquakes by Holden (1898) and by Townley and Allen (1939), for example, provided the statistical basis of most seismicity risk studies, both local and regional, in West Coast States. The intensity information for Pacific Coast earthquakes (1769–1927) summarized in those catalogues has been variously converted to modified Mercalli intensities, Richter magnitudes, tectonic energy contours, and even peak ground acceleration and velocities. Only recently have these early contributions, necessarily limited in scope and depth, been subjected to much critical analysis and augmentation. Unfortunately, a substantial amount of this new material is in the form of proprietary and special purpose reports, not published through scientific journals. Finding and referencing such studies are becoming difficult tasks.

Illustrations are given in the following sections of the types of seismicity cataloguing and research that are now needed. First, the available information on felt and damage reports from historical earthquakes needs analytic study of the type given the central California earthquakes of the mid-nineteenth century by Louderback (1944). In this connection, also, a recent examination by Marine Advisers (1965) of the evidence for a purported large tsunami associated with the California earthquake of December 21, 1812, led to doubts that sea waves were generated, as implied in some earlier editions of *Earthquake History of the United States*. This re-evaluation involved the assessment of unpublished notes by G. D. Louderback, which are now held in the Bancroft Library, University of California, Berkeley.

Second, some of the larger earthquakes in the first five decades or so of this century in the western United States were recorded at sufficient seismographic stations in North America and overseas to make it worthwhile to redetermine their hypocenters by using modern methods. Hypocentral solutions adopted contemporaneously with the earthquakes were sometimes based on limited data and graphical methods. These solutions are reported in *Earthquake History of the United States* (Coffman and von Hake, 1973) and international catalogues, such as the "International Seismological Summary." Many examples have been found where least-squares readjust-

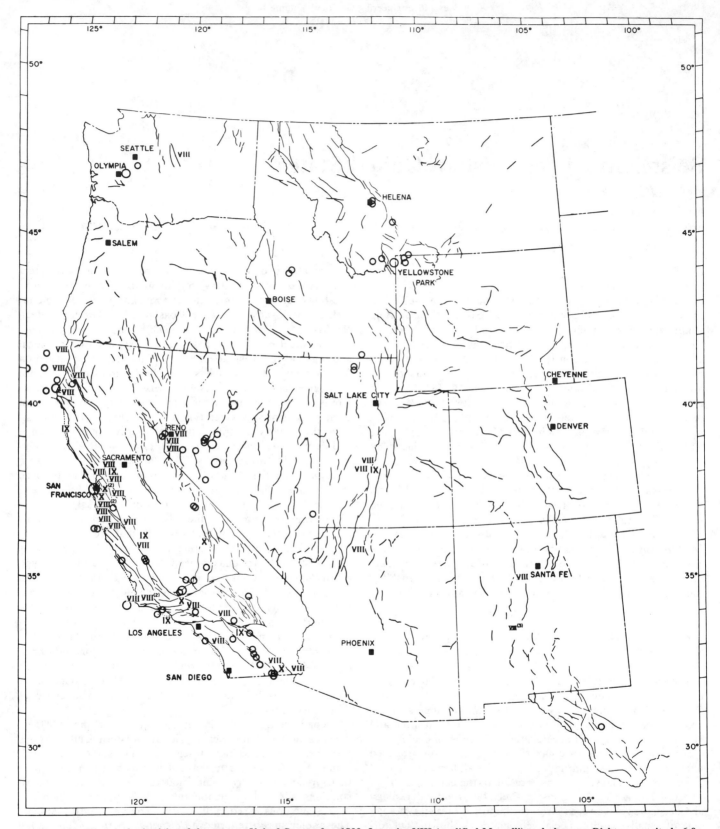

Figure 1. Historical seismicity of the western United States after 1800. Intensity VIII (modified Mercalli) and above or Richter magnitude 6.0 and above.

TABLE 1. LARGE EARTHQUAKES OF THE WESTERN UNITED STATES FROM 1800 ($M_L \geq 6.0$ OR MM INTENSITY $\geq$ VIII)

California

Date	Locality	Lat (°N)	Long (°W)	M_L	Int (MM)
10/11/1800	San Juan Bautista	36.83	121.58		VIII
12/ 8/1812	San Juan Capistrano	33.50	117.67		VIII
12/21/1812	Offshore S. California	34	120		IX
6/10/1836	East of S.F. Bay	37.67	122.08		X
6/ - /1838	San Francisco	37.50	122.50		X
11/ 9/1852	Fort Yuma	33	114.5		VIII
1/ 9/1857	Fort Tejon	34.84	118.92		X
11/26/1858	San Jose	37.33	121.92		VIII
7/ 4/1861	San Ramon	37.72	121.94		VIII
10/ 1/1865	Eureka	40.83	124.17		VIII
10/ 8/1865	Santa Cruz Mtns.	37	122		VIII
10/21/1868	Hayward	37.67	122.08		X
- / - /1871	Imperial Valley	33.0	115.5		X
3/26/1872	Owens Valley	36.58	118.08		X
11/22/1873	Crescent City	41.75	124.17		VIII
1/24/1875	Verdi	39.3	120.3		VIII
4/11/1885	East of King City	36.25	120.80		VIII
4/24/1890	Monterey Bay Area	36.92	121.75		VIII
10/11/1891	Napa and Sonoma	38.25	122.33		VIII
4/19/1892	Vacaville	38.33	122.00		IX
4/21/1892	Winters	38.50	122.00		VIII
4/ 4/1893	Newhall, L.A.	34.42	118.50		VIII
6/20/1897	Hollister	36.83	121.42		VIII
4/14/1898	Mendocino County	40.83	124.17		IX
7/22/1899	Cajon Pass	34.33	117.50		VIII
12/25/1899	San Jacinto	33.75	116.92		IX
3/ 2/1901	Stone Canyon	36.08	120.58		IX
5/19/1902	Elmira and Vacaville	38.33	121.92		VIII
7/27/1902	Los Alamos, Lompoc	34.75	120.25		VIII
7/31/1902	Los Alamos, Lompoc	34.75	120.25		VIII
8/ 2/1903	San Jose	37.33	121.92		VIII
4/18/1906	San Francisco	37.76	122.48	8.25	X
4/18/1906	Brawley	33.00	115.50		VIII
10/28/1909	NW California	40.58	124.17		VIII
7/ 1/1911	San Jose	37.25	121.75	6.6	VII
1/11/1915	Los Alamos	34.75	120.75		VIII
6/22/1915	Imperial Valley	32.75	115.50	6.25	VIII
6/22/1915	Imperial Valley	32.75	115.50	6.25	VIII
12/31/1915	SW of Eureka	41.00	125.00	6.5	III
4/21/1918	San Jacinto	33.75	117.00	6.8	VIII
7/15/1918	SW of Eureka	41.00	125.00	6.5	VI
3/10/1922	Cholame Valley	35.75	120.25	6.5	IX
1/22/1923	Off Cape Mendocino	40.50	124.50	7.2	IX
7/22/1923	San Bernadino Valley	34.00	117.25	6.25	VII
6/ 4/1925	NW of Eureka	41.50	125.00	6.0	
6/29/1925	Santa Barbara	34.30	119.80	6.25	IX
10/22/1926	Monterey	36.61	122.35	6.1	VIII
10/22/1926	Monterey	36.57	122.18	6.1	VII
8/20/1927	Arcata	41.00	124.60		VIII
9/18/1927	NW of Bishop	37.50	118.75	6.0	VII
11/ 4/1927	W of Pt. Arguello	34.9	120.67	7.3	IX
6/ 6/1932	Humboldt County	40.75	124.50	6.4	VIII
3/10/1933	Long Beach	33.60	118.00	6.3	IX
6/ 7/1934	Parkfield	35.80	120.33	6.0	VIII
3/25/1937	Terwilliger Valley	33.41	116.26	6.0	VII
5/18/1940	SE of El Centro	32.70	115.50	6.7	X
6/30/1941	Santa Barbara	34.40	119.60	5.9	VIII
9/14/1941	Owens Valley	37.57	118.73	6.0	VI
10/ 3/1941	SW of Eureka	40.40	124.80	6.4	VI
10/21/1942	Borrego Valley	32.97	116.00	6.5	VII
3/15/1946	N of Walker Pass	35.70	118.10	6.3	VIII
4/10/1947	East of Barstow	34.98	116.55	6.2	VII
12/ 4/1948	Desert Hot Springs	33.93	116.38	6.5	VII
7/21/1952	Kern County	35.00	119.00	7.7	X
7/21/1952	Kern County	35.00	119.00	6.4	V
7/23/1952	Kern County	35.37	118.56	6.1	VII
7/29/1952	Kern County	35.38	118.85	6.1	VII
11/22/1952	San Simeon	35.73	121.20	6.0	VII
3/19/1954	Santa Rosa Mtns.	33.28	116.18	6.2	VI
12/21/1954	E of Eureka	40.78	123.87	6.5	VII
9/12/1966	Truckee Area	39.42	120.15	6.0	VII
4/ 9/1968	S of Ocotillo Mtn.	33.19	116.13	6.4	VII
2/ 9/1971	San Fernando	34.41	118.40	6.4	XI

Nevada

Date	Locality	Lat (°N)	Long (°W)	M_L	Int (MM)
- / - /1852	Pyramid Lake	39.5	119.5		VIII
- / - /1860	Carson - Virginia City	39.3	119.7		VIII
- / - /1869	Reno	39.5	120		VIII
10/ 2/1915	Pleasant Valley	40.5	117.5	7.75	X
12/20/1932	Cedar Mtn.	38.75	118.00	7.2	X
6/25/1933	Wabuska	39.08	119.33	6.1	VII
1/30/1934	SE of Hawthorne	38.28	118.36	6.3	IX
12/29/1948	Verdi	39.55	120.08	6.0	VII
7/ 6/1954	E of Fallon	39.42	118.53	6.8	IX
7/ 6/1954	SE of Fallon	39.30	118.50	6.0	VIII
8/23/1954	E of Fallon	39.58	118.45	6.8	IX
12/16/1954	Dixie Valley	39.32	118.20	7.2	X
12/16/1954	E of Fallon	39.50	118.00	7.1	X
3/23/1959	Dixie Valley	39.60	118.02	6.3	VI
6/23/1959	E of Yerington	39.08	118.82	6.1	VI
8/16/1966	SE Nevada	37.4	114.2	6.0	

Washington

Date	Locality	Lat (°N)	Long (°W)	M_L	Int (MM)
12/14/1872	Winesap	47.80	120.35		VIII
4/13/1949	Olympia	47.1	122.7	7.0	VIII
4/29/1965	Seattle	47.4	122.3	6.5	VIII

Oregon

None recorded with $M_r > 6.0$ and/or $I > VIII$

Idaho

Date	Locality	Lat (°N)	Long (°W)	M_L	Int (MM)
7/12/1944	Cascade	44.5	115.5	6.1	
2/14/1945	Cascade	44.7	115.4	6.0	
3/27/1975	Pocatello Valley	42.1	112.5	6.3	

Montana

Date	Locality	Lat (°N)	Long (°W)	M_L	Int (MM)
6/27/1925	E of Helena	46.0	111.2	6.75	VIII
10/18/1935	Helena	46.6	112.0	6.25	VIII
10/31/1935	Helena	46.6	112.0	6.0	VIII
11/23/1947	SW Montana	44.8	112.0	6.25	VIII
8/17/1959	Hebgen Lake	44.8	111.1	7.1	X
8/18/1959	Yellowstone	45.0	110.5	6.5	
8/18/1959	Yellowstone	44.8	110.7	6.0	VI
8/18/1959	Yellowstone	44.9	110.7	6.5	
8/18/1959	SW Montana	44.9	111.6	6.0	V

Wyoming

None recorded with $M_L \geq 6.0$ and/or $I \geq VIII$

Colorado

None recorded with $M_L \geq 6.0$ and/or $I \geq VIII$

Utah

Date	Locality	Lat (°N)	Long (°W)	M_L	Int (MM)
11/13/1901	Beaver, S Utah	38.7	112.1		IX-X
9/29/1921	Elsinore	38.8	112.2		VIII
10/ 1/1921	Elsinore	38.8	112.2		VIII
3/12/1934	Kosmo	41.7	112.8	6.6	VIII
3/12/1934	Kosmo	41.7	112.8	6.0	VIII

Arizona

Date	Locality	Lat (°N)	Long (°W)	M_L	Int (MM)
8/18/1912	N of Flagstaff	36.0	112.0		VIII

New Mexico

Date	Locality	Lat (°N)	Long (°W)	M_L	Int (MM)
7/12/1906	Socorro	34.0	107.0		VIII
7/16/1906	Socorro	34.0	107.0		VIII
11/15/1906	Socorro	34.0	107.0		VIII
5/28/1918	Santa Fe	35.5	106.6		VIII

Texas (Western portion)

Date	Locality	Lat (°N)	Long (°W)	M_L	Int (MM)
8/16/1931	Mt. Livermore	30.9	104.2	6.4	VIII

ments, using modern machine programs (for example, Bolt, 1960; Dewey, 1972) and other statistical methods, led to significant changes in epicenters.

Any such adjustments must be fully tested and documented before adoption and publication. Revisions should also be sufficiently sizable and significant compared to the original location to make amendments worthwhile. Thus there are major problems for compilers of catalogues as to when to allow a revision and when to avoid the confusion of several conflicting solutions for one earthquake.

THE HISTORICAL EARTHQUAKE RECORD

Figure 1 is a map showing major historical seismicity of the western United States. Data for the plot are given in Table 1 by State. For this compilation, all earthquakes with modified Mercalli (MM) intensity VIII and above or Richter magnitude 6 and above were selected from the main historical and modern catalogues. The record essentially begins after 1800 for all the states west of the Rocky Mountains. For California and the Pacific States, the basic catalogue is that of Townley and Allen (1939). This catalogue has some entries for the 18th century back to 1775, but these early data may not be complete. Reports of earthquakes in Washington State become more or less regular after 1840, and those in the western mountain region about 1850. A general discussion and listing of the early earthquakes are given in the revised edition of *Earthquake History of the United States* (Coffman and von Hake, 1973) and will not be repeated here. The demands for regional seismicity lists have led to special compilations, with data drawn from various primary and secondary sources (see Smith, 1978).

A handy recent set of summaries of seismicity in the western states has been published in the *Earthquake Information Bulletin,* now published bimonthly by the U.S. Geological Survey. Montana, Nevada, and New Mexico earthquakes were treated by von Hake (1974a, 1974b, 1975). Similar summaries appeared earlier for Arizona (NOAA [National Oceanic and Atmospheric Administration], 1970a), Colorado (NOAA, 1970b), Idaho (NOAA, 1972), and California (NOAA, 1971). The seismicity of Wyoming was discussed earlier by Benioff (1960), of Oregon by Berg and Baker (1963), of Washington by Rasmussen (1967), of Utah by Cook and Smith (1967), and of the Great Plains by Lander (1960).

Only Oregon and Colorado show no earthquake sources with intensities exceeding the adopted bounds (see Fig. 1). Most of Arizona, New Mexico, and Wyoming have also been free of large intensity earthquakes, although none of the western states is without some reported earthquakes (see Fig. 2). Broadly, the largest earthquakes fall in four zones of most significant historical activity: the San Andreas fault system, Owens Valley and central Nevada, northwest Washington, and the intermountain seismic belt along the western limits of the Rocky Mountains. The contemporary tectonic understanding of these zones indicates no abatement of seismic activity in the short term, but provides no quantitative estimates of periods between earthquakes (except perhaps in the first zone).

The need for quantitative analysis of the historical seismicity has led to recent revisions of the catalogues. The Townley and Allen catalogue has now been re-edited carefully, taking into account modern studies. The result is an abstracted list with some revisions that is available on magnetic tape at the National Geophysical Data Center, NOAA, in Boulder, Colorado. The type allows earthquake data to be retrieved according to geographic region. Also, for California, seismicity information based on seismographic readings has recently been condensed into two summary lists, one for southern California (Hileman and others, 1973) and one for northern California (Bolt and Miller, 1975). These catalogues supersede in key aspects the individual bulletins published for many years by the California Institute of Technology in southern California and the University of California at Berkeley in northern California. So many special studies of California earthquake occurrences, particularly along the San Andreas fault, have been published (see Cloud, 1960; Niazi, 1964; Allen and others, 1965; Bolt and Miller, 1971; Lee and others, 1972) that no attempt will be made to discuss them here. The California Division of Mines and Geology has recently produced a combined catalogue on magnetic tape for California earthquakes with some revisions (Real and Toppozada, 1978).

Valuable studies of a similar kind have been published for Washington (Crosson, 1972; Unger and Mills, 1973), Utah (Cook and Smith, 1967), Nevada (Slemmons and others, 1965), and Colorado (NOAA, 1969; Gibbs and others, 1973). The seismicity and tectonic relations of the western Cordillera have been discussed recently by Smith (1978).

Rather unsystematic reworking of the historical record has been stimulated by three developments. First, seismic site evaluation for nuclear power reactors must meet stringent requirements. Second, the network of large storage dams in the western United States requires that the authorities involved—particularly the U.S. Corps of Engineers, the U.S. Bureau of Reclamation, and the California State Department of Water Resources—ascertain any seismic hazard by means of seismicity reports. A third stimulus came from the program carried out after the 1971 San Fernando earthquake by the U.S. Veterans Administration (Bolt and others, 1975). Consultants were retained to study the seismic and geologic hazards at each site of existing and proposed hospitals. The work was begun in California and progressed into other areas, including Washington and Utah.

The large expenditures of funds involved in construction of large engineered structures make it feasible to spend considerably more time investigating historical accounts of damage in the field. Two representative examples of some importance can be given here. The first was carried out by Diana C. Dale during the preparation of the Preliminary Site Analysis Report (PSAR; Docket 50522) for the proposed Skagit nuclear reactor in northern Washington State. In this case, a great deal of local historical investigation in Washington, Idaho, and Oregon, including examination of local newspapers and interviews in towns and villages throughout the central area, showed that the Washington State earthquake of December 14, 1872, had been previously mislocated. The *Earthquake History of the United States* places this event near Puget Sound with MM intensity VI, and a recent study by Milne (1956) located it near the Canadian border. The incorrect Puget Sound location can be traced to a single report used by Holden (1898). The

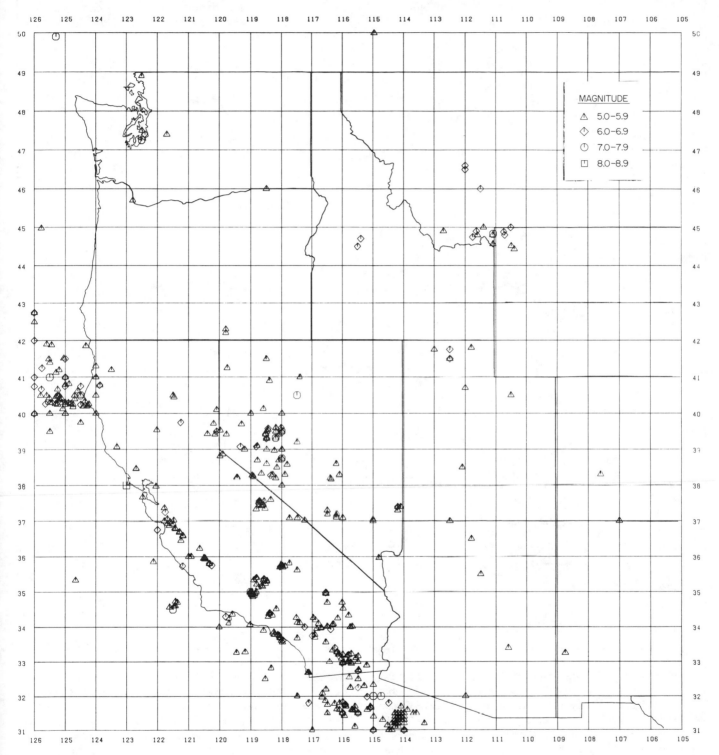

Figure 2. Earthquake epicenters, mainly obtained from analysis of readings of seismic waves from seismograms, for the western United States from 1900 to 1974 (courtesy of J. Lander, NOAA). Local magnitude greater than 5.0.

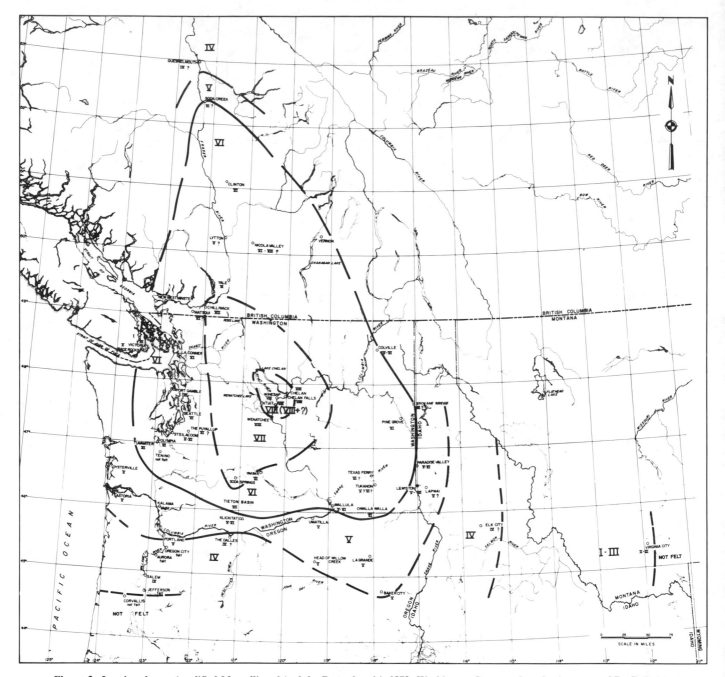

Figure 3. Isoseismal map (modified Mercalli scale) of the December 14, 1872, Washington State earthquake (courtesy of D. C. Dale).

analysis of the much wider range of material gathered by Dale demonstrated that the source of the earthquake was about 150 km to the east of Puget Sound, perhaps near Lake Chelan. (A special review panel, chaired by H. A. Coombs, on this earthquake later concluded that the earthquake source probably lay in an elliptical area about 50 km from east to west and about 80 km from north to south which includes Lake Chelan.) Isoseismals based on Dale's work are shown in Figure 3 and indicate a maximum MM intensity of VIII+.

The second case of interest is the Owens Valley earthquake of March 26, 1872. Several recent studies have been published (see Oakeshott and others, 1972; Evernden, 1975). There is

little published information on the effects of this earthquake, although ground shaking was felt throughout most of California and Nevada, in Oregon and Arizona, and as far away as Salt Lake City, Utah. Plaster fell and brick walls were damaged in Chico, California, 480 km from the center of the disturbance. The maximum MM intensity has been rated X in the Independence–Lone Pine area. A comparison with the isoseismals of the 1906 San Francisco earthquake shows clearly that the 1872 earthquake shook a larger region.

Because both location and size of historical earthquakes are fundamentally important to modern risk mapping, it is surprising that little critical attention has been given to optimal estimation of seismic intensity. Assessed intensities are usually biased upward in two ways. First, estimates of intensity at a particular place in a shaken area usually depend on that item rated highest in the descriptive scale. In particular, reports of landslides commonly cause a site to be rated VIII to IX on the Mercalli scale, although landslides may be triggered even without earthquakes. Secondly, isoseismals are commonly drawn as contours separating areas having uniform intensity level. This enveloping of the data again places an upper bound on intensity. What is needed is careful revision of the descriptive material in the light of modern knowledge of statistical analysis and of effects of ground shaking on buildings of different kinds. For example, descriptions of swinging pendulums can be used together with the theory of forced harmonic motion to estimate velocity of strong ground motion, and modern theory on the response of structures can give at least a limit to the acceleration of the ground which produced cracks in masonry of various kinds.

THE MODERN EARTHQUAKE RECORD

Seismographic stations in various western states have produced systematic and continuous earthquake bulletins of great value. The catalogues of the California Institute of Technology began to be published in 1932, and those of the University of California in Berkeley in 1910. However, the geographic coverage and quality of this instrumentally located seismicity in the western United States are uneven. An example of the material now available on computer printout by request is given in Figure 2. This computer plot contains all listed earthquakes with magnitudes (local magnitude in most cases) above 5 for the years 1900 to 1974. The list from which the plot came, however, is known to be incomplete. "The hypocenter data file for the region is clearly not complete for magnitude 5 earthquakes in the Rocky Mountain area up into the 1960s" (J. Lander, 1977, written commun.).

Another difficulty is the assessment of magnitude. After the definition of local magnitude by Richter in 1935, it was many years before the parameter was used widely in the western states. It was not routinely calculated for the University of California Berkeley *Bulletin* until the 1942 issue, although Wood-Anderson seismographs were introduced in 1928. Some instrumental magnitudes of western earthquakes early in this century were worked out by Gutenberg and Richter (1954) from measurements made afterward from the old seismograms. Undoubtedly, much remains to be done to complete the magnitude record from stored seismograms that have never been analyzed in this way.

Modern mapping of instrumentally determined hypocenters in the western United States has more or less established the base patterns of seismicity (see Fig. 2). These patterns have commonly been related to Quaternary faulting and crustal stress patterns. It remains difficult, however, to deal with certain locations in general terms. For example, there is a background of small to moderate earthquakes not clearly associated with the broad structural trends related to Cenozoic deformations that have taken place west of the Rocky Mountains. The understanding of the history of the present geologic evolution of the region, in terms of location, depth, size, and mechanism

of earthquakes, is hampered by the variation in the quality and homogeneity in earthquake recording in the western states. Up to 1960, seismographic station coverage was, judged by standards needed for tectonophysics, inadequate and sparse. Since 1960 there has been an increase in the coverage of seismographic networks and in their sensitivity. The increase, however, has not been geographically uniform, and there are problems in gathering measurements and making optimal solutions.

Another problem is the uneven evolution of methods of estimating hypocenters and magnitudes during the modern era. During World War II, for example, general lack of interest meant that detailed attention was not often given to earthquakes below a threshold of magnitude 5. Uncertainties in location vary with time and region and are difficult to assess in a general way. Perhaps the best statement would be that apart from special studies or circumstances, up to at least 1965, published earthquake locations in the western region should be regarded as having epicentral uncertainties of ±20 km and uncertainties in focal depth of about 20 km. Threshold magnitudes vary throughout the region; since the 1960s, some earthquakes down to magnitude 2.5 were reported near to sensitive seismographic stations, whereas in more remote places only earthquakes down to magnitude 4.5 were uniformly included. This variability in the sample makes research on earthquake frequency in the western United States both difficult and equivocal. Only through special studies can one expect to obtain data sets with sufficient stability in the sampling procedures to warrant detailed statistical analysis. A few recent studies (see Knopoff, 1964) have remedied some problems and must be consulted for the levels of precision appropriate to the region.

An illustration comes from an examination of the seismicity of the Coast Ranges of central California (Bolt and others, 1968). The analysis of 300 regional earthquakes from 1962 through 1965 indicated that methods of location feasible using the telemetry network in the region gave average uncertainties of epicenters in the Coast Ranges of about 5 km. This imprecision was made up of an error from reading scatter of the P times and systematic errors due to the unreality of the crustal models used. Solutions, however, obtained by the local network were often in sharp contrast with published preliminary locations obtained by the routine methods for global earthquakes employed by national and international centers. The routine methods systematically placed near the coastline the epicenters of earthquakes actually centered in the central Coast Ranges of California (and mainly associated with the San Andreas fault). This westward bias of about 30 km evidently arose because of the use of a standard program with Jeffreys-Bullen traveltime tables and because there is no station control to the west. An example of the westerly bias of solutions found in the global catalogues is the earthquake of December 28, 1967 ($M_L = 5.0$), which was centered (see Fig. 2) north of Gilroy, California, at lat 37.4°N, long 121.63°W, as determined by the University of California Seismographic Station network. The epicenter of this earthquake was computed by the International Seismological Centre as lat 37.00°N, long 121.89°W, a shift of about 30 km southwest from its actual position toward the city of Santa Cruz on the coast. Interestingly, the continental shelf, west of the San Andreas fault, does have a definite but low rate of seismic activity (Uhrhammer, 1977).

Currently available seismicity maps show quiescent gaps, some of which probably arise not from the absence of local earthquakes, but from a continued lack of detection and analysis ability. A striking example is in the far north of California. Here, earthquakes were mapped up until 1973 by using readings from seismographic stations at Mineral (1939 to present), Shasta (1942 to 1964), Arcata (1948 to present), and Fickle Hill (1968 to present). Since 1973 a major effort has been made to resolve the regional seismicity more precisely with the June 1973 establishment of a highly sensitive broadband instrument at Whiskeytown Dam. This station, Fickle Hill, Mineral, and Oroville all record over telephone lines onto one develocorder at Berkeley (see Fig. 4). Earthquakes down to Richter magnitudes 2.0 and even less were located from April 1973 through March 1976 as closely as possible by swinging arcs and by

using P and S arrival times. Because earthquake size is small and stations few, some locations may contain large errors. Nevertheless, if the population is regarded in a statistical sense, an important picture of the microseismicity emerges for the first time (Fig. 4).

In this preliminary study, attention was focused on a band extending eastward from Cape Mendocino and limited mainly between lat 40.0°N and 41.0°N. Absence of epicentral plots outside this band does not necessarily indicate no earthquakes there, but rather lack of resolution and analysis. Within the detection band, however, four critical results emerge. First, there is a concentration of earthquakes in the coastal area at lat 40.25°N along an eastward extension of the Mendocino Escarpment onto the continent near Cape Mendocino. This concentration of stress release through rock fracture must reflect some mechanical connection between the Mendocino

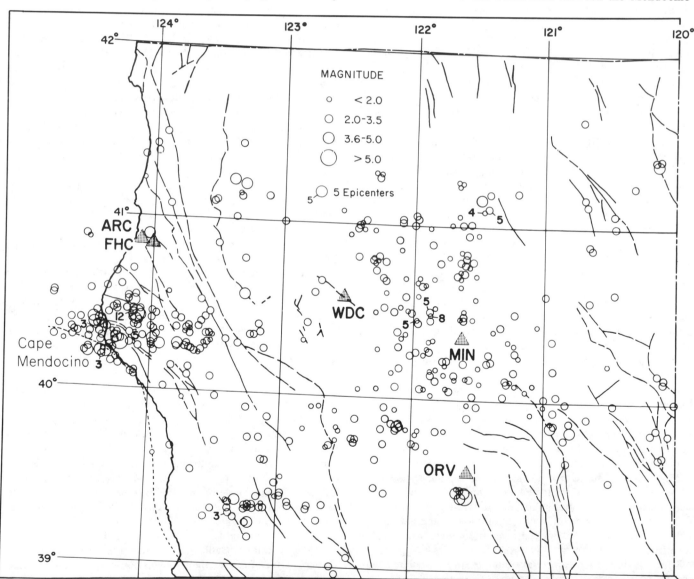

Figure 4. Detailed earthquake pattern of part of northern California, April 1973–March 1976 (solutions from the seismographic station at University of California, Berkeley). Dashed lines are generalized major faults. Seismographic stations (triangles): ARC, Arcata; FHC, Fickle Hill; WDC, Whiskeytown Dam; MIN, Mineral; ORV, Oroville.

escarpment and the westward movement of the western United States. Its explanation may throw light on the mechanics of deformation near a junction of tectonic plates (Bolt and others, 1968).

Second, from long 122.3°W to about 123.2°W and north of lat 40°N, there are almost no earthquakes, even though this section of the band contains the sensitive Whiskeytown station. The Whiskeytown seismograph would detect earthquakes down to at least magnitude 1.0 if they occurred within 50 km of the station. To the east of this seismic gap lies a dispersed zone of minor activity in the region of recent volcanic activity running north of the Sierra Nevada through Mount Lassen National Park and into the Cascades to lat 41°N. Incidentally, it is worth noting that from 1973 to 1976, no epicenters were located adjacent to the Mineral station near Mount Lassen.

Third, between the Mineral and Oroville seismographic stations (Fig. 4) there appears to be a boundary to the seismicity about lat 40°N, near the northern end of the Sierra Nevada batholiths. There is no continuation of the minor seismicity to the south toward the Foothills fault system with which the 1975 Oroville earthquake sequence has been associated. (This sequence is indicated by a group of epicenters just south of Oroville station.) Fourth, there is a scattered but more or less continuous trend of earthquake epicenters running southwest from Mineral across the Sacramento Valley into the Coast Ranges to about lat 39.3°N, long 123.2°W. Many foci, generally related to earthquakes with magnitudes between 2 and 3.5, may underlie the Great Valley sedimentary sequences. Although precise hypocenters have not been individually determined, taken together they presumably indicate some deeper crustal strain release whose origin at present is not understood. It should be remarked that the largest earthquake centered in the northern Great Valley in modern times occurred on May 24, 1966 (M_L = 4.6), at lat 39.78°N, long 121.77°W (not plotted in Fig. 4). The focal depth of this earthquake was found to be 20.8 ± 5.7 km (Lomnitz and Bolt, 1967).

The detailed picture of small earthquake occurrence in northern California shown in Figure 4 is quite new and poses many intriguing questions. We can only speculate what the complete seismicity pattern would look like for the western United States if the sensitivity of recording and analysis similar to that in Figure 4 was available for the whole region.

INCREASED DENSITY OF SEISMOGRAPHIC STATIONS

In the 1970s a jump occurred in the number of seismographic stations recording in the western United States. This increased observation grew largely from the need for special studies to determine the seismic risk to large structures, such as dams and nuclear reactors. Reference can be made to several representative examples.

A large network of short-period seismographs, mainly along the San Andreas fault in central California, was established in the 1960s by the U.S. Geological Survey (USGS) with partial support from the U.S. Atomic Energy Commission (Lee and others, 1972). This network, which was later extended into southern California in collaboration with the California Institute of Technology, is a basic tool in the studies of the USGS

into methods of earthquake prediction. During the same time, a network of stations was operated around the nuclear test site in Nevada after it had been suggested that there was a correlation between the firing of large nuclear devices underground and outbreaks of natural earthquakes in Nevada (see Smith and others, 1972). In California, a network of telemetry stations was emplaced around a number of newly constructed large dams, including Oroville in northern California and Castaic in southern California, by the State Department of Water Resources. These telemetry networks transmit signals to a center in Sacramento where a watch is kept for changes in background seismicity associated with the impounding of water in these reservoirs. For the same purpose, in April 1972 the USGS installed a special network of eight stations around the New Melones Dam site in the central western foothills of the Sierra Nevada. In eastern Washington State, a linked network of sensitive short-period seismographs has operated for nearly a decade in the Hanford area to determine earthquake patterns and tectonic trends. The monitoring there is related to questions of risk in the storage of radioactive wastes in underground tanks and the operation of processing plants. At the suggestion of the U.S. Nuclear Regulatory Commission, Pacific Gas and Electric Company set up a special seismic network in northern California around the nuclear reactor at Humboldt Bay (Smith, 1975). Sixteen stations (mostly south of FHC in Fig. 4) became fully operational in mid-August 1974. During the next 12 months, 425 earthquakes were located by the network in the region described; the network thus provided the most precise control of seismicity ever achieved over a limited area in this region. After a period of shutdown in early 1976, the utility restarted network operation in mid-1976. A dense USGS seismograph network around The Geysers in northern California (Bufe and others, 1976) has detected many shallow microearthquakes throughout the geothermal field.

Very significant increases also took place during this period in the number of seismographic stations operated in the Puget Sound area by the University of Washington (Crosson, 1974), in Nevada by the University of Nevada in Reno (Ryall and others, 1973), in Utah by the University of Utah (Smith and Sbar, 1974), and in Montana by the University of Montana at Missoula (A. Qamar, 1977, written commun.). All this work and that of other universities and governmental agencies has been augmented by seismicity studies involving portable high-gain seismographs throughout the whole region. One example is a study in which six portable high-gain seismographs were used to detect earthquakes in the Hebgen Lake–Yellowstone area (Trimble and Smith, 1975). This study was in addition to work done by seismologists in a wider region of the Rocky Mountains (Dewey and others, 1972). The results indicate a close correlation between the earthquake foci occurring from 1925 to 1971 in this region and the Cenozoic faults that trend eastward from the Hebgen fault zone along the north side of the Centennial Range and terminate at Yellowstone.

A new effort is an attempt using ocean-bottom seismographs to locate more precisely the submarine earthquakes along the Pacific coast of the western United States. The first installation of an ocean-bottom seismographer to record local earthquakes was OBS-3, built at Lamont Geological Observatory and emplaced off the coast of northern California at lat 38°09.2′N, long 122°54.4'W (see Fig. 1) on May 18, 1966, at a water depth of 3,903 m (Nowroozi, 1973). Although the instrument was not expected to run for more than 1 or 2 yr, many of the seismographic sensors remained operational until September 11, 1972, when the cable to shore developed a fault. This instrument provided important information on both local and distant earthquakes (Auld and others, 1969). A number of temporary installations of ocean-bottom seismographs have been made in the same area in recent years by several groups. One experiment carried out in 1975 (Asada and others, 1975) placed tethered ocean-bottom seismographs on the bottom of the Gorda Basin northwest of Cape Mendocino (see Fig. 4) in water depths of greater than 3,000 m. Recordings showed that the seismicity of the basin is higher than previously believed, with many swarms of local earthquakes. Further work with ocean-bottom seismographs of this kind is needed for understanding of the structure of the western continental margin and its interaction with the Gorda and Juan de Fuca spreading ridges.

Much more attention is now being given in the western United States to the relation between general seismicity and faults, particularly those of Quaternary age. In part, this is due to the requirements of the Nuclear Regulatory Commission and other governmental groups to determine for hazard estimation purposes whether faults are capable or active (Adair, this volume). It is also a consequence of the realization that seismograms can give key information on present crustal deformation and tectonic trends. Precise location of the foci of small earthquakes is a decisive tool in mapping zones where crustal strain is now being relieved. Other data from seismograms besides traveltimes are playing a role. For example, the first motions of seismic P waves have allowed—with the increased density of seismographic networks—fault-plane solutions for local earthquakes to be worked out; therefore, the mechanisms of small earthquakes in various zones can be determined (Smith and Lindh, 1978). An early study showed that most earthquakes along the San Andreas fault in northern California are the result of right-lateral strike slip (Bolt and others, 1968); a more recent study found that normal fault motions with north-south tensions are common in the Hebgen Lake–Yellowstone area (Trimble and Smith, 1975). More crucial

from a tectonic point of view are those fault-plane solutions that are significantly abnormal for a given region. Not much attention has been given to the statistics of groups of fault-plane solutions region by region; I have discussed the theory necessary for this work (Bolt and others, 1978).

The more precise seismicity mapping of recent times provides a basis for hypotheses on crustal and lithospheric deformation and mechanical models for earthquake source processes in various areas in the western United States. Recent examples are the detailed study of the relation between earthquake mechanisms and tectonics along the western coast of North America (Chandra, 1974) and the review by Smith (1978) for the western Cordillera.

Two cases of special import will be described here. First, the research reported in the previous section on microearthquakes in northern California required a structural model for further discussion. The hypothesis of McKenzie and Morgan (1969) and others is that near Cape Mendocino there is a triple junction between the North American, Gorda, and Pacific plates. Here the plates are separated by three tectonic discontinuities: the San Andreas fault, the Mendocino Escarpment, and a presumed trench. The implication is that subduction has taken place (or still is taking place) under the continental coast north of Cape Mendocino (see Fig. 4). The consequence of a slab (or stack of slabs) dipping eastward under the Klamath Mountains should be testable by seismological means. Recently, evidence has accumulated that earthquake foci are significantly deeper in the Cape Mendocino region (as much as 30 km or so) than in central California, say, where depths seldom exceed 15 km. Although the depth to the Mohorovičić discontinuity is not well known in this area, there is a strong indication that the deeper earthquakes occur below the crust proper, in a layer at the top of the upper mantle. Several recent detailed studies of the seismicity of the area agree (Nowroozi, 1973; Simila and others, 1975; Smith, 1975) that although shallow earthquakes with foci in the top 5 km of the crust do occur (but are not clearly associated with mapped surface faults), even more foci are detected at depths below 18 km. There is a suggestion of a slight increase in focal depth toward the east. Furthermore, the latest evidence leans toward the existence of a nearly aseismic layer between the two active zones.

For the purpose of further testing, a hypothetical structural model that explains most of the present evidence is given in Figure 5. One interpretation of the subcrustal active zone is that it coincides with a brittle subducted slab with contemporary internal strain. It is not known how far eastward such a dipping slab could be reasonably postulated to extend, although the evidence presented in Figure 4 is that seismicity dies out about 100 km to the east. Speculation, based on the model in Figure 5 and the active volcanoes running from Mount Lassen in northern California northward into Oregon and Washington, hints at a structural continuum with increasingly steep dip under the Great Valley. If this is the case, very infrequent intermediate-focus earthquakes may occur below the Whiskeytown area (see Fig. 4)—perhaps as deep as those in Puget Sound.

The second structural model, shown in Figure 6, is for the Puget Sound region and summarizes much recent work (Crosson, 1972; Docket 50522, 1976). The largest earthquakes in northwest Washington in modern times have been those of

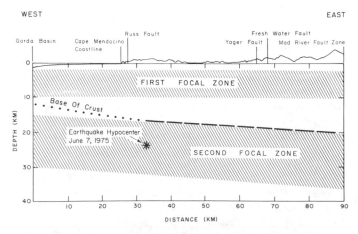

Figure 5. Conjectured model of tectonic structure in Humboldt County, northern California.

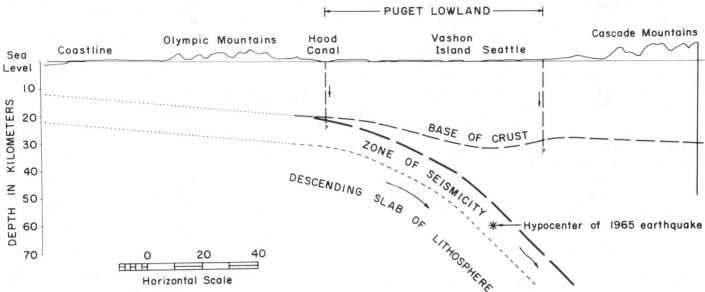

Figure 6. Conjectured model of tectonic structure of the Puget Sound region, Washington. Star shows focus of earthquakes (after J. Litehiser).

April 13, 1949, and April 29, 1965, centered in southern Puget Sound, with depths of about 60 km and surface-wave magnitudes of about 7.0 and 6.5, respectively. In earthquake risk assessment in the Puget Sound region, the question therefore arises whether earthquakes of this size could occur at more shallow depths or whether they are restricted for mechanical reasons to depths greater than 50 km. McKenzie and Julian (1971) presented evidence from seismic traveltime anomalies that a subduction zone might dip eastward under this area. Guided by measurements in analogous tectonic regions, the geometry of the subduction zone shown in Figure 6 is at least reasonable.

It is interesting to note that the foci of the 1949 and 1965 earthquakes fall in the section of maximum flexure of the postulated slab as it dips beneath the Puget lowland. The preferred focal mechanism of the 1965 earthquake (Algermissen and Harding, 1965) was tensional fracture (normal faulting) with northwest strike in agreement with observed mechanisms of earthquakes in similar sections of other subduction slabs. In addition, on May 16, 1976, for example, in the Georgia Straits (to the north of Puget Sound), an earthquake with a focal depth of 62 km and Richter magnitude 5.3 occurred at lat 48°48′N, long 123°21′W. The focus of this earthquake would also fall within the dipping slab if the curvature of the slab turned northeast to follow the continental margin.

REVISION OF PUBLISHED HYPOCENTERS

Scientific requirements and the needs of risk evaluation have recently demanded that many past solutions for hypocenters based on recorded traveltimes be revised for earthquakes in the western states. Such revisions may be worthwhile because more satisfactory crustal models and local traveltimes have become available. Computer programs and more robust computational algorithms for the location of earthquake foci have been developed and tested in the 1970s. A fruitful idea has been the use of "master" earthquakes: an explosion or earthquake whose location is known with high precision is used as a standard, and cross-correlation is made with traveltimes from either contemporary earthquakes or earthquakes from past times to reduce bias. An early example of the use of the method is the revision of the location of the 1906 San Francisco earthquake focus (Bolt, 1968) by comparison with measurements from the 1957 San Francisco earthquake. The revised solution placed the principal focus nearer to the Golden Gate than the earlier estimate (Coffman and von Hake, 1973) by H. F. Reid, which was near Olema to the north. (Fig. 1 shows the revised epicenter, Fig. 2 the original estimate.)

Another case is the suggested relocation of the central California coastal earthquake ($M_L = 7.3$) that occurred on November 4, 1927. Byerly (1930) calculated a location of the epicenter about 70 km west of Point Arguello based on the arrival times at three seismographic stations—Berkeley, California; Mount Hamilton, California; and Tucson, Arizona. Based on readings at overseas stations, the International Seismological Summary estimated the epicenter at lat 34.9°N, long 121.00°W. Gawthrop (1978), using the 1969 Santa Lucia Bank earthquake as a master event and weighting the stations, obtained a location at lat 34.95°N, long 120.7°W with an uncertainty of about 35 km. This solution yields consistently negative P residuals (early onsets) at many overseas stations, however, so the revision remains in doubt. Using traveltimes of S and P waves from local stations, Hanks (1978, written commun.) preferred a location off Point Arguello; this is consistent with the isoseismals.

A general improvement in the precision of hypocenter determination in the western states could be achieved if the area were divided into appropriate tectonic regions and the method of group estimation of hypocenters used (Bolt and others, 1978). With local networks, the method gives more consistent relative locations of epicenters, and the bias of the "center of mass" can be checked against master events when these become available. For teleseisms, Dewey (1972) has programmed an algorithm which is based on this method and which has been tested and proved to be very satisfactory. In one application, epicenters of 90 historical earthquakes in the Hebgen Lake–Yellowstone area (see Fig. 1) were recomputed using the method (Dewey and others, 1972). This suggested an east-trending zone north of the main Hebgen fault scarps. Similar algorithms and statistical methods should now be adopted for routine local earthquake determinations by regional networks (Dewey, this volume). A group location program with master events has been adopted at the Seismographic Station at Berkeley to routinely locate earthquakes since January 1977 in the central Coast Ranges of California.

ACKNOWLEDGMENTS

The crucial help of D. Seeburger (who re-edited the Townley and Allen catalogue under my supervision), R. Miller, and R. McKenzie with seismicity lists and maps is much appreciated. Diana C. Dale made available her paper on re-evaluation of historical earthquakes before its publication. Critical reviews were provided by O. Nuttli and J. Dewey. John Meeker is responsible for most of the work involved in Figure 4. This study was supported by National Science Foundation Grant EAR76-00118.

REFERENCES CITED

Adair, M. J., 1979, Geologic evaluation of a site for a nuclear power plant, in Hatheway, A. W., and McClure, C. R., Jr., eds., Geology in the siting of nuclear power plants: Geological Society of America Reviews in Engineering Geology, v. IV (this volume).

Algermissen, S. T., and Harding, S. T., 1965, The Puget Sound, Washington, earthquake of April 29, 1965: U.S. Coast and Geodetic Survey Preliminary Seismological Report, 26 p.

Allen, C. R., St. Armand, P., Richter, C. F., and Nordquist, J. M., 1965, Relationship between seismicity and geologic structure in the southern California region: Seismological Society of America Bulletin, v. 55, p. 753–798.

Asada, T., Bolt, B. A., Shimamura, H., Takano, K and Moriya, T., 1975, Earthquake studies in the Gorda Basin with ocean bottom seismographs [abs.]: EOS [American Geophysical Union Transactions], v. 56, p. 1024.

Auld, B., Latham, G., Nowroozi, A., and Seeber, L., 1969, Seismicity off the coast of northern California determined from ocean bottom seismic measurements: Seismological Society of America Bulletin, v. 59, p. 2001–2015.

Benioff, H., 1960, Observation of the Lamb-Pekeris ground-response pattern in the Yellowstone earthquake of August 18, 1959 [abs.]: Geological Society of America Bulletin, v. 71, p. 2049.

Berg, J. W., Jr., and Baker, C. D., 1963, Oregon earthquakes, 1841–1958: Seismological Society of America Bulletin, v. 53, p. 95–108.

Bolt, B. A., 1960, The revision of earthquake epicenters, focal depths and origin-times, using a high-speed computer: Royal Astronomical Society Geophysical Journal, v. 3, p. 433–440.

——1968, The focus of the 1906 California earthquake: Seismological Society of America Builletin, v. 58, p. 457–472.

Bolt, B. A., and Miller, R. D., 1971, Seismicity of northern California and central California, 1965–1969: Seismological Society of America Bulletin, v. 61, p. 1831–1847.

——1975, Catalog of earthquakes in northern California and adjoining areas, 1910–1972: Berkeley, University of California, Seismographic Station, Special Publication, 567 p.

Bolt, B. A., Lomnitz, C., and McEvilly, T. V., 1968, Seismological evidence on the tectonics of central and northern California and the Mendocino escarpment: Seismological Society of America Bulletin, v. 58, p. 1725–1767.

Bolt, B. A., Johnson, R. G., Lefter, J., and Sozen, M. A., 1975, The study of earthquake questions related to VA hospital facilities: Seismological Society of America Bulletin, v. 65, p. 937–950.

Bolt, B. A., Okubo, P., and Uhrhammer, 1978, Optimum station distribution and determination of hypocenters for small seismographic networks: U.S. Army Corps of Engineers Waterways Experiment Station, Geotechnical Laboratory, Miscellaneous Paper 2-78-9, p. 1–42.

Bufe, C. G., Pfluke, J. H., Lester, F. W., and Marks, S. M., 1976, Map showing preliminary hypocenters of earthquakes in the Healdsburg quadrangle, Lake Berryessa to Clear Lake, California: U.S. Geological Survey, Open-File Map 76-802, scale 1:100,000.

Byerly, P., 1930, The California earthquake of November 4, 1927: Seismological Society of America Bulletin, v. 20, p. 53–66.

Chandra, U., 1974, Seismicity, earthquake mechanisms and tectonics along the western coast of North America, from 42°N to 61°N: Seismological Society of America Bulletin v. 64, p. 1529–1549.

Cloud, W. K., 1960, Earthquake recorded by low-cost instrument [abs.]: Geological Society of America Bulletin, v. 71, p. 2054.

Coffman, J. L., and von Hake, C. A., 1973, Earthquake history of the United States: Washington, D.C., U.S. Department of Commerce Publication No. 41-1, revised edition (through 1970), 208 p.

Cook, K. L., and Smith, R. B., 1967, Seismicity in Utah, 1850 through June 1956: Seismological Society of America Bulletin, v. 57, p. 689–718.

Crosson, R. S., 1972, Small earthquakes, structure, and the tectonics of the Puget Sound region: Seismological Society of America Bulletin, v. 62, p. 1133–1171.

——1974, Compilation of earthquake hypocenters in western Washington: Washington Department of Natural Resources, Information Circular 56.

Dewey, J. W., 1972, Seismicity and tectonics of western Venezuela: Seismological Society of America Bulletin, v. 62, p. 1711–1752.

——1979, A consumer's guide to instrumental determination of hypocenters, in Hatheway, A. W., and McClure, C. R., Jr., eds., Geology in the siting of nuclear power plants: Geological Society of America Reviews in Engineering Geology, v. IV (this volume).

Dewey, J. W., Dillinger, W. H., Taggert, J., and Algermissen, S. T., 1972, A technique for seismic zoning: Analysis of earthquake locations and mechanisms in northern Utah, Wyoming, Idaho and Montana, in Proceedings, Microzonation Conference: Seattle, University of Washington, v. 2, p. 879–894.

Docket 50522, 1976, PSAR, Skagit NPS (units 1 and 2), Skagit County, Washington: Seattle, Washington, Puget Sound Power & Light Company.

Evernden, J., 1975, Seismic intensities, "size" of earthquakes and related parameters: Seismological Society of America Bulletin, v. 65, p. 1287–1313.

Gawthrop, W., 1978, The 1927 Lompoc, California, earthquake: Seismological Society of America Bulletin, v. 68, p. 1705–1716.

Gibbs, J. F., Healy, J. H., Raleigh, C. B., and Coakley, J., 1973, Seismicity in the Rangely, Colorado, area, 1962–1970: Seismological Society of America Bulletin, v. 63, p. 1557–1570.

Gutenberg, B., and Richter, C. F., 1954, Seismicity of the Earth: Princeton, N.J., Princeton University Press, 310 p.

Hileman, J. A., Allen, C., and Nordquist, J. M., 1973, Seismicity of the southern California region, 1 January 1932 to 31 December 1972: Pasadena, California Institute of Technology, Seismological Laboratory, 487 p.

Holden, E. S., 1898, A catalogue of earthquakes on the Pacific coast, 1769–1897: Smithsonian Institution, Miscellaneous Contribution 1087, 253 p.

Knopoff, L., 1964, The statistics of earthquakes in southern California: Seismological Society of America Bulletin, v. 54, p. 1871–1873.

Lander, J., 1960, Seismicity of the Great Plains [abs.]: Geological Society of America Bulletin, v. 71, p. 2037.

Lee, W.H.K., Meagher, K. L., Bennett, R. E., and Matamoros, E. E., 1972, Catalog of earthquakes along San Andreas fault system in central California for year 1971: U.S. Geological Survey Open-File Report, 67 p.

Lomnitz, C., and Bolt, B. A., 1967, Evidence on crustal structure in California from the Chase V explosion and the Chico earthquake of May 24, 1966: Seismological Society of America Bulletin, v. 57, p. 1093–1114.

Louderback, G. D., 1944, The reputed destructive earthquake of January 16–18, 1840: Seismological Society of America Bulletin, v. 34, p. 103–108.

Marine Advisors, Inc., 1965, Examination of tsunami potential at San Onofre Nuclear Generating Station: La Jolla, California, Southern California Edison Company, Report A-163.

McKenzie, D., and Julian, B., 1971, Puget Sound, Washington, earthquake and the mantle structure beneath the northwestern United States: Geological Society of America Bulletin, v. 82, p. 3519–3524.

McKenzie, D. P., and Morgan, W. T., 1969, The evolution of triple junctions: Nature, v. 224, p. 125–133.

Milne, W. G., 1956, Seismic activity in Canada, west of the 113th meridian, 1841–1951: Dominion Observatory Ottawa Publications, v. 18, no. 7, p. 119–146.

National Oceanic and Atmospheric Administration, 1969, Denver, Colorado, sustains most damaging shock in history: Earthquake Information Bulletin, v. 1, no. 8.

——1970a, Earthquake history of Arizona: Earthquake Information Bulletin, v. 2, no. 2, p. 26–27.

——1970b, Earthquake history of Colorado: Earthquake Information Bulletin, v. 2, no. 6, p. 24–27.

——1971, Earthquake history of California (p. 22–26); the California earthquake of February 9, 1971 (p. 3–9); the great San Francisco earthquake (p. 15–19): Earthquake Information Bulletin, v. 3, no. 2.

——1972, Earthquake history of Idaho: Earthquake Information Bulletin, v. 4, no. 2, p. 26–29.

Niazi, M., 1964, Seismicity of northern California and Nevada: Seismological Society of America Bulletin, v. 54, p. 845.

Nowroozi, A. A., 1973, Seismicity off the Mendocino escarpment and the aftershock sequence of June 26, 1968; ocean bottom seismic measurements: Seismological Society of America Bulletin, v. 63, p. 441–456.

Oakeshott, G. B., Greensfelder, R. W., and Kahle, J. E., 1972, The great Owens Valley earthquake, one hundred years later: California Geology, v. 25, p. 51–61.

Rasmussen, N., 1967, Washington state earthquakes, 1840–1965: Seismological Society of America Bulletin, v. 57, p. 463–476.

Real, C. R., and Toppozada, T., 1978, Earthquake catalog of California, January 1, 1900–December 31, 1974 (first edition): California Division of Mines and Geology Special Publication 52.

Ryall, A. S., and others, 1973, Bulletin of Seismological Laboratory, October 1 to December 31, 1971: Mackay School of Mines, University of Nevada, Reno, 48 p.

Simila, G. W., Peppin, W. A., and McEvilly, T. V., 1975, Seismotectonics of the Cape Mendocino, California area: Geological Society of America Bulletin, v. 86, p. 1399–1406.

Slemmons, D. B., Jones, A. E., and Gimlet, J. I., 1965, Catalog of Nevada earthquakes, 1852–1960: Seismological Society of America Bulletin, v. 55, p. 537–583.

Smith, B. E., Coakley, J. M., and Hamilton, R. M., 1972, Distribution, focal mechanisms and frequency of earthquakes in the Fairview Peak area, Nevada, near the time of the Benham explosion: Seismological Society of America Bulletin, v. 62, p. 1223–1240.

Smith, R. B., 1978, Seismicity, crustal structure, and intraplate tectonics of the interior of the western Cordillera, in Smith, R. B., and Eaton, G. P., eds., Cenozoic tectonics and regional geophysics of the western Cordillera: Geological Society of America Memoir 152, p. 111–144.

Smith, R. B., and Lindh, A. G., 1978, Fault-plane solutions of the Western United States: A compilation, in Smith, R. B., and Eaton, G. P., eds., Cenozoic tectonics and regional geophysics of the western Cordillera: Geological Society of America Memoir 152, p. 107–110.

Smith, R. B., and Sbar, M. L., 1974, Contemporary tectonics and seismicity of the intermountain seismic belt: Geological Society of America Bulletin, v. 85, p. 1205–1218.

Smith, S. W., 1975, Annual report, Humboldt Bay seismic network, August 1974–August 1975, to Pacific Gas and Electric Company: Berkeley, California, Tera Corp., Report TR-75-4013, 49 p.

Townley, S. D., and Allen, M. W., 1939, Descriptive catalogue of earthquakes of the Pacific coast of the United States, 1769 to 1928: Seismological Society of America Bulletin, v. 29, p. 1–297.

Trimble, A. B., and Smith, R. B., 1975, Seismicity and contemporary tectonics of the Hebgen Lake–Yellowstone Park region: Seismological Society of America Bulletin, v. 65, p. 733–741.

Uhrhammer, R. A., 1977, Seismicity in the vicinity of the Farallon Escarpment: Geophysical Research Letters, v. 4, p. 469–472.

Unger, J. D., and Mills, K. F., 1973, Earthquakes near Mount St. Helens, Washington: Geological Society of America Bulletin, v. 84, p. 1065–1068.

von Hake, C. A., 1974a, Earthquake history of Montana: Earthquake Information Bulletin, v. 6, no. 4, p. 30–34.

——1974b, Earthquake history of Nevada: Earthquake Information Bulletin, v. 6, no. 6, p. 26–29.

——1975, Earthquake history of New Mexico: Earthquake Information Bulletin, v. 7, no. 3, p. 23–26.

MANUSCRIPT RECEIVED BY THE SOCIETY JULY 13, 1978
MANUSCRIPT ACCEPTED NOVEMBER 13, 1978

Geological Society of America
Reviews in Engineering Geology, Volume IV
1979

A consumer's guide to instrumental methods for determination of hypocenters

JAMES W. DEWEY

U.S. Geological Survey, Denver Federal Center, Denver, Colorado 80225

ABSTRACT

In nuclear power plant siting, redetermination of hypocenters of instrumentally recorded earthquakes in the site region may be better than relying on routinely determined hypocenter locations listed in standard earthquake catalogues. Routinely determined hypocenters, particularly those of small earthquakes or of earthquakes occurring before the mid-1950s, may be so mislocated that they present a misleading picture of the seismotectonics of the site region. The preferred method for redetermining a hypocenter depends on the earthquake being considered. The hypocenters of many pre-1954 earthquakes may be more accurately redetermined by now-standard computerized location techniques that were not available when the earthquakes were initially catalogued. Some important earthquakes are so poorly recorded that they cannot be assigned a hypocenter that is mathematically unique; however, it may be possible to pose a hypothesis such that the significance of the earthquake to a proposed power plant can be tested without explicitly locating the earthquake. A well-recorded earthquake whose hypocenter is suspected of being biased by lateral variations of seismic wave velocities can be more accurately located by ray-tracing methods, provided that the lateral variations of velocity are known. In an attempt to infer a fault or seismic zone from a group of hypocenters, a relative-location method—such as the master-event method or joint hypocenter determination—should be used. All methods for determining hypocenters involve assumptions over which seismologists may disagree; in the safety analysis of a nuclear power plant, these assumptions must be explicitly discussed and shown to be conservative as to their implication for the design of the plant. In addition, confidence ellipses should be given for the hypocentral coordinates, in order to assess the errors that might occur even if the assumptions of the location method are correct.

WHY REDETERMINE HYPOCENTERS?

Locations of previous earthquakes are of great importance in defining the characteristics of the seismicity of a nuclear power plant site. Hypocenters[1] or epicenters[2] of historical earthquakes are used to assess the likelihood of future earthquakes on mapped geologic faults. These locations are used to determine whether earthquakes have occurred in one or more well-defined seismic zones in the site region or whether they may instead have occurred throughout the site region. A catalogue of earthquake hypocenters may be used to develop a broad tectonic model of the site region.

Earthquakes occurring worldwide are located routinely by the U.S. Geological Survey (USGS), which uses data contributed by seismological observatories around the world. Many seismological centers with local or regional networks of stations routinely compute, on their own, hypocenters of earthquakes occurring within their networks. Data compiled by the USGS and local or regional networks are collected by the International Seismological Centre (ISC), which publishes the "last word" in routinely determined hypocenters of earthquakes that have occurred anywhere in the world.

Unfortunately, some catalogued hypocenters may be seriously inaccurate, enough so as to cause misleading assessments of the seismic hazard associated with particular sites. This is likely to be the case especially for routinely determined hypocenters of small earthquakes that did not occur within a dense regional network of seismographic stations. The user of a catalogued hypocenter must remember, for example, that a magnitude 4.0 earthquake, which might be used to assess the activity of a fault passing near a nuclear power plant, was 1 of perhaps 10,000 earthquakes of that magnitude or larger to have occurred in 1 yr. At the time it occurred, the earthquake may have been considered of little importance and received only routine attention from the group locating it. In many cases, however, the hypocenter of such a previously "neglected" earthquake can be redetermined to much higher accuracy by use of techniques that are not yet routine in hypocenter determination. The present paper reviews several

---

[1] Hypocenter—the estimated point in the Earth from which seismic waves first originate.
[2] Epicenter—point on the Earth's surface vertically above the hypocenter.

methods by which improved hypocenter accuracy can be obtained.

LEAST–SQUARES DETERMINATION OF HYPOCENTERS

Let t = the time of origin of the earthquake, x = its latitude, y = its longitude, and z = its depth. Also let (t_0, x_0, y_0, z_0) = the coordinates of a provisional hypocenter. Then corrections (δt, δx, δy, δz) are calculated to obtain a better estimate of the true hypocenter of the earthquake. The simplest form for the equations of condition for (δt, δz, δy, δz) is

$$\delta t + f_{0j}(T)\,\delta x + g_{0j}(T)\,\delta y + h_{0j}(T)\delta z = r_j \qquad j = 1, J. \qquad (1)$$

J = the total number of stations; $f_{0j}(T)$, $g_{0j}(T)$, and $h_{0j}(T)$ = functions of the provisional hypocenter, the location of the jth station, and the theoretical traveltime T for an assumed velocity model for seismic waves passing through the Earth; and r_j = the residual, which is the observed arrival time of the earthquake waves at the jth station minus the theoretical arrival based on (t_0, x_0, y_0, z_0) and T.

Equation 1 is a first-order, or linear, approximation to a nonlinear equation. The unknowns are δt, δx, δy, δz; the other parameters are considered known, although all of them depend on assuming a velocity model for seismic waves in the Earth. A set of more than four simultaneous equations, each in the form of equation 1, is usually solved by the method of least squares so as to minimize the sum of the residuals, Σr_j^2. The computed corrections (δt, δx, δy, δz) are used to adjust the old provisional hypocenter to obtain a new one, and the whole process is repeated until a convergence criterion is met.

REASONS FOR ERRORS IN HYPOCENTERS

Earthquakes Poorly Recorded

Some earthquakes have not been well-enough recorded by the global network of seismographs to permit accurate location from instrumental data. The number of stations (J in eq. 1) may be fewer than four, or the earthquake may have been recorded by stations from only a few regions of the globe, so that many of the J equations of condition are almost linearly dependent.

Modern-day poorly recorded shocks are usually small earthquakes occurring in regions with few seismographs. For example, the teleseismic epicenter of the Managua, Nicaragua, earthquake of January 4, 1968, was computed to lie about 50 km from the actual epicenter (Fig. 1). This earthquake, though locally damaging (Algermissen and Brown, 1970; Algermissen and others, 1974), was at the threshold of detection for the global seismographic network. Another class of modern-day earthquakes that are often seriously mislocated are small shocks that were recorded only by the stations of a local array but that occurred outside the limits of the array (Peters and Crosson, 1972; Buland, 1976).

Going back in time to when the number of seismograph

stations was much smaller, seismographs less sensitive, and seismograph clocks less reliable, one finds that some very destructive earthquakes were so poorly recorded that their positions cannot be determined to within 100 km from instrumental data. For example, the instrumental epicenter of the disastrous Managua, Nicaragua, earthquake of March 31, 1931, is listed in some catalogues as lat 13.2°N, long 85.8°W, which is 130 km from the true position at Managua (Fig. 1). A computer search for all epicenters within 100 km of Managua would fail to list the earthquake of March 31, 1931, which destroyed much of the town and killed more than 1,000 people (Freeman, 1932). Conversely, by listing the epicenter of the 1931 earthquake at lat 13.2°N, long 85.8°W, the catalogues suggest a higher risk than is probably justified for that location.

When earthquakes are recorded only by seismographs from a limited range of azimuths, errors in latitude may be strongly correlated with errors in longitude. Computed epicenters of earthquakes occurring even at a point source would then be distributed in an elongated ellipse suggestive of a fault zone where none exists.

Earthquakes Never Individually Located

Epicenters of some earthquakes occurring in the first half of the twentieth century have never been specifically determined. Before the days of electronic computers, it was the practice of the International Seismological Summary (ISS), the predecessor of the ISC, to specifically locate only the first earthquake from a region and assign subsequent shocks from the same source region to the epicenter of the first shock. This practice may cause errors of many tens of kilometres in the listed epicenters of subsequent earthquakes. These errors may be corrected simply by redetermining the location of the subsequent earthquakes with a standard computer program (for example, Bolt, 1960; Engdahl and Gunst, 1966; Herrin and others, 1962). The ISS used a computer to individually locate large earthquakes occurring in 1954–1963, but the ISS catalogues for this period are not complete for earthquakes of magnitude less than 6.

Inappropriate Velocity Model Assumed in Location Process

Locations of hypocenters from a source region may be systematically biased by kilometres or even tens of kilometres because of variations of seismic wave velocity through the Earth that are not accounted for in the theoretical traveltime T in equation 1. In effect, the Earth acts as a distorting lens to seismic waves. Systematic location bias may exist even for earthquakes that are widely recorded. For example, the epicenter of the Managua, Nicaragua, earthquake of December 23, 1972, was computed by routine methods to lie about 25 km northeast of the true position in Managua (Fig. 1; Algermissen and others, 1974). The 1972 Managua earthquake was widely recorded; the error in its computed location is apparently not due to erratic arrival-time data but rather to seismic P waves traveling with a higher velocity through the material toward the northeast and with a lower velocity through the material lying in other directions. There may be nothing in the character of arrival-time data or in the distribution of seismographic stations to suggest that the location of a particular earthquake is biased by an inappropriate velocity model.

Linear Approach to Nonlinear Problem

Some classes of earthquake-location problems are highly nonlinear, so that the first-order equations of condition, such as equation 1, are valid only if the provisional hypocenter is very near the true position. Otherwise, the location method may converge to different solutions for different, physically reasonable provisional hypocenters. This is a particular difficulty in the location of local earthquakes with data from small networks.

Poor Determination of Focal Depth

Even if the epicenter of an earthquake is accurately determined, the focal depth may be poorly determined. For earthquakes occurring in the uppermost 50 km of the Earth, the focal depth is particularly hard to determine solely from teleseismically recorded P waves.

STRATEGIES FOR IMPROVING HYPOCENTER DETERMINATIONS OF POORLY RECORDED EARTHQUAKES

Additional Data

Arrival-time data are published in bulletins of the ISC (or of its predecessor the ISS) and in the *Earthquake Data Report* of the USGS [or of its predecessors in routine epicenter determination, the U.S. Coast and Geodetic Survey (USCGS) and the National Oceanic and Atmospheric Administration (NOAA)]. If these compiled data are not sufficient to accurately locate an earthquake, additional data should be sought from the bulletins of seismological observatories near the region of the earthquake. One should also try to read seismograms from stations near the earthquake that did not originally report data to bulletins, on the chance that seismic waves from the earthquake were overlooked.

For earthquakes that occurred before 1919, Gutenberg and Richter (1954) found that compilation of earthquake data was incomplete, and they had to search bulletins of individual seismographic stations to supplement data listed in compilations. Gutenberg and Richter (1954, p. 5) listed the types of data available in individual station bulletins.

For earthquakes occurring from 1919 to 1952, arrival-time data were compiled quite completely by the ISS.

For earthquakes occurring from 1953 to 1963, arrival-time data were compiled by the ISS only for earthquakes of magnitude 6.0 or greater, except for smaller shocks of unusual significance. The bulletins of the Bureau Central International Seismologique (BCIS) for this period include data on many smaller shocks that are not listed by the ISS, again with data compiled from bulletins of individual seismological centers.

Since 1964, the USGS (and its predecessors) and the ISC have been publishing arrival times for every earthquake they can locate from the data sent to them. In addition, for earthquakes that occurred since the early 1960s, seismograms of the World-wide Standardized Seismograph Network (WWSSN) are readily available from the Environmental Data Service of NOAA. Traveltimes from some of the WWSSN stations are not regularly reported to the USGS or ISC; in reading these seismograms, one often finds important data not listed in the compilations of the USGS or ISC.

Subsidiary Phases

The USGS and the ISC use only the arrival times of initial P waves and pP phases in routine hypocenter determination. Most later-arriving P waves, S waves, and surface waves are not used in routine hypocenter determination because their identification is sometimes uncertain, their velocities are often not as well determined as those of the initial P wave, and the statistical properties of their arrival times are not well known.

On the other hand, for poorly recorded earthquakes, the use of later-arriving phases may significantly improve location accuracy (James and others, 1969; von Seggern, 1972). In principle, provided the above-mentioned problems are overcome, the use of later-arriving phases together with initial P waves permits better determination of hypocenters from station networks that are poorly distributed with respect to the earthquakes. The use of later-arriving phases may more than double the number of readings for a particular earthquake; much more confidence may thereby be placed in the precision of the solution.

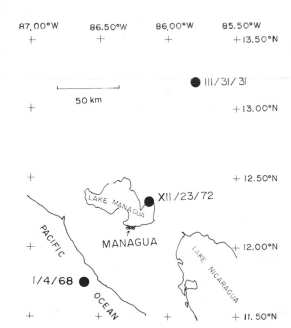

Figure 1. Epicenters of three damaging Nicaraguan earthquakes determined from instrumentally recorded data. Independent evidence indicates that all three earthquakes occurred in, or within several kilometres of, Managua. Errors in the instrument determined epicenters of III/31/31 (ISS) and I/4/68 (ISC) are due to these earthquakes not being well-recorded by the global network of seismographs. Error in the instrument-determined epicenter of XII/23/72 (ISC) is due to lateral variations of seismic wave velocity not accounted for in the routine location procedure.

Figures 2 and 3 show a particularly impressive example of the use of subsidiary phases in redetermination of hypocenters. The above-mentioned problems with subsidiary phases were minimized by the use of joint hypocenter determination (see below, under Strategies for Minimizing Location Bias . . .).

The epicenters shown in Figures 2 and 3 are those of the Dulce, New Mexico, earthquake of January 23, 1966, and aftershocks that occurred within 4 d of the main shock. A seismotectonic study based on the routinely determined epicenters of the ISC (Fig. 2) might conclude that the source area associated with the Dulce earthquake was over 2,000 km^2. (The routinely determined USCGS epicenters for these earthquakes show similar scatter.) However, there was good reason to think that the earthquakes shown in Figure 2 had actually occurred in a small region, because they were aftershocks to a moderate earthquake ($M = 5\frac{1}{2}$) and were felt in a small area (von Hake and Cloud, 1968). Figure 3 confirms that the early aftershocks occured in a small area, probably less than 100 km^2.

The improvements in the locations of the Dulce earthquakes were obtained by using the phases $\bar{P}$ (as defined by Pakiser, 1963) and the corresponding shear wave phase $\bar{S}$ in addition to the first-arriving P_n phase, which was the only phase used by the ISC to locate most of the hypocenters. For these earthquakes, the $\bar{P}$ and $\bar{S}$ phases were remarkably consistent— the sample variances for the $\bar{P}$ and $\bar{S}$ phases were as small as that for the P_n. For most of the earthquakes, the use of $\bar{P}$ and $\bar{S}$ phases more than doubled the number of readings. In computing the original hypocenters, the $\bar{P}$ phases of small earthquakes at some stations were misinterpreted as P_n, the real P_n being lost in the seismic noise. In the recomputation, I made the following decision: if a station reported an emersive P_n and an impulsive $\bar{P}$ for larger aftershocks, but only an impulsive "P_n" for small aftershocks, I assumed that the phase reported as P_n was in fact $\bar{P}$.

It must be emphasized that the value of using later arrivals in hypocenter calculation depends on the later arrivals being correctly identified and read with high consistency. If the sample variance of the traveltime residuals of a later-arriving phase is high (which suggests either that the phase is misidentified or that the arrival time of the phase is difficult to measure accurately), the readings of that later-arriving phase should receive correspondingly low weights in the computation of the hypocenter.

Different Provisional Hypocenter or Computational Method

If, starting with a certain provisional hypocenter in equation 1, a satisfactory solution cannot be obtained for an earthquake recorded by a sparse local network, a satisfactory hypocenter may sometimes be obtained by changing the provisional hypocenter. Buland (1976) has proposed in addition that the location of hypocenters from data of small local networks would be much more efficient and stable if, in hypocenter-location programs, seismologists used several new computational algorithms developed by numerical analysts for least-squares solution of a system of equations such as equation 1.

Testing Hypotheses with Sparse Data

As a last resort, if data for a particular earthquake are too sparse to permit determination of a hypocenter, one may sometimes frame a hypothesis that can be tested with the sparse data without actually determining a hypocenter.

For example, a particular poorly recorded earthquake may be of concern only because it might have occurred on a geologically mapped fault that passes near a plant site. Traveltime data from only one or two seismographic stations may be sufficient to establish that the earthquake did not occur on the fault, even if these data do not establish where the earthquake did occur. One would seek to select, from the infinite number of hypocenters consistent with the sparse data, that hypocenter which is nearest the geologically mapped fault. One also needs an estimate of the precision to which that

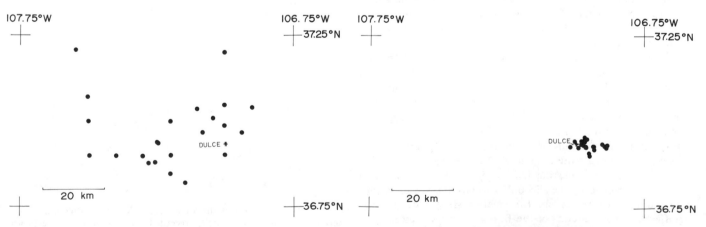

Figure 2. Epicenters that were routinely determined by the ISC for regionally recorded earthquakes occurring near Dulce, New Mexico, January 23–26, 1966. Figure 3 shows redetermined epicenters of these same earthquakes.

Figure 3. Epicenters of earthquakes shown in Figure 2, determined by the method of joint hypocenter determination, using P_n, $\bar{P}$, and $\bar{S}$ phases from regional stations. Small aftershocks located by Tosimatu Matumoto (written commun.) were used to constrain these epicenters to the region immediately to the east of, and including, Dulce. All the epicenters are estimated to be accurate to within 10 km, at a 90% level of confidence.

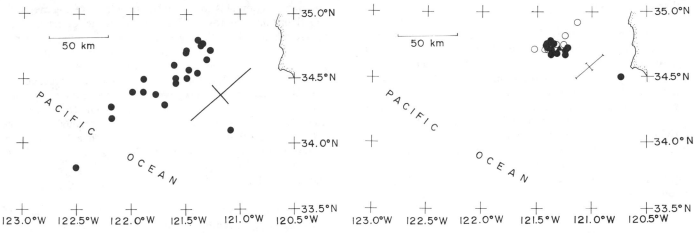

Figure 4. An example of a spurious lineament of hypocenters caused by the correlation of errors in latitude with errors in longitude. These are epicenters computed by the ISC (those computed by the USCGS were similar) with *P*-wave arrivals from 10 or more stations. The earthquakes occurred off the coast of central California in October–December 1969. Redetermined epicenters of these earthquakes are shown in Figure 5. Principal axes of a typical 90% confidence ellipse for the epicentral coordinates of these earthquakes are plotted southeast of the principal zone of epicenters.

Figure 5. The earthquakes shown in Figure 4, redetermined by the method of joint hypocenter determination. Solid symbols represent those epicenters whose 90% confidence ellipses have semi-axes less than 15 km long. Principal axes of a typical confidence ellipse are plotted to the southeast of the principal group of aftershocks. The calibration event for these epicenters is the earthquake of November 05, 1969, 17:54 GMT, whose epicenter (triangle) was restrained to the ISC epicenter at lat 34.72°N, long 121.28°W.

"nearest hypocenter" can be determined under the assumption that the sparse data may contain errors. If the nearest hypocenter is significantly far from the fault, as indicated by the estimate of precision, then one may reject the hypothesis that the poorly recorded earthquake occurred on the fault.

Bolt (1970) discussed the problem of "locating" sparsely recorded earthquakes by use of the generalized inverse matrix; he solved the particular case of determining that hypocenter (with three stations) or epicenter (with two stations) which is nearest a postulated point in the Earth or on the Earth's surface. His equations may be used in testing, for example, how close to a plant site the hypocenter of an earthquake recorded by only three stations could be.

STRATEGIES FOR DETECTING SPURIOUS LINEAMENTS CAUSED BY CORRELATION OF ERRORS IN HYPOCENTRAL COORDINATES

Confidence Ellipses

An eccentric confidence ellipse (see section entitled Estimating Precision of Hypocenters, below) parallel to an elongated group of hypocenters plotted on a map or cross section is a warning that the fault suggested by the hypocenters may be spurious, a result of correlation of errors in hypocentral coordinates. Such correlations of errors arise when seismographic stations are unevenly distributed in distance and azimuth relative to the earthquakes being located so that the seismograph network can resolve hypocentral errors in some directions better than in other directions. The epicenters plotted in Figure 4, for example, are more than 100 km from the nearest seismograph, and most of the associated earthquakes were recorded

only by stations to the north and east. From the principal axes of the confidence ellipse in Figure 4, one sees that small errors in the arrival-time data for an earthquake may cause a large mislocation to the northeast or southwest.

Relative-Location Methods

Relative-location methods reduce the effects of systematic arrival-time anomalies in the readings from a station. The systematic anomalies are no longer "errors" in the mathematical model used in the location process, and the errors in computed hypocenters are correspondingly reduced. Use of relative-location methods cannot, of course, change the configuration of seismographic stations that recorded the earthquake. Therefore, the hypocenters computed with a relative-location method will still tend to be mislocated in certain directions, which are indicated by the confidence ellipses. Figure 5 shows the result of relocating the epicenters of Figure 4 by joint hypocenter determination (a relative-location method discussed in more detail in the section Strategies for Minimizing Location Bias). Figure 5 indicates that the northeast-striking trend seen in Figure 4 is spurious, as had been suggested by the confidence ellipses of the epicenters. In fact, the elongation in the principal cluster of epicenters in Figure 5 that is statistically significant at the 90% confidence level is the west-northwest elongation nearly perpendicular to the major axis of the confidence ellipse. The revised hypocenters are also consistent with a study of these earthquakes by Gawthrop and Engdahl (1975), who greatly added to the data used in locating the earthquakes in Figure 5 and who made a convincing case for a northwest-trending fault as the source of most of these earthquakes. The isolated earthquake near lat 34.5°N, long 120.7°W is evidently from a different source than the other shocks.

Subsidiary Phases

If subsidiary phases such as S are correctly identified and consistently read, they may help minimize the tendency for hypocenters to be mislocated in certain directions. Subsidiary phases are particularly useful when earthquakes are located outside of the network of recording stations. In this case, the P waves alone can be used to satisfactorily determine only the direction of earthquakes from the seismographic network; arrival times of subsidiary phases or time intervals between phases (such as the time interval between the arrival of the P wave and the S wave) also enable one to make a good estimate of the distance of the earthquakes from the stations in the network.

STRATEGIES FOR MINIMIZING LOCATION BIAS CAUSED BY LATERAL VARIATIONS OF SEISMIC WAVE VELOCITIES

Ray-tracing

One may compute theoretical traveltimes by ray-tracing through an Earth model that contains lateral variations in velocity (for example, Jacob, 1970; Julian, 1970; Sorrels and others, 1971, Aki and Lee, 1976, Engdahl and Lee, 1976). With knowledge of the variation of velocity between a seismic source and a seismographic station, one may compute traveltimes that are more appropriate to the source-station pair than are the "worldwide-average" traveltimes normally used in hypocenter determination. Ray-tracing may thereby be used to obtain hypocenters unbiased by lateral variations of seismic wave velocity. Engdahl (1973) has shown how ray-tracing methods may be incorporated directly into a hypocenter-location program.

For a nuclear power plant safety analysis, ray-tracing will be most effective if (1) the earthquakes to be located are well-recorded, so that any mislocations would be the result of velocity anomalies rather than reading or timing errors, and (2) the velocity model used in the ray-tracing can be convincingly supported. For example, it is clear (Herrin and Taggart, 1962) that upper-mantle P-wave velocities in the western United States change quite rapidly between different tectonic provinces and that these changes may cause location biases of tens of kilometres. Although much study remains to clarify the detail of these velocity changes, they are probably sufficiently well known that ray-tracing methods could be used to reduce the location bias for earthquakes in the western United States (Herrin and Taggart, 1962).

Ray tracing would also be effective for analysis of seismicity of power plant sites near subduction zones. There is strong evidence (For example, Davies and McKenzie, 1969) that high seismic wave velocities associated with inclined seismic zones (Benioff zones) produce systematic bias of tens of kilometres in hypocenters computed for earthquakes in the zones. Unfortunately, beyond the existence of high velocities in the inclined seismic zones, the variations of seismic velocities in subduction zones are not well known. As a result, for a nuclear power plant site near a subduction zone, one cannot confidently claim

to predict location bias to within 10 km by ray-tracing methods. Instead, one may use ray-tracing to get an "order of magnitude" understanding of how the high velocity in the inclined seismic zone will bias routinely computed hypocenters. Does the high-velocity zone produce, in general, location bias toward or away from the plant site, and how does the presence of such bias affect the conservativeness of the vibratory ground motion for which the plant is to be designed? To answer these questions, one would use ray-tracing through a simple model, such as that of Engdahl (1973), with a high-velocity slab corresponding to the inclined seismic zone.

Relative-Location Methods

A "calibration event" of known location may be used to remove from hypocenters of neighboring events the location bias due to regional variations of seismic wave velocity. The other events are located relative to the calibration event; if the calibration event is mislocated, the other events will be systematically mislocated in the same way as the calibration event. Relative-location methods generally assume that a travel time anomaly at a station is the same for a particular calibration event and all earthquakes located with that calibration event. The greater the distance between hypocenters of two seismic events, the more likely it is that this assumption will be violated.

The master-event method of earthquake location (Evernden, 1969b) is the simplest to use of the relative-location methods; the traveltimes of the earthquakes to be located are adjusted by subtracting traveltime residuals of the calibration event, and the earthquakes are located by a conventional location program. For optimal use of the master-event method, the calibration event must be clearly recorded by the stations that are used to locate the other earthquakes, and the statistical properties of the traveltime data must be known so that weighting functions can be developed to minimize the effect of extreme residuals (Dewey, 1971). In practice these conditions are often sufficiently well met that the master-event method can be used with confidence.

Joint hypocenter determination (Douglas, 1967; Dewey, 1971, 1972) is the preferred location method when the calibration event is not recorded by many of the stations that are to be used in the relocation of a group of earthquakes. In joint hypocenter determination, one computes simultaneously the epicenters of a group of earthquakes and traveltime adjustments for the stations used in locating the earthquakes. The joint computation of hypocenters and station adjustments enables one to use data from stations that recorded the calibration event to compute adjustments to traveltimes at stations that did not record the calibration event; it is not necessary that all stations used in the joint computation have recorded the calibration event. For example, one may wish to relocate earthquakes occurring over several decades, during which the global network of seismographic stations has changed appreciably. To do so, one exploits the overlaps in the time periods for which the different stations were operating to compute simultaneously the epicenters of the earthquakes and station adjustments for all the stations used. I have satisfactorily determined 15 hypocenters and 100 station adjustments at a time with the current version of the program that I described earlier (Dewey, 1971). Joint treatment of a group of hypocenters should be used when the statistical properties of the arrival times are not sufficiently well known to construct a function to weight observations. By treating a large number of data simultaneously, one may reliably estimate the variance of observations for use in weighting functions. This is particularly important when subsidiary phases are to be used in the location process, for it is often difficult to estimate from prior experience the variances of observations of subsidiary phases.

For regions with a dense seismographic network and many different seismic sources, a form of joint hypocenter determination may be used to estimate unbiased earthquake hypocenters, station adjustments, and, in addition, corrections to a provisional velocity structure (Lilwall and Douglas, 1970; Crosson, 1976). The revised velocity structure may then be used to obtain improved hypocenter estimates for earthquakes occurring before the installation of the dense seismographic network.

Relative-location methods may frequently be used advantageously even when there is not a calibration event with a reliable location known to be unbiased. In this case, the absolute location of all events will be systematically in error in the same way as the calibration event, but the relative precision of the hypocenter will be improved, sometimes dramatically. This will allow inferences to be made on the tectonic structure that produced the earthquakes. For example, the absolute position of the group of Dulce, New Mexico, epicenters shown in Figure 3 is uncertain by several kilometres because the position of the calibration event is uncertain by that amount. The important inference to be drawn from Figure 3 is that the Dulce earthquakes occurred in a very limited area and that the large source region suggested by the routinely determined epicenters of these earthquakes (Fig. 2) is spurious.

WHAT TO DO WHEN THE COMPUTED HYPOCENTER CHANGES WITH THE CHOICE OF PROVISIONAL HYPOCENTER

For a widely recorded earthquake, any reasonable choice of provisional hypocenter will lead to convergence at the same hypocenter when the same location algorithm is used. For a poorly recorded earthquake, however, adequate convergence may require that the provisional hypocenter be quite close to the final hypocenter. For the poorly recorded earthquake, starting the location process at different seismologically plausible provisional hypocenters may lead to convergence to different computed hypocenters. Fortunately, many of these final computed hypocenters will be obviously "suspicious" because they will have associated with them very high standard errors of the traveltime residuals. If a nonlinear problem of this sort is suspected, a number of different provisional hypocenters should be tried for a particular earthquake, including some provisional hypocenters that are consistent with a "worst-case" tectonic model. For example, if the activity of a certain fault is to be determined, then provisional hypocenters of the earthquake should be set on different segments of the fault, in order to test the possibility that the earthquake may have occurred on the fault.

STRATEGIES FOR ESTIMATING ACCURATE FOCAL DEPTHS

The easiest way to estimate accurate focal depths from teleseismic data is to use depth-phases such as pP or sP (Jeffreys and Bullen, 1958; Herrin and others, 1968). To avoid the possibility of misidentifying other phases as pP or sP, observations of possible depth-phases should be made at stations at different distances from the epicenter.

Focal depths more accurate than those routinely determined from P waves alone may be obtained by using such subsidiary phases as $\bar{P}$ or S (see strategies for Improving Hypocenter Determinations . . .) and by using relative-location methods (see Strategies for Minimizing Location Bias . . .).

Valuable and essentially independent estimates of focal depths of earthquakes occurring in the Earth's crust may be obtained by comparing recorded seismograms with synthetic seismograms (for example, Helmberger, 1974; Langston, 1976) or by performing spectral analyses of seismic surface waves (Tsai and Aki, 1970; Massé and others, 1973).

If the focal depth of a crustal earthquake cannot be determined to closer than 15 km, the effect of an incorrect focal depth on the teleseismically determined epicenter is likely to be minimal. For a poorly recorded earthquake, it is better to estimate the focal depth at a geophysically reasonable value rather than trying to compute the focal depth from inadequate data. For example, the focal depths of the earthquakes in Figure 5 were restrained to 5 km; the epicenters are nearly identical to what would have been computed if the focal depths had been restrained to 20 km.

ESTIMATING PRECISION OF HYPOCENTERS

A computed hypocenter should be accompanied by an estimate of how accurate it is likely to be. A valuable estimate of hypocentral precision is given by the α percent joint marginal confidence ellipses on pairs of hypocentral coordinates (Flinn, 1965; Everndsen, 1969a), where α corresponds to a statistical level of confidence. For example, principal axes of 90% joint marginal confidence ellipses on the epicentral coordinates are plotted in Figures 4 and 5 for a typical earthquake in each group. When the axes are centered on the computed epicenter, the area within the confidence ellipse is an estimate of the area within which the true epicenter should be located at 90% level of confidence.

In Figures 4 and 5, the axes of the confidence ellipses show that the epicenters are likely to be much more in error in the northeast-southwest directions than in the northwest-southeast direction; the confidence ellipses are thus important aids in interpreting patterns of hypocenters. If focal depth is an important parameter for a particular hypocenter, then one should compute confidence ellipses for the pairs of coordinates latitude-depth and longitude-depth.

The advantage of confidence ellipses over the more commonly used estimates of the standard error of hypocentral coordinates is that the confidence ellipses show the directions in which errors are likely to be greatest and those in which errors are likely to be least. Neither type of estimate of hypocentral precision takes into account the possibility of location bias caused by an inappropriate model of seismic wave velocity. Similarly, in a relative-location method, such as those discussed above, the estimates of hypocentral precision cannot detect a mislocation of the calibration event; rather they estimate the precision of computed hypocenters relative to the calibration event. The sizes of both the confidence ellipses and estimated standard errors depend on how the statistical properties of the traveltime observations are estimated (Evernden, 1969a).

Most estimates of precision of computed hypocenters, such as confidence ellipses or standard errors, assume that the location problem is nearly linear (Flinn, 1965). Because local earthquake location is frequently nonlinear, Lee and Lahr (1975) have included in their widely used HYPO71 computer program an option to test whether points in the vicinity of a computed hypocenter may actually be more consistent with the traveltime data than the computed hypocenter itself. This option, the "map of auxiliary RMS values," is an important aid in identifying poorly determined hypocenters and should be used in local earthquake location with sparse networks.

HOW MUCH ACCURACY CAN THE CONSUMER EXPECT?

In contemplating the redetermination of hypocenters of earthquakes occurring near a power plant site, one must first be aware of the accuracy that is likely to be attained with the data that are available. In general, the further back in time the earthquake, the more difficult it will be to obtain accurate locations.

As a rough guide to the level of accuracy attainable with the methods discussed in this paper, consider a magnitude 6.5 earthquake occurring in the Northern Hemisphere. Assume that the problem of location bias due to lateral variations of seismic wave velocities has been removed by one of the methods discussed above (see Strategies for Minimizing Location Bias . . .). The level of precision to which the epicenter can be determined at a 90% level of confidence is highly dependent on the location of the earthquake with respect to the global network of seismographic stations, but it might be expected that the epicenter of such an earthquake occurring today could be located with instrument-recorded data to within 5 or 10 km of the true epicenter. The same earthquake, recorded by the seismographic network of the 1950s would be locatable with a precision of between 10 and 20 km. Recorded by the seismographic network of the 1930s, this earthquake would be locatable with a precision of between 20 and 30 km. If the earthquake had been recorded by the global network that existed prior to 1930, the epicenter would probably not be locatable to within 30 km by using only arrival-time data recorded by seismographs. In each case, the error in focal depth is likely to exceed the error in the epicentral coordinates. These estimates of hypocentral accuracy do not mean, of course, that more nearly correct locations cannot be obtained for some early earthquakes, but they do indicate the limits

that the quality of traveltime data may impose on even the most sophisticated location methods. One should set against the above figures the fact that many pre-1950 epicenters located by the ISS or Gutenberg and Richter (1954) are not accurate to within 100 km (Gutenberg and Richter, 1954, p. 11).

CONCLUSION

The special redetermination, by any of the techniques discussed above, of an earthquake epicenter that is crucial to the design of a nuclear power plant should be accompanied by a detailed analysis of factors on which the computed hypocenter depends:

1. The manner in which focal depth is determined should be discussed.

2. A confidence ellipse on the epicentral coordinates should be computed to show the kind of error the epicenter might have because of random normal errors in the arrival-time data. If focal depth is an important parameter, confidence ellipses should be computed for latitude-depth and longitude-depth. Possible violations of the statistical assumptions (Flinn, 1965; Evernden, 1969a) used in the construction of confidence ellipses should be discussed.

3. Justification must be given for the throwing away of any data whose inclusion in the hypocenter location process would significantly change the computed hypocenter.

4. The effect of hypocenter mislocation due to systematic traveltime anomalies will not appear in the computed confidence ellipses. Therefore, if the hypocenter has been redetermined by a relative-location technique, uncertainty in the epicenter of the calibration event must be explicitly discussed. If the hypocenter has been determined by ray-tracing techniques, uncertainties in the assumed velocity model must be explicitly discussed as well as the effects that errors in the velocity model would have on the computed hypocenter.

5. If the hypocenter has been determined with a sparse local network of seismographs, it should be demonstrated that the computer program has not converged to a grossly incorrect solution because of the nonlinearity of the local hypocenter-determination problem.

ACKNOWLEDGMENTS

I thank William Gawthrop for discussion on the 1969 San Luis Banks earthquakes off the coast of California; his criticism of my initial hypothesis on these earthquakes caused me to reconsider and revise a statistical weighting scheme with which I was experimenting. He also let me experiment with his own data for these earthquakes.

Tosimatu Matumoto kindly gave me the results of an unpublished study on the Dulce, New Mexico, earthquakes.

I gratefully acknowledge helpful reviews by Bruce Bolt, Bruce Julian, Joe Litehiser, Phil Romig, and James Taggart.

REFERENCES CITED

Aki, K., and Lee, W.H.K., 1976, Determination of three-dimensional velocity anomalies under a seismic array using first P arrival times from local earthquakes; 1, A homogeneous initial model: Journal of Geophysical Research, v. 81, p. 4381–4399.

Algermissen, S. T., and Brown, R. D., 1970, The Managua, Nicaragua, earthquake of January 4, 1968 ([abs.]: Seismological Society of America, Program, Annual Meeting, Hayward, California.

Algermissen, S. T., Dewey, J. W., Langer, C. J., and Dillinger, W. H., 1974, The Managua, Nicaragua, earthquake of December 23, 1972: Location, focal mechanism, and intensity distribution: Seismological Society of America Bulletin, v. 64, p. 993–1004.

Bolt, B. A., 1960, The revision of earthquake epicenters, focal depth, and origin times using a high-speed computer: Geophysical Journal, v. 3, p. 433–440.

——1970, Earthquake location for small networks using the generalized inverse matrix: Seismological Society of America Bulletin, v. 60, p. 1823–1828.

Buland, R., 1976, The mechanics of locating earthquakes: Seismological Society of America Bulletin, v. 66, p. 173–187.

Crosson, R. S., 1976, Crustal structure modeling of earthquake data; 1, Simultaneous least-squares estimation of hypocenter and velocity parameters: Journal of Geophysical Research, v. 81, p. 3036–3046.

Davies, D., and McKenzie, D. P., 1969, Seismic travel-time residuals and plates: Royal Astronomical Society Geophysical Journal, v. 18, p. 51–63.

Dewey, J. W., 1971, Seismicity studies with the method of joint hypocenter determination [Ph.D. dissert.]: Berkeley, University of California, 164 p.

——1972, Seismicity and tectonics of western Venezuela: Seismological Society of America Bulletin, v. 62, p. 1711–1751.

Douglas, A., 1967, Joint Epicenter determination: Nature, v. 215, p. 47–48.

Engdahl, E. R., 1973, Relocation of intermediate depth earthquakes in the central Aleutians by seismic ray tracing: Nature, v. 245, p. 23–25.

Engdahl, E. R., and Gunst, R. H., 1966, Use of a high speed computer for the preliminary determination of earthquake hypocenters: Seismological Society of America Bulletin, v. 56, p. 325–336.

Engdahl, E. R., and Lee, W.H.K., 1976, Relocation of local earthquakes by seismic ray tracing: Journal of Geophysical Research, v. 81, p. 4400–4406.

Evernden, J. F., 1969a, Precision of epicenters obtained by small numbers of world-wide stations: Seismological Society of America Bulletin, v. 59, p. 1365–1398.

——1969b, Identification of earthquakes and explosions by use of teleseismic data: Journal of Geophysical Research, v. 74, p. 3828–3856.

Flinn, E. A., 1965, Confidence regions and error determinations for seismic event location: Reviews of Geophysics, v. 3, p. 157–185.

Freeman, J. R., 1932, Earthquake damage and earthquake insurance: New York, McGraw-Hill.

Gawthrop, W. H., and Engdahl, E. R., 1975, The 1927 Lompoc earthquake and the 1969 San Luis Bank earthquake sequence, a comparative study [abs]: EOS (American Geophysical Union Transactions), v. 56, p. 1028.

Gutenberg, B., and Richter, C. F., 1954, Seismicity of the earth and associated phenomena: Princeton, N.J., Princeton University Press, 310 p.

Helmberger, D. V., 1974, Generalized ray theory for shear dislocations: Seismological Society of America Bulletin, v. 64, p. 45–64.

Herrin, E., and Taggart, J., 1962, Regional variations in P_n velocity and their effect on the location of epicenters: Seismological Society of America Bulletin, v. 52, p. 1037–1046.

Herrin, E., Taggart, J., and Brown, C. F., Jr., 1962, Machine computation of earthquake hypocenters: Journal of the Graduate Research Center, Southern Methodist University, v. 30, p. 79–106.

Herrin, E., chairman, and others, 1968, 1968 seismological tables for P phases: Seismological Society of America Bulletin, v. 58, p. 1193–1252.

Jacob, K. H., 1970, Three-dimensional seismic ray tracing in a laterally heterogeneous spherical earth: Journal of Geophysical Research, v. 75, p. 6675–6689.

James, D. E., Sacks, I. S., Lazo L., E., and Aparicio G., P., 1969, On locating local earthquakes using small networks: Seismological Society of America Bulletin, v. 59, p. 1201–1212.

Jeffreys, H., and Bullen, K. E., 1958, Seismological tables: London, Burlington House, British Association for the Advancement of Science, Gray-Milne Trust, Office of the British Association, 50 p.

Julian, B., 1970, Ray tracing in arbitrarily heterogeneous media: Lexington, Massachusetts, Lincoln Laboratory, Massachusetts Institute of Technology, Technical Note 1970-45.

Langston, C. A., 1976, A body wave inversion of the Koyna, India, earthquake of December 10, 1967, and some implications for body wave focal mechanisms: Journal of Geophysical Research, v. 81, p. 2517–2529.

Lee, W.H.K., and Lahr, J. C., 1975, HYPO71 (Revised): A computer program for determining hypocenter, magnitude, and first motion pattern of local earthquakes: U.S. Geological Survey Open-File Report 75-311, 113 p.

Lilwall, R. C., and Douglas, A., 1970, Estimation of P-wave travel-times using the joint epicentre method: Royal Astronomical Society Geophysical Journal, v. 19, p. 165–181.

Massé, R. P., Lambert, D. G., and Harkrider, D. G., 1973, Precision of the determination of focal depth from the spectral ratio of Love/Rayleigh surface waves: Seismological Society of America Bulletin, v. 63, p. 59–100.

Pakiser, L. C., 1963, Structure of the crust and upper mantle in the Western United States: Journal of Geophysical Research, v. 68, p. 5747–5756.

Peters, D. C., and Crosson, R. S., 1972, Application of prediction analysis to hypocenter determination using a local array: Seismological Society of America Bulletin, v. 62, p. 775–788.

Sorrels, C. G., Crowley, J. B., and Veith, K. F., 1971, Methods for computing ray paths in complex geological structures: Seismological Society of America Bulletin, v. 61, p. 27–53.

Tsai, Y. B., and Aki, K., 1970, Precise focal depth determination from amplitude spectra of surface waves: Journal of Geophysical Research, v. 75, p. 5729–5743.

von Hake, C. A., and Cloud, W. K., 1968, United States earthquakes 1966: U.S. Department of Commerce, 110 p.

von Seggern, D., 1972, Relative location of seismic events using surface waves: Royal Astronomical Society Geophysical Journal, v. 26, p. 499–513.

Manuscript Received by the Society July 13, 1978
Manuscript Accepted November 13, 1978

PART 3

TECHNIQUES

Geological Society of America
Reviews in Engineering Geology, Volume IV
1979

Application of remote-sensing data to nuclear power plant site investigations

ROLAND C. McELDOWNEY
Dames & Moore, 605 Parfet Street, Denver, Colorado 80215

RICHARD F. PASCUCCI
Dames & Moore, 6 Commerce Drive, Cranford, New Jersey 07016

ABSTRACT

Remote-sensing data for studies of nuclear power plant sites are acquired by aerial surveys and satellite programs and include satellite photography (Landsat and Skylab); conventional black-and-white, color, and color infrared photography; thermal infrared imagery; radar imagery (side-looking airborne radar); and airborne geophysical surveys, such as aeromagnetic and aeroradiometric surveys.

In general, existing data from such surveys are relatively inexpensive to obtain and offer a synoptic overview of the area, provide a large amount of information for the scale involved, and afford a technique of sampling that does not disturb the sample.

In current methods of analysis, the photography, images, and maps are brought to a common scale, and existing structural geologic data are compared with a new data set, usually in the form of lineaments. The field investigations that follow include reconnaissance and detailed geologic investigations of the lineaments to detect evidence of faulting; then ground geophysical surveys, boreholes and trench studies are made. These field investigations add "ground data" to the remote-sensing base and aid in evaluating the significance of any geologic structure so defined.

Two examples of recent fault studies for nuclear power plant sites, one conducted in the Virginia Piedmont tectonic province and the other in the Maryland Coastal Plain province, illustrate the potential value of remote sensing in the site selection process. When correlation of geologic maps with the several remote-sensing techniques is undertaken early in the planning stages of the siting study, it is possible to locate the nuclear power plant away from potentially hazardous geologic structures or to avoid such ambiguous geologic features as are impossible to adequately define in terms of site safety.

INTRODUCTION

In recent years, remote-sensing data have become increasingly significant in site selection and evaluation investigations.

Recent fault studies (in accord with Code of Federal Regulations, 1978) conducted by Dames & Moore for nuclear power plant sites have included analyses of Landsat, side-looking airborne radar (SLAR), thermal infrared (TIR), and aerial photography (black and white, color, and color infrared). In addition, aeromagnetic and aeroradioactivity maps have been studied when available. Linear features evident on the images, photographs, and maps have been examined in the field. The most persistent throughgoing lineaments, which could not be explained or dated by mapping, have been studied by seismic techniques or other geophysical methods. When identified as faults, the most suspicious or important features have been drilled and trenched to determine the date of last movement.

The purpose of this paper is to document the recording capabilities and limitations of remote sensors; to describe the methods of remote-sensor data analysis; and to present two case histories that demonstrate, in a practical environment, the methods and sequence of a site investigation using remote sensing.

ACQUISITION OF REMOTE-SENSOR DATA

Review of General Capabilities and Advantages of All Remote Sensors

Remote sensors offer a synoptic overview wherein point observations are integrated by eye into their relationship with the whole, so that they present a visual set of data patterns, not merely a group of data points.

Remote-sensor imagery has a very high information density compared to other graphic, textual, or electronic storage media. However, although high-resolution imagery is an ideal medium of data storage, the quantity and reliability of the information retrieved and the rapidity of retrieval are largely a function of the interpretative facility of the retriever.

Remote-sensors offer a technique of sampling that does not disturb the sample. One of the practical advantages to be realized from their use, as compared to ground survey techniques, becomes evident when one considers the tendency of property to appreciate in value when a field crew is introduced into a study area.

Remote sensors provide a more complete inspection of the terrain than do ground survey methods. Although the level of detail recorded by the sensor is not so high as that recorded by the observer on the ground, the sensor brings the entirety of the terrain under surveillance rather than merely selected portions of it. Ground surveys can, of course, be made sufficiently exhaustive to bring under close inspection all terrain units of as small a size as desired; however, the cost/benefit ratio of such a procedure is usually too high to be practical except for small, site surveys.

The costs to acquire existing remotely sensed data are relatively low in terms of both time and funds expended. This is particularly the case for Landsat and other remote-sensing data held by Federal and State agencies.

Landsat Data

The capabilities of the two Landsat systems currently in operation include provisions for gathering data from the entire globe in 185 × 185 km increments from an orbital altitude of about 926 km. This orbit was designed so that data are always gathered at a constant sun angle (about 9:30 a.m. local time). The only change in illumination occurs as a result of the seasonal variation in sun elevation.

Each satellite repeats coverage of any given swath of the Earth every 18 d, and with the two satellites now operating, each swath is covered every 9 d. This greatly increases the probability of cloud-free coverage. Cloud-free coverage is currently available for all of the continental United States.

The sensor system aboard the satellites is a multispectral line-scanner. This system generates individual scenes, with each scene scanned in four different wavelengths to produce four similar images simultaneously, as follows: green band, 0.5 to 0.6 μm; red band, 0.6 to 0.7 μm; and two infrared (IR) bands, 0.7 to 0.8 and 0.8 to 1.1 μm.

As the satellite travels along its orbit, each frame overlaps the previous one by about 10% so as to provide continuous coverage. Adjacent, parallel orbits are spaced so that side-lap coverage is about 10% at the equator with greater side-lap nearer the poles, which means that a minimum of 20% of each Landsat frame can be viewed stereoscopically, a great aid to analysis.

The observations of the Earth are transmitted as electrical signals to ground-receiver antennas and are subsequently converted to facsimile images in the laboratory. The ground resolution of this imagery is about 61 m.

Landsat imagery can be purchased from the U.S. Geological Survey Data Center at Sioux Falls, South Dakota, at scales of 1:1,000,000; 1:500,000; and 1:250,000. Prices in 1978 ranged from $8 for a black-and-white image at 1:1,000,000 to $50 for a color infrared composite at 1:250,000.

Skylab

The remote-sensing systems of the Skylab satellite differ from that of Landsat in that they acquire photography in addition to facsimile imagery. Two photographic sensing systems were carried on Skylab—a six-lens multispectral camera and an Earth terrain camera.

The multispectral camera consists of a six-lens array that records stereo photos (60% forward overlap) on six 70-mm film types simultaneously. The film types are two black-and-white infrared emulsions filtered in the 0.7- to 0.8-μm and 0.8- to 0.9-μm region; color infrared and color films; and high-resolution, panchromatic black-and-white films filtered in the 0.5- to 0.6-μm and 0.6- to 0.7-μm bands. The estimated ground resolution from this camera system ranges from about 30 m for black-and-white films to about 76 m for the infrared films. Scales can be enlarged up to 1:250,000 with almost no loss in information content. Ground coverage per scene recorded by the six-lens camera system is 161 × 161 km.

The Earth terrain camera is a long–focal length camera that records scenes of 109 × 109 km in area onto film 12.7 cm wide. The original photo scale is expandable to about 1:125,000 with little loss in resolution, which ranges from 17 m for high-definition black-and-white to 30 m for color infrared.

Skylab photography is obtainable from the U.S. Geological Survey Data Center at prices that ranged in 1978 from $8 for a black-and-white photo at 1:1,000,000 to $50 for a color photo at 1:125,000.

Side-Looking Airborne Radar

One of the most important capabilities of side-looking airborne radar (SLAR), one that is especially applicable in areas in which persistent cloud cover is a problem, is its day-night, all-weather operation. The all-weather capability stems from the fact that SLAR is an active sensor; that is, it provides its own source of "illumination." This illumination has a frequency ranging between 8,000 and 40,000 MHz for commercially available sets; thus, the physical length of individual waves—being large relative to the size of cloud droplets—enables it to penetrate all cloud types except cumulonimbus. The specific advantages consequent upon this capability are (1) in certain parts of the world that are persistently cloud covered, SLAR is the only remote sensor that can acquire imagery; (2) in areas that have a large proportion of cloudy days, even during the best flying season, SLAR affords a means of acquiring imagery without incurring the cost of excessive time on station for aircraft, crew, and sensor; in Arctic and Antarctic regions, data can be gathered even during the months of winter darkness.

In scale, synoptic presentation, and resolution (which is about 15 m), SLAR is similar to the satellite remote-sensing systems.

Existing SLAR coverage can be purchased from the National Cartographic Information Center, in Reston, Virginia; from

Goodyear Aerospace Corporation and Motorola, Litchfield Park, Arizona; and from Westinghouse Electric Corp. of Philadelphia, Pennsylvania. Prices vary, but in 1978 were on the order of \$40 per 1,600 to 2,400 km^2.

Airborne Geophysical Methods

Aerial magnetic and radioactivity surveys appear to be the most useful of the airborne geophysical methods (which include electromagnetic and recently developed aerogravimetric methods) for detecting subsurface geologic structure in site studies.

Magnetic methods employ either flux-gate or proton-precession magnetometers in the "towed bird" configuration behind a helicopter or airplane. Flux-gate magnetometers record the total magnetic intensity with an accuracy of approximately 1γ. The proton magnetometer records the Earth's total field.

Flight lines are laid out on aerial photographic mosaics at right angles to the known or suspected structural trend, spaced usually at 400 to 800 m or closer. The optimum altitude for the survey is 30 to 150 m above the terrain along the predetermined traverse lines (admittedly difficult to accomplish in rough country). The locations of traverses are precisely plotted on the photomosaic with the aid of simultaneous strip photos taken along the lines during the survey and are then linked with the magnetometer readings, which are collected continuously on a paper strip. The magnetic values (in gammas) are plotted on topographic maps and profiled. Magnetic-response contour maps are subsequently developed from the profiles. The interpretation and use of these contour maps are discussed below.

Airborne radioactivity surveys generally measure gamma ray flux from three principal sources: from radioactive sources in the rock or soil (usually no more than 30 cm below the ground surface); from reflected cosmic rays; and from radon gas emitted at ground-level. Because the intensity of radiation from the surface decreases rapidly with increasing height above the source, radiometric surveys should be carried out very close (within 30 m) to the ground surface. Gregory (1960) and Moxham (1960) have provided excellent descriptions of procedures and interpretations of aeroradioactivity surveys, as have Pitkin and others (1964).

Flight line layout and reduction of data to contour maps are accomplished in the same manner as in aeromagnetic surveys.

The relative advantages of aerial versus ground magnetometer and/or radioactivity surveys have been summarized by Dobrin (1960), as follows: The most obvious advantage of the aerial magnetometer survey is its speed; because of this advantage of speed, the cost of an aerial survey is much lower than an equivalent ground survey over areas that are large enough to justify the high fixed costs. Also, because of the speed, the effects on instrument drift and diurnal variation are minimized. The airborne magnetometer can be used over water and over terrain that is inaccessible to ground operations. Because of the height of the plane, spurious magnetic materials (pipes, rails, in buildings) on the Earth's surface do not affect the record, whereas such extraneous sources of magnetism continually interfere with the usability of ground-acquired magnetic data. In the same way, the effects of extraneous magnetic rocks, sediments, and dikes at or just below the surface will not interfere with the recognition of anomalies caused by deep subsurface bodies. Finally, smoothness of the data allows freer use of analytical methods.

However, there are disadvantages as well (Dobrin, 1960): The accuracy of the results in aerial work is always limited by the accuracy of the base map on which the magnetic data are transcribed. The minimum cost of an aeromagnetic survey is high because of the basic investment in the special aircraft instrument platform employed. The typical cost for 250 km^2 was about \$20,000 in 1978.

Aeromagnetic maps of many areas of the United States are available through the United States Geological Survey (USGS) and State geological surveys. The U.S. Department of Energy (DOE), formerly the Energy Research and Development Administration (ERDA), is conducting systematic, high-sensitivity, airborne radioactivity and magnetic mapping of the United States to evaluate uranium potential. Aeroradioactivity maps of parts of the United States are available through the DOE offices in Grand Junction (Public Affairs Office, DOE, Grand Junction, Colorado 81501).

Thermal Infrared Imagery

Unlike SLAR, thermal infrared (TIR) is a passive sensor, which is to say that it does not emit a signal but, rather, receives that part of the Earth's electromagnetic emission lying in the infrared range, specifically in the "atmospheric windows" of 3 to 5 and 8 to 14 μm. Any body having a temperature above absolute zero emits energy in the infrared as well as other regions of the electromagnetic spectrum and does so at an intensity directly proportional to the fourth power of the absolute temperature. In addition to temperature, the rate of emission is also a function of the emissivity of the object; a perfect black body has an emissivity of 1.0. Thus, terrain components having different temperatures and different emissivities will appear different, except in the special case in which the product of the higher temperature and lower emissivity of the one is exactly equaled by the lower temperature and higher emissivity of the other.

Very little of the Earth's surface has been covered by thermal surveys so that, in most cases, it must be acquired on an *ad hoc* basis. Many aerial survey firms have the capability of flying thermal coverage, at costs generally somewhat higher than those for flying large-scale photographic coverage.

A recent satellite, the Heat Capacity Mapping Mission (HCMM), is currently acquiring thermal infrared data over the United States and portions of foreign countries. The information will initially be made available (in 1979) to the public on computer compatible tapes and will eventually be sold as hard-copy images. Resolution is expected to be on the order of 0.5 km. No cost information is currently available. The data will be sold through the National Space Science Data Center, Goddard Space Flight Center, Greenbelt, Maryland (contact John Price).

Aerial Photography

The techniques and applications of aerial photography are too well known to require documentation here. Suffice it to say that the principal advantages offered by aerial photos are their unsurpassed resolution (usually about 1 m) and the relatively large scale at which they are usually available. (Most off-the-shelf aerial photography acquired by the U.S. Government agencies falls between 1:20,000 and 1:50,000.) These aspects of scale and resolution make them ideally suited for complementary work with, or for follow-up work after, satellite and SLAR imagery, because they provide the means for integrating a localized, detailed analysis into the synoptic overview. In 1978, existing aerial photographs of any area in the United States could be purchased for $3 per 9-in. black-and-white frame from the files of the following Federal agencies: Agricultural Stabilization and Conservation Service; Soil Conservation Service; Forest Service; Geological Survey; Bureau of Land Management; Tennessee Valley Authority; National Ocean Survey; and National Aeronautics and Space Administration. Aerial photos may also be acquired on an *ad hoc* basis by private flying companies at much higher prices, which vary according to scale, film emulsion used, and size of the area of interest.

The interested reader can find excellent treatments of the subject in the *Manual of Photographic Interpretation* (Colwell, 1960) and the *Manual of Remote Sensing* (Reeves and others, 1975).

ANALYSIS OF REMOTE-SENSING DATA

This section of the paper presents an overview of remote-sensor data analysis and includes examples of this kind of analysis from the literature. In power plant site selection and evaluation, the principal effort of remote-sensor data analysis is directed toward the detection of geologic structural features. Of primary importance among these is the detection of lineaments that may indicate faults and/or fractures. As a guide to the analysis and interpretation of image-type data, ten criteria (more fully described under "Landsat Analysis") are commonly employed, of which five are concerned with alignments on the images and another five with offset of the same alignments—namely, drainage, rock contacts, landforms, vegetation, and optical density (when the density anomaly cannot be assigned to any of the preceding four).

In addition to lineaments, the imagery is examined for evidence of (1) folded structures, the axes of which are determined by observations of strike and dip direction, and (2) rock type, which is differentiated on the basis of color, tone, drainage density, drainage pattern, geomorphic expression, and land use.

Airborne geophysical data, which are reduced to the form of contour maps, are analyzed according to a somewhat different set of criteria, which includes terminations and alignments of highs, lows, and changes in gradient. These are discussed more fully below under "Aeromagnetic Analysis."

Landsat Analysis

The great utility of Landsat imagery for determining regional structural geology lies in (1) the broad overview that it affords, (2) the low sun elevation at which its images are made (9:30

a.m., local time), and (3) the fact that it records in four different spectral bands.

The broad overview, encompassing about 34,000 km^2 per frame, permits the geologist to observe the entire area of interest as a single entity and reveals structural patterns and relationships that are often not detected on aerial photos.

The low sun elevation, especially in winter scenes, is a distinct aid in the detection of structural features, because the shadows emphasize and exaggerate minor differences in topography and vegetation. This results in the detection of many lineaments that may be the surface expression of faults or fractures. This advantage has been emphasized by almost all Landsat investigators. Figure 1 is a good example of the expression of lineaments on a Landsat image.

As mentioned above, analyses and interpretations of lineaments are usually postulated on the basis of ten criteria. In most, but by no means all cases, alignments of the following five items would be designated as evidence of a "possible fault": (1) Drainage—segments of a stream, river, or lake (if a valley is observed, but not the stream itself, criterion 3 is used). (2) Rock contacts—rectilinear contact between two rock types. (3) Geomorphic features—straight ridge lines and valleys that do not appear to be caused by bedding. (4) Vegetation—rectilinear interfaces between vegetation types, as well as long, straight, narrow bands of vegetation, such as those bordering a watercourse. (5) Optical density (tone)—this criterion is employed when the cause of an observed alignment cannot be identified further, that is, when only a rectilinear tonal difference can be seen.

Likewise, offsets of these items are criteria regarded as evidence of a "probable fault": (6) A rectilinear lateral displacement of any drainage segment—a stream, river, or lake. (7) A rectilinear discontinuity in the strike of a contact. In most instances, lineaments that are probably caused by an offset in a contact between rock types are more easily identified as an offset of geomorphic features. This is because the interpretation of geomorphic features is virtually certain, whereas the interpretation of rock type is more subtle and therefore conjectural. Thus, an offset in a ridge or scarp falls under criterion 8 even though the ridge or scarp was probably the manifestation of a resistant rock unit. (8) A rectilinear lateral displacement in a geomorphic feature such as a ridge or valley. (9) A rectilinear lateral displacement of vegetation type. (10) Offset of optical density (tone)—the offset of a feature not otherwise identified.

A striking example of lineament detection has been presented by Barthelemy and Dempster (1975). They discovered an extremely dense lineament system while mapping a horizontal sedimentary sequence in Lesotho in southern Africa.

Another example of lineament detection especially relevant to power plant siting was recorded by Goetz and others (1973). In a Landsat study, the investigators were able to extend the Bright Angel and Butte faults (in Arizona) to twice their previously detected length and were able to make a probable correlation of these extensions with modern seismic events.

A similar study, having similar results, was described by Abdel-Gawad and Silverstein (1972). As described by these investigators, "A fault lineament, apparently not previously mapped, was identified in the Uinta Mountains, Utah. Part

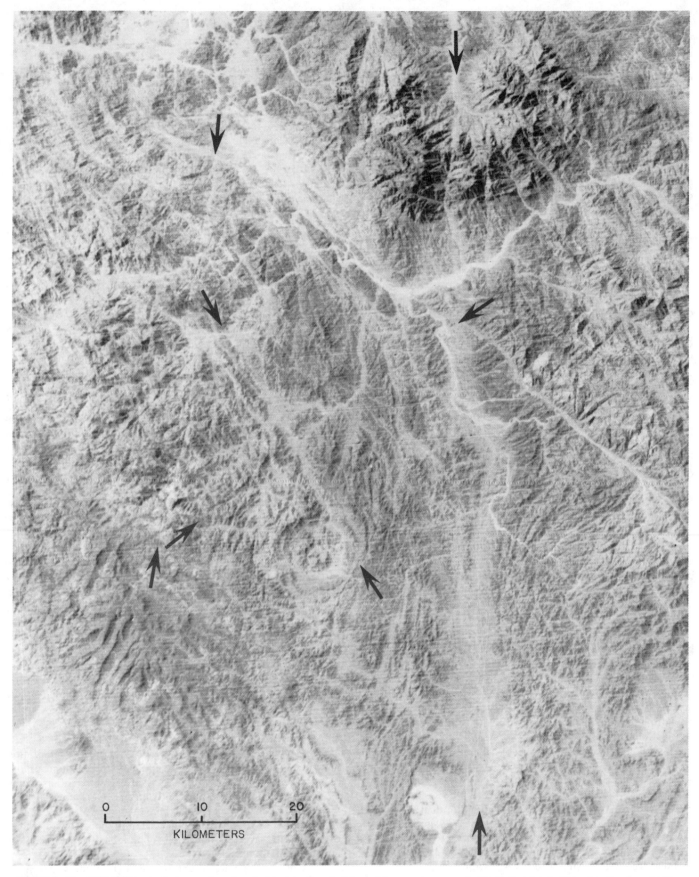

Figure 1. Example of lineaments (arrows) on Landsat image of central Iran. Lineaments are probably fault related. Note also circular structures on image.

of the lineament shows evidence of recent faulting that corresponds to [the location of] a moderate earthquake cluster."

The use of Landsat in differentiating rock types has been less successful but has achieved some notable results in unmapped or poorly mapped areas. For example, Correa (1975) reported good results in mapping rock units in the Sao Francisco River area of eastern Brazil. Correa differentiated between rock units on the basis of drainage patterns, landforms, vegetation, and land use.

The third capability of Landsat—recording in four different spectral bands—has permitted the differentiation of rock units on the basis of spectral, rather than spatial, criteria. Levine (1975) described the use of Landsat computer-compatible data storage tapes in distinguishing between several rock types (or, more precisely, the soils formed in situ on the rocks) by determining and comparing their spectral response. A limitation of this method, also described by Levine, is that the spectral reflectance of the soils is obscured by the vegetation growing on it (in this case, grass). The method was only successful during the dry season or after a grass fire.

Similar results have been reported by Carter (1975), who commented on the results of a multispectral computer analysis that differentiated between granitic rocks and andesite and between rhyolitic tuffs and basalts. Carter did not, however, describe the type and density of the vegetation.

In summation, then, it can be said that using Landsat data allows significant contributions to siting studies not only in poorly mapped areas, where it can contribute new structural and lithologic information, but also in well-mapped areas, where it can detect evidence of faulting and fracturing not previously observed on the ground or on aerial photos.

Skylab Analysis

In general, the useful features of Landsat imagery are repeated in Skylab imagery, including the synoptic view and the multispectral data acquisition. The sun elevation may or may not be low, however, because the photographs are taken in accordance with weather conditions and the astronaut's schedule, rather than at a preset, invariable time.

The principal difference between Landsat and Skylab data involves resolution. Skylab photos have superior resolution because the negatives are physically returned to Earth along with the astronauts, rather than telemetered back as discrete bits, as are Landsat images. Resolution is on the order of 15 m for Skylab as compared to 61 for Landsat data. This means that Skylab imagery reveals (1) finer details of topography, drainage, and vegetation, which can result in more accurate delineation of rock types, and (2) smaller lineaments and smaller, local changes in strike and dip direction, which can result in the detection of more folded structural features. Another significant difference between Skylab and Landsat data is that Skylab photos usually overlap by 60% to ensure full stereoscopic coverage. The resulting optical illusion of three dimensions is of inestimable value in analysis. The effects of these differences on the sequence of interpretation are described below in the section, Methods and Sequence of an Ideal Remote-Sensing Site Investigation.

Side-Looking Airborne Radar Analysis

It has been said above that, in respect to scale and resolution, SLAR is similar to the satellite remote-sensing systems. However, SLAR has the additional advantage of the low "look angle" (high angle of incidence) at which the radar energy is propagated to the Earth's surface. This is analogous to a very low sun angle in aerial photography, being equivalent, at the outer extremes of the beam, to a solar altitude of about 20° above the horizon. This angle produces a radar "shadow" having a length of about 2.5 times the height of the radar-illuminated object. The length of these exaggerated shadows emphasizes small changes in elevation, and the shape and density of small individual shadows call attention to subtle changes in relief pattern and texture; thus SLAR is an excellent means to detect faults and fractures. Indeed, SLAR is unparalleled, even by Landsat, in its capability to portray lineaments. Figure 2 is an example of the expression of lineaments on an SLAR image. Nearly all SLAR investigators have commented on this capability, which is readily apparent even to the uninitiated. Gribben and others (1971) discussed this at length in their comparison of available SLAR systems.

It should be mentioned that, of all the remote sensors in general use, SLAR is the only "active" sensor. Satellite sensors, airborne geophysical sensors, and thermal infrared sensors all passively record reflected or emitted energy, but SLAR actively emits a signal in the form of a discrete radar pulse and measures and records the strength of the signal that is returned to the antenna-receiver. The factors that determine the amplitude of the back-scattered signal are surface roughness and the dielectric constant of the terrain materials. It is intuitively apparent that the slope and geometric aspects of the surface relative to the propagation direction of the radar energy is a determinant of the proportion of the signal returned to the radar antenna, the return varying inversely as the incidence angle, all else being equal. Somewhat less apparent, perhaps, are the casual effects that surface roughness or microrelief exercises on reflection. In general, surfaces composed of particle sizes having a diameter of less than $\lambda/10$ act as specular reflectors, whereas surfaces composed of particles having diameters of λ or greater act as diffuse reflectors. In practice, however, the only natural surfaces that act as true specular reflectors are unruffled water and smooth ice, although playa deposits and flat expanses of very fine sand sometimes approach this. The combined sensitivity that SLAR exhibits to slope changes (macrorelief) and to surface roughness (microrelief) allows fine-tuned differentiation of rock types and detection of structures.

In contradistinction to the synoptic presentation of SLAR, it is also possible, once the advantages of large-area integration have been realized, to enlarge the imagery and produce a more detailed degree of interpretation. Enlargements of as much as eight diameters have been utilized and have continued to yield levels of mappable detail commensurate with that expanded scale, levels that are on the order of one to two orders of magnitude greater than that obtainable at the scale of acquisition (Holmes, 1969).

Most of the regional structural geologic studies that have

Figure 2. Example of side-looking radar image, northern California.

been conducted with SLAR have been performed for mining companies, and the results are, of course, proprietary. Following, however, are some of the publicly documented results of investigators who have used SLAR in both a research and operational mode.

Pascucci (1971) reported detecting a semi-annular structure in a granitic complex that, although immediately obvious on SLAR imagery, is extremely obscure on a photo mosaic having a scale almost twice as large.

Brennan and Lintz (1971), using SLAR imagery at a scale of about 1:160,000, were able to extend the trace of a known (mapped) fault by nearly 2 km. This extension, not previously noted on the ground, was also not obvious on aerial photography.

Del Campo (1971) reported that SLAR was far superior to all other sensors for detecting faults in a test site in Mexico. This is especially impressive since the SLAR data were of relatively poor quality, and the data with which the SLAR data were compared included color photography, color IR photography, and thermal infrared imagery.

Komarov and Starostin (1975) reported the successful use of SLAR in studies of "geomorphology, tectonic composition, lithology, soil [and] vegetation." They, too, commented on lineament detection, especially linearly oriented intrusions such as dikes, and reported that Soviet investigators have "isolated terrigenic, carbonaceous, volcanogenic, intrusive, and metamorphic" rocks by this method.

Investigators for the U.S. Bureau of Mines (Elder, and others, 1974) have found SLAR to be a useful tool in geologic structural mapping and analysis. "Three major, superimposed joint sets and several fault or fractured zones were identified by SLAR lineament analysis. The fault and joint systems were verified by surface and in-mine observations."

Aeromagnetic Analysis

The interpretation of aeromagnetic maps has generally taken three forms: modeling of anomalies (quantitative method); correlation of magnetic intensity with rock type (qualitative method); and linear analysis of anomaly edges, trends, and so forth to produce aeromagnetic lineaments.

Parasnis (1972) indicated that modeling of magnetic anomalies is the ideal procedure for studying magnetic contour maps. He presented several excellent approaches to modeling, as well as case histories; Vacquier and others (1951) and Dobrin (1960) did likewise. This quantitative method assumes a model of homogeneous magnetism and attempts a best fit to the magnetic anomaly, considering the model's depth, magnetic intensity, and dimensional parameters.

In the second, or qualitative, method of interpreting aeromagnetic maps, the intensity of the anomaly is correlated with a rock type, and the geologic unit is assumed to extend to the edge of the anomaly. Neuschel (1970) gave an excellent example of this method of interpretation, and Dobrin (1960, p. 310) discussed its limitations. Many recent papers on regional aeromagnetic studies include interpretations that combine both the quantitative and qualitative methods.

A relatively little known but effective method of interpretation is the lineament analysis technique described by Gay (1972).

This method is more directly concerned with locating geologic structure than the two methods described above. The theory is that the edge or position of change in the anomaly configuration represents a geologic boundary. It is thus the most probable location for geologic contacts and structure. This "edge" usually has a linear alignment with other "edges," such that aeromagnetic lineaments can be produced. The criteria noted by Gay for recognizing the lineaments include termination of highs or lows; changes in gradient; linear contour patterns; alignments of highs and lows; long, linear "alteration" lows; and combinations of the above criteria.

Although the analysis of gravity maps is beyond the scope of this paper, the methods of analysis are similar to those employed in aeromagnetic interpretation. Gravity maps are commonly interpreted in conjunction with aeromagnetic data. McGinnis and Ervin (1974) indicated correlation of faults with edges of gravity anomalies or gradients (lineaments) in the Illinois basin. Historic earthquakes were correlated with "high gravity gradient areas on the edges of closures or in the lower gradient areas lying between closures." Thus, Gay (1972) and McGinnis and Ervin (1974) advocated a similar correlation technique for different data systems.

Because the object of remote-sensing interpretation in nuclear plant siting is to define the location, extent, and recency of faulting in a region, the last two qualitative methods seem most useful; however, modeling of anomalies can lend support to field geologic interpretations of amount of offset and dip of a fault plane. Once aeromagnetic lineaments are determined, their locations should be compared to other remote-sensing lineations and to known fault locations. Large, throughgoing (and often quite ancient) geologic structures usually become apparent using this method.

Aeroradioactivity Analysis

Structural interpretation of anomalous radioactivity is a qualitative procedure, usually done in conjunction with aeromagnetic maps or other airborne geophysical methods. Quantitative estimates of the radioactive contents of rocks have been more related, in the past, to uranium exploration than to structural geologic investigations. Moxham (1960) discussed this in some detail.

In comparing magnetic maps of an area in Virginia with radiometric maps of the same area, Neuschel (1970) noted a striking linearity on both maps that reflected the structural grain of the rocks. Radioactive highs occurred over magnetic lows, and where magnetic data were rather flat and featureless, radioactivity data were detailed, and vice-versa. Thus, Neuschel was able to correlate rock units with both radioactivity and magnetic expressions and to predict geologic contacts and structure. Parts of Neuschel's maps are reproduced as Figures 8 and 9 and discussed below in the section on case histories.

Thermal Infrared Imagery Analysis

Although thermal infrared imagery has thus far proven to be less effective, overall, than most other remote sensors in detecting geologic features, it remains a valuable remote-sensing system in that it has the capability to detect features that cannot be detected by any other sensor. For example, Pascucci (1971) compared SLAR and thermal infrared imagery obtained over a test area that included parts of the California Coast Ranges, the San Joaquin Valley, and the Sierra Nevada foothills. It was found that the SLAR images contained more lithologic and structural data than did the thermal infrared images, but the latter revealed six small intrusions and one large fault that were not visible on the SLAR images. In this case, there was a thermal difference between the intrusions, the fault, and their surroundings where no topographic or textural difference existed. It was concluded that thermal infrared should be used as a supplementary, rather than as the primary, sensor.

Sabins (1969) described a striking example of the unique capability of thermal infrared. He compared co-aerial views of an aerial photograph and a thermal infrared image taken over the Imperial Valley in California. The photo is nearly featureless, while the infrared imagery is replete with geologic structure, the most conspicuous feature of which is a fault-truncated anticline. These structures are all covered by a thin sheet of windblown sand, described by Sabins as rarely exceeding "a few feet in thickness." The anticline consists of alternate layers of sandstone and siltstone, and the propagation to the surface of temperature differences congruent with these layers is presumed to be due to their different conductivities. In a subsequent investigation of the same area (Howard and Mercado, 1970), however, it was found that vertical aerial photography taken at a low sun elevation (30° above the horizon) detected more geologic data than did the thermal infrared imagery of Sabins. It should be added that this imagery was acquired over an unirrigated part of the Imperial Valley; in more humid areas, vegetation and weathering would tend to mask temperature differentials induced by near-surface phenomena.

It should be emphasized that thermal anomalies must be interpreted with great care. For example, thermal infrared flown during daylight hours, especially if the day is sunny, will produce an image having a radiant flux pattern of light and dark tones that closely follows the insolation pattern of sun and shade on the terrain; that is, terrain radiation will be primarily a function of differential solar heating and only secondarily of differences in rock type. Ideally, therefore, acquisition of thermal infrared imagery should be restricted to nighttime hours. Several investigators (Watson and others, 1971) have found that best results are obtained using predawn imagery. The following examples cite some results achieved in thermal infrared surveys.

Rowan and others (1970) found that dolomite (warm) and limestone (cool) could be distinguished on predawn imagery; facies changes between them could be distinguished as well. The investigation was carried out at the USGS Mill Creek, Oklahoma, test site, which has a vegetation cover consisting of grass on gently rolling topography. It is interesting to note that it had not been possible to consistently discriminate between these rock types using black-and-white, color, and color infrared photography.

In a thermal infrared survey conducted over a desert terrain and described by van Dijk and others (1971), indications were given that thermal infrared "might be useful for the detection of a near-surface salt dome with little or no topographic expression." Rock types were differentiated; and in some cases,

structural features were more clearly seen, at least locally, than on black-and-white photography.

During thermal infrared investigations of volcanic and geothermal areas, Friedman and Williams (1968) reported thermal emissions from both effusive- and explosive-type volcanoes; thermal anomalies from volcanic areas generally regarded as dormant; convective heat transfer from craters, vents, fractures, faults, porous scoriaceous rock, primary and secondary fumaroles and solfataras, and various forms of hydrothermal activity; relative degree of activity or intensity of thermal emission; the relationship of thermal anomalies to tectonic patterns; and near-surface hydrologic flow.

We examined a chip of thermal infrared imagery showing a fault in the Anadarko basin. An anonymous description on the chip declared that the surface expression of this important fault, a controlling structure for the Gageby Creek gas field, was first discovered on the thermal infrared imagery.

Brennan and Lintz (1971) reported that rocks in a stratigraphic sequence that looked "rather uniform" displayed "considerable contrast" on thermal infrared imagery; that discrimination between bedrock and surrounding alluvium was readily accomplished on nighttime infrared imagery; and that loose sand and weakly cemented sandstone (1% cement) were easily differentiated. The test site selected by these investigators was arid and had minimal vegetative cover.

A problem that is occasionally encountered in power plant site evaluation is the determination of the existence and location of underground cavities. Satellite and SLAR imagery contribute to solving this problem only insofar as the lineaments detected by them may be the controlling structures of solution cavities. However, Rinker (1974) described a special case in which a thermal infrared study yielded direct evidence of cavity openings. The detection was based on the facts that the temperature in a known cavern was 7 to 9 °C warmer than the outside temperature during the early morning hours and that this time period was coincident with a small decrease in atmospheric pressure. Thermal infrared data revealed warm exhalations at two openings of the cavern. Warren and Wielchowsky (1973) evaluated infrared photography, thermography, and SLAR for studying subsidence and collapse in carbonate terranes. They thought that these methods were useful in beginning studies of carbonate solution problems, but that more detailed ground exploration, such as the methods evaluated by Fountain and others (1975), was necessary.

Aerial Photographic Analysis

Although aerial photos have been, and continue to be, one of the most useful of remote-sensing tools, their capabilities are sufficiently well-known to require only a brief reminder of their use in identifying new geologic features and in confirming those found by other sensors. Their generally large scale and excellent resolution make them invaluable in detecting geologic features that often add to information detected on images from other sensors.

The principles and methods of photo analysis are thoroughly described and documented in two excellent, standard texts: the *Manual of Photographic Interpretation* (Colwell, 1960) and the *Manual of Remote Sensing* (Reeves and others, 1975).

Color and black-and-white photography have been used for mapping irregularities in carbonate bedrock surfaces and for locating zones of increased permeability and conduit development in limestone. Parizek (1971) indicated success with photographs in mapping sinkholes; bedrock outcrops and strike; traces of high-angle and thrust faults; systematic joint sets; zones of fracture concentration; undrained valleys; variations in stream alluvium, colluvium, alluvial fans, and residual and transported soils; carbonate units that favor cavity development; springs and areas of diffuse groundwater discharge; areas of surface-water loss; and regional lineations reflecting increased permeability development in bedrock.

Growth faults related to nontectonic events, such as growth of salt domes, have been noted on conventional aerial and infrared photographs of the Houston, Texas, area (Reid, 1973). The location of growth faulting must be well-documented because of the hazard of ground rupture, even though earthquakes are not related to these structures.

An example of the use of conventional black-and-white vertical photographs in conjunction with other types of photography for locating active fault zones is presented by Babcock (1971). Babcock found that oblique color infrared aerial photographs, conventional black-and-white vertical aerial photographs, and ground studies were effective combinations for locating active faults in the agricultural lowland of the Imperial Valley, California. Additional discussion on the use of aerial photos for detailed analysis of lineaments is presented in the following section.

METHODS AND SEQUENCE OF AN IDEAL REMOTE–SENSING SITE INVESTIGATION

The ideal, though seldom encountered, remote-sensing site investigation is one in which the area of interest is covered by all of the major remote-sensing systems that have been described above.

The question sometimes arises as to the rationale for using multiple remote sensors, especially those that yield a relatively small amount of information, when sensor records yielding more information are available. The reason for this is that different sensor systems detect different phenomena, and although one, such as SLAR, may have an overall superiority to another, such as thermal infrared, thermal infrared has the capability of detecting thermal effects that SLAR cannot, as has been described above. Similarly, an investigation conducted by Clark (1971), comparing SLAR with aerial photography, demonstrated the overall superiority of the photos, but simultaneously showed that SLAR, in some cases, portrays textural differences in surficial materials that are not detected on the photography. The conclusion is that remote-sensing systems should be used as complementary—rather than competing—tools, and the first step in a remote-sensing investigation should be to determine the extent and kinds of remote-sensor coverage that are available.

When records from all, or at least most, of the remote sensors are available, a definite sequence of analysis should be followed. This sequence consists of review of available regional geologic mapping, followed by local geologic and confirmatory mapping.

Regional mapping is usually carried out within a radius of from 80 to 320 km of the site; local mapping is generally confined within a 6- to 8-km radius. Confirmatory mapping is undertaken in special "target" areas defined during the image interpretation. In general, the sequence is from smaller scale to larger scale, from lower information content to higher information content (not necessarily information content as a whole, just that part applicable to the problem at hand—in this case, nuclear power plant siting). This sequence is given below, along with some of the analytical methods that should be used.

The first sensor record to be interpreted should be Landsat data. (It is assumed that a thorough search and study of the available geologic literature has been conducted before beginning the remote-sensor work.) The reason for using Landsat first is that it provides the broadest overview. The scale of the Landsat coverage should be either 1:500,000 or 1:250,000. Scales smaller than 1:500,000 are generally too small for the display of information; scales larger than 1:250,000 generally result in an unacceptable degradation of image quality.

In addition to refining the basic tectonic and lithologic information for the region, the Landsat coverage also serves as a good base map on which to record the analyses of the other sensor records, although its cartographic properties leave something to be desired. [Colvocoresses and McEwen (1973) reported that 1:1,000,000 is the largest scale at which bulk-processed multispectral Landsat imagery meets U.S. National Map Accuracy Standards for accurate placement of planimetric data.]

The Landsat image should first be examined for evidence of alignments and/or offsets indicative of faulting, as described above, and next for patterns of drainage, vegetation, texture, and tone that are indicative of lithologic differences and folded structure. Good general rules of interpretation are (1) that the image should be rotated in 45° intervals or less, from time to time, so as to preclude directional biases of the eye (some analysts tend to preferentially see north-south and east-west lineaments, whereas others have a bias for the northwest-southeast and northeast-southwest directions), and (2) the interpretation and analysis process should be broken up into a series of 1- to 2-h periods, rather than carried out in a single session, because efficiency drops off rapidly beyond the 2-h period.

For geologic information, it is best to analyze spectral bands 5 and 7 and a color infrared composite. Usually each of these spectra has recorded information that is not apparent on either of the others.

Finally, and most importantly, the work of one analyst should be checked by another, and proposed additions, deletions, or other recommendations should be discussed by the two. The most seasoned professional is occasionally overzealous or overcautious. In nuclear power plant site investigations, "quality assurance" programs require that such checking be done.

At this point, the results of the Landsat analysis should be transferred to a base map, at a scale of 1:250,000, or the Landsat image itself may be used as the base map. In either case, known structural and lithologic features from published maps, if any, should be combined with the Landsat analysis. The known structures should be delineated in a different color so that the two can be readily distinguished from one another.

When known structures have been detected by Landsat, this should be indicated. A simple, mnemonic annotation is sufficient, such as K for "known" and L for "Landsat." Progressively, the analysis of each available sensor record (Skylab, SLAR, aeromagnetic survey, aeroradioactivity survey, and so forth) will be transferred to this base map, and multiple detections of structures by different sensors will be identified by multiple combinations of letters, such as the designation LSR for a feature detected by Landsat, Skylab, and radar (SLAR). The structures can then be assigned a relative probability of existence, with those detected by a greater number of sensors being more probable than those detected by a lesser number.

The resulting regional map will be a synthesis of the analyses of all the small-scale remote-sensor records, namely, Landsat, Skylab, SLAR, aeromagnetic surveys, and aeroradiometric surveys, and may include lineaments from gravity maps as well. When this regional map has been completed and the regional structural framework has been established, the analytical effort shifts to the analysis of the large-scale sensor records—aerial photos and thermal infrared—to establish the local structure.

The base map for local structure should be USGS 7½-minute quadrangle sheets at the scale of 1:24,000. The geologic structures are transferred from the regional map to the appropriate local base map; next, a detailed, systematic analysis of the aerial photos is made, and the results are added to the map (now a photogeologic map). The final remote-sensing analysis is to examine the thermal infrared records for thermal anomalies, determine which of these appear to have a structural or lithologic cause, and add them to the photogeologic map of the site area.

Up to this point, the locations of lineaments detected by the remote sensors have been "validated" by noting the number of remote sensors on which detection has occurred. No geophysical or field-geologic examination has yet been performed. The next and final level of study of the local area of interest— field verification of lineaments within 5 to 8 km of the site—is much more costly in terms of time and personnel, transportation, subsistence, and geophysical instrument rental or purchase.

Field investigations usually begin with reconnaissance geologic mapping along lineaments annotated on aerial photographs (stereo pairs); this mapping should be at a scale of 1:24,000 or larger. The object of this work is not only to verify that a feature such as a fault or sink hole exists or does not exist, but also to examine the surficial materials for evidence of recent movement. Evidences for faulting are too numerous to describe here, but have been well documented by, among others, Lahee (1961, p. 245–268). Faults and fractures should be described in detail, especially relationships that indicate termination or renewal of movement, with plan-view and cross-section sketches and, if possible, photographs. Detailed geologic mapping (scale 1:1,200 or larger) may be required in critical junction areas or areas of complex geology.

Field investigation of aeromagnetic and aeroradioactivity lineaments and anomalies can include collection of rock samples for analysis of magnetic susceptibility and radioactivity. Detailed ground geophysical follow-up (seismic, magnetic, gravity, and scintillometer surveys) can more accurately locate the position of the anomaly so that boreholes or trenches can be made.

Once the lineament has been verified to be a fault zone or similar geologic structure potentially hazardous for the nuclear power plant, an evaluation of its capability is made. This is done in accordance with U.S. Nuclear Regulatory Commission (NRC) criteria (see Code of Federal Regulations, 1978), by attempting to correlate local seismicity with the fault zone, and by examining evidence from trenches, boreholes, or outcrops of the fault zone's capability or noncapability for future seismic activity.

CASE HISTORIES OF RECENT FAULT STUDIES FOR NUCLEAR POWER SITES USING REMOTE-SENSING TECHNIQUES

Brandywine Dome

The Brandywine domal structure (Fig. 3) was first identified by Washington Gas Light Company in Atlantic Coastal Plain sediments near Brandywine, Maryland, about 24 km southeast of Washington, D.C., and 39 km northeast of the Douglas Point nuclear power site. Figure 3 shows the location of the dome as defined by a structure-contour map on the top of the Marlboro Clay, a distinctive 9-m-thick index unit within the Eocene Nanjemoy Formation.

The buried geologic structure in the Brandywine region was disclosed during an investigation by the Washington Gas Light Company, preliminary to an underground gas storage project. Aeromagnetic and gravimetric maps and more than 5,000 water-well logs of the Brandywine region had been studied in an early stage of the company's investigation to select sites for more detailed investigation. Further work by Washington Gas Light, including deep drilling and seismic reflection studies using the Vibroseis[1] technique (Jacobeen, 1972), showed unmistakable displacements of the basement surface and disturbance of Cretaceous and Tertiary sediments overlying the basement offset. The main fault was interpreted as a reverse fault. It is up-thrown on the east, is rooted in the basement, and dips progressively less steeply and with decreasing displacement of the overlying sediments as the upper limit of the Vibroseis record is approached.

Consultation with Frank Jacobeen of Washington Gas Light and review of selected parts of his data indicated that the Brandywine fault system was present in an area extending from northeast of the town of Brandywine in Prince Georges County, southwestward, passing near the town of Danville and into northern Charles County toward Port Tobacco (Fig. 4). Geophysical evidence along the fault trace on either side of the Danville area and subsurface information from several deep boreholes in the area indicated the presence of the basement discontinuity. The significance of this basement discontinuity was evaluated in terms of the NRC (then AEC) criteria, and further detailed investigation of the fault system was undertaken.

---

[1] Registered trademark of Continental Oil Company.

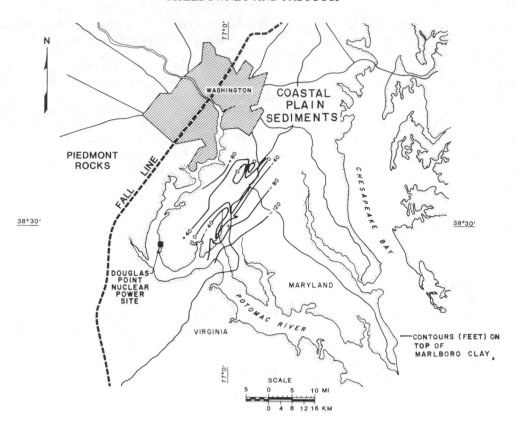

Figure 3. Location of Brandywine domal structure.

The investigation (Docket 50448-2, 1974) included drilling with continuous sampling, gamma ray and electric borehole logging, surface geologic mapping, photogeology including infrared photography and SLAR, compilation of all published well data, and a Vibroseis seismic reflection program. The objectives of the Brandywine fault investigation were to define the position, extent, and geometry of the fault and to determine the date of its most recent movement.

The locations of lineaments that were visible on the photographs are shown in Figure 4. These lineaments were not faults in themselves, but they served as a guide in planning the Vibroseis lines and drilling programs, as did the contour map on the Marlboro Clay. Field investigation found the lineaments to result from topographic and vegetative alignments in stream valleys. No surface rupture, surface warping, or geomorphic offsets were found. Although the surface lineaments and drainage patterns appear to reflect subsurface faulting, evidence indicates that these features are the result of structural control by the Marlboro Clay of subsurface drainage affecting surface drainage.

Figure 5 shows the results of the drilling program at Danville, Maryland, just west of Brandywine. This was one of two drilling investigations (including the Brentland drill site) designed to determine the date of last movement of the faults in the basement, as defined by the Vibroseis study.

The subsurface investigation at Danville consisted of 13 boreholes supplemented by backhoe trenches and pits. This area was selected primarily because of property accessibility and the availability of data from previous Washington Gas Light Company investigations. A program of continuous sampling and electric logging in closely spaced boreholes was employed until the basic structural and stratigraphic control was revealed. Significant structural relief within the lower Tertiary section and the presence of a locally continuous unconformity were determined early in the drilling program.

A number of supplementary boreholes were drilled between boreholes 101 and 103 to evaluate the nature of the 30 m of structural relief encountered in the Marlboro Clay. More specifically, with such close control, it was possible to see that the structural relief is uniformly distributed over a distance of less than 30 m, as opposed to being concentrated in an even shorter horizontal distance. The uniformly distributed relief clearly demonstrates the presence of a monocline, rather than fault offset or rupture.

Trenches were dug to a depth of 3 m across the area of structural relief. No stratigraphically continuous marker was revealed within the coarse fluvial gravels and discontinuous sand and clay layers of the upland gravels; however, no indications of faulting or folding could be found among the sedimentary and erosional surfaces that were exposed.

The Danville drilling program indicated the existence of a truncated west-facing monocline in Eocene materials, overlain unconformably by relatively flat lying Miocene sediments. These were covered by a veneer of undeformed Pliocene-

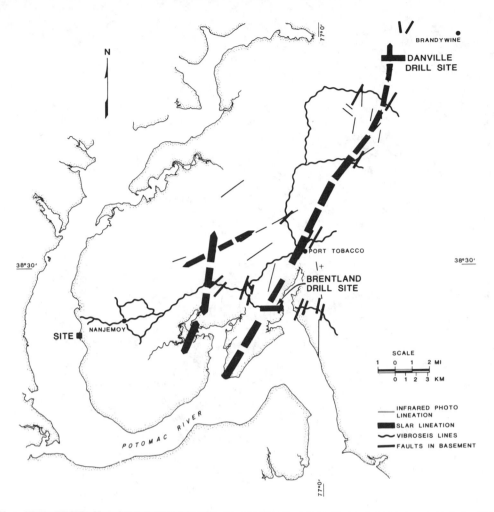

Figure 4. Basic data map, Brandywine domal structure.

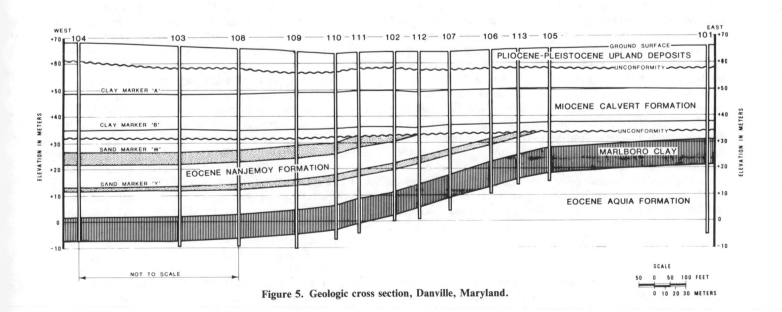

Figure 5. Geologic cross section, Danville, Maryland.

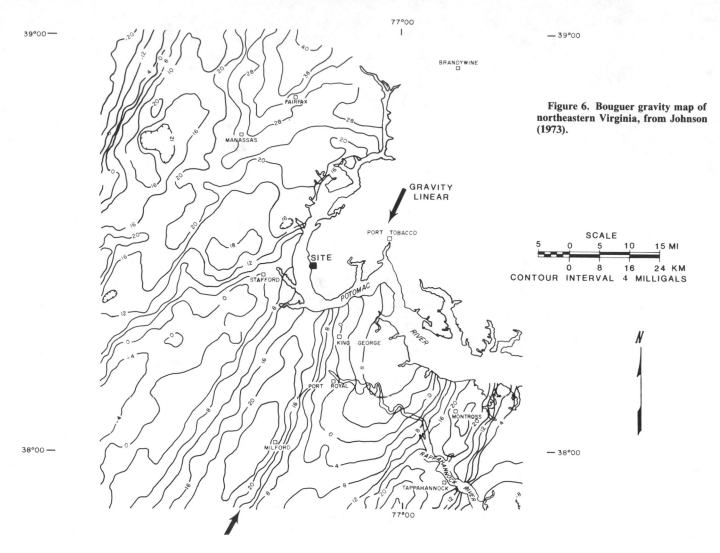

Figure 6. Bouguer gravity map of northeastern Virginia, from Johnson (1973).

Pleistocene upland deposits. Correlation of these features with regional structure suggested that this folding could be related to a regional gravity anomaly. Figure 6 shows a northeast-trending linear feature in Virginia that appears to align with the Brandywine domal structure. To the southwest, just north of Richmond, this lineament coincides with a Triassic border fault. Weighing against a direct correlation of the Brandywine dome and the Triassic basin at Richmond are the following two facts: (1) Normal faults are not known in the Brandywine area; although thin Triassic sediments were encountered there, these sediments are not found consistently on one side or the other of the reverse faults. (2) On the basis of detailed stratigraphic correlations of Cretaceous through Miocene units in Virginia (Tiefke, 1973), the Brandywine dome does not continue southward of a point due east of Fredericksburg, Virginia.

Faults at North Anna

The North Anna Power Station is located in northern Virginia in the Appalachian Piedmont tectonic province about 112 km southeast of Washington, D.C. During excavation for generation units 3 and 4, four minor northeast-trending fault zones were exposed and examined in detail on site (Docket 50404-53, 1973). The relationship of these zones to larger structures in the region was the object of reconnaissance geologic mapping of parts of five 7½-minute quadrangles around the site.

The geologic map of the Contrary Creek quadrangle and a part of the Partlow quandrangle, Virginia (Fig. 7), displays two major structural zones that strike northeastward across the area. Three to five kilometres northwest of the site, garnet and actinolite schists lie in the axis of the apparent continuation of the Louisa or Columbia synclinorium, described in part by Hopkins (1960), Smith and others (1964), and Brown (1937). This structure plunges at a low angle to the northeast and appears to be slightly overturned to the northwest. About 2 km southeast of the site lies the axis of an anticline that is cored by a granite body and that, in most aspects, appears to be a classical gneiss dome.

The plant site is located on the northwestern side of the dome, which is gently overturned to the northwest. The fold, which forms the northern end of the dome, plunges at about

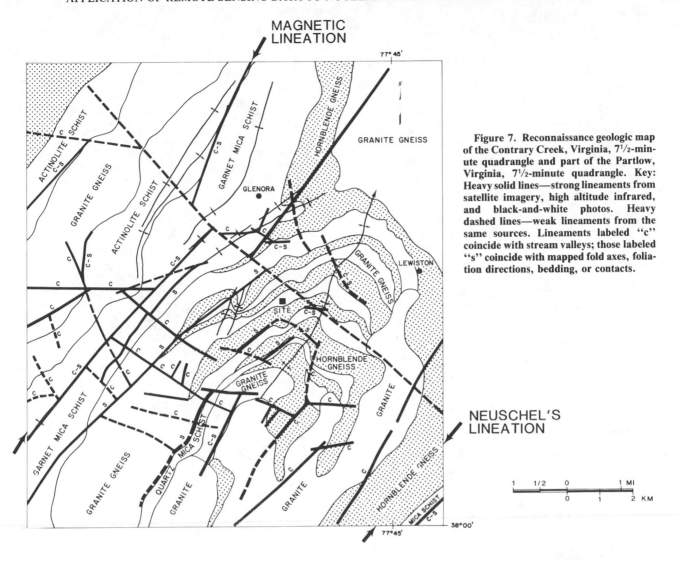

MAGNETIC LINEATION

NEUSCHEL'S LINEATION

Figure 7. Reconnaissance geologic map of the Contrary Creek, Virginia, 7½-minute quadrangle and part of the Partlow, Virginia, 7½-minute quadrangle. Key: Heavy solid lines—strong lineaments from satellite imagery, high altitude infrared, and black-and-white photos. Heavy dashed lines—weak lineaments from the same sources. Lineaments labeled "c" coincide with stream valleys; those labeled "s" coincide with mapped fold axes, foliation directions, bedding, or contacts.

20°NE to 30°NE. The massive layers of biotite-hornblende gneiss and granitic gneiss, which are the predominant rock types in the plant area, dip about 45°NW.

Aeromagnetic and aeroradioactivity maps (Neuschel, 1970) of the area outline the general rock types quite well (Figs. 8 and 9). These maps, plus other USGS published and open-file geophysical maps, were studied during the investigation and were compared to geologic maps and to lineaments found on the photographs. The plant site, located generally at the northeastern end of a broad aeromagnetic low and a tight aeroradioactivity low, is almost entirely surrounded by magnetic and aeroradioactivity highs. The strong linear magnetic anomaly just northwest of the site coincides with outcrops of a peridotite dike and other rocks in the Columbia synclinorium that contain magnetite. An equally strong anomaly occurs about 6 km southeast of the site. This particular anomaly was postulated by Neuschel (1970) to be a fault, "because the break in magnetic values is almost identical with the break in radioactivity and because the boundary is so rectilinear." Owing to the proximity of these two regional linear anomalies to the site, parts of

both were included in the area covered by the reconnaissance geologic map, and both features were examined in detail in the field for evidence of faulting (especially surface rupture, warping, or geomorphic offset). In neither area could evidence of geologically young faulting be found; however, in both areas, magnetite-rich rocks were found that undoubtedly gave rise to the anomalies. Neuchel's linear anomaly was traced southward on USGS open-file aeromagnetic maps and published geologic maps, where a number of Triassic dikes are indicated to cut across the linear anomaly with no reported offset. Work is currently underway on the northern extension of the linear anomaly at its intersection with the Fall Line; the structure may involve Cretaceous and Eocene sediments in folds and faults in a fashion similar to that found along the Brandywine dome.

To aid in the mapping and to identify possible areas of surficial rupture, detailed examination of Landsat, black-and-white aerial photos, and color infrared photographs was undertaken before, during, and after the field mapping part of the investigation. Figure 7 shows the geology in an approximately 8-km

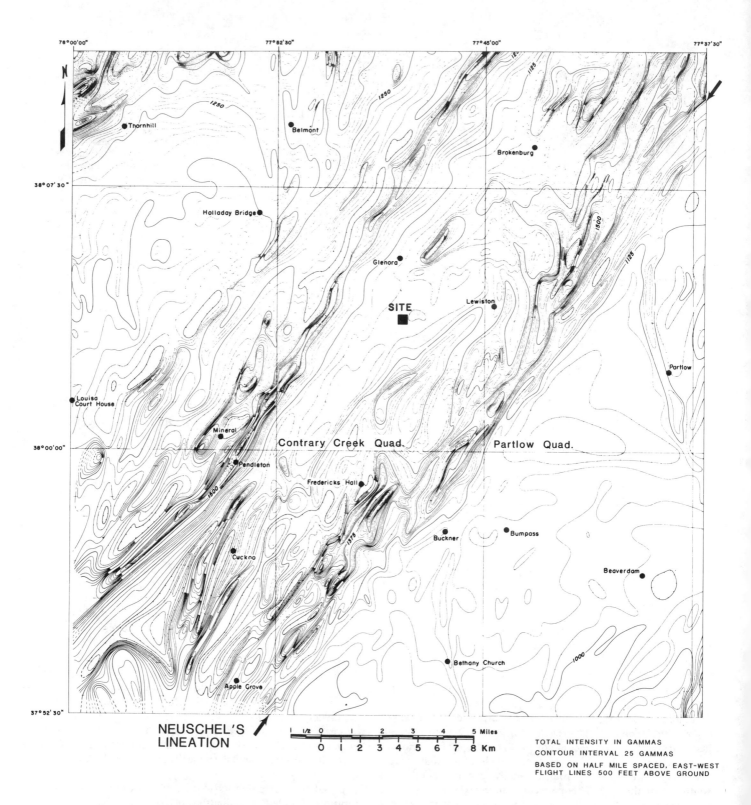

Figure 8. Aeromagnetic map of the Spotsylvania area, Virginia, from Neuschel (1970, Fig. 2).

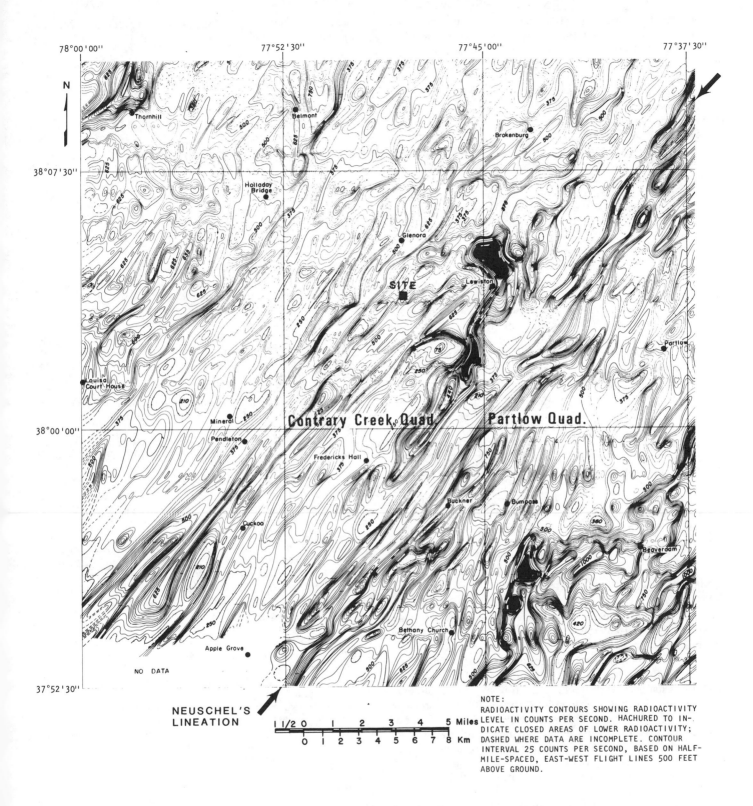

Figure 9. Aeroradioactivity map of the Spotsylvania area, Virginia, from Neuschel (1970, Fig. 3).

radius around the site, with photolineaments superimposed on the map. Each lineament topographically above the level of Lake Anna (just north of the site) was field checked. Nearly all of the lineaments coincide with stream valleys and strike generally northeast, northwest, or due east. These trends compare favorably with joint maxima contoured on stereo plots of the site area. As shown in Figure 7, most of the strong, throughgoing lineaments trend northeast and coincide with mapped fold axes, foliation and bedding directions, or contacts. The weak northwest-trending lineament (long dashed line in Fig. 7) connects the straight northwest-trending stretches of the North Anna River (not shown in Fig. 7).

Of particular importance during the investigation were photolineaments detected near the site and in the area of the magnetic and radioactivity lineaments. As shown in Figure 7, no lineaments could be found in the area of Neuschel's (1970) anomaly; however, several northeast-trending lineaments were found near the magnetic anomaly northwest of the site. On the basis of mapping, these lineaments coincide with fold axes and contacts in the Columbia synclinorium but, significantly, do not appear to cross the weak northwest-trending lineament that parallels stretches of the North Anna River.

In the site area, the closest lineament occurs approximately 1 km northwest of the powerblock. This lineament coincides with land use and drainage pattern alignments. It also reflects contacts between granitic gneiss and hornblende gneiss along parts of its length. No lineament could be found associated with the faults in the site area.

The four faults exposed at the site were examined in several trenches in rock, saprolite, and soil. Trenches in rock disclosed the presence of a mineralized set of northtrending fractures that offset three of the faults and intersect a fourth. Studies of the faults saprolite indicate that they have not moved since its formation, a minimum of 500,000 yr ago. Examination of the highly developed red-yellow podzolic soils overlying the faulted saprolite indicates that the soils have not been disturbed during a time span of possibly more than 1 m.y.

SUMMARY AND CONCLUSIONS

To summarize, the geologic analysis of remote-sensing data is playing an important role in nuclear power plant siting. The synoptic overview provided by satellite and SLAR imagery, used in conjuction with geophysical and thermal data and backed up by the highly detailed data afforded by aerial photographs, constitutes an invaluable technology for first-phase geologic investigation. Recent investigations for faults near nuclear power sites have disclosed the presence of Tertiary faulting beneath the Atlantic Coastal Plain province of the East Coast, coincident with gravity, SLAR, and photogeologic lineaments. Studies of aeromagnetic, aeroradioactivity, and photogeologic lineaments in rocks of the Piedmont province indicate good correlation with geologic structures and/or major rock units.

It is concluded that correlation of data from geologic maps with data from remote-sensing techniques can result in the definition of regional fault zones. If this correlation is carried out early in the planning stages of the siting study, it is possible

to locate the nuclear power plant away from potentially dangerous geologic structures.

ACKNOWLEDGMENTS

We acknowledge the very helpful editorial reviews of Joseph A. Fischer, Bernard Archer, James G. McWhorter, Allen Hatheway, and Vernon Anderson.

REFERENCES CITED

Abdel-Gawad, M., and Silverstein, J., 1972, Earthquake epicenters and fault intersections in central and southern California: Greenbelt, Maryland, Goddard Space Flight Center, Type II Progress Report, 23 p.

Babcock, E. A., 1971, Detection of active faulting using oblique infrared aerial photography in the Imperial Valley, California: Geological Society of America Bulletin, v. 82, p. 3189–3196.

Barthelemy, R., and Dempster, A., 1975, Geological interpretation of the ERTS-1 satellite imagery of Lesotho, and possible relations between lineaments and kimberlite pipe emplacement, in Proceedings, 10th International Symposium on Remote Sensing of Environment: Ann Arbor, Environmental Research Institute of Michigan, p. 915–924.

Brennan, P. A., and Lintz, J., Jr., 1971, Remote sensing of some sedimentary rocks, in Proceedings, 7th International Symposium on Remote Sensing of Environment: Ann Arbor, Environmental Research Institute of Michigan, p. 253–268.

Brown, C. B., 1937, Outline of the geology and mineral resources of Goochland County, Virginia: Virginia Division of Mineral Resources, Bulletin 48, 68 p.

Carter, W. D., 1975, Mineral resource investigations in South America using LANDSAT data, in Proceedings, 10th International Symposium on Remote Sensing of Environment: Ann Arbor, Environmental Research Institute of Michigan, p. 1029–1030.

Clark, M. M., 1971, Comparison of SLAR images and small-scale, low-sun aerial photographs: Geological Society of America Bulletin, v. 82, p. 1735–1742.

Code of Federal Regulations, 1978, Title 10, Energy; Part 100 [10 CFR 100], Reactor site criteria; Appendix A, Seismic and geologic siting criteria for nuclear power plants: Washington, D.C., U.S. Nuclear Regulatory Commission.

Colvocoresses, A. P., and McEwen, R. B., 1973, Progress in cartography, EROS Program, in Freden, S. C., and Becker, M. A., eds., Symposium on Significant Results Obtained from the Earth Resources Technology Satellite: Scientific and Technical Information Office, National Aeronautics and Space Administration, SP-327, p. 887–898.

Colwell, R. N., ed., 1960, Manual of photographic interpretation: Falls Church, Virginia, American Society of Photogrammetry, 868 p.

Correa, A. C., 1975, A regional mapping program and mineral resources survey based on remote sensing data, in Proceedings, 10th International Symposium on Remote Sensing of Environment: Ann Arbor, Environmental Research Institute of Michigan, p. 1057–1066.

Del Campo, C. A., 1971, Some practical results of remote sensing over test site 701, El-Oro Tlalpujahua, Mexico, in Proceedings, 7th International Symposium on Remote Sensing of Environment: Ann Arbor, Environmental Research Institute of Michigan, p. 2295–2302.

Dobrin, M. B., 1960, Introduction to geophysical prospecting (second edition): New York, McGraw-Hill Book Company, p. 321–338.

Docket 50404-53, 1973, PSAR, North Anna NPS (units 3 and 4), Louisa County, Virginia, Supplemental geologic data, Report by Dames & Moore: Richmond, Virginia, Virginia Electric & Power Company, 158 p.

Docket 50448-2, 1974, PSAR, Douglas Point NPS, Volume 2, Charles County, Maryland, Report by Dames & Moore: Washington, D.C., Potomac Electric Power Company, 390 p.

Elder, C. H., Jeran, P. W., and Keck, D. A., 1974, Geologic structure analysis using radar imagery of the coal mining area of Buchanan County, Va.: Association of Engineering Geologists, Program and Abstracts, Annual Meeting, p. 23.

Fountain, L. S., Herzig, F. X., and Owen, T. E., 1975, Detection of subsurface cavities by surface remote sensing techniques: Federal Highway Administration Report no. FHWA-RD-75-80, 126 p.

Friedman, J. D., and Williams, R. S., 1968, Infrared sensing of active geologic processes, in Proceedings, 5th International Symposium on Remote Sensing of Environment: Ann Arbor, Environmental Institute of Michigan, p. 787–815.

Gay, S. P., Jr., 1972 Fundamental characteristics of aeromagnetic lineaments, their geological significance, and their significance to geology: Salt Lake City, Utah, American Stereo Map Company, Technical Publication no. 1, 94 p.

Goetz, A.F.H., Billingsley, F. C., Elston, D. P., and others, 1973, Geologic applications of ERTS images in the Colorado Plateau, Arizona, in Proceedings, Third Earth Resources Technology Satellite Symposium, Volume 1: Greenbelt, Maryland, Goddard Space Flight Center, p. 719–744.

Gregory, A. F., 1960, Geological interpretation of aeroradiometric data: Canada Geological Survey Bulletin, v. 66, 29 p.

Gribben, H. R., Hockeborn, H., and Pascucci, R. F., 1971, SLAR—A status report: Falls Church, Virginia, American Society of Photogrammetry, Proceedings, 37th Annual Meeting, Report no. 71-148.

Holmes, R. F., 1969, Side-looking airborne radar survey: Alexandria, Virginia, Autometric Operation Raytheon Company, 8 p.

Hopkins, H. R., 1960, Geology of western Louisa County, Virginia [Ph.D. thesis]: Ithaca, New York, Cornell University, 98 p.

Howard, A. D., and Mercado, J., 1970, Low-sun-angle vertical photography versus thermal infrared scanning imagery: Geological Society of America Bulletin, v. 81, p. 521–524.

Jacobeen, F. H., 1972, Seismic evidence for high angle reverse faulting in the coastal plain of Prince George's and Charles Counties, Maryland: Maryland Geological Survey Information Circular 13, 21 p.

Johnson, S. S., 1973, Bouger gravity in northeastern Virginia and the Eastern Shore Peninsula: Virginia Division of Mineral Resources, Report of Investigations 32, 48 p.

Kamarov, V. B., and Starostin, V. A., 1975, Place and significance of radar survey in the complex of remote sensing methods used in the USSR for study of environment, in Proceedings, 10th International Symposium on Remote Sensing of Environment: Ann Arbor, Environmental Research Institute of Michigan, p. 825–834.

Lahee, F. H., 1961, Field geology (6th edition): New York, McGraw-Hill, 926 p.

Levine, S., 1975, Correlation of ERTS spectra with rock soil types in Californian grassland areas, in Proceedings, 10th International Symposium on Remote Sensing of Environment: Ann Arbor, Environmental Research Institute of Michigan, p. 975–984.

McGinnis, L. D., and Ervin, C. P., 1974, Earthquakes and block tectonics in the Illinois basin: Geology, v. 2, p. 517–519.

Moxham, R. M., 1960, Airborne radioactivity surveys in geologic exploration: Geophysics, v. 25, p. 408–432.

Neuschel, S. K., 1970, Correlation of aeromagnetics and aeroradioactivity with lithology in the Spotsylvania area, Virginia: Geological Society of America Bulletin, v. 81, p. 3575–3582.

Parasnis, D. S., 1972, Principles of applied geophysics (second edition): London, Chapman and Hall Ltd., 214 p.

Parizek, R. R., White, W. B., and Langmuir, D., 1971, Hydrogeology and chemistry of folded and faulted carbonate rocks of the central Appalachian type and related land use problems: University Park, Pennsylvania, Pennsylvania State University, College of Earth and Mineral Sciences, Circular 82, 184 p.

Pascucci, R. F., 1971, Comparative contribution of three remote sensors to geologic mapping: Falls Church, Virginia, American Society of Photogrammetry, Proceedings, 37th Annual Meeting, Report no. 71-128, p. 219–225.

Pitkin, J. A., Neuschel, S. K., and Bates, R. G., 1964, Aeroradioactivity surveys and geologic mapping, in Adams, J.A.S., and Lowder, W. M., eds., The natural radiation environment: Chicago, University of Chicago Press, p. 723–736.

Reeves, R. G., Anson, A., and Landen, D., eds., 1975, Manual of remote sensing, Volumes I and II: Falls Church, Virginia, American Society of Photogrammetry, 2,144 p.

Reid, W. M., 1973, Active faults in Houston, Texas: Geological Society of America Abstracts with Programs v. 5, p. 777–778.

Rinker, J. N., 1974, Infrared thermal detection of caves: Falls Church, Virginia, American Society of Photogrammetry, Proceedings, 40th Annual Meeting.

Rowan, L. C., Offield, T. W., Watson, K., Cannon, P. J., and Watson, R. D., 1970, Thermal infrared investigations, Arbuckle Mountains, Oklahoma: Geological Society of America Bulletin, v. 81, p. 3549–3562.

Sabins, F. F., 1969, Thermal infrared imagery and its application to structural mapping in southern California: Geological Society of America Bulletin, v. 80, p. 387–404.

Smith, J. W., Milici, R. C., and Greenberg, S. S., 1964, Geology of Fluvanna County, Virginia: Virginia Division of Mineral Resources, Bulletin 79, 62 p.

Tiefke, R. H., 1973, Stratigraphic units of the Lower Cretaceous through Miocene Series, Part 1; Geological Studies, Coastal Plain of Virginia: Virginia Division of Mineral Resources, Bulletin 83, 78 p.

Vacquier, V., Steenland, N. C., Henderson, R. G., and Zietz, I., 1951, Interpretation of aeromagnetic maps: Geological Society of America Memoir 47, 151 p.

van Dijk, C., Mulder, C. J., and others, 1971, Exploration for (shallow) geological structures with the thermal infrared imagery technique in some desert areas of Oman, in Proceedings, 7th International Symposium on Remote Sensing of Environment: Ann Arbor, Environmental Research Institute of Michigan, p. 2115–2131.

Warren, W. M., and Wielchowsky, C. C., 1973, Aerial remote sensing of carbonate terrains in Shelby County, Alabama: Ground Water, v. 11, p. 14–26.

Watson, K., Rowan, L. C., and Offield, T. W., 1971, Application of thermal modeling in the geologic interpretation of IR images, in Proceedings, 7th International Symposium on Remote Sensing of Environment: Ann Arbor, Environmental Research Institute of Michigan, p. 2017–2041.

MANUSCRIPT RECEIVED BY THE SOCIETY JULY 13, 1978
MANUSCRIPT ACCEPTED NOVEMBER 13, 1978

Geological Society of America
Reviews in Engineering Geology, Volume IV
1979

Application of microfacies analysis to the identification of stratigraphic marker beds in the Tertiary strata of northern Puerto Rico

ROBERT H. OSBORNE
Department of Geological Sciences, University of Southern California, Los Angeles, California 90007

WALTER R. JUNGE*
FUGRO, Inc., 3777 Long Beach Boulevard, Long Beach, California 90807

GEORGE A. SEIGLIE
Department of Geology, University of Puerto Rico, Mayaguez, Puerto Rico 00708

ABSTRACT

Microfacies analysis is a mature and sophisticated set of procedures for solving a variety of stratigraphic problems. One of the most important of these problems is the identification and definition of surfaces for stratigraphic correlation. There is virtually no end to the list of potential correlative surfaces that can be defined by microfacies analysis, particularly when used in conjunction with available mathematical techniques for the quantification of geologic data. Such procedures are particularly useful in stratigraphic units characterized by complex facies relationships, such as reef-associated paleoenvironments. The utility of microfacies analysis in evaluating potential sites for nuclear power plants and other engineered structures is exemplified by studies performed in conjunction with the NORCO-NP-1 nuclear power plant site in northern Puerto Rico. The definition of three microfacies (Globigerinidea, *Nummulites cojimarensis*, and *Amphistegina* spp., in ascending order) within the Quebradillas Limestone (Tertiary) at the NORCO-NP-1 nuclear power plant site demonstrated that two surfaces along which important natural gamma ray peaks occur are stratigraphically controlled rather than being controlled by dislocation surfaces, unconformities, jointing, or karstification. This was accomplished by showing that the surfaces defined by the gamma ray peaks are parallel or subparallel to two depositional surfaces, the base and top of the *N. cojimarensis* microfacies, within the apparently massive carbonates of the Quebradillas Limestone.

**Present address: Colorado Geological Survey, 1313 Sherman Street, Denver, Colorado 80203.

INTRODUCTION

The siting of nuclear power plants and other structures sensitive to faulting may necessitate the correlation of stratigraphic sections within sedimentary intervals displaying complex facies relationships. In such cases, the probability of tracing a single bed or set of beds throughout an area of interest may be rather small, and it may not be either geologically or economically feasible to seek stratigraphic markers above or below such intervals. Furthermore, facies relationships may be more conspicuous than structural features in areas with little structural relief. This paper is concerned with the use of microfacies analysis to identify marker beds within stratigraphic intervals characterized by complex facies relationships. Such strata are exemplified by Tertiary carbonates in northern Puerto Rico. The extended introduction is addressed to engineering geologists, geophysicists, and physical geologists who may not be familiar with the terminology, literature, correlative utility, and quantitative aspects of microfacies analysis. The remainder illustrates an application of microfacies analysis to the identification of stratigraphic marker beds at the NORCO-NP-1 nuclear power plant site in northern Puerto Rico.

Two major lines of research during the past several decades have made it possible to better understand sedimentary intervals with complex facies relationships. (1) A limited number of depositional models have been identified, and the lateral and vertical associations of such models have been determined. This synthesis has been accomplished by the integration of petrographic, lithologic, and surface microtextural and biologic information with primary and secondary sedimentary structures and vertical sequences of sedimentary structures. There is still a great deal to be learned about Holocene and ancient depositional environments, but available models provide useful conceptual frameworks for many sedimentological studies. (2) Insight has been gained into many diagenetic processes so that diagenetic effects can be recognized in rocks and often may be separated from features associated with formative processes which acted during sediment accumulation.

Although geochemical and geophysical methods offer promise for future paleoenvironmental analysis, petrographic study has been and probably will continue to be instrumental in the interpretation of the depositional environment of sedimentary strata, particularly when combined with knowledge of associated sedimentary structures, biological information, grain-surface microtextures, and so forth. In fact, petrographic data commonly can explain the meaning of geochemical and geophysical characteristics. The acquisition of lithologic, biologic, textural, fabric, and diagenetic information at the microscopic scale is fundamental to the subject of microfacies analysis.

Microfacies Analysis

Definitions. The term "facies" may be defined as the sum of all primary lithologic and paleontologic characteristics exhibited by a sedimentary rock from which its origin and environment of formation may be inferred (Teichert, 1958). The term "microfacies" was proposed by Brown (1943) for the features, composition, or appearance of a rock or mineral as seen in thin section or under the microscope. This term was used by Cuvillier (1951) and Fairbridge (1954) to refer to lithologic and biologic properties, or a certain "look," recognizable in thin sections of sedimentary rocks. Inasmuch as the certain "look" of a sedimentary rock may be due partly or entirely to diagenetic alteration of primary constituents, the term "microfacies" is restricted to the consideration of primary lithologic and biologic characteristics in this paper. This restriction tends to equate the definitions of facies and microfacies except for obvious difference in scale. This restriction is not intended to diminish the significance of the petrologic and stratigraphic analysis of diagenetic units. In fact, it is usually imperative to see through a diagenetic "mask" to estimate the composition and volume of each primary constituent, to identify original textures and fabrics, and to distinguish between primary and diagenetic structures. The importance of recognizing diagenetic effects will be demonstrated in the second part of this paper.

Studies of Carbonate Microfacies. Horowitz and Potter (1971, p. 18–31) presented a concise history of carbonate petrology emphasizing those studies that have made major use of the petrographic microscope. Their list of 144 annotated references (p. 20–31) arranged in chronologic order (1851–1970) is particularly informative concerning the historical development of knowledge of carbonates. Furthermore, they provided a list of 28 annotated references (p. 82–83) concerning major studies in carbonate microfacies. Cuvillier (1951) should probably be credited with the concept of interpreting microfacies in terms of depositional environments, and Carozzi (1951) was among the first to quantify microfacies analysis by showing temporal and spatial variations in the major mineral and organic components of stratigraphic units. Carozzi and others (1972) have

written a definitive volume concerning the microfacies of the Jurassic System of the western Aquitaine. This microfacies atlas includes the stratigraphy, petrography, diagenesis, geochemistry, petrophysics, and depositional environment of samples assigned to the Jurassic System within a geographically well-defined area. All lithostratigraphic units discussed in Carozzi and others' volume are based on the petrographic examination of thin sections, although certain of these units are also recognizable in the field and/or by subsurface methods. Wilson (1975) has synthesized a great deal of information regarding carbonate depositional patterns to identify recurring depositional models in various sedimentary basins through geologic time. He has recognized 24 standard microfacies and grouped them into eight major depositional environments (facies belts). Wilson developed this synthesis by directing attention to both petrographic analysis and the stratigraphic relations of carbonate bodies. Wilson (1975, p. 63) credited Flügel (1972) with adding sedimentological criteria to the basic paleontological approach used by many European researchers in microfacies analysis; Wilson also credited Flügel with the recognition of many of the basic microfacies types.

Studies of Terrigenous Sand and Sandstone Microfacies. Pettijohn and others (1972) have amassed a wealth of information concerning the composition, petrography, texture, fabric, transportation, sedimentary structures, depositional environments, tectonic setting, diagenesis, and evolution of sand and sandstone. Their work includes a number of excellent reference lists, and the annotated bibliographies (75 entries) of comprehensive petrographic analyses of sandstone (p. 245–250) and sand (p. 250–252) are of particular interest to this discussion. Terrigenous sandstone sequences in sedimentary basins commonly have distinct populations of detrital constituents that occupy unique spatial and temporal configurations. Such populations constitute operational stratigraphic units defined as "sandstone petrofacies" (Dickinson and Rich, 1972). It is clear that the concept of sandstone petrofacies is closely related to the concept of microfacies. The distribution of these constituent populations may provide important depositional and/or diagenetic information concerning basinal development. Microfacies analyses are not yet common in recent literature on sand and sandstone because of the large quantity of information and data processing required to define them and because many important questions regarding sandstone petrogenesis can be answered by stratigraphic and paleocurrent information. The utility of the petrofacies or microfacies concept in the analysis of terrigenous sand and sandstone is demonstrated in recent studies by Fuchtbauer (1964, 1972), Davies and Ethridge (1975), Shukis and Ethridge (1975), Stanley (1976), Rice and others (1976), Lobo and Osborne (1976), and Combellick and Osborne (1977).

Stratigraphic Correlation by Microfacies Analysis. Stratigraphic correlation refers to the demonstration of equivalency of lithostratigraphic, biostratigraphic, chronostratigraphic, or other types of stratigraphic units. In each case it is necessary to identify the nature of the equivalency unless the context of the usage makes this clear. Krumbein and Sloss (1963) sagaciously discussed the principles of stratigraphic correlation. As they pointed out, technological advances for measuring and recording geologic properties of strata have and will continue to broaden the scope of criteria available for stratigraphic correlation. Furthermore, the bounding surfaces of natural units defined by newer analytical techniques may not coincide with more traditional stratigraphic contacts. Many such units defined by heavy-mineral composition, insoluble residues, trace-element content, seismic velocity, electrical properties, and so forth may be defined as "parastratigraphic units" that commonly lack either mappability or lithologic homogeneity, both of which are required to define lithostratigraphic units at the formational rank. The definition of formal biostratigraphic units does not require mappability as a factor, and the biologic consistency required is dependent on the type of unit. The aspect of a given microfacies commonly depends on both lithologic and biologic characteristics of a sediment or sedimentary rock. Thus the boundaries of a given microfacies may coincide with those of traditional lithostratigraphic or biostratigraphic units, or they may be unrelated to traditionally defined boundaries. Fairbridge (1954) pointed out the importance of microfacies analysis for stratigraphic correlation.

Griffiths (1967) introduced the general problem of sampling sedimentary strata; provided a useful summary of operational definitions commonly used to measure grain size, grain shape,

grain packing, and modal analysis of sediment and sedimentary rocks; and introduced the concepts of data processing and reduction. Carver (1971) provided a useful guide to currently conventional methods of measurement and analysis in sedimentary petrology. Many of these analytical techniques are fundamental to the identification and definition of microfacies. Whereas Carver (1971) presented an excellent discussion of the techniques of experimental analysis, Griffiths (1967) addressed the entire methodology involved in the analysis of sediments and sedimentary rocks.

The problem of statistically sampling a geologic population is difficult in most cases, and there is generally no simple solution. Griffiths (1966) and Griffiths and Ondrick (1968) discussed some of the problems involved in obtaining a representative sample from sedimentary strata. The number of samples required and the vertical and/or lateral spacing of these samples are a function of the purpose of the sampling, the number of variables being examined, the abundance of each variable, the degree of accuracy required, the precision required, the variance of each variable, the funding available, the time available, the analytical expertise available, and so forth. In most studies it is desirable to develop an experimental

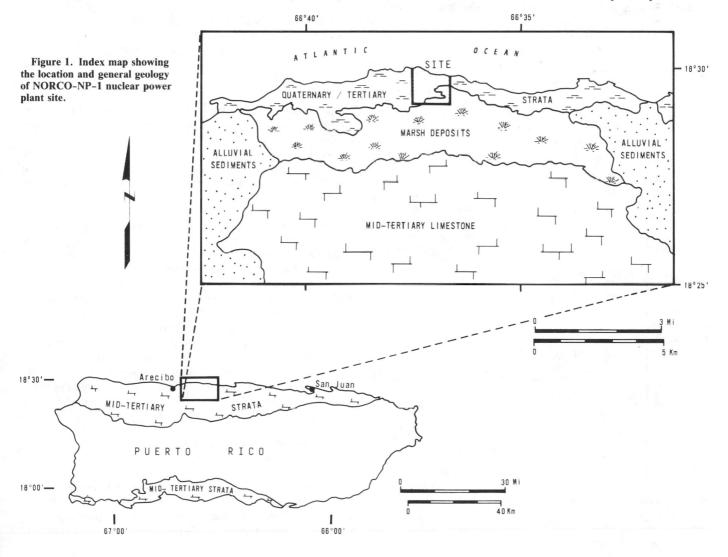

Figure 1. Index map showing the location and general geology of NORCO-NP-1 nuclear power plant site.

design that maximizes the information obtained and minimizes the investment in time and money. Normally a pilot study is performed to afford estimates of variance and to locate critical stratigraphic levels of potential correlative importance. Then detailed studies are designed to evaluate the correlative utility of these stratigraphic surfaces. The spacing of samples depends largely on the degree of accuracy required to define a given stratigraphic surface. Inasmuch as surface and subsurface samples commonly are obtained during studies of potential sites for major structures, thin sections can be prepared wherever additional information is required. A classic study in microstratigraphy was performed by Goldman (1926), who used microfacies analysis on only two samples to determine whether a stratum 2 cm thick should be assigned to the Ordovician or Mississippian System. Carozzi and others (1972) and Wilson (1975) discussed methods and problems of stratigraphic correlation in carbonate microfacies.

Data obtained by microfacies analysis are usually sequential, which means they are characterized by their position along a single line, for example, a succession of lithologic, biologic, geochemical, and geophysical variables along a core or borehole. Davis (1973) presented an excellent discussion of the analysis of sequential data including topics such as runs tests,

transition matrices, autoassociation and cross-association, Fourier analysis, autocorrelation and cross-correlation, time-trend analysis, and regression analysis. These statistical techniques may be employed to aid in the identification and definition of potential correlative surfaces. The selection of a particular technique depends largely on the measurement scale of each variable and whether the spacing between successive observations is regular or irregular. Davis (1973) and Harbaugh and Merriam (1968) discussed many examples illustrating the geologic application of these mathematical techniques. Anderson and Koopmans (1963) and Anderson and Kirkland (1966) employed time-series analysis for intrabasinal varve correlation, and Dean and Anderson (1967) used a similar methodology for the stratigraphic correlation of turbidite strata. Mrakovich and others (1976) successfully used Fourier analysis to define shape zones of quartz clasts which have correlative significance in the Louisiana offshore Pliocene. There is virtually no end to the list of potential correlative surfaces that can be defined by microfacies analysis, particularly when used in conjunction with available mathematical techniques for the quantification of geologic data.

IDENTIFICATION OF STRATIGRAPHIC MARKER BEDS, NORCO-NP-1 NUCLEAR POWER PLANT SITE, NORTHERN PUERTO RICO

Geologic Setting

Puerto Rico is an island near the northeast corner of the Caribbean Sea. The island, approximately rectangular in shape, is about 175 km long (east-west) and about 65 km wide (north-south). Puerto Rico includes three main geomorphic divisions: a mountainous area that comprises the southern two-thirds of the island, a belt of rugged karst terrain in the north-central and northwestern parts of the island, and a discontinuous fringe of relatively flat coastal plain.

In northern Puerto Rico, strata of Tertiary age crop out in a belt that extends from Loiza Aldea (about 20 km east of San Juan) westward to the westernmost tip of the island (Fig. 1). This belt is quite narrow at the extremities, but it widens to a maximum of about 26 km near Arecibo. The NORCO-NP-1 nuclear power plant site lies within this belt of Tertiary strata (Fig. 1). Two formations of Tertiary age occur in the site exploratory boreholes: the lower is the Aymamon Limestone, and the upper is the Quebradillas Limestone (Fig. 2). These two formations are separated by a well-defined unconformity in the site area. The Quebradillas Limestone is unconformably overlain by undifferentiated strata of Quaternary age. Monroe (1973) presented a general description of the stratigraphy in northern Puerto Rico.

Stratigraphic Position of Natural Gamma Ray Peaks, Quebradillas Limestone

Two natural gamma ray peaks were found within the Quebradillas Limestone in each of the NORCO-NP-1 boreholes so logged (Fig. 3). Both of these natural gamma ray peaks appeared to be due to concentrations of uranium daughters, particularly

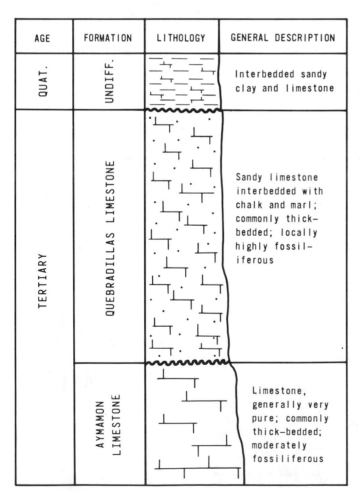

AGE	FORMATION	LITHOLOGY	GENERAL DESCRIPTION
QUAT.	UNDIFF.		Interbedded sandy clay and limestone
TERTIARY	QUEBRADILLAS LIMESTONE		Sandy limestone interbedded with chalk and marl; commonly thick-bedded; locally highly fossiliferous
	AYMAMON LIMESTONE		Limestone, generally very pure; commonly thick-bedded; moderately fossiliferous

Figure 2. Generalized stratigraphic column of rocks penetrated at NORCO–NP–1 site.

[214]Bi. The occurrence of these peaks was of particular interest because they represented potential marker horizons for correlative use for both site and off-site boreholes.

One major problem that had to be resolved before either the lower or upper natural gamma peak could be used for correlative purposes was whether each of these peaks was stratigraphically controlled. The facts that the natural gamma ray peaks were persistent, that the distance between the peaks was relatively consistent (6.1 to 12.2 m), that the thickness of the response intervals was relatively consistent (0.6 m to 2.1 m), and that the major peaks bore a consistent relationship to less definitive responses between them indicated that the gamma peaks were controlled by primary or secondary stratigraphic features. These facts in themselves, however, did not constitute proof of primary or secondary stratigraphic control, because these same relationships can develop along surfaces not directly controlled by stratigraphy. Horizontal to low-angle, subparallel surfaces within a relatively small area can be produced by gravity sliding and thrust faulting (such dislocation surfaces are commonly obscure in carbonate sequences), major collapse structures resulting from karstification, joints, unconformities, and so forth.

The strongest line of evidence to demonstrate stratigraphic control for each peak was the general parallelism of that peak with depositional surfaces within the Quebradillas Limestone. It was necessary to relate the peaks to conformable units within the Quebradillas Limestone, because the Quebradillas Limestone was bounded by unconformities in the site area. Even though the surfaces defined by the two peaks were subparallel, initially the stratigraphic position of the lower peak was questionable. In places the lower peak appeared to be near the base of the Quebradillas Limestone but elsewhere appeared to be within the upper part of the Aymamon Limestone; this indicated that the lower peak apparently occurred at different positions across a well-defined unconformity. The situation suggested that (1) the peaks developed along surfaces that were not stratigraphically controlled, (2) there were a number of discontinuous strata yielding high natural gamma ray responses, or (3) the stratigraphic contacts were misidentified in some cases.

Approach to Solving the Problem

It was necessary to identify depositional markers within the upper Aymamon Limestone and Quebradillas Limestone to determine whether the natural gamma ray peaks were stratigraphically controlled. The Quebradillas Limestone had long been thought to represent a massive unit incapable of being subdivided into smaller stratigraphic units; however, microfacies analysis demonstrated that this is not the case.

Although the microfacies in the site area have been named after numerically important foraminifera (Seiglie and Moussa, 1975), both lithologic and biologic criteria contribute to the aspect of each microfacies. Consequently, the general lithology and then the foraminiferal micropaleontology and age for each microfacies will be discussed in that order.

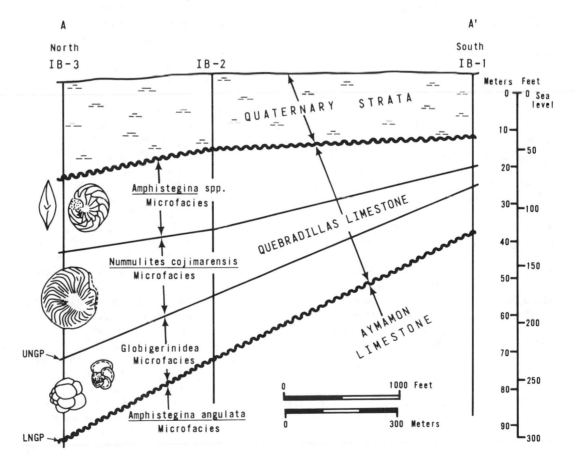

Figure 3. Stratigraphic cross section through boreholes IB-1, IB-2, and IB-3 showing the sequence of Tertiary microfacies in the upper Aymamon Limestone and the Quebradillas Limestone. The location of this cross section is indicated in Figures 6 and 7.

Aymamon Limestone

Lithology. The Aymamon Limestone extends from Loiza Aldea at the eastern edge of the depositional basin west to the coast north of Aquadilla (Monroe, 1973). The upper part of the Aymamon Limestone is a thick-bedded to massive, dolomitic limestone which is commonly free from detrital quartz clasts. It contains abundant recrystallized or dolomitized fossils including coralline algae, corals, echinoderms, mollusks, and foraminifera. Petrographically, the limestone is algal-foraminiferal biomicrite, and micrite apparently accounts for as much as 80% to 85% by volume. Much of the micrite in these samples has been recrystallized to microspar or is partly dolomitized so that its genesis is difficult to ascertain. Of the five major fossil groups represented, only benthonic foraminifera (1% to 3%) and coralline algae (8% to 16%) are volumetrically significant. Although recrystallization and dolomitization have masked much of the original limestone fabric, these framework elements often appear to float in a micritic matrix. Examination by means of cathodoluminescense shows that coralline algae are much more extensive than superficially appears. Therefore, some of these samples may be bound, at least partly, by coralline algae.

Amphistegina angulata **Microfacies.** The *Amphistegina angulata* microfacies includes the total section of the Aymamon Limestone penetrated in the NORCO-NP-1 site boreholes (Fig. 3). This microfacies (Fig. 4A) is defined by the relative abundance of *A. angulata,* which ranges from 75% to 100% of the total foraminiferal assemblage. Other benthonic foraminifera in this microfacies occur in very small percentages. The most significant ones are *Orbitolites? americana, Gypsina* spp., *Heterostegina* sp., *Archais* sp., and several species of Miliolidae. *A. angulata* occurs mainly in fore-reef environments. The presence of abundant *A. angulata,* relatively abundant coralline algae and mollusks, the absence of green algae and back-reef foraminifera, and the presence of some planktonic foraminifera suggest a fore-reef or reef-talus depositional environment for strata assigned to the upper part of the Aymamon Limestone. It is likely that these strata were deposited at water depths from 20 to 30 m.

The benthonic foraminifera in the Aymamon Limestone have a long stratigraphic range. *A. angulata* ranges from middle Miocene to Pliocene, *O.? americana* ranges from latest early Miocene to late Miocene and possible early Pliocene, and the other species have even longer ranges. Among the mollusks, *Orthaulax* ranges from middle to late Miocene in Puerto Rico, and *Ostrea haitensis* occurs in the Ponce Limestone in Puerto Rico, which is late Miocene or even Pliocene (Bold, 1969). Macsotay (1965) reported *O. haitensis* in the *Globorotalia acostaensis* Zone, which is late Miocene. The most probable age for the upper part of the Aymamon Limestone in the NORCO-NP-1 site is late Miocene.

Quebradillas Limestone

Lithology. The Quebradillas Limestone occurs in a discontinuous belt that extends from the Rio de la Plata west to Isabela (Monroe, 1973). The basal beds of the Quebradillas Limestone are commonly pinkish- to reddish-gray in contrast to the very pale orange to light gray of the Aymamon Limestone. Although the Quebradillas Limestone is predominantly limestone, most of this unit contains appreciable quantities of detrital quartz silt or sand. The carbonates of the Quebradillas Limestone are generally biomicrites in the site area, but some calcarenites also occur, particularly in the upper part of this unit. Micrite constitutes approximately 56% to 77% by volume of the samples analyzed, sparite 2% to 11%, skeletal grains 12% to 13%, and detrital clasts 3% to 12%. Although there are some important differences, the carbonate framework elements consist of the same major fossil groups as occur in the samples from the Aymamon Limestone. The foraminifera in the lower Quebradillas Limestone are dominantly planktonic, whereas those in the upper Aymamon Limestone are dominantly benthonic. Seiglie and Moussa (1975) demonstrated that the foraminiferal content varies stratigraphically within the Quebradillas Limestone. In the site area, samples from the Quebradillas Limestone tend to have a greater volume percentage of foraminifera and mollusk grains than do samples from the Aymamon Limestone, whereas samples from the Aymamon Limestone tend to have a greater volume percentage of coralline algae.

The occurrence of detrital quartz clasts and authigenic glauconite is restricted to the Quebradillas Limestone in the site boreholes. Detrital ilmenite-magnetite is restricted to the Quebradillas Limestone except for one borehole, where the ilmenite-magnetite occurs just below the contact between the Aymamon Limestone and Quebradillas Limestone. This occurrence of ilmenite-magnetite in the uppermost Aymamon Limestone probably represents detrital clasts washed into a scour or solution pit associated with the unconformity at the top of the Aymamon Limestone.

Detrital quartz grains range from 0.12 to 0.40 mm in apparent (thin-section) grain diameter and generally coarsen upward through the Quebradillas Limestone. Both monocrystalline and polycrystalline quartz grains occur; these display either straight or slightly undulose extinction. The grains range from subangular to round and are usually subangular to subround. There are generally fewer than five subunits in the polycrystalline grains; this suggests derivation from a silicic plutonic source rock. There are no highly sheared or foliated clasts suggestive of a metamorphic source terrane.

Glauconite commonly occurs as greenish pellets and as fillings in foraminiferal tests within the Quebradillas Limestone. The formation of glauconite is exclusively marine, and where it occurs as fillings in foraminiferal tests there is little doubt of its authigenic character. The glauconite in the Quebradillas Limestone is commonly partly or almost completely altered to iron oxides. Examination of even highly altered glauconite by means of cathodoluminescence permits traces of unaltered glauconite to be identified.

There is little evidence of extensive recrystallization or dolomitization within the Quebradillas Limestone. Micrite is partially altered to microspar, and occasional clusters of euhedral dolomite rhombs occur usually within fields of micrite and microspar. The basal part of the Quebradillas Limestone displays slightly greater secondary alteration in certain localities, which is probably a result of ground-water movement along the unconformity at the top of the Aymamon Limestone.

In general near the site, the Quebradillas Limestone has been less affected by secondary alteration than has the Aymamon Limestone. Therefore, the use of the highest stratigraphic occurrence of largely recrystallized and partly dolomitized limestone (Aymamon Limestone) to identify the stratigraphic position of the contact between the Aymamon Limestone and Quebradillas Limestone usually is justified.

The Quebradillas Limestone contains three well-differentiat-ed microfacies that represent three environments related to different depths of water (Seiglie and Moussa, 1975). In ascending stratigraphic order these are the Globigerinidea microfacies, the *Nummulites cojimarensis* microfacies, and the *Amphistegina* spp. microfacies (Fig. 3).

Globigerinidea Microfacies. The Globigerinidea microfacies is defined by the relative abundance of planktonic foraminifera (Fig. 4B), which constitute 75% to 99% of the total foraminiferal

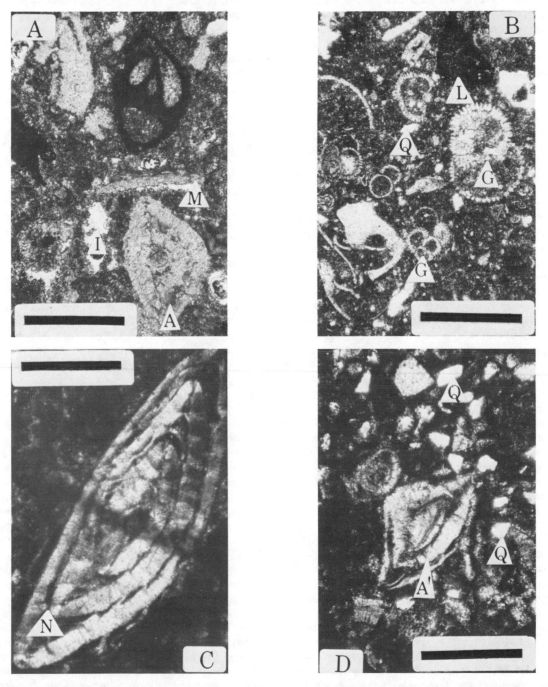

Figure 4. Photomicrographs of microfacies. A, *Amphistegina angulata* microfacies (IB-1; elev, −70.1 m). B, Globigerinidea microfacies (IB-2; elev, −67.7 m). C, *Nummulites cojimarensis* microfacies (IB-2; elev, −50.6 m). D, *Amphistegina* spp. microfacies (IB-2; elev, −36.6 m). Shown at the upper apex of lettered white triangles are *A. angulata* (A), mollusk grain (M), interstices (I), Globigerinidea (G), limeclast (L), *N. cojimarensis* (N), *A.* sp. (A′), and quartz clasts (Q). Each scale bar represents 0.5 cm.

assemblage, except near the contact with the Aymamon Limestone where it includes large amounts of reworked benthonic foraminifera from the *A. angulata* microfacies (Fig. 5A). The planktonic foraminifera of the Globigerinidea microfacies commonly consist only of inner molds of glauconite or iron oxides, which formed from the oxidation of glauconite. This microfacies contains reworked *Amphistegina* spp., as well as agglutinated foraminifera of the general *Textulariella*, *Spiroplectammina*, and *Vulvulina* types which represent fairly deep water. This microfacies contains the largest number of foraminifera per square centimetre of thin section. The number of planktonic foraminifera ranges from $300/cm^2$ to $550/cm^2$ (except for beds where the tests and molds have been highly altered by recrystallization and dolomitization) and represents from 6,000 to 12,000 foraminifera in the area of a 5-cm core, which is comparable to a deep-water globigerine ooze. The Globigerinidea microfacies represents a slope environment with water depths from 100 to 300 m or deeper.

The planktonic foraminiferal zones are referred to by an N followed by a number according to the classification of Blow (1969). Zone N 16 (*Globorotalia acostaensis–Globorotalia merotumida* Zone) and Zone N 17 (*Globorotalia tumida plesio-tumida* Zone) are late Miocene. The limit between the Miocene and the Pliocene is the middle of Zone N 18 (*Globorotalia tumida tumida–Sphaeroidinellopsis subdehiscens paenadehiscen* Zone), and Zone N 19 (*Sphaeroidinella dehiscens dehiscens–Globoquadrina altispira altispira* Zone) is early Pliocene. The most important taxa in the Globigerinidea microfacies are *Globorotalia margaritae* (Zones N 16 to N 19), *G. tumida plesio-tumida* (Zones N 17 to N 18), *G. tumida tumida* (Zone N 18 to present), and *Sphaeroidinellopsis subdehiscens immatura*. The appearance of *S. dehiscens immatura* with a dorsal secondary aperture indicates the beginning of the Pliocene. However, the presence of the secondary dorsal aperture may be caused by partial solution of the test of *S. subdehiscens paenadehiscens* so the evolutionary significance of this structure is in question. According to Bolli (1970), *Globorotalia margaritae* is limited to the Pliocene and his *G. margaritae* Zone is earliest Pliocene. *G. margaritae* is rare in this microfacies, but its scarcity may be due to solution or recrystallization. It is considered most probable that the Globigerinidea microfacies ranges in age from Zone N 17 to the top of Zone N 18, that is, late Miocene into Pliocene.

Nummulites cojimarensis **Microfacies.** The overlying *Nummulites cojimarensis* microfacies (Fig. 3) is named after the most abundant species of benthonic foraminifera (Fig. 4C) contained in these strata; however, *Amphistegina* sp. is most abundant in several samples examined. Planktonic foraminifera make up 6% to 53% of the total foraminiferal assemblage. The major taxa of foraminifera present in this microfacies suggest sediment accumulation at water depths from 20 to 70 m. Pebbles and cobbles reworked from the underlying Globigerinidea microfacies occur at several stratigraphic levels in the *N. cojimarensis* microfacies. Although this may suggest the presence of an unconformity, the fact that such clasts did not occur in all site boreholes suggests that these clasts were more likely reworked from the Globigerinidea microfacies and transported northward while the sediments of the *N. cojimarensis* microfacies were accumulating.

N. cojimarensis was reported by Bronnimann and Rigassi (1963) from rocks of middle to latest Miocene age in Cuba and by Robinson and Jung (1972) from rocks of late early Miocene age in Carriacou, West Indies. *N. cojimarensis* must range to the Pliocene in Cuba with recent adjustments of the biostratigraphic zonations; therefore, this species is not a useful stratigraphic index. The planktonic foraminifera in the *N. cojimarensis* microfacies are less abundant and have a lower diversity (number of different components of which a biologic community is composed) than in the Globigerinidea microfacies. *Globorotalia acostaensis humerosa* (*G. dutertrei* of Bermudez and Seiglie, 1969) is the only subspecies that does not occur in the Globigerinidea microfacies. This subspecies ranges in other areas from Zone N 16 to Zone N 23, and its late appearance in northern Puerto Rico is probably caused by ecological conditions. The most probable age for the *N. cojimarensis* microfacies in the site area is early Pliocene.

Amphistegina **spp. Microfacies.** The overlying *Amphistegina* spp. microfacies (Figs. 3, 4D) is characterized by two species of *Amphistegina*, one of which is *A. angulata*. Both species of *Amphistegina* are transported, as are minor quantities of planktonic foraminifera. This microfacies was probably deposited in water no deeper than 20 m, and its most probable age is Pliocene. The *A.* spp. microfacies is overlain unconformably by undifferentiated Quaternary strata.

Discussion of Results

Sedimentological Considerations. The identification of carbonate microfacies based on lithologic and micropaleontologic information from the NORCO–NP–1 site yielded the following important results. The geologic age of the Aymamon Limestone and Quebradillas Limestone was determined to be from middle (?) to late Miocene and from latest Miocene to early Pliocene, respectively. The *A. angulata* microfacies is restricted to the upper part of the Aymamon Limestone. The lithologic discontinuity between the Aymamon Limestone and the Quebradillas Limestone was found to coincide with the biostratigraphic discontinuity between the *A. angulata* microfacies and the Globigerinidea microfacies. The Globigerinidea, *N. cojimarensis,* and *A.* spp. microfacies occur in ascending order within the Quebradillas Limestone. A possible unconformity may exist between the Globigerinidea microfacies and the *N. cojimarensis* microfacies; however, it seems more likely that clasts from the Globigerinidea microfacies were reworked and transported northward while the strata assigned to the *N. cojimarensis* microfacies were accumulating in the site area. The decrease in percentages of planktonic foraminifera relative to total foraminiferal assemblages and the increase in the grain-size and quantity of detrital quartz from the Globigerinidea microfacies through the *A.* spp. microfacies indicate that the Quebradillas Limestone represents an emergent sedimentary sequence.

Relation of Natural Gamma Ray Peaks to Microfacies Boundaries. The identification of the four microfacies present in the upper Aymamon Limestone and Quebradillas Limestone permitted the recognition of the following stratigraphic markers: (1) the top of the *A. angulata* microfacies (Aymamon Limestone); (2) the highest stratigraphic occurrence of highly recrystallized and dolomitized limestone with abundant casts and molds of corals and mollusks (Aymamon Limestone); (3) the base of the Globigerinidea microfacies (top of the *A. angulata* microfacies); (4) the lowest stratigraphic occurrence of detrital quartz and, usually, magnetite-ilmenite; (5) the lowest stratigraphic occurrence of glauconite; (6) the base of the *N. cojimarensis* microfacies (top of the Globigerinidea microfacies); (7) the base of the *A.* spp. microfacies (top of the *N. cojimarensis*

microfacies); and (8) the base of the undifferentiated Quaternary strata (top of the *A.* spp. microfacies). Markers 1 through 5 may be used to define the unconformable contact between the Aymamon Limestone and the Quebradillas Limestone, and marker 8 may be used to define the unconformable contact between the Quebradillas Limestone and overlying Quaternary strata. Inasmuch as markers 6 and 7 are subparallel depositional

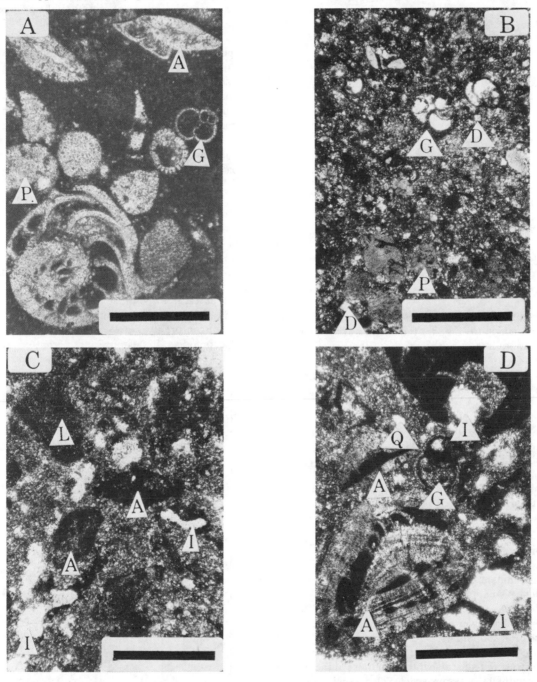

Figure 5. Photomicrographs illustrating the effects of reworking and partial dolomitization. A, Basal part of Globigerinidea microfacies with many abraded *Amphistegina angulata* reworked from the Aymamon Limestone (IB-2; elev, −73.2 m). B, Partly dolomitized Globigerinidea microfacies (IB-1; elev, −41.6 m). C, Dolomitized *A. angulata* microfacies (IB-1; elev, −43.3 m). D, Partly dolomitized Globigerinidea microfacies with reworked *A. angulata* (IB-1; elev, −41.6 m). Note overall similarity of photomicrographs 5C and 5D. Shown at the upper apex of lettered white triangles are *A. angulata* (A), Globigerinidea (G), pelmatozoan grains (P), dolomite rhomb (D), limeclast (L), interstices (I), and quartz clast (Q). Each scale bar represents 0.5 cm.

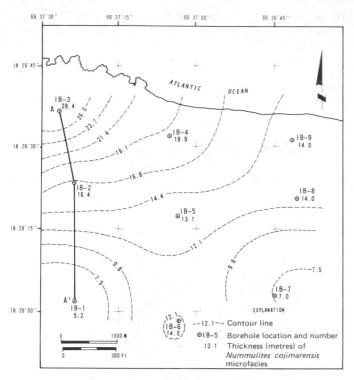

Figure 6. Isopach map of *Nummulites cojimarensis* microfacies.

surfaces within the Quebradillas Limestone, these are meaningful surfaces with which to compare the positions of the natural gamma ray peaks to determine the extent of their stratigraphic control.

The position of the upper natural gamma ray peak coincides with the base of the *N. cojimarensis* microfacies within the NORCO–NP–1 site (Fig. 3); therefore, this peak is clearly stratigraphically controlled in this area.

The lower natural gamma ray peak occurs within the basal part of the Globigerinidea microfacies; therefore, the position of this peak is controlled by sedimentological characteristics in the basal Quebradillas Limestone rather than by secondary deposition along the unconformity separating the Aymamon Limestone from the Quebradillas Limestone. The configuration of the surface defined by the lower peak clearly reflects the shape of the underlying erosional surface plus the effects of differential compaction over erosional relief developed on this unconformity.

The initial assignment of the lower natural gamma ray peak to the uppermost Aymamon Limestone in some boreholes and the basal Quebradillas Limestone in others was due to differential diagenesis in the lowermost Quebradillas Limestone. In cores from several boreholes, recrystallization and partial dolomitization of basal strata of the Quebradillas Limestone rendered these strata indistinguishable from those of the Aymamon Limestone at the megascopic scale. Petrographic examination of samples from this stratigraphic interval permitted the identification of the *A. angulata* microfacies (Fig. 5C) and the Globigerinidea microfacies (Figs. 5B, 5D) even though these microfacies are strongly masked by diagenetic effects. Identification of these microfacies demonstrated that initially the

major source of error was the misidentification of the contact between the Aymamon Limestone and the Quebradillas Limestone. When these strata were assigned to the proper lithostratigraphic units, the lower peak consistently occurred in the basal Quebradillas Limestone.

Microfacies analysis also served to demonstrate that the two natural gamma ray peaks are of different stratigraphic age. This negates the possibility of their being one surface that has been faulted and then superimposed.

The identification and substantiation of markers 6 and 7 also permit the construction of a computer-generated isopach map of a continuous sedimentary sequence (Fig. 6) as well as a structure-contour map (Fig. 7) based on a depositional surface. The comparison of isolith, isopach, and structure-contour maps of isochronous or nearly isochronous stratigraphic intervals is extremely useful for interpreting the tectonic and sedimentological history of a given area through the application of isopach-lithofacies analysis (Krumbein and Sloss, 1963; Harbaugh and Merriam, 1968).

SUMMARY AND CONCLUSIONS

The utilization of microfacies analysis achieved the following important results at the NORCO–NP–1 nuclear power plant site. Subdivision of the apparently massive limestone of the Quebradillas Limestone permitted the recognition of two depositional surfaces in contrast to the unconformities that bound this unit. Microfacies information added greatly to the definition of the unconformity between the Aymamon Limestone and the Quebradillas Limestone and permitted strata near this

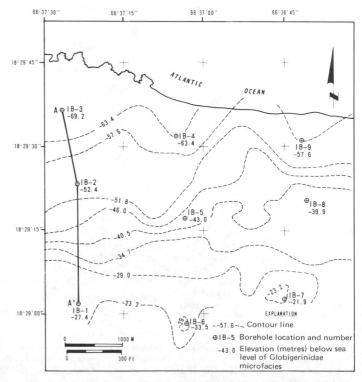

Figure 7. Structure contour map on the base of the *Nummulites cojimarensis* microfacies (top of the Globigerinidea microfacies).

contact to be assigned to the proper stratigraphic unit. Before this analysis, strata of the lower Quebradillas Limestone that had been altered diagenetically were sometimes wrongly assigned to the Aymamon Limestone. This analysis demonstrated that the lower natural gamma ray peak always occurred in the basal part of the Quebradillas Limestone. The lower and upper natural gamma ray peaks were shown to be parallel to subparallel to two depositional surfaces within the Quebradillas Limestone and that they occurred in strata of different ages. Therefore, it was demonstrated that the surfaces along which the natural gamma ray peaks occur are stratigraphically controlled and are not a single surface juxtaposed by faulting. Microfacies analysis also assisted in the solution of off-site potential structural problems by small-scale correlations across trenches and along sets of boreholes drilled across possible dislocation surfaces that were identified initially by photogeologic interpretation. These results indicate that microfacies analysis is a useful, relatively inexpensive, and sometimes necessary method for the solution of stratigraphic continuity problems.

ACKNOWLEDGMENTS

We acknowledge skillful administrative support from Allen W. Hatheway, who was instrumental in the initiation and completion of our work concerning the NORCO–NP-1 nuclear power plant site. Richard O. Shmitka was invaluable in coordinating the field and laboratory studies during the course of this work. The manuscript was critically reviewed by Gerald Friedman and James L. Wilson; we thank them. Barbara Hitchens prepared the line drawings.

REFERENCES CITED

Anderson, R. Y., and Kirkland, D. W., 1966, Intrabasin varve correlation: Geological Society of America Bulletin, v. 77, p. 241–256.

Anderson, R. Y., and Koopmans, L. H., 1963, Harmonic analysis of varve time series: Journal of Geophysical Research, v. 68, p. 877–893.

Bermudez, P. J., and Seiglie, G. A., 1969, Age, paleoecology, correlation and foraminifers of the uppermost Tertiary formation of northern Puerto Rico: Caribbean Journal of Science, v. 10, nos. 1–2, p. 17–33.

Blow, W. H., 1969, Late middle Eocene to Recent planktonic biostratigraphy, in Proceedings, First International Conference on Planktonic Microfossils, Geneva, 1967, Volume 1: Leiden, E. J. Brill, p. 199–421.

Bold, W. A. van den, 1969, Neogene Ostracoda from southern Puerto Rico: Caribbean Journal of Science, v. 9, nos. 3–4, p. 177–233.

Bolli, H. M., 1970, The foraminifera of sites 23–31, Leg 4, in Initial reports of the Deep Sea Drilling Project, Volume 4: Washington, D.C., U.S. Government Printing Office, p. 577–643.

Bronnimann, P., and Rigassi, D., 1963, Contribution to the geology and paleontology of the area of La Habana, Cuba, and its surroundings: Eclogae Geologicae Helvetiae, v. 56, p. 193–480.

Brown, J. S., 1943, Suggested use of the word microfacies: Economic Geology, v. 38, p. 325.

Carozzi, A., 1951, Rhythmes de sédimentation dans le Crétacé Helvétique: Geologisches Rundschau, v. 39, p. 177–195.

Carozzi, A., Bouroullec, J., Deloffre, R., and Rumeau, J. L., 1972, Microfacies of the Jurassic of Aquitaine, petrography-diagenesis-geochemistry-petrophysics: Bulletin du Centre de Recherches de Pau, 594 p.

Carver, R. E., ed., 1971, Procedures in sedimentary petrology: New York, Wiley-Interscience, 653 p.

Combellick, R. A., and Osborne, R. H., 1977, Sources and petrology of beach sand from southern Monterey Bay, California: Journal of Sedimentary Petrology, v. 47, p. 891–907.

Cuvillier, J., 1951, Corrélations stratigraphiques par microfacies en Aquitaine occidentale: Leiden, E. J. Brill and Co., 23 p.

Davies, D. K., and Ethridge, F. G., 1975, Sandstone composition and depositional environment: American Association of Petroleum Geologists Bulletin, v. 59, p. 239–264.

Davies, J. C., 1973, Statistics and data analysis in geology: New York, John Wiley & Sons, Inc., 550 p.

Dean, W. E., Jr., and Anderson, R. Y., 1967, Correlation of turbidite strata in the Pennsylvanian Haymond Formation, Marathon region, Texas: Journal of Geology, v. 75, p. 59–75.

Dickinson, W. R., and Rich, E. I., 1972, Petrologic intervals and petrofacies in the Great Valley sequence, Sacramento Valley, California: Geological Society of America Bulletin, v. 83, p. 3007–3024.

Fairbridge, R. W., 1954, Stratigraphic correlation by microfacies: American Journal of Science, v. 252, p. 683–694.

Flügel, E., 1972, Mikrofazielle Untersuchungen in der Alpinen Triassic—Methoden und Probleme: Mitteilung der Gesellshaft der Geologie und Bergbaustudenten in Wien, v. 21, p. 9–64.

Fuchtbauer, H., 1964, Sedimentpetrographische Untersuchungen in der älteren Molasse nördlich der Alpen: Eclogae Geologicae Helvetiae, v. 57, p. 157–298.

——1972, The Tertiary Alpine molasse, in Crawford, F. D., ed., Arenaceous deposits: Sedimentation and diagenesis: Calgary, Alberta, University of Alberta and Alberta Society of Petroleum Geologists, p. 205 218.

Goldman, M. I., 1926, Petrology of the contact of the Ordovician Ellenburger Limestone and the Mississippian limestone of Boone age in San Saba County, Texas, in Mississippian formations of San Saba county, Texas, Part IV: U.S. Geological Survey Professional Paper 146, p. 44–59, Pls. 7–33, 1 Fig.

Griffiths, J. C., 1966, Sampling a geological population: Notes from a premeeting short course, Geological Society of America, San Francisco, 85 p.

——1967, Scientific method in analysis of sediments: New York, McGraw-Hill, 508 p.

Griffiths, J. C., and Ondrick, C. W., 1968, Sampling a geologic population: Kansas Geological Survey Computer Contribution 30, 53 p.

Harbaugh, J. W., and Merriam, D. F., 1968, Computer applications in stratigraphic analysis: New York, John Wiley & Sons, Inc., 282 p.

Horowitz, A. S., and Potter, P. E., 1971, Introductory petrography of fossils: New York, Springer-Verlag, 302 p., 100 pls.

Krumbein, W. C., and Sloss, L. L., 1963, Stratigraphy and sedimentation: San Francisco, W. H. Freeman and Company, 660 p.

Lobo, C. F., and Osborne, R. H., 1976, Petrology of late Precambrian–Cambrian quartzose sandstones in the eastern Mojave Desert, southeastern California: Journal of Sedimentary Petrology, v. 46, p. 829–846.

Macsotay, O., 1965, Carta faunal de macrofosiles correspondientes a las formaciones cenozoicas de la peninsula de Araya, Estado Sucre: Geos, no. 13, p. 37–50.

Monroe, W. H., 1973, Stratigraphy and petroleum possibilities of middle Tertiary rocks in Puerto Rico: American Association of Petroleum Geologists Bulletin, v. 57, p. 1086–1099.

Mrakovich, J. V., Ehrlich, R., and Weinberg, B., 1976, New techniques for stratigraphic analysis and correlation—Fourier grain shape analysis Louisiana offshore Pliocene: Journal of Sedimentary Petrology, v. 46, p. 226–233.

Pettijohn, F. J., Potter, P. E., and Siever, R., 1972, Sand and sandstone: New York, Springer-Verlag, 618 p.

Robinson, E., and Jung, P., 1972, Stratigraphy and age of marine rocks, Carriacou, West Indies: American Association of Petroleum Geologists Bulletin, v. 56, p. 114–127.

Rice, R. M., Gorsline, D. S., and Osborne, R. H., 1976, Relationships between sand input from rivers and the composition of sands from the beaches of southern California: Sedimentology, v. 23, p. 689–703.

Seiglie, G. A., and Moussa, M. T., 1975, Paleoenvironments of Quebradillas Limestone (Tertiary), northern Puerto Rico, and their geologic significance: American Association of Petroleum Geologists Bulletin, v. 59, P. 2314–2321.

Shukis, P. S., and Ethridge, F. G., 1975, A petrographic reconnaissance of sand-sized sediment, upper St. Francis River, southeastern Missouri: Journal of Sedimentary Petrology, v. 45, p. 115–127.

Stanley, K. O., 1976, Sandstone petrofacies in the Cenozoic High Plains sequence, eastern Wyoming and Nebraska: Geological Society of America Bulletin, v. 87, p. 297–309.

Teichert, C., 1958, Concept of facies: American Association of Petroleum Geologists Bulletin, v. 42, p. 2718–2744.

Wilson, J. L., 1975, Carbonate facies in geologic history: New York, Springer-Verlag, 471 p.

MANUSCRIPT RECEIVED BY THE SOCIETY JULY 13, 1978

MANUSCRIPT ACCEPTED NOVEMBER 13, 1978

CONTRIBUTION NO. 361, DEPARTMENT OF GEOLOGICAL SCIENCES, UNIVERSITY OF SOUTHERN CALIFORNIA

Geological Society of America
Reviews in Engineering Geology, Volume IV
1979

Dating techniques in fault investigations

PHILIP J. MURPHY
JOHN BRIEDIS
JOHN H. PECK
Stone & Webster Engineering Corporation, P.O. Box 2325, Boston, Massachusetts 02107

ABSTRACT

Determining the time of most recent fault movement is an important part of assessing a possible site for a nuclear power plant. The purpose of this paper is not to present research information but to provide a practical guide to some of the dating techniques available to the engineering geologist working on nuclear power plant siting. Emphasis is placed on the practical aspects, such as usable minerals, conditions necessary for them to yield correct dates, degree of accuracy, sample collection, sample size, and sample packaging.

In this paper, we have taken for granted the usual geologic field techniques—such as those used in stratigraphy, paleontology, and structural analysis—for assessing fault history. We discuss laboratory techniques used in conjunction with or supplemental to field methods. The specific radiometric methods discussed are ^{14}C (carbon-14), fission track, K-Ar (potassium-argon), thermoluminescense, Rb-Sr (rubidium-strontium), and U-Th (uranium-thorium). Racemization of amino acids, paleomagnetism, and fluid-inclusion techniques are the nonradiometric methods that are discussed. Our experiences with some of these techniques are described as well.

INTRODUCTION

Determining the time that has elapsed since the last movement along a fault is an important phase of site studies for nuclear power plants. In the nuclear industry, the potential for movement to recur along a fault has been based on the history of faulting within the past 500,000 yr. In regulatory jargon, this is defined as the capability of the fault; U.S. Nuclear Regulatory Commission (NRC) criteria define a capable fault as a fault that has exhibited one or more of the following characteristics (Code of Federal Regulations, 1978): (1) Movement at or near the ground surface at least once within the past 35,000 yr or movement of a recurring nature within the past 500,000 yr. (2) Macroseismicity instrumentally determined with records of sufficient precision to demonstrate a direct relationship with the fault. (3) A structural relationship between a fault and a capable fault according to the above characteristics, such that movement on the capable fault could be reasonably expected to be accompanied by movement on the other fault.

These criteria are used to assess the potential for movement based on either the history of near-surface movement along known faults or close association with seismicity. Dating the time of last movement, therefore, becomes an important part of assessing the history of the faulting and site feasibility.

The intent of this paper is to present the geologist or engineering geologist engaged in the siting of nuclear power plants with a concise summary of laboratory dating techniques most often used on projects of this nature. These are (1) radiometric techniques, (2) racemization of amino acids, (3) paleomagnetism, and (4) fluid-inclusion techniques. The paper does not present original research in these dating techniques, nor does it deal with the basic structural, stratigraphic, and paleontologic methods familiar to geologists and engineering geologists.

Certain radiometric techniques are most often applied to establishing the age of some undisturbed rock, saprolite, or soil horizon overlying or transecting the fault zone; others are applied to dating materials within the fault zone itself. There are commonly no overlying strata to date the faulting, especially in much of the northern part of the Midwest and New England, where the bedrock is of Paleozoic age or older, has been considerably deformed, and is overlain (if at all) by soil or other postglacial materials that are too young (Holocene or late Pleistocene) to satisfy NRC criteria. In such geologic settings, radiometric techniques applied to minerals that have grown in the fault zone itself since its last movement may be of most use. For these techniques to be applicable, however, some gouge or mineralization containing datable minerals must be present.

Of the radiometric techniques discussed in this paper, ^{14}C (carbon-14), fission track, and K-Ar (potassium-argon) are the most often used in the dating of horizons overlying or transecting the fault zone. The K-Ar technique is the most versatile and is also used in dating minerals within the zone itself. Other less commonly used methods are U-Th-Pb (uranium-thorium-lead), Pb-Pb (lead-lead), U-^{230}Th (uranium-ionium), and U-Th-

He (uranium-thorium-helium). These may also have an application in limited circumstances.

When local geologic conditions indicate that the radiometric techniques discussed cannot be applied, the fault zone may be datable by other laboratory techniques that may give at least a good approximation of the minimum age. The techniques discussed in this category are the pressure-temperature fluid-inclusion method, paleomagnetism, and racemization of amino acids.

Figure 1 is a schematic sketch of a hypothetical fault exposed by trenching. It illustrates the possible application of laboratory methods of age determination discussed in this paper relative to their geologic setting.

CARBON-14 OR RADIOCARBON METHOD

The ^{14}C technique can be used where the strata to be dated contain charcoal, wood, peat, shells, bone, pollen, or any other organic C-bearing material.

The ^{14}C method was used effectively in a preliminary site study in Oregon. The material within the youngest marine terrace affected by faulting (see Fig. 2) was dated at 31,000 yr B.P. The ^{14}C method was also used in determining the age of carbonaceous strata overlying faulted saprolite of Piedmont crystalline bedrock in Virginia to be about 300 yr. There may have been secondary calcite mineralization which affected the final date. In any case, the date was too young to be of any use in fulfilling NRC criteria.

Description of Technique

The radiocarbon method of dating is based on the decay of the radioactive isotope ^{14}C, which is manufactured in the Earth's upper atmosphere and absorbed along with ^{12}C by living organisms. An organism maintains a relatively constant equilibrium ratio of ^{14}C/^{12}C as long as the organism is alive. After death, this equilibrium ratio no longer is maintained, and the ^{14}C begins to decay. The most accurate half-life, based on recent determinations, is 5,730 yr, but most analysts still use the international standard half-life of 5,568 ± 40 yr established by Libby (1963), with 1950 as the reference or zero age.

The type of pretreatment of a sample for radiocarbon analysis is determined from the nature of the material. Obvious foreign matter such as roots or packaging is removed, and HCl (hydrochloric acid) is used to remove inorganic or surface carbonate contaminants. In some cases, the sample is treated with a NaOH (sodium hydroxide) solution to remove absorbed humic acids.

The cleaned sample is burned to completion in oxygen and purified to remove any halides, sulfur compounds, nitrogen oxides, and any other impurities, such as radon, which may affect the counting characteristics of the gas. The purified CO_2 (carbon dioxide) may be counted directly or converted to methane and passed through low-background beta counters (if the sample is small) or to benzene which is counted in a liquid scintillation counter (if the sample is large).

The precision of the analysis ranges from ±60 yr for recent C samples to about 3% of the age of older samples. The preci-

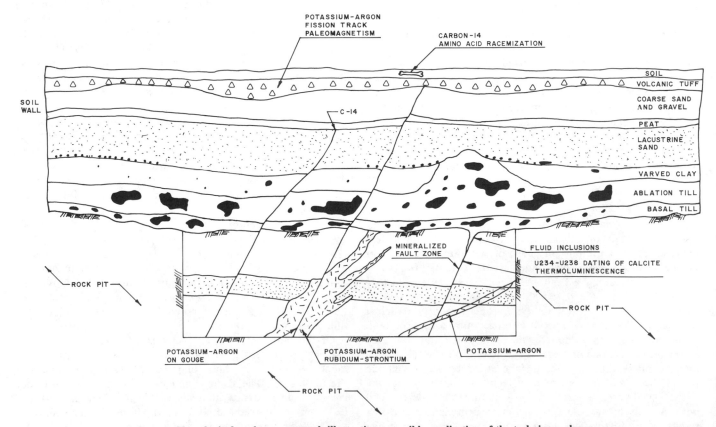

Figure 1. Hypothetical exploratory trench illustrating a possible application of the techniques shown.

sion decreases rapidly for samples older than 30,000 yr up to 50,000 yr because of contamination by younger C and the limiting amount of residual ^{14}C that can be detected. The sample is run through the counting process twice, at different times, to ensure reproducibility and eliminate the possibility of error due to traces of residual radioactive radon gas, unless radon-removal procedures are applied.

Sample Collection

The major precaution, other than careful packaging, is to prevent contamination of the sample by foreign carbonaceous material. The sample must be uniform, that is, of one C-bearing type of material, and be of a quantity sufficient for analysis (see Table 1). Samples should be shipped wrapped in several layers of aluminum foil, within sterile glass or metal containers, and under no conditions should preservatives, cotton, or paper be used in packaging the samples. The size of the sample for radiocarbon dating varies with both the expected age and the C content. Old samples or those samples low in C should be larger. Also, liberal amounts ensure that duplicate analyses may be run, if necessary. Table 1 gives the required amounts for various C-bearing materials.

Sources of Error

The major source of error is the basic assumption that the ^{14}C content of the atmosphere has been stable over long periods of time. This is dependent on the variability of the average cosmic ray intensity, the magnitude of the Earth's magnetic field, and the degree of mixing of the oceans. However, the radiocarbon age scale has been calibrated by the correlation of ^{14}C dating with tree rings in redwood, Douglas fir, and the bristlecone pine that have recorded the variations of the ^{14}C content for the past 8,000 yr (Libby, 1961).

The biggest unknown is the amount of contamination of the sample by foreign C of a different ^{14}C content. The sources of ^{14}C contamination are (1) percolating water, (2) decomposi-

tion by-products that may carry off a disproportionate amount of one C isotope, or (3) contamination by carbonaceous material entering porous structures. In the case of carbonate minerals, the organism may synthesize its skeletal structures using older inert C sources; this would result in ^{14}C dates that are older than the organism. Other possible sources of error affecting ^{14}C dates are (1) bicarbonate precipitated on or within the sample from ground water (2) rootlets too small for identification, and (3) soluble organic material borne by ground water (Olson and Broecker, 1958).

Other potential sources of contaminants are fossil CO_2 from the combustion of fossil fuels, which dilute the ^{14}C content, and atmospheric atomic tests, whcih can increase the amount of ^{14}C [variations of 3% have been noted (Libby, 1963)].

Accuracy

Treatment of samples to eliminate the above sources of error has reduced the expectable error to ±3% for samples younger than 25,000 yr and to 15% in samples as old as 50,000 yr. The errors are within reasonable limits considering the time spans and half-life involved.

Limitations of Technique and Interpretation of Date

The most limiting factor for radiocarbon dating is its geologically short half-life. However, technological advances and improvements in equipment, especially in ^{14}C counters, may extend ^{14}C dates beyond 50,000 yr in the future. Some samples as much as 75,000 yr old have been dated with some degree of reliability (Stuiver, 1977). Another limitation is the absence of datable carbonaceous material in most fault zones. Fault zones and rock units generally do not provide datable carbonaceous material, so the technique is generally limited to soils.

FISSION-TRACK DATING

This technique is useful in some rocks and minerals not datable by other radiometric techniques. The minerals that can be dated by fission tracks are zircon, sphene, apatite, muscovite, epidote, garnet, allanite, hornblende, and natural

Figure 2. A low-angle reverse fault in a coastal marine terrace in southern Oregon with about 30 cm (maximum) of dip-slip displacement. The age determined by the ^{14}C method on carbonaceous material in the terrace was 31,000 yr. Faulting is considered capable.

TABLE 1. DRY SAMPLE SIZE FOR ^{14}C ANALYSIS

Material	Optimum (g)	Minimum (g)
Charcoal	8–12	1
Wood	10–30	3
Shell*	30–100	5
Peat	10–25	2
Bone	50–500	5
Carbonate	30–100	5

Note: From Geochron, Inc. (1977, personal commun.).

*Shell material must be fresh and show no alteration to another type of carbonate mineral such as low-magnesian calcite. Oysters have the best shells for dating, as the shells are originally low-magnesian calcite.

glasses. The age that is determined by this technique is a minimum age for the last thermal event or drop in geothermal temperature that affected the mineral dated.

Description of Technique

A fission track is formed when the two nuclei from a fissioning heavy element travel through a solid. The original heavy-element nucleus breaks up, with the liberation of energy, into two lighter nuclei of approximately equal mass. The two nuclei travel away from each other in opposite directions. These nuclei are highly charged and, by their rapid movement, disrupt the electron structure of the ions in the lattice along their path. The nuclei leave behind a zone of positive charge that causes the positively charged ions in the lattice to repel each other; this results in a dislocation or track in the crystal structure. This track is stable in nonconductive solids at temperatures less than 100 °C (Doherty, 1975).

Those nuclei that spontaneously undergo fission are ^{238}U. Their tracks in the natural state are too small to be seen except with an electron microscope; for this reason, the minerals are etched to enhance analysis under an optical microscope. Each mineral requires a different technique for mounting, polishing, and etching for fission-track analysis; the method of etching should be left to the analyst. In general, by choosing the proper chemical etchant (nitric, hydrofluoric, and hydrochloric acids and concentrated sodium hydroxide solutions), it is possible to etch the damaged zone and not dissolve the crystal (Doherty, 1975). The etched tracks can be seen and counted under an optical microscope for the fossil track density. Another sample or the second half of the original sample is heated so that the fossil tracks are annealed; it is then irradiated with a suitable neutron source. The resulting tracks in the sample are called the induced tracks. (Muscovite is used as a control during irradiation. Counting the tracks in the muscovite is necessary for calibration.) The radiometric age can then be calculated from the ratio between the fossil and induced track density and the radioactive decay constants (Naeser and Dodge, 1969).

Sample Collection

Only fresh (unweathered) samples should be examined. Depending on the information desired, the samples ordinarily should not have been exposed to thermal events younger than the faulting because this would affect the age determination. Samples should be large enough to allow for the preparation of several thin sections. The minerals listed in Table 2 are the most suitable for fission-track age determination.

Sources of Error

The largest source of error is the possibility of postmineralization thermal events that will anneal the fission tracks, alter their density, and, hence, decrease the apparent age. The fission tracks do not appear until the mineral has reached a temperature below its annealing temperature. They will be "erased" if the mineral again is heated to its annealing temperature, even by the geothermal gradient. Metamorphism or a nearby intrusion can also reset the date. This sensitivity to temperature, however,

can be useful in determining the minimum age of the last major fault movement, if the mineral is very close to or within the fault zone.

Mineral zonation can affect the date that is determined. Zircon especially is subject to this type of error. In a zoned crystal, the center of the crystal is older than its outer layers. Thus, dates derived from zoned zircon will be hybrid minimum ages. Because of the high content of fissionable material in zircon and the concomitant high density of fission tracks, ages older than Cenozoic are impossible to ascertain with any accuracy (Fleischer and others, 1964).

The type of etchant used can also affect the age that is determined, though standardization of etching time and strength of the etchants have minimized this problem. Detailed work on sphene indicated an error equal to that caused by a temperature of 150 °C if HCl is used instead of NaOH (Doherty, 1975). In addition, the distribution of the fissionable material in the mineral is important. Apatite is a desirable mineral from this standpoint, because its crystallographic geometry allows an even distribution of radiogenic atoms. Other potential sources of error are high lithostatic pressures, ionizing radiation, and high water pressure.

The more serious sources of error in the laboratory analysis lie in the accurate determination of the neutron flux for each irradiated sample, the mathematics of counting statistics, and the value of the fission-decay constant for ^{238}U. There are two fission-decay values currently in contention, the "geologic" value of 6.85×10^{-17} yr^{-1} and the value of 8.46×10^{-17} yr^{-1}, based on dating of uranium glass from Grant's Tomb and on other laboratory data. The geologic constant gives concordant agreement with isotopic ages; the other constant does not (J. B. Lyons, 1977, written commun.).

The degree of accuracy of fission-track dates is as follows: sphene, 8% to 10%; zircon, 10%; epidote, 5% to 10%; allanite, 5% to 10%; and apatite, 10%. In New England, however, no ages determined from apatite correlate with other isotopically determined ages from the same rock. This may be the result of the low annealing temperature of apatite, which could have been reached by cooling during the Cretaceous as a result of uplift and erosion (Zimmerman and Reimer, 1974).

TABLE 2. MINIMUM TEMPERATURES AND TIME REQUIRED FOR ANNEALING FISSION TRACKS

	Temperature (°C)	Time (yr)
Epidote	375–630	1,000,000 (Naeser and others, 1969)
Zircon	350–400	1,000,000 (Fleischer and others, 1964)
Sphene	325–420	1,000,000 (Naeser and Faul, 1969)
Apatite	75–170	1,000,000 (Naeser and Faul, 1969)

Note: 75 °C can be obtained at approximately 2.5- to 8-km depth, depending on the geothermal gradient of the area (Naeser and others 1971). We have no information on the minimum temperatures of annealing for muscovite, garnet, allanite, hornblende, and natural glasses.

Limitations of Technique and Interpretation of Data

The large variations (10%) of fission-track results compared with the relatively small laboratory errors (2%) of other radiometric techniques do not allow the use of fission tracks for exact dating. The date is limited by temperature and may be only the reflection of depth of burial and the time when the temperature dropped below the annealing temperature of the mineral.

Correction factors that have been developed to account for postmineralization effects on the fission tracks are not adequate to eliminate all error due to these effects (C. W. Naeser and R. L. Fleischer, 1977, written commun.). More often than not, the assumptions on which the correction factors are based are not realistic. These assumptions are based on generalized ideal conditions that never are attained in nature.

The technique is useful in dating minerals that cannot be radiometrically dated by other techniques and in dating thermal events. The sensitivity of fission tracks to temperature can be useful in determining the time of the last fault movement.

Generally, two minerals should be used in the analysis. In many cases, however, this would yield two different fission-track ages because of the difference in annealing temperatures of the two minerals. The size of the difference should be

Figure 3. Fault where attempts to date by the K-Ar method were made. The fault is in the Austin Glen Formation in eastern New York. Movement was right over left. The dates of the shale and of the fault gouge were 488 ± 18 m.y. (shale–whole rock) and 476 ± 17 m.y. (less than 10-μm fraction—1 Md illite in the gouge). Faulting was either nearly contemporaneous with deposition or was not intense enough to disturb the age yielded by the clay minerals derived from the rock.

evaluated as to whether the fission-track technique is suitable for the particular case in question.

We have not resorted to this technique during the course of our fault investigations, but it may prove useful in certain situations, such as a case where epidote is the only datable mineral found in a fault zone.

POTASSIUM-ARGON

The K-Ar method is frequently used to determine the time of last movement on faults. This is due to the method's wide range of time (10,000 to more than 1,000,000,000 yr) over which it is applicable, the large number of datable minerals found in all types of rock, and the minerals found in fault zones, especially the 1 Md illite (a muscovite polymorph) found in some gouge materials.

We have often used this method to date material crosscutting, overlying, or located within a fault (see Fig. 1). However, the most widely used application has been dating of 1 Md illite in fault gouge. The 1 Md illite is important because it is a main constituent of fault gouge and yields absolute ages that are in reasonably close agreement with the age of the faulting (Lyons and Snellenburg, 1971). Lyons and Snellenburg considered the illitic fraction to be the product of mechanical abrasion that accompanied faulting and therefore to be authigenic.

One such application of the K-Ar technique was on a plant site in southern Connecticut. The samples from fault zones and from a faulted pegmatite were X-rayed to determine mineral composition and were found to be suitable for dating. The age of the fault gouge was about 175 m.y., and the fault cut a pegmatite found to be 230 to 260 m.y. old. Other faults were found but were not datable because of insufficient gouge material. Their physical character, orientation, and sense of movement were the same as those faults that were dated. They were interpreted to be of the same age by correlation. None of the faults displaced the overlying glacial material.

Displacement along the datable faults ranged from 1 to 35 ft (less than 1 to 12 m). The smaller faults had movement less than 1 ft and appeared to have formed along pre-existing joints. Thin-section analyses of the fault gouge indicated a complex history, including hydrothermal activity and differential weathering that was inversely proportional to the degree of hydrothermal silicification. The K-Ar ages then could be considered minimum ages and thus would satisfy NRC requirements by showing the faults to be not capable.

There are cases where K-Ar ages are not conclusive enough. One such case involved a plant site on the Hudson River. A sample from the fault gouge was determined by K-Ar analysis to be the same age as that of the faulted wall rock. A comparison of the X-ray diffraction patterns of the fault gouge and undisturbed shale showed identical minerals. Because faulting had not sufficiently reset the radiometric clock, another technique was needed to determine the age of last fault movement. Thus, fluid-inclusion studies on quartz crystals found within the fault zone were performed as well (see Fig. 3).

The K-Ar method of dating relies on the radioactive decay of ^{40}K to its radiogenic daughter atom ^{40}Ar. Because ^{40}Ar is a gas, there are unique problems associated with this method. A melt will not usually retain the gaseous ^{40}Ar, so the radiometric clock is not set until a mineral solidifies and cools sufficiently to retain the ^{40}Ar. The initial K-Ar ratio will be retained by the mineral unless disturbed by another thermal event, such as metamorphism or intense fault movement. This disturbance may allow for the escape of ^{40}Ar and a reset of the "clock." The initial setting of the "clock" may cover millions of years. For an intrusive rock for which cooling is slow, K-Ar dates of different K-bearing minerals may vary, because different minerals precipitate out of the melt and reach radiogenic stability at different temperatures; therefore, the K-Ar date will fall somewhere between the time of intrusion and time of cooling. The K-Ar date of extrusive rocks, however, will establish the time of solidification. Metamorphic rocks may yield an assortment of dates; this possibility depends on the severity of the thermal event and the susceptibility to Ar loss that the K-bearing minerals may have. In general, anything that will affect the Ar-retention capabilities of minerals—including thermal events, weathering, and alteration—will, at least partially, affect the K-Ar date.

Description of Technique

The minerals of interest are separated (except in the case of whole-rock dates) and placed into an ultra-high vacuum system utilizing a completely fluxless, radio-frequency (RF) induction-heating (fusion) procedure to extract the Ar. This method ensures completely quantitative Ar removal, while it minimizes atmospheric contamination, a factor that becomes particularly critical in dating very young samples with low initial amounts of K. The amount of radiogenic Ar is measured by the stable-isotope dilution method, which uses a precisely known quantity of highly purified ^{38}Ar during fusion. After fusion, the sample is analyzed for ^{40}Ar on a mass spectrometer, which is attached directly to the Ar-extraction apparatus (Geochron, Inc., 1977, personal commun.; Teledyne Isotopes, Inc., 1977, personal commun.).

The sample is treated differently to measure K. The sample is dissolved in hydrofluoric, sulfuric, and nitric acids. Silicon is removed as SiF_4 by evaporation. After the remaining solution is diluted with water, a standard quantity of lithium is added, which serves as an internal standard. This use of lithium minimizes indirect effects from other elements (matrix effects) during flame photometry.

Solutions for flame photometry are made by dissolving a known amount of a K-bearing salt to get a known concentration of K (for calibration) and adding it to the above solution. The solution is passed through a flame photometer for K analysis.

With the known decay constant of ^{40}K (half-life, 1.3 b.y.) and the K/Ar ratio analytically determined, the age can be calculated.

Sample Collection

Sample collection methods depend on the purpose of the dating study. However, in all cases, the least-weathered samples should be obtained. Whole-rock samples (for example, of basalt and diabase) may be collected if the rock has not been affected by any subsequent thermal event; the Cenozoic volcanic rocks in the western United States are an example. Whole-rock samples would not be usable if the rock is Devonian and had been deeply buried. In studies of faults, three distinct types of material might be obtained: (1) original wall-rock minerals that have been recrystallized and that can be cleanly separated from unrecrystallized minerals, (2) fault-produced minerals (for example, 1 Md illite), and (3) replacement minerals or fissure fillings.

As minerals may lose part of their accumulation of Ar because of the heat generated during faulting, detailed petrographic studies of the fault zone are necessary to define the appropriate minerals for dating. X-ray diffraction analysis may be required for 1 Md illite (Lyons and Snellenburg, 1971).

The amount of sample to be collected is dependent on the mineral to be dated and the estimated age of the sample. As an example, for a clean, reasonably homogeneous fine-grained biotite or muscovite, the *minimum* sample sizes necessary for dating are 0.5 g for Precambrian material and 2 to 3 g for Cretaceous material. Larger amounts of other minerals are necessary. Discussions with the dating laboratory will determine the amount of sample needed (Geochron, Inc., 1977; personal commun.).

Whole-rock samples may be sent to the laboratory as is. No special precautions need be taken in the choice of wrapping materials. Samples that need separation of K-bearing minerals from the rock sample to ensure their purity, as determined by petrographic inspection, can be separated by the laboratory or by an independent consultant with access to X-ray equipment.

Desirable Minerals

In order to be useful for K-Ar dating, a mineral must meet three basic criteria: (1) The mineral must retain Ar at "normal" geologic temperatures, that is, 100 to 200 °C or less. (2) The mineral must be relatively resistant to alteration and to dissolution by ground water. (3) The mineral must contain enough K to make analytical determinations possible; this can also include K impurities in other minerals (Dalrymple and Lanphere, 1969). Minerals used in K-Ar dating are listed in Table 3; their useful ranges are plotted in Figure 4.

Whole-rock samples may be used in dating volcanic and metamorphic rocks; however, volcanic rock samples should not be taken from the tops, bottoms, or margins of units because of the significant contamination by the entrapment or solution of atmospheric ^{40}Ar. Also, contamination by dissolved excess radiogenic Ar and incorporation of xenolithic material or detrital material may prove significant to the suitability of the sample for dating (Damon, 1977).

Sources of Error

Dalrymple and Lanphere (1969) discussed several sources of error in the K-Ar dating method. Analytical error may result from using unsatisfactory material or material with excess ^{40}Ar. Excess ^{40}Ar can be detected by using two minerals, one with a high Ar retention and one with a low retention capability during heating. Concordance of ages means no postformational thermal events. An incorrect age assignment may result from postformational heating (see above) or from inherited ^{40}Ar being present because the crystal lattice is contaminated by inclusions of impurities. Problems may also arise if the sample was altered or weathered or if it had an anomalous K content (which can be checked by X-ray diffraction before dating because the crystal lattice will be disrupted).

Accuracy

The accuracy of the date is determined by conducting precise analytical tests for K and Ar contents several times. The subsequent dates are plotted and averaged using a best-fit curve with the ranges of dates in the plus or minus portion.

Limitations of Technique and Interpretation of Date

In the absence of a later and distinctly separate thermal event, K-Ar ages usually approximate crystallization ages, but this is not always true. For example, intrusive or metamorphic rocks may remain at elevated temperatures long after the minerals have formed and the rocks have solidified, in which case a K-Ar age would indicate the time of final cooling. If

high postcrystallization temperatures are maintained by deep burial, then K-Ar ages may represent the time of eventual uplift rather than the time of crystallization. For example, biotite can lose Ar at temperatures as low as 150 to 200 °C and glauconite at 150 °C; thus, it is important to date two different minerals when thermal activity is suspected. The usefulness of a K-Ar age depends not only on the heating and cooling history of the rock but also on the effectiveness of the mineral(s) as an Ar trap.

THERMOLUMINESCENCE

The thermoluminescence technique can be applied to samples of limestone and dolomite (carbonates) as young as 25,000 yr. The level of natural thermoluminescence in a rock reflects its radiation and thermal history. The potential for thermoluminescence is related to radiation damage and to crystallographic and chemical defects of a mineral. Natural radioactive decay results in ionized mobile electrons that can be caught in metastable traps formed by chemical impurities or crystal lattice defects. The release of a trapped electron by heating the mineral results in the dissipation of energy in the form of light. If the total radiation dose of a mineral can be determined and the rate of accumulation can be measured, then the length of exposure, that is, the age of the rock, can be calculated (Zeller, 1968).

The thermoluminescence dosimetry technique for dating is based on several assumptions. It is assumed that the number of traps remained constant throughout the geologic history of the rock and that these traps accumulated excited electrons as the result of ionization caused by decay of radioactive impurities contained within the rock (Zeller, 1968). The first step in dating a rock is to measure the level of its natural thermoluminescence. A powdered sample is heated at a constant rate, and the emitted light is measured with a photomultiplier tube. The light intensity can be plotted directly on an X-Y recorder as a function of temperature, and the resultant curve is referred to as the glow curve. A high-temperature glow peak is observed, and the height of the peak or the area of the peak is used to indicate the magnitude of thermoluminescence. Several samples should be analyzed and an average value used.

The next step is to develop a calibration curve. Four to six powder splits of the sample are drained of all natural thermoluminescence by heating the samples to about 300 °C for several hours or by subjecting the samples to ultraviolet radiation. The drained samples are then exposed to increasing amounts of artificially induced radiation, such as from X-ray or gamma ray sources. The calibration curve is constructed by plotting the thermoluminescence peak of each irradiated sample versus the radiation dosage. The relative equivalent radiation dose of the sample can be determined by projecting the value of natural thermoluminescence on the graph to find the corresponding radiation dose (Medlin, 1968).

Before the age of the sample can be determined, the natural radioactivity of the sample must be measured. Alpha scintillation counters are commonly used, as well as Geiger counters and gamma ray spectrometers (Zeller, 1968; Johnson, 1963).

TABLE 3. MINERALS USED IN K-Ar DATING

Volcanic	Plutonic	Metamorphic	Sedimentary
Sanidine	Biotite	Biotite	Glauconite[§]
Anorthoclase	Muscovite	Phlogopite	Illite[§#]
Plagioclase	Hornblende	Muscovite	Chlorite[#]
Biotite	Nepheline*	Hornblende	
Hornblende	Lepidolite*		
Leucite*	Pyroxene*[†]		
Nepheline*			
Pyroxene*[†]			

*Minor minerals.

[†]Pyroxene may have extremely low K and Ar contents and may have incorporated Ar during crystallization (Dalrymple and Lanphere, 1969).

[§]Glauconite and illite may have lost a considerable amount of their initial Ar because of their very small grain size (Hurley, 1966).

[#]Illite and chlorite samples must be X-rayed to determine the presence of other fine-grained contaminants (Lyons and Snellenburg, 1971).

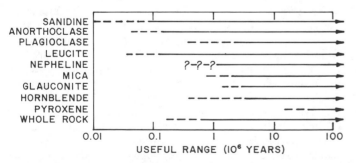

Figure 4. Useful range of some K-Ar datable minerals (from Dalrymple and Lanphere, 1969).

U-Th decay is a major source of alpha and beta activity in rock samples. The level of radioactive decay can be calculated by dividing the relative equivalent radiation dose by the rate of natural radioactivity. The calculated value may equate to the age of the rock or the time since a past thermal event.

The number of lattice traps filled by mobile charges may eventually reach the saturation level where few original traps remain. When this happens, the increase in thermoluminescence of the rock is dependent on the rate of creation of new trapping centers by radiation damage and not on the natural rate of radioactive decay.

An age determined by the thermoluminescence dosimetry method for a rock that had reached thermoluminescence saturation would be a minimum age indicative of the time to reach saturation. Johnson (1963) estimated a time of about 100,000 yr for carbonate rocks to reach saturation, whereas Hutchison (1968) reported ages in excess of 260 m.y. on carbonates, using essentially the same technique.

Zeller (1968) proposed a different approach to thermoluminescence dating, the artificial thermoluminescence method, which is based on the assumption that additional trapping centers are created by radiation damage in the crystal lattice. It is not necessary to measure the level of natural thermoluminescence. A middle-temperature glow peak is used for the analysis, and it is assumed that the middle-temperature glow peak is absent from newly precipitated minerals. The theoretical basis for this assumption is not established, although empirical evidence suggests that recent carbonates have a small middle-temperature peak, and older (Paleozoic) carbonates show a large, well-developed middle-temperature peak. The analytical technique consists of subjecting five or six powdered samples to increasing dosages of high-energy artificial radiation and then testing for thermoluminescence glow curves. The calibration curve should depict a sharp rise in thermoluminescence up to a plateau representing the saturation level of the sample. The value obtained by dividing the peak height at saturation by the natural radioactivity is a function of the geologic age of the sample. This resulting value must be corrected for the differing trap-producing efficiencies of each mineral.

A sound approach to dating rocks by thermoluminescence techniques would be to analyze each sample by both methods. Natural thermoluminescence saturation should be checked during any analysis.

Desirable Minerals

Thermoluminescence dating techniques are commonly applied to carbonate minerals (Johnson, 1963; Zeller, 1968; Hutchison, 1968). Successful results have been obtained with quartz (Kaul and others, 1968; Ganguli and Kaul, 1968); attempts at dating feldspar phenocrysts from lava flows (Aitken and others, 1968; Hwang, 1970) have been less successful.

Sampling Procedures

Core samples are more desirable than outcrop samples because the rock would not have been exposed to potential surficial thermal increases caused by sunlight or forest fires. Although natural thermoluminescence is stable at temperatures found at the Earth's surface, partial annealing of low- to moderate-temperature glow peaks can occur from long-term exposure to surface temperatures.

Samples should be stored away from sources of heat or light. Brief exposure to solar ultraviolet radiation may partially drain thermoluminescence. Rock from blasting zones should not be sampled, because of the possibility of shock-induced thermoluminescence changes.

Sample Preparation

Samples are generally ground and sieved to a size fraction of 60 to 100 mesh to facilitate handling and to ensure reproducibility (Lewis, 1968). Grinding may induce thermoluminescence effects and thereby partially drain the samples before measurement of the glow curve. Grinding effects are most pronounced on the finest particles and can be minimized if this fraction is sieved out and the powder size is kept nearly constant.

Accuracy and Sources of Error

Care must be exercised to avoid selecting samples with thermoluminescence partially drained. Effects of grinding will be minimized by careful attention to preparation of the sample. Measurements of thermoluminescence can be held to an accuracy of $\pm 5\%$ if the apparatus is frequently calibrated with a standard light source. A calibrated source of radiation is required to accurately calculate the artificial radiation dosage. The largest single possible error in the analytical technique is from the measurement of the natural radioactivity of the sample. Decay rates are generally very low, and counting times are relatively short; these factors result in errors of as much as 50% (Zeller, 1968). Further inaccuracies can be introduced by failure to account for all types of natural radiation and their relative efficiencies for producing thermoluminescence. Beta activity and gamma radiation, as well as alpha activity, should be measured (Johnson, 1963). It may also be necessary to account for the relative efficiency of each type of radiation in producing thermoluminescence and crystal defects (Hwang, 1970; Durrani and Christodoulides, 1969).

Limitations of Technique and Interpretation of Dates

Although techniques for thermoluminescence dating have been developed, some details of the release mechanism for a few substances are not fully explained. There are many possible errors when dating rocks by this method. A review of current literature on thermoluminescence dating reveals a wide divergence of analytical practices. Even though there are many problems with dating rocks by thermoluminescence, useful information can be obtained. The dates are a measure of the length of radiation exposure since the formation of the crystal or since the last thermal event, so an understanding of the geologic history is necessary to interpret the dates.

Perhaps the real potential for thermoluminescence is in direct dating of faults. This may be accomplished by dating minerals in shear zones, if it is assumed that heat generated during shearing was sufficient to drain previously acquired thermoluminescence. We have not used thermoluminescence for dating as yet, but it may be applicable to fault studies as geologic circumstances dictate.

RUBIDIUM–STRONTIUM

The Rb-Sr dating technique is based on the beta decay of ^{87}Rb into ^{87}Sr; the ^{87}Rb has a half-life of 4.7×10^{10} yr. Because of the long half-life, the Rb-Sr technique is most reliable for rocks older than 80 m.y., because by that age they would have a quantity of radiogenic ^{87}Sr sufficient to measure. Certain minerals normally have a low initial amount of ^{87}Rb and thus may not be datable by the Rb-Sr method until they are much older (see Table 4).

TABLE 4. MINERALS USED IN Rb-Sr DATING

Mineral	Minimum usable age (m.y.)
Biotite	80–100
Muscovite	80–100
Lepidolite	80–100
Microcline	300–400
Sanidine	300–400
Hornblende	1,000–1,500
(Whole rock)	500–1,000
Glauconite	80–600*

*If the temperature was near-surface (that is, <50 °C) and the mineral was well crystallized, 80 to 600 m.y. is the usable range, but 80 to 200 m.y. is the limit for good accuracy.

Description of Technique

The first step in preparing the samples is dissolving the sample in hydrofluoric and perchloric acid and adding a known quantity of a tracer isotope, either ^{87}Rb or ^{86}Sr. The Sr is separated from other elements by cation-exchange techniques and is then precipitated out as an oxalate and placed on rhenium filaments for analysis in a mass spectrometer.

After the Sr is precipitated from solution and removed, Rb is precipitated out as the perchlorate; after washing, this Rb compound is converted to the sulfate and placed in the mass spectrometer for analysis.

The absolute amount of the isotopes is determined at least ten times. The age is calculated from the decay constant of Rb and the ratios of $^{87}Sr/^{86}Sr$ and $^{87}Rb/^{86}Sr$.

Sample Collection

The samples should contain at least 1 to 5 g of clean, unweathered, and unmetamorphosed mineral. If whole-rock age determinations are desired, the dimensions of the sample should be at least ten times the textural variations. For best results, the larger the grain size of the mineral, the more accurate the date.

The samples of the mineral to be tested may be submitted to the dating laboratory as components of a rock sample, or they may be crushed and sieved for homogeneity. In either case, between 1 and 5 g of the mineral must be submitted.

Whole Rock

The whole-rock technique is useful in Rb-Sr dating. There is a loss of radiogenic ^{87}Sr from minerals during geologic time. This loss can be accelerated if the minerals are reheated after cooling, as a result of metamorphism or reburial, which increases the temperature as a result of the geothermal gradient. However, the radiogenic ^{87}Sr lost from the minerals is absorbed by the matrix of the rock. Thus, analyzing the rock will be more accurate than just dating individual minerals (Fairbairn and others, 1961).

Most igneous rocks are well suited to Rb-Sr whole-rock dating. However, young mafic volcanic rocks are generally not suited to such dating because of their very low Sr content. Metamorphic rocks can be used as well as sedimentary rocks. Marine shale is the best sedimentary rock type to use because it has a lower probability of containing detrital 2M mica polymorph and feldspar than do the other types of sedimentary rock. However, X-ray diffraction should be used to determine the actual content of mica or feldspar before dating is attempted. The original Rb-Sr content is that of the parent sea water, which has apparently not fluctuated much in geologic history (Compston and Pidgeon, 1962).

Isochron Plots

A plot is originated by computing the $^{87}Rb/^{86}Sr$ versus $^{87}Sr/^{86}Sr$ ratios of several samples. These sample points are used to determine the initial $^{87}Sr/^{86}Sr$ ratio, which is obtained by drawing a straight line through the experimentally determined points and projecting the line back so that it intercepts the $^{87}Sr/^{86}Sr$ axis. This is the original $^{87}Sr/^{86}Sr$ ratio. From the slope, formed by the points, the date can be mathematically derived. The alignment of points on a straight line indicates a closed system (Moorbath, 1964).

Sources of Error

One of the major sources of error is the base exchange of ions, due to the action of ground water. This type of alteration usually lowers the Rb-Sr age, while leaving the K-Ar age much less affected. Thus, if base exchange has occurred, the K-Ar age will be greater than the Rb-Sr age, whereas the opposite will be true if thermal alteration has occurred.

The second major source of error is the effect of temperature. Diffusion caused by temperature increases due to metamorphism, igneous intrusions, or geothermal gradients affects micas, especially fine-grained biotite, more than the other minerals. Radiogenic Sr isotopes are much less prone to diffusion than the gaseous Ar.

Other sources of error are more specific to individual minerals in different types of rock. Glauconite can have (in addition to base exchange) thermal changes, poor crystallization, recycled glauconite from older units, and/or a diagenetic addition of Rb and detrital minerals in the center of the glauconite pellets. Glauconite can also undergo diffusion loss of the isotopes (Thompson and Hower, 1973).

A whole-rock analysis of shale must use the assumption of a uniform $^{87}Sr/^{86}Sr$ ratio of sea water. This source of error is in addition to the possible presence of detrital micas and feldspars (Compston and Pidgeon, 1962).

In general, a small grain size (which facilitates ion diffusion), the length of time required for cooling, and metamorphic events can adversely affect the age determination.

Accuracy

The accuracy of determining the Rb and Sr contents is ±2%. However, with the other sources of error included in the history of the samples themselves, the accuracy drops to ±5%. The younger samples have a considerably higher variance because the ratio of inherited ^{87}Sr atoms to radiogenic ^{87}Sr atoms (resulting from decay of parent ^{87}Rb) is higher.

Limitations of Technique and Interpretation of Date

For dating faults, the major limitation of the Rb-Sr technique is the unsuitability of many fault-zone materials. A Stone & Webster study on one fault zone showed that the micas and feldspars of the original rock were not sufficiently affected by the faulting to have their Rb-Sr clocks reset. A large amount of recrystallization apparently is needed.

During geologic time, a protracted, but simple uplift and cooling history of a large deep-seated plutonic or metamorphic complex could produce a discordant age pattern, because different minerals become radiogenically closed systems at different temperatures. This age pattern is analogous to one obtained in an area of superimposed thermal events. Whole-rock age determinations are more likely to yield the true age of emplacement at depth (Moorbath, 1964). Because of this, whole-rock and separated-mineral isochron studies should be conducted when using the Rb-Sr method.

URANIUM-THORIUM DATING OF CALCITE

The U-Th dating technique may be used on samples of inorganic and organic calcite and is effective to a maximum of about 300,000 yr. It has been used for a plant site site on Lake Ontario in northern New York. A sample of calcite was collected from a fault zone in which the calcite coated a set of horizontal slickensides (see Fig. 5). The age of the sample was determined to be 81,000 to 170,000 yr, but must be considered a minimum because of the introduction of ^{232}Th contaminants. The contamination probably resulted from the incorporation of Fe compounds, which preferentially absorb Th. Some of the contamination may have been derived from ground water percolating through the overlying glacial till.

Description of Technique

The isotopes involved are ^{238}U, ^{234}U, ^{230}Th, and ^{232}Th. The radiometric clock starts after the formation of the calcite. The ^{238}U isotope enters the system in the form of uranyl carbonate

complex ions, $UO_2(CO_3)_3^{-4}$, which are soluble and found in natural ground water (Ku, 1975). The ^{234}U isotope is created by the radioactive decay of ^{238}U until equilibrium is reached; therefore, the $^{238}U/^{234}U$ ratio should equal one. Any other value would indicate diffusion of ^{234}U in or out of the system, because ^{234}U is more mobile and more readily forms compounds. The ^{234}U isotope decays into ^{230}Th. The determination of the $^{234}U/^{238}U$, $^{230}Th/^{234}U$, $^{230}Th/^{232}Th$, and $^{228}Th/^{232}Th$ ratios together with the known disintegration rate of each isotope yields the age of the sample. The technique assumes that the carbonate was a closed system which initially did not contain any Th. Another assumption is that the rates of diffusion of ^{234}U and the rates of accumulation of additional ^{238}U and ^{234}U remained constant. Finally, the remainder of ^{234}U and all of the ^{238}U that produces the mobile ^{234}U are constant (Ku, 1965).

It is evident that the assumptions are not geologically realistic and only represent ideal conditions. Carbonate is not a closed system, and contamination does occur. Th enters the system in compounds with silicates and iron hydroxides, and the rates of accumulation and diffusion vary with the geochemical environments (Ku, 1976). There are numerous correction factors in the formulas from which the data are derived to take into account the imperfections of the technique and reflect the real situation. To evaluate the data, the geologic setting and ground-water conditions should be known in as much detail as possible.

Sample Collection

Usable samples of calcite are those that do not display any signs of leaching or erosion and are in the fault zone to be dated. The calcite should be white or colorless (any other color indicates impurities that will contribute to Th contamination) and be undeformed. Only 5 to 10 g of calcite are required (Ku, 1976). If at all possible, the calcite sample should remain on the rock and a composite sample sent to the laboratory for treatment and selection of the calcite to be analyzed.

Only calcite should be submitted for dating. Other carbonates

Figure 5. Photograph of undisturbed calcite lying on a set of horizontal slickensides. The fault is in the Upper Ordovician Oswego Formation. The minimum age of the calcite was determined by the U-Th method to be between 81,000 and 170,000 yr B.P.

such as siderite, ankerite, and rhodochrosite contain iron and other impurities that could introduce Th into the system.

Limitations of Technique and Interpretation of Date

Because the calcite precipitates out of ground water, a pure mineral is not to be expected, particularly if there is a heterogeneous zone, such as terrigenous soil or glacial till, above the calcite deposit. In such localities, water percolation will carry a much greater amount of contaminants down to the locality of precipitation. Since the calcite forms by numerous crystallization stages, the deposit is layered. During sample preparation the entire calcite sample is ground up, and isolation of the oldest layer is not possible; thus, although the age determined is an average, it is also a minimum age of faulting, if all crystallization postdates the last movement.

RACEMIZATION OF AMINO ACIDS

The technique of racemization of amino acids may be of use where the stratigraphic units to be dated contain bones, teeth, or unaltered organic carbonate. In the case of mollusk shells, the racemization rate varies in different structural units of the shell; therefore, it is essential to use comparable shell structures when making comparisons (Hare, 1977).

In southern California, we reviewed a siting study where dating of an undisturbed marker horizon overlying a fault was done by amino acid racemization. The horizon contained bone fragments and vertebrae. The ^{14}C method showed the bone to be older than 50,000 yr. Analysis of the degree of racemization of amino acids contained in the bone proved its age to be about 80,000 yr (Ku, 1975).

Description of Technique

Racemization is the process by which protein amino acids (L-isomers) such as aspartic acid, alanine, glutamic acid, isoleucine, and leucine decay with time into nonprotein amino acids (D-isomers). The ratio between the isomers indicates the age. The acids are, in order of their minimum and maximum usable ages (rate of racemization is dependent on several factors; this accounts for the range of time): aspartic acid, 5,000 to 70,000 yr; alanine, 20,000 to 150,000 yr; glutamic acid, 20,000 to 150,000 yr; isoleucine, 50,000 to 300,000 yr; leucine, 50,000 to 350,000 yr.

These usable age ranges for each particular acid are temperature dependent. The higher the temperature, the younger the limit. One of the slowest to decay is isoleucine, which is the best amino acid to analyze for dates beyond the range of ^{14}C (50,000± yr) (Bada, 1972).

Isoleucine decays to alloisoleucine. Test samples are washed with dilute HCl to remove surface contaminants, rinsed thoroughly with distilled water, and dried under vacuum. The samples are then incubated at 100 °C for 15 min under a partial vacuum. After heating, the samples are treated with $6M$ HCl for 24 h. More chemical treatments with HCl, NaOH, and NH$_4$OH and heating in a vacuum are required before the sample is ready for the amino acid analyzer (Bada, 1972).

Sample Collection

About 2 g or more of the sample are required for processing; however, recent advances in liquid and gas chromatography, together with fluorescent detection and a specific nitrogen detector, make possible the analysis of 1 mg or less (Hare, 1977). The best results are obtained from samples of bone, teeth, or other organic fragments (sometimes from nodules) collected from arid areas characterized by relatively constant temperature, low humidity, and very little ground-water percolation since the time the organic material was formed (Bada and Shou, 1976). Information about the climatic history and the location of the sample, as well as a specimen of the enclosing strata, should be sent to the dating laboratory with the sample.

Sources of Error

In order to determine the kinetic rate of racemization, the temperature history of the samples needs to be evaluated (Bada and Protsch, 1973). Environmental factors such as the pH of ground water and the rainfall history need to be evaluated also. An error of ±2 °C can produce a ±50% error in the age date (Bada, 1972).

Other sources of error can be amino acids introduced into the sample by microbial decomposition of the flesh and other tissues originally surrounding the sample, excessive handling of the sample during excavation and shipment preparation, and the addition of preservatives to the sample. The contamination from these sources is confined to the surface of the sample, and the treatment with HCl can eliminate this problem (Bada, 1972). Another possible source of error is percolation through the sample of ground water containing recently formed amino acids (Bada and others, 1973). This source of contamination is more serious in very old samples because of the longer exposure time and the decomposition of some of the original amino acids in the samples.

Accuracy

Because of the temperature uncertainties, this method can never approach the accuracy obtained by ^{14}C and should only be used if ^{14}C dating shows the sample to be older than 50,000 yr as in the California siting study mentioned above. Temperature history can be determined using oxygen isotopes in carbonates if the carbonates are associated with the datable samples. It may be possible to calibrate the in situ rate of racemization by comparing ^{14}C dates with amino acid analysis from the same sample or another expendable sample (Bada and Protsch, 1973; Bada and others, 1974). The assumptions made in calibration of the rate of racemization are that the amount of the sample is sufficient and young enough for ^{14}C dating and that the samples are representative of the thermal history of burial. Rates thus calibrated may then be used to date older material from the same area.

Limitations of Technique and Interpretation of Date

The greatest limiting factor of this technique is the requirement for a nearly stable temperature history. Areas that have been subjected to glaciation (or other major climatic changes) and changing hydrologic conditions (that is, transgressive-regressive shorelines, and so forth) probably will not be suitable. Temperature (not just temperature changes) affects the range of usefulness. For example, a sample exposed to a relatively constant 15 to 20 °C will be usable for dating if it is between 20,000 and 40,000 yr old, whereas a sample exposed to 3 °C will be usable for from 300,000 to 9,000,000 yr (Bada, 1972). In all instances, samples have to be at least 5,000 yr old because of the threshold limits of the amino acid analyzer for detecting small amounts of nonprotein amino acids.

PALEOMAGNETISM

Paleomagnetism is most commonly used for determining the age of soil or rock strata (which must contain at least one magnetic mineral). Paleomagnetism can also be used in fault zone studies for dating fault gouge or an overlying stratigraphic horizon.

Description of Technique

The technique depends on determining the original paleomagnetic direction of the sample and comparing that direction with the paleomagnetic reversal time scale.

The original paleomagnetic direction (declination and inclination) may be masked by secondary (later) magnetization acquired during the existence of the sample. This secondary magnetization may be removed by thermal or electromagnetic laboratory methods (Runcorn, 1969).

In treating the sample electromagnetically, it is taken through a demagnetization cycle by applying a field of the intensity of the coercive force to those grains that carry it. The sample is rotated in an alternating field (A.C.) that is reduced smoothly to zero, the rotation being arranged so that no direction in the rock is preferentially oriented with respect to the applied field. The demagnetization field strength is increased by steps until the direction of the remanent magnetization (that is, the original paleomagnetic direction) no longer changes (Runcorn, 1969).

Thermal treatment of the sample requires heating above the blocking temperature (that is, the temperature at which the secondary magnetization is formed) of the grains carrying the secondary magnetization and then cooling in a neutral field. The heating is taken in steps of 50 to 100 °C until the direction of the remanent magnetization remains unchanged (Runcorn, 1969).

When the original direction of magnetization of a sample has been recovered, the values of the declination and inclination are plotted on a stereographic projection. Directions from a homogeneous population (that is, more than one sample from the same site or distributed through one formation) can be statistically examined. The vector sum of the directions of each sample or samples provides the best estimate of the direction of the mean geomagnetic field during the polarity epoch considered. A cone of confidence of appropriate semiangle can be calculated such that the true direction will lie within the cone with a probability of 95%. A survey of paleomagnetism

shows that the geomagnetic field varies three different ways: secular variations (small changes in the intensity and orientation of the magnetic field), geomagnetic reversals, and polar wandering (Runcorn, 1969).

Sample Collection

The samples should be collected as close together as possible to minimize secular variations. Usually, four short (20 cm) drilled cores spaced a few metres apart, a single drilled core several metres long (if rock), or at least four blocks separated by a few metres (if friable) are sufficient for paleomagnetic determinations. The samples should be as unweathered as possible (Gough, 1967). The samples must contain at least one of the following magnetic minerals: hematite, ilmenite, magnetite, ulvospinel, spinel, or pyrrhotite. The best exposures to collect from are those lowest in elevation within the particular strata of interest. This minimizes weathering and lightning effects.

The single most important part of sample collection and processing is proper documentation of the sample in the field. Suitable orientation marks must be placed on the sample, usually strike and dip. However, difficulty in finding plane surfaces renders necessary the selection of imperfect surfaces for marking, and this can lead to considerable inaccuracies. Some surfaces can be built with plaster of Paris, or a portable drilling apparatus with an oriented core can be used. If the rock is sufficiently magnetic to influence a Brunton compass so that it cannot be used to determine true north, an azimuth must be obtained. A visual sighting on the sun with the use of appropriate tables or plotting an azimuth from the sample location to an identifiable object on a topographic map is sufficient. An accuracy of 0.5° is required (Girdler, 1967).

Sources of Error

A rock may have become magnetized antiparallel to the prevailing magnetic field. There is no generally applicable test available that will positively indicate the presence or absence of this phenomenon, called self-reversal, even though it requires a particular magnetochemistry (McDougall and Chamalaun, 1966).

Magnetic instability results when secondary magnetization and mineralogic changes—such as the secondary formation of magnetite, the formation of titanomaghemite, or exsolution in the ferromagnetic phases—produce another secondary magnetic component that tends to be more stable than the just-mentioned forms of secondary magnetization. Such affects can be removed using A.C. or thermal demagnetization techniques (McDougall and Chamalaun, 1966).

Finally, if the samples have been moved or rotated by tectonic processes, no accurate paleomagnetic analysis can be made, unless the samples can be structurally rotated back to their original position.

Accuracy

The accuracy of the paleomagnetic work is dependent on the adjustments made with regard to secondary magnetization, as well as proper sampling and documentation. The geomagnetic reversal scale has been established back to 6.5 m.y. B.P. (McDougall and others, 1977). Beyond this, the spread of correlative K-Ar dates makes an accurate assessment of the older geomagnetic history impossible. However, the data may be used to correlate with geomagnetic pole positions determined for older geologic periods.

The length of time that our present normally polarized magnetic field has existed is 700,000 yr (the Brunhes normal epoch). Paleomagnetic ages older than 700,000 yr (the time of the first magnetic reversal) would satisfy NRC criteria for the last fault movement older than 500,000 yr.

Limitations of Technique and Interpretation of Date

The technique, with regard to faulting, is useful in determining the age of fault gouge (if dates are less than 1 m.y., the minimum age for effective K-Ar dating) or the age of overlying undisturbed strata. This technique should be corroborated with other techniques if possible. The results should be evaluated using the following criteria: the determination of polarity was carried out by conventional techniques, a proper method of sampling and documentation was utilized, multiple samples from the same stratigraphic horizon were used for polarity determination, the scatter of magnetic directions was not excessive, and demagnetization procedures were successful. The fault gouge or soil that is used for paleomagnetic determinations may have differing polarities because of different degrees of weathering at different depths; thus, it is important to sample from just one area.

The paleomagnetic reversal data may not indicate a date but a generalized time span. However, polar-wandering curves have been calibrated by radiometric dating (^{14}C and K-Ar); by plotting the paleomagnetic pole position with respect to these curves, a minimum age may be determined.

FLUID–INCLUSION TECHNIQUE

The fluid-inclusion technique will not yield a direct age determination, but rather an estimate of the minimum age. The fluid-inclusion method is a pressure-temperature technique that indicates the environment of formation of the examined crystals. Combining this information with that from the present environment and using a conservative erosion rate, it may be possible to establish a minimum age of crystal formation. To be applicable to dating fault movement, it must be shown that the dated minerals have grown since faulting and have not been disturbed by subsequent movement. The analysis is performed according to an established technique used in the mining industry to determine ore fluid temperatures and pressures.

The technique has been used at a nuclear power plant site along the Hudson River and at another in southern Connecticut. At the Hudson River site, large, euhedral quartz crystals from a fault zone were analyzed and found to have formed from an aqueous CO_2-bearing solution in a near-neutral or alkaline reducing environment. The temperature of formation was in excess of 160 °C and under a hydrostatic pressure of 44 to 150 bars (Kelly, 1975). The evidence pointed to an environment of formation at depths of at least 2 km. An estimated 60 m.y. would be required to erode 2 km of rock.

Another example of its use was the analysis of euhedral, unfractured quartz crystals found in a fault zone on a plant site in southern Connecticut. The study showed that the crystals were emplaced in the fault zones at temperatures of 148 to 243 °C and several kilometres deep. The time of the last fault movement was interpreted to be Jurassic-Triassic on the basis of fluid-inclusion analysis and geologic orientation of the faults.

Description of Technique

During and following faulting, hot aqueous solutions may penetrate the fault zone and, upon cooling, precipitate minerals—commonly, quartz, calcite, and/or sulfide minerals. Within the crystals are irregularities formed by localized solution pitting and related chemical activity during crystal growth. These pits and cavities are frequently filled by residual fluids. As the crystal cools, the trapped fluids contract more rapidly than the solid material. As a result, both a gaseous and liquid phase develop. The cooling liquid may also precipitate minerals in the form of daughter salts. The liquid-vapor inclusions may be water and CO_2 or a highly saline solution and CO_2 or other gas. Such inclusions are termed "primary inclusions."

There are two types of secondary fluid inclusions. The first type forms at some time after complete growth of the crystal along fractures. Postcrystallization fluids penetrate the crystals along these fractures and precipitate minerals along the walls of the fractures up to the point of healing them. The second type, sometimes called "pseudo-secondary fluid inclusions" form along minute fractures that occur during crystal growth and are healed by the precipitating minerals. The difference between the two lies in the location of the fracture genesis. The former starts at the crystal surface while the latter begins growing internally. The origin of these secondary fractures is genetically important but is often difficult to determine with confidence. These inclusions are grouped under the term "fracture-controlled inclusions" without any implication of their relative age to the parent crystal.

The fundamental assumption of inclusion geothermometry is that the inclusion is filled with fluid that is still at the pressure and temperature under which it was formed. Therefore, if the original pressure approximated the vapor pressure of the solution at the temperature of formation and if the inclusion has not leaked, the liquid should expand and refill the cavity when the crystal is reheated and the temperature of formation is reached. Pressure correction factors have been calculated to explain situations in which the pressure of formation was higher than the vapor pressure of the fluid.

The procedures commonly followed in the analysis (Kelly, 1975) are as follows: A binocular microscope study is made of all specimens to select appropriate crystals for inclusion study. Polished plates are prepared from the crystals. The polished plates are impregnated with dye to determine any leakage of inclusions. The inclusions are studied, classified, and interpreted through the use of petrographic microscopes. Selected inclusions are frozen and others are heated to evaluate fluid salinities, and selected inclusions to evaluate fluid salinites.

Finally the plates are crushed to determine the amount and kind of compressed gas.

Limitations of Fluid-Inclusion Analysis of Quartz

The technique of analysis has certain geologic limitations. Not all fluid inclusions are suitable for such study. The analysis requires inclusions that have not leaked throughout geologic time. The subject of leakage is fully treated by Roedder and Skinner (1968), who showed that, in general, fluid inclusions do not leak in nature. However, postformational changes in the inclusions can be recognized in thin sections. Certain stress conditions can develop pressures that plastically deform weak ductile materials or explode the inclusions. Deformed inclusions yield anomalously high temperatures and pressures. Such inclusions can be recognized and eliminated.

In a given fluid inclusion, especially if irregular in shape, the precipitating mineral matter may separate the original inclusion into a group of small inclusions. If this separation takes place during cooling, then a group of inclusions will form from the parent and will inherit inhomogeneous proportions of gas, liquids, and daughter salts. These inclusions can be identified and eliminated from consideration. The inclusions also must be large enough to perform heating, freezing, and crushing tests on them. Impurities in the minerals must not be opaque so as to make examination of the inclusions impossible. The accuracy of the analysis depends to a large extent on the interpolation of fluid refilling temperatures. Irregularities in the inclusion walls may cause uncertainties amounting to 3 °C. These uncertainties translate into further inaccuracy in the estimation of formation depth.

Determinations from the Analysis

When the pressure and temperature conditions of formation of the crystals are determined, an estimated depth of crystallization in the fault zone can be developed. A standard erosion rate is assumed for the area under study, and the amount of time to expose these crystals at the Earth's surface is calculated. Commonly, only an age range can be determined, because of the range of temperature and pressure conditions experimentally derived from the crystals.

Collection of Samples

The collection of samples should be carried out in such a manner as not to physically damage the crystals. Crystals that have grown in open spaces and that have not been crushed or recemented by later solutions are preferred. The inclusions in these crystals are likely to be primary. Any crystals containing visible solid inclusions should also not be overlooked; such solid inclusions could provide valuable indicators of formation temperature. The location of the sample must be surveyed and documented photographically. A brief geologic description of the sample, making note of the genetic relationships, should be written. Above all, before any sampling is done, if at all possible, the prospective analyst or laboratory should be contacted concerning any special sampling procedures that might be required for the analysis.

Interpretation of Data

Fluid-inclusion analysis is a useful method to determine time of fault movement. It should, however, be used with knowledge of its limitations. The method of analysis is one that is sharpened by experience. There is a degree of interpolation needed when estimating the filling temperatures and freezing temperatures. This interpolation may be difficult in poor specimens.

The inclusion method can be used to corroborate other field or laboratory data. The analysis alone may not stand, simply because of the analytical uncertainty in the technique. This is not to say that the technique is usually worthless, but simply a warning against blind faith in it (Kelly, 1975).

SUMMARY

The dating techniques available from many academic and commercial laboratories have proved useful in determining the age of faulting at many nuclear power sites. We have discussed some techniques that have been used by us and some that we have not used yet. Our basic philosophy has been to use any and all methods that will fit a given problem and provide data helpful in the determination of fault history.

Geology is not an exact science; any analyses are controlled by the geologic parameters, not vice versa. In spite of, but aware of, the limitations of all laboratory techniques, the geologist attempts to obtain as much information as possible through their use.

In unusual situations, one method such as ^{14}C or K-Ar, coupled with good geologic field data, may be sufficient to prove a fault not capable and satisfy all NRC criteria. In many other situations, however, the field data will not be definitive, and several dating methods must be used in order to provide sufficient clues to decipher faulting history. Because of the limitations of any one method, two or more methods may be used in order to increase the confidence in the results. We have found that in fault investigations on nuclear power plant sites, duplicated or corroborating results from different techniques are essentail in providing broad-based arguments and supportive data for final determination of fault capability.

All the techniques we have discussed were developed by geologic research in branches of the science other than engineering geology. None of the techniques was developed for fault dating per se. However, the geologist concerned with nuclear plant siting needs to be aware of laboratory methods and techniques that might be useful in solving specific problems. We hope that those we presented will be added to and that more innovations for faulting investigations will be publicized.

ACKNOWLEDGMENTS

We wish to express our gratitude to our co-workers for stimulating discussions and arguments concerning dating techniques. Much of the data were compiled from notes and detailed observations on many different projects. We also deeply appreciate the critical review of the early manuscript by J. B. Lyons and H. Krueger.

REFERENCES CITED

Aitken, M. J., Fleming, S. J., Doell, R. R., and Tanguy, J. C., 1968, Thermoluminescent study of lavas from Mt. Etna and other historic flows: Preliminary results, *in* McDougall, D. J., ed., Thermoluminescence of geological material, Proceedings NATO Advanced Research Institute, Spoleto, Italy: New York, Academic Press, p. 359–366.

Bada, J. L., 1972, The dating of fossil bones using the racemization of isoleucine: Earth and Planetary Science Letters, v. 15, p. 223–231.

Bada, J. L., and Protsch, R., 1973, Racemization reaction of aspartic acid and its use in dating fossil bones: National Academy of Sciences Proceedings, v. 70, p. 1331–1334.

Bada, J. L., and Shou, M., 1976, Effects of various environmental parameters on amino acid racemization rates in fossil bones: Geological Society of America Abstracts with Programs, v. 8, p. 762–763.

Bada, J. L., Kvenvolden, R. A., and Peterson, E., 1973, Racemization of amino acids in bones: Nature, v. 245, p. 308–310.

Bada, J. L., Schroeder, R. A., Protsch, R., and Berger, R., 1974, Concordance of collagen-based radiocarbon and aspartic-acid racemization ages: National Academy of Sciences Proceedings, v. 71, p. 914–917.

Code of Federal Regulations, 1978, Title 10, Energy; Part 100 [10 CFR 100], Reactor site criteria; Appendix A, Seismic and geologic siting criteria for nuclear power plants: Washington, D.C., U.S. Nuclear Regulatory Commission.

Compston, W., and Pidgeon, R. T., 1962, Rubidium-strontium dating of shales by the total-rock method: Journal of Geophysical Research, v. 67, p. 3493–3502.

Dalrymple, G. G., and Lanphere, M. A., 1969, Potassium-argon dating: Principles, techniques, and applications to geochronology: San Francisco, W. H. Freeman and Company, 258 p.

Damon, P. E., 1977, K-Ar dating applied to Quaternary geochronologic problems: Geological Society of America Abstracts with Programs, v. 9, p. 941–942.

Doherty, J. T., 1975, Apatite and zircon fission track ages of the White Mountain plutonic-volcanic series intrusives [M.A. thesis]: Hanover, N.H., Dartmouth College, 106 p.

Durrani, S. A., and Christodoulides, C., 1969, Allende meteorite: Age determination by thermoluminescense: Nature, v. 223, p. 1219–1221.

Fairbairn, H. W., Hurley, P. M., and Pinson, W. H., 1961, The relation of discordant Rb-Sr mineral and whole-rock ages in an igneous rock to its time of crystallization and to the time of subsequent Sr^{87}/Sr^{86} metamorphism: Geochimica et Cosmochimica Acta, v. 23, p. 135–144.

Fleischer, R. L., Price, P. B., and Walker, P. B., 1964, Fission-track ages of zircons: Journal of Geophysical Research v. 69, p. 4885–4888.

Ganguli, D. K., and Kaul, I. K., 1968, The age of radioactive mineralization of placer deposits of Kerala (Travancore), India: Economic Geology, v. 63, p. 838–840.

Girdler, R. W., 1967, The collection and orientation of rock samples, *in* Collinson, D. W., Creer, K. M., and Runcorn, S. K., eds., Methods in paleomagnetism, developments in solid earth geophysics, Volume 3: New York, Elsevier, p. 8–10.

Gough, D. I., 1967, Notes on rock sampling for paleomagnetic research, *in* Collinson, D. W., Creer, K. M., and Runcorn, S. K., eds., Methods in paleomagnetism, developments in solid earth geophysics, Volume 3: New York, Elsevier, p. 2–7.

Hare, P. E., 1977, Amino acid dating, limitations, and potential: Geological Society of America Abstracts with Programs, v. 9, p. 1004–1005.

Hurley, P. M., 1966, K-Ar dating of sediments, *in* Schaeffer, O. A., and Zahringer, J., eds., Potassium-argon dating: New York, Springer-Verlag Inc., p. 134–150.

Hutchison, C. S., 1968, The dating by thermoluminescence of tectonic and magmatic events in orogenesis, *in* McDougall, D. J., ed., Thermoluminescence of geological material, Proceedings, NATO Advanced Research Institute, Spoleto, Italy, 1966: New York, Academic Press, p. 341–358.

Hwang, F.S.W., 1970, Thermoluminescence dating applied to volcanic lava: Nature, v. 227, p. 940–941.

Johnson, N. M., 1963, Thermoluminescence in contact metamorphosed limestone: Journal of Geology, v. 71, p. 593–616.

Kaul, I. K., Bhattacharya, P. K., and Tolpaid, S., 1968, Factors in age determination by thermoluminescence of smoky quartz, *in* McDougall, D. J., ed., Thermoluminescence of geological material, Proceedings, NATO Advanced Research Institute, Spoleto, Italy, 1966: New York, Academic Press, p. 327–340.

Kelly, W. C., 1975, Analysis of fluid inclusions in quartz crystals: Power Authority of the State of New York (Docket 50549, PSAR, Greene County NPS, Greene County, New York, App. 2C).

Ku, T. L., 1965, An evaluation of the U^{234}/U^{238} method as a tool for dating pelagic sediments: Journal of Geophysical Research, v. 70, p. 3457–3474.

——1975, ESSR, Age dating of desert caliche by Th^{230}/U^{234}, Appendix 2.5 J, Sundesert nuclear power plant, Riverside County California.

——1976, Uranium-series age dating of calcite material: Los Angeles, University of Southern California, unpublished Geochemical Report No. SW-1 to Stone & Webster Engineering Corporation, Nine Mile nuclear power station, unit no. 2, Oswego County, New York.

Lewis, D. R., 1968, Effect of grinding on thermoluminescence of dolomite, calcite, and halite, *in* McDougall, D. J., ed., Thermoluminescence of geological material, Proceedings, NATO Advanced Research Institute, Spoleto, Italy: New York, Academic Press, p. 125–132.

Libby, W. F., 1961, Radiocarbon dating: Science, v. 133, p. 621–629.

——1963, Accuracy of radiocarbon dates: Science, v. 140, p. 278–280.

Lyons, J. B., and Snellenburg, J., 1971, Dating faults: Geological Society of America Bulletin, v. 82, p. 1749–1752.

McDougall, I., and Chamalaun, F. H., 1966, Geomagnetic polarity scale of time: Nature, v. 212, p. 1415–1418.

McDougall, I., Saemundsson, K., Johannesson, H., Watkins, N. D., and Kristjanssen, L., 1977, Extension of the geomagnetic polarity time scale to 6.5 m.y.: K-Ar dating, geological and paleomagnetic study of a 3,500-m lava succession in western Iceland: Geological Society of America Bulletin, v. 88, p. 1–15.

Medlin, W. L., 1968, Thermoluminescence growth curves in calcite, *in* McDougall, D. J., ed., Thermoluminescence of geological material, Proceedings, NATO Advanced Research Institute, Spoleto, Italy: New York, Academic Press, p. 91–102.

Moorbath, S., 1964, The rubidium-strontium method: Geological Society of London Quarterly Journal, v. 120, p. 87–98.

Naeser, C. W., and Dodge, F.C.W., 1969, Fission track ages of accessory minerals from granitic rocks of the central Sierra Nevada batholith, California: Geological Society of America Bulletin, v. 80, p. 2201–2212.

Naeser, C. W., and Faul, H., 1969, Fission track annealing in apatite and sphene: Journal of Geophysical Research, v. 74, p. 705–710.

Naeser, C. W., Engels, J. C., and Dodge, F.C.W., 1969, Fission track annealing and age determination of epidote minerals: Journal of Geophysical Research, v. 75, p. 1579–1584.

Naeser, C. W., Kistler, R. W., and Dodge, R.C.W., 1971, Ages of coexisting minerals from heat-flow borehole sites, central Sierra Nevada batholith: Journal of Geophysical Research, v. 76, p. 6462–6463.

Olson, E. A., and Broecker, W. S., 1958, Sample contamination and reliability of radiocarbon dates: New York Academy of Science, ser. II, v. 20, p. 593–604.

Roedder, E., and Skinner, B. J., 1968, Experimental evidence that fluid inclusions do not leak: Economic Geology, v. 63, p. 715–730.

Runcorn, S. K., 1969, The paleomagnetic vector field, *in* Hart, P. J., ed., The earth's crust and upper mantle: American Geophysical Union Geophysical Monograph No. 13, p. 447–457.

Stuiver, M., 1977, Recent developments in ^{14}C dating: Geological Society of America Abstracts with Programs, v. 9, p. 1192–1193.

Thompson, G. R., and Hower, J., 1973, An explanation for low radiometric ages from glauconite: Geochimica et Cosmochimica Acta, v. 37, p. 1473–1491.

Zeller, E. J., 1968, Geologic age determination by thermoluminescence, *in* McDougall, D. J., ed., Thermoluminescence of geological material, Proceedings, NATO Advanced Research Institute, Spoleto, Italy, 1968: New York, Academic Press, p. 311–325.

Zimmerman, R. A., and Reimer, G. M., 1974, Cretaceous fission-track dates of New England apatites: Geological Society of America Abstracts with Programs, v. 5, p. 88–89.

MANUSCRIPT RECEIVED BY THE SOCIETY JULY 13, 1978
MANUSCRIPT ACCEPTED NOVEMBER 13, 1978

Geological Society of America
Reviews in Engineering Geology, Volume IV
1979

Trenching as an exploratory method

ALLEN W. HATHEWAY
Haley & Aldrich, Inc., 238 Main Street, Cambridge, Massachusetts 02142

F. BEACH LEIGHTON
Leighton & Associates, 17975 Skypark Circle, Irvine, California 92714

ABSTRACT

The critical nature of siting nuclear power plants has led to increased emphasis on exploratory trenching. Trenching is the most definitive of all subsurface exploratory methods; it permits inspection of a continuous geologic section by both geologists and regulatory authorities and makes possible the preparation of a graphic log that delineates both obvious and subtle geologic features. About one of every two nuclear plant licensing efforts utilizes exploratory trenching. Many geologic hazards, such as "capable" faults, can be detected from trench exposures; they may otherwise remain undetected.

Trenches must be judiciously located, survey-controlled, excavated safely and adequately shored, logged in detail, and properly diagnosed. Useful techniques of trench logging include thorough cleaning of the trench walls, teamwork between geologist and recorder, logging against a carefully surveyed baseline and vertical reference grid, and panoramic photography. Soils, including paleosols, and glacial and glaciofluvial deposits present some of the most difficult media to log.

Trench logs must be thoroughly interpreted and correlated so that they document the geologic conditions governing suitability of the site. Age-determination techniques utilized in exploratory trenching include petrographic analyses, quartz inclusion studies, clay mineralogic analyses, and radiometric methods.

TRENCHING AS AN EXPLORATORY METHOD

Trenching by bulldozer or backhoe produces a slot that reveals the third dimension of earth materials. It is probably the most valuable as well as the most neglected exploratory method used in the siting of nuclear power plants and other important facilities. In the past, trenching has taken a back seat to geophysical work and exploratory drilling, but much progress has been made in its application to solving geologic problems on all types of development projects.

The urge to open the earth to expose buried geologic features and solve geologic problems has always been second nature to most geologists. Highway and railway cuts, exposures along bridge and dam abutments, mine shafts, excavated basements, tunnels, and cut-off trenches for dams are examples of excavations comparable to trench exposures. They all contain geologic information that can be viewed and recorded directly by the geologist. However, the critical nature of siting engineering structures in geologic hazard areas has led to increased emphasis on trenching prior to site design and construction in order to identify the nature of suspect features that will be uncovered during foundation excavation activities (Table 1).

The history of exploratory trenches for engineering works extends practically to the birth of engineering geology as both an art and a science and to the advent of powered machinery for trench excavation. At first the exploratory trench was commonly incorporated into the project excavation and was made to gather general geologic information on the site. Accounts of early exploratory work of this type are provided by many prominent geologists, including Lapworth (1911) and Burwell and Moneymaker (1950). Louderback (1950) was an early advocate of the use of exploratory trenching for investigation of fault ruptures, a key factor in nuclear power plant siting. A recent concise treatment of the advantages of trenching applied to assessing fault activity is that of Taylor and Cluff (1973).

With the arrival of regulatory control for siting engineering structures (about 1960), trenching became an important exploration method for the engineering geologist in both hillside and flatland areas. This has not been a sudden or steady evolution, rather an evolution marked by progress in spurts, chiefly in response to damaging natural events such as earthquakes or heavy rains, and to subsequent tightening of building and grading codes. Logging of geologic information from trenches has gradually become more systematic and a more formal part of geologic reports submitted for review and approval by the regulatory agencies. Critical structure siting underlines the ultimate need for detailed and accurate records

TABLE 1. EXAMPLES OF EXPLORATORY TRENCHING PERFORMED IN NUCLEAR POWER PLANT SITING

Site, location, reference	Purpose of trenching	Geologic material	Techniques applied
Diablo Canyon NPS,* California, 50323-3†	Explore continuously mantled bedrock on topographic terrace adjacent to faulted sea cliff	Obispo Tuff, pre-Monterey mudstone, Monteray Fm; sandstone, shale, siltstone, and limestone; Miocene	Eventually eight trenches in rectangular grid pattern; 1,550 m total length; mapped at 1:25 scale; 1 to 13 m deep; evidence of undisplaced reference features dating fault activity; thin-section analyses of deformed microfossils
Trojan NPS, Oregon, 50344-38	Expose complex stratigraphy in interbedded tuffs and massive basalts	Goble Fm; Eocene	Placed trench in topographic depression for maximum depth penetration; utilized adjacent inclined boring; trench 120 m long, 9 m deep
Limerick NPS, Pennsylvania, 50352-70	Small fault offset detected in foundation excavation; previously predicted by geotechnical consultant; displacement of 140-m.y.-old dike in late Triassic or early Jurassic time	Brunswick Fm, Newark Gp; red shales, siltstone, sandstones; Triassic	Absence of glacial cover; clay minerals used for K-Ar dating
Limerick NPS, Pennsylvania, 50352-79	Faulting dated at 150 to 200 m.y. by independent board of academic consultants; offsite trenching also utilized	As above	Low level of deformation in delicate shear-zone minerals; continuity of overlying soils shown by mineralogy; in-situ stress determination; depth of crystallization by geothermometry and geobarometry; age dating by alluvial terraces; two 45-m-long trenches across offset dike located by magnetometer survey
Hope Creek NPS, New Jersey, 50354-171	Demonstrate suitable foundation materials; variable degree of calcite cementation present	Vincentown Fm; quartzose glauconitic sand; Paleocene-Eocene(?)	Block samples of representative material extracted for lab testing of strength parameters; to 4.5 m below foundation grade
McGuire NPS, North Carolina, 50369-9	Ancient small-scale shear zones detected in rock core at site; includes slickensides	Metagabbro, granite, diorite; pre-Triassic	15-m-deep test pit; sampling and petrographic analysis; K-Ar age determination; striated calcite on slickensides related to Lower Triassic displacement; features found cut by 450-mm-wide Triassic mafic dike
North Coast NPS, Puerto Rico, 50376-57	Investigate nature of five prominent aerial photographic linears	Aguada and Aymamon tropical marine limestones; Miocene-Pliocene	Nine trenches; total 760 m long to 9 m deep; rock blasting and bulldozer, extended to depth in one case by backhoe along trench center; supplemented by adjacent boreholes and geophysical logging; microscopic paleontological determinations
Susquehanna NPS, Pennsylvania, 50387-76	Minor shear zones, breccia, slickensides, and calcite-healed fractures; mainly discovered in excavations for containment vessel No. 1	Wisconsin outwash and till, over Hamilton Gp shale (Middle to Upper Devonian)	Zone of weathering and iron staining found to be unbroken over glacial till
Shearon Harris NPS, North Carolina, 50400-4	Demonstrate stratigraphic continuity of power-block area	Residual sandy clay and sandy silt over Sanford Fm; claystone, siltstone, sandstone; Triassic(?)	Four major trenches; total 3,600 m long, 0.6 to 3.5 m deep, plus five minor trenches 15 to 30 m long; mapping at 1:120 scale
North Anna NPS, Virginia, 50404-53	Explore shear zone discovered in foundation excavations for units 3 and 4	Soil (horizons A through C), over saprolite, over biotite-hornblende and granite gneiss of Wissahickon Schist	Shear zone traced by series of trenches 3 to 105 m long and 3 to 5 m deep; mapping at scales as large as 1:24; clay mineral determination; radiometric age determination; structural fabric analysis; shear zone determined to be reactivated last in Triassic time (200 m.y.)
Catawba NPS, South Carolina, 50413-2	Trenches excavated for exploration of conditions expected to be present; numerous joints; one small fault with 3 to 13 mm gouge zone	Saprolite and weathered adamellite (syenite) and metagabbro; pre-late Triassic	Three trenches excavated by backhoe and dragline; total length 55 m, depth 5.5 to 9.5 m; boreholes placed on linear extension
Catawba NPS, South Carolina, 50413-13	Reverse fault in fluvial gravels of Pee Dee River; reported in literature; minimum distance of 64 km from site	Fluvial gravels; undetermined age; slickensided gouge; brecciated zone in bedrock; minor brecciation of saprolite	14 test pits over 107-m trace; organic material in fault zone determined to be at least 1,400 yr old; recent alluvium undisturbed
Catawba NPS, South Carolina, 50413-107	Three breccia zones, to 1.5 m wide, to 33 mm displacement, found in pipe trench and excavation for power block; reported by applicant to NRC	In saprolite and adamellite	Excavation halted on NRC order; detailed face mapping at 1:60 and 1:360 specified

TABLE 1. *(Continued)*

Site, location, reference	Purpose of trenching	Geologic material	Techniques applied
Catawba NPS, South Carolina, 50413-108	As above	As above	NRC specifies face mapping to follow format similar to U.S. Army (1975)
Catawba NPS, South Carolina, 50413-115 50413-120	As above; report on breccia zones 2 and 3	As above	K-Ar determination of laumontite, of hydrothermal origin, at ± 86 m.y.; additional backhoe trenches across extension; breccia zone 3 traced to point of being overlain by undisplaced and unfaulted alluvial material and saprolitre B horizon; logging at 1:120, numerous attitude measurements; movement considered to be 56 to 150 m.y. B.P.
Catawba NPS, South Carolina, 50413-122	As above; brecciated zones 5, 6, 7 reported and investigated by independent geologic review panel	As above	Paragenetic mineral study demonstrated relationships similar to those above; strained laumonite in related dilatation fractures; tabulation of geologic events affecting site as related to those of regional nature
Millstone 3 NPS, Connecticut, 50423-109 50423-144	Fault discovered in bedrock excavation of category I foundations	Monson Gneiss; lower Paleozoic	Fault zones mapped in detail; constituent minerals sampled, petrographic identification, clay mineral determination, fluid inclusion dating; petrogenetic sequence developed
Perry NPS, Ohio, 50440-58	Small-scale asymmetric bedrock folds and faults beneath Pleistocene glacial till in foundation excavation	Chagrin Shale, Bedford Fm; Upper Devonian–Lower Mississippian	Machine-scraped excavation of hillside and roadcut exposures
Perry NPS, Ohio, 50440-136	FSAR[§] floor mapping of foundation excavation	As above	Results showed features shallow, nontectonic, with strikes normal to regional glacial movement; due to basal drag of Pleistocene ice sheet
Perry NPS, Ohio, 50440-154	FSAR; continued mapping of excavated faces; photographs presented	As above	As above
Perry NPS, Ohio, 50440-165	FSAR; continued mapping of excavated faces; photographs presented	As above	Use of boulder stratum in till to demonstrate stratigraphic continuity
Fulton NPS, Pennsylvania, 50463-5	Investigate several zones of deep weathering parallel to strike of cleavage in bedrock	Peach Bottom Slate Member of Peters Creek Fm; lower Paleozoic	Cleavage demonstrated continuous; undisplaced dike located
Fulton NPS, Pennsylvania, 50463-10 50463-75	Renewed NRC interest in Peach Bottom fault	As above	Foliation planes in juxtaposed slate and schist shown to be similar, that is, movement only prior to regional metamorphism (345 to 470 m.y.); small trenches to explore shear zones found in borings; K-Ar dating employed; 630 m of trenches to 8 m deep
Fulton NPS, Pennsylvania, 50463-86	Continued exploration of Peach Bottom fault	As above	Magnetometer surveys to locate undisplaced Triassic dikes; folding of fault planes related to older orogenic period; supplementary backhoe pits to define trends found in trenches (up to 60 m long); trenches segmented on basis of stereographic projections of poles to lineations; clay mineralogy to distinguish between depositional features, fractures, and faults
Allens Creek NPS, Texas, 50466-34	Investigate supposed relationship between linear tonal anomalies on remote imagery and growth faults common to gulf coast region	Beaumont Fm; Pleistocene preconsolidated fluvial-deltaic clays	120-m trench to 3 m deep, along N–S axis of plant; mapped at 1:60; remote imagery interpretation and seismic reflection profiling (330 to 450-m depth); trenching ultimately unsuccessful in producing actual evidence of linears
Allens Creek NPS, Texas, 50466-85	NRC requested trench examination of linears detected by Texas Bureau of Economic Geology suspected to be related to effects of groundwater withdrawal and subsidence	As above	As above
Allens Creek NPS, Texas, 50466-95	Consultant declined to utilize further trenching on basis of lack of definite presence of linears in trenches	As above	Further remote imagery interpretation and inspection of riverbank exposures at intersection with linears

Continued on next page

TABLE 1. (Continued)

Site location, reference	Purpose of trenching	Geologic material	Techniques applied
Cherokee NPS, South Carolina, STN-50491-139	Ancient small-scale shear features discovered in rock core and test pits; features considered older than 170 m.y.; displacements of no more than several inches	Mafic and felsic gneiss, schist, metaconglomerate, and quartzite; Precambrian to lower Paleozoic; overlain by saprolite	Applicant committed to trenching as PSAR Appendix F effort, to be submitted to NRC
Montague NPS, Massachusetts, 50496-4 50496-34	Determine nature of slickensides observed in drill core	Interbedded Mt. Toby Conglomerate and Turners Falls Sandstone; Upper Triassic	1,260 m of trenches to 6 m deep; 1:120 scale; features determined to be stress effects on undisplaced joints, related to basin-wide folding in Triassic time
Pebble Springs NPS, Oregon, 50514-94	Expose unusual clastic dikes in volcanic sequence	Ellensburg Fm; (Pomona basalt)	620 m of trenches exposed several clastic dikes that did not transect overlying Rattlesnake Ridge Member
Palo Verde NPS, Arizona, STN-50528-12	Define nature of fault mapped at ground surface within 8 km of site; also linear at Arlington, Arizona	Miocene basalt overlies clayey sand and silty clay	31 backhoe trenches excavated, 610-m fault trace; 100 borings; geophysical borehole logging; K-Ar dating; mineralogical studies of clay soil horizon; undisturbed paleosols 2-m.y.-old basalt lies over four paleosols
Fort Calhoun NPS, Nebraska, 50548-93	Reverse-sense offset in outwash/glaciofluvial sand and gravel exposed in distant, off-site road cut; reported by Nebraska State Geological Survey; entire location determined to be mass wastage containing several Pleistocene units	Pleistocene glacial and glaciofluvial deposits and Peoria loess	Radiometrically datable material lacking; resorted to time-stratigraphic units and paleosols, pebble count of tills, analyses of remote imagery and areal geologic mapping
Sundesert NPS, California, 50582-12	Determine existence of possible faults	Bouse Fm; Pliocene and various Quaternary units	51 trenches; total of 2,925 m lineal extent
Skagit NPS, Washington, STN-50522-100	Exploratory trenching of remote imagery linears; shear zone; close fractures, crushed rock, clay; other minor bedding-plane fractures	Chuckanut Fm (sandstone and siltstone); Paleocene Shuksan metamorphic suite	Shear zone investigated by 12 exploratory trenches at 1:120; traced to local pinch-out; unbroken mantle of glacial till; carbon-14 age determination

Note: This table contains information concerning the use of exploratory trenching on only those sites with which the authors are familiar or at which they have worked.

*Nuclear Power Station.

†Reference document is identified by Federal Docket Number; available from National Technical Information Service, U.S. Department of Commerce, Springfield, Virginia 22141. Complete citations are found at the end of this paper.

§Final Safety Analysis Report (see McClure and Hatheway, this volume).

of subsurface conditions, compiled under quality assurance procedures (see Appendix 1).

Despite the widespread use of trenching today, written treatises on the subject are practically nonexistent. In fact, in the tables of contents and indexes of most engineering geology texts, trenching is not mentioned and is not even treated under the subjects of subsurface exploration and subsurface geology. Yet trenching is to the engineering geologist today what wells are to the petroleum geologist and ground-water geologist and what coring is to the mining geologist. This is demonstrated in construction disputes over the question, What exploration could have been undertaken to most effectively diagnose this subsurface condition prior to construction? Often the answer is, More exploratory trenching was needed. The days are rapidly disappearing when visual inspection provided the summary

basis for acceptance or rejection of subsurface conditions. Nowadays when geologic hazards become controversial, it is in the exploratory trench that the bulk of the critical evidence is found and weighed.

Objectives of Trenching

Trenches permit mapping in detail of earth materials, including their lithology and subsurface distribution, the sampling and testing of earth materials, and the determination of their rippability in excavation. In this way, trenching has been used to work out geologic puzzles on both a site-specific and areal basis (Tables 1, 2).

Many geologic and foundation problems that would otherwise remain undetected can be recognized and interpreted from

TABLE 2. LEVELS OF STUDY RELATED TO SUBSURFACE INVESTIGATIONS

Type of study	Chief objectives	Common types of subsurface exploration	Products
1. Regional appraisal of geotechnical conditions over large areas (>1,000 acres)	Geologic framework; broad planning parameters; guidelines for future development	Geophysical surveys	Medium- to small-scale maps (1:24,000 to 1:62,500); basic data compilations
2. Tract investigations (<1,000 acres)	Geotechnical analysis of information for specific tract layout, or alternative types of development; guidelines for site investigation	Backhoe or bulldozer pits; borings, geophysical surveys	Subsurface logs Large-scale maps and sections (1:2,400 to 1:7,200)
3. Detailed site evaluation	Diagnosis of site constraints and opportunities in detail	Trenching and boring on a large-scale grid	Detailed trench logs, maps and cross sections (1:60 to 1:1,200)

trench exposures. More specifically, nuclear power plant siting astride or near "capable" faults (see Adair, this volume), solution cavities, slope failures, and other geologic hazards can be prevented.

As soon as a site for the nuclear power block has been selected, its geologic safety must be proved. This objective is most fully accomplished by a trenching program that is carefully planned, executed safely, recorded as a lasting graphic record, and properly diagnosed.

Advantages of Trenching

The trench permits direct visual inspection and study of a continuous horizontal and vertical section of earth materials, unlike geophysical methods that are indirect and unlike borings that lack horizontal continuity. Trenches enable recognition and interpretation of geologic hazards such as faults, landslides, ground-water problems, and subsidence conditions. They have an advantage over boreholes in places where the geology is complicated and where a detailed picture of the geologic section is necessary.

The trench commonly becomes the test arena for evaluation of nearly all geologic hazards that are of sufficient magnitude to result in rejection of a nuclear power plant site. The essentially continuous display of subsurface features cannot only be recorded, illustrated, sampled, and tested, but it can be revisited and evaluated by investigators and regulatory agency officials.

Site suitability rests heavily on the identification and depiction of geologic features in the trenches. If there is evidence of recent fault displacement or other major adverse conditions, the site may have to be rejected. On the other hand, quantification of certain hazard parameters may permit the site to be handled safely and economically by engineers. Because of the complexity and interaction of geologic processes, conflicting evidence regarding geologic features is common and may require further probing to eliminate multiple hypotheses regarding the type and degree of risk.

Costs of trenching may be a source of concern to the payer, but the savings from the results obtained can more than compensate for the expenses. A bulldozer or backhoe can be used to produce a trench at considerably less cost than the drilling of traditional boreholes. And, more importantly, the proving out of a site by trenching may result in the saving of large sums of money (perhaps millions) that otherwise may have to be invested in structural reinforcing steel and other engineering design measures.

Philosophy of Trench Logging

There are basically two philosophies of trench logging: *subjective* and *objective.* Simply stated, subjective logging recognizes that a condition exists and then undertakes to portray the log as a primary graphic framework in which the condition is illustrated first and the supporting rock or soil matrix is added in secondary importance. Such logging begins after close inspection reveals obvious key factors regarding faults and displacements. The logging tends to be somewhat schematic, such as is shown on Figure 1. The schematic nature does not detract from the accuracy of logging; features are accurately placed with reference to the mapping grid. However, subordinate or accessory details not necessary in proving the underlying supposition are omitted. The fact that faulting is present and that its nature and age of last movement have been correctly defined in the trench log is sufficient. A significant amount of trenching performed to aid in the preparation of the Preliminary Safety Analysis Report (PSAR) has produced such subjectively schematic logs, but to rely on this technique is to invite additional regulatory questioning and costly time delays.

In contrast, objective logging attempts to portray equally all physical features of the trench face, larger than a threshold of resolution, in an impartial manner and without regard to relative importance. Both obvious and subtle features are shown with equal resolution, and little subjective interpretation is made during the recording process. Trench logging for nuclear plants should usually be conducted so that whatever data are collected must be carefully recorded, in both graphic and note form, and must not be biased by interim decisions as to their relative value in the process of judging fault capability. To this end, the most successful of nuclear plant exploratory trench logs

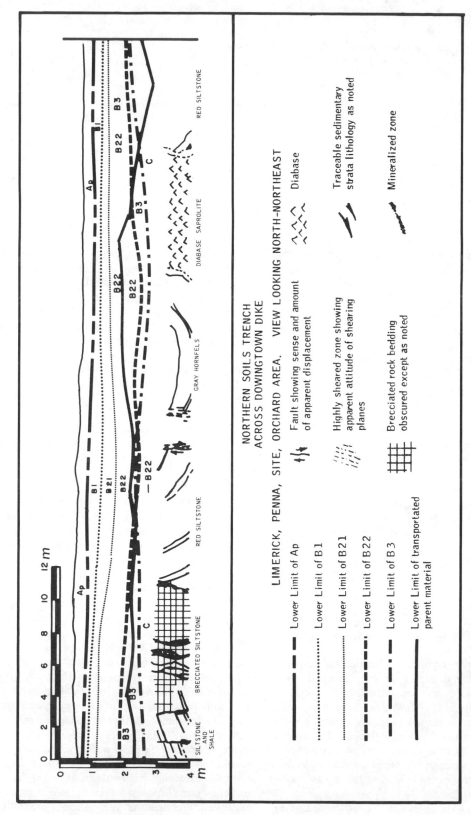

Figure 1. A *subjective* trench log; particular detail is not shown. Contacts and structural features have been portrayed in a schematic fashion, subduing the detail of the host rock. This type of logging is more useful when faulting is known to exist and evidence relating to its capability is rather straightforward. Limerick NPS, Pennsylvania (Docket 50352-79, 1974).

are clear portraits of all components: matrix, rock discontinuities, inclusions, color variations, apparent contacts, and boundaries, such as seen in Figure 2. It is important not to draw in subtle boundaries and contacts; rather it is important to draw definitively only the absolutely defined parts of the puzzle. This is objective trench logging.

SITING CONSIDERATIONS

A sound understanding of the stratigraphic and structural framework of the proposed site must be developed prior to planning trench locations. This framework should extend over at least the immediate 2.5 km^2 that surround the prime siting area for the reactor containment vessel. Photogeologic work and field mapping may serve to eliminate some of the possible power-block sites, thus reducing or expanding the area of consideration and alleviating expensive trench programs in at least certain portions of the initial area under consideration. On the other hand, some exploratory trenching (and drilling) may be necessary to establish the stratigraphic-structural framework, including even a possible second stage of subsurface exploration.

The practical effect of the *Code of Federal Regulations, Title 10, Part 100 (1978)* is that a plant foundation cannot be traversed by "capable" faults that make stringent and costly design measures necessary in order to construct a safe and seismically resistant structure. A "capable" fault is defined as one that has experienced a single displacement in the past 35,000 yr or recurring displacements during the past 500,000 yr. It is incumbent upon the applicant utility and its consultants to show beyond any reasonable doubt that capable faults are absent. To do this, it should be shown that the site of the trench contains a cover of late Quaternary materials against which faults or other deformational structures can be observed to terminate, or through which they may be seen to cut. Without materials of appropriate age, proof of the age relationships of suspicious features can be quite difficult or even impossible to demonstrate. A case in point is that of units 3 and 4 of the North Anna (Virginia) Nuclear Power Station (NPS) in which foundation excavation mapping for the Final Safety Analysis Report (FSAR) revealed an apparent shear zone in schistose rock under only a thin cap of saprolite (Docket 50404-53, 1973). Saprolite generally results from long-term alteration of igneous and metamorphic rock by climatically controlled weathering processes. Because saprolite is not the product of a Quaternary depositional process, ordinary stratigraphic dating techniques are ineffective, and geochemical and radiometric studies are often required to determine the ages of materials present in suspicious shear zones.

The power-block location is chosen with careful consideration of foundation engineering properties as well as the basic geologic suitability. Therefore, an early effort is made to select the best possible locations for exploratory trenches, not only to demonstrate the fault-free nature of the power-block site, but to assist the geotechnical engineers in providing essential design information for both static foundation design and the governing soil-structure dynamic analyses.

Extensive on-site trenching should not be undertaken until completion of the first review of site geologic and foundation characteristics by the soil dynamics specialists. This permits screening of the most desirable power-block location within the site preserve. Power plant design features are generally standardized to such a degree with each Nuclear Steam Supply System manufacturer that a typical outline and geometry of the power-block and appurtenant structures can be furnished by the architect-engineer (Fig. 3).

Geologic conditions are examined so as to place exploratory trenches in the immediate vicinity of class I structures, To facilitate this, the trial plant layout is superimposed on geotechnical maps. The trenches are generally planned to intersect suspected or observed earth features, as well as to afford inspection of key foundation areas. In one of the first uses of trenching in nuclear plant siting (Diablo Canyon, California; Jahns, 1969—50323-3), R. H. Jahns chose to have a rectangular grid of four wide bulldozer trenches constructed on a broad marine topographic terrace adjacent to a sea cliff exhibiting faulting.

The long axis of such trenches should be placed as nearly perpendicular as possible to the stratigraphic-structural feature or linear to be examined. Existing exposure and borehole data can aid in decreasing the number or extent of some trenching programs. On slopes it is commonly possible to produce exploratory cut faces without making a two-sided trench. A small shored trench at the foot of the slope may be necessary. In places trench width can be narrowed by placing a small backhoe trench within the confines of a bulldozer trench. Existing inferior exposures and some drainage channels containing thin surficial deposits can be scraped to produce the necessary geotechnical information equivalent to that found in a standard shored trench.

Geophysical techniques such as seismic refraction will assist in identifying troublesome zones of deep weathering (typical in the Appalachian province), and the portable proton magnetometer will detect dike rocks of sufficient contrast (more than about 150 gammas) against country rocks.

Geomorphology is important in the selection of trench locations. Geomorphic study of landforms, both in the field and on aerial photographs, is useful in distinguishing earth features such as linears, lineaments, soil and rock contacts, earth processes such as active faulting and landsliding, and earth history stages, youthful and old. Image interpretation is treated by McEldowney and Pascucci (this volume).

PLANNING THE TRENCH LAYOUT

In order to be a useful and positive part of the site investigation, on-site trenches must be survey-located and carefully maintained after logging for as long as required for a confirmatory visit by the regulatory agencies.

Survey Control

Some trenches are successful enterprises in themselves without vertical survey control. That is because they may prove to provide such irrefutable evidence of stratigraphic continuity that nearby exploratory boreholes and/or downhole geophysi-

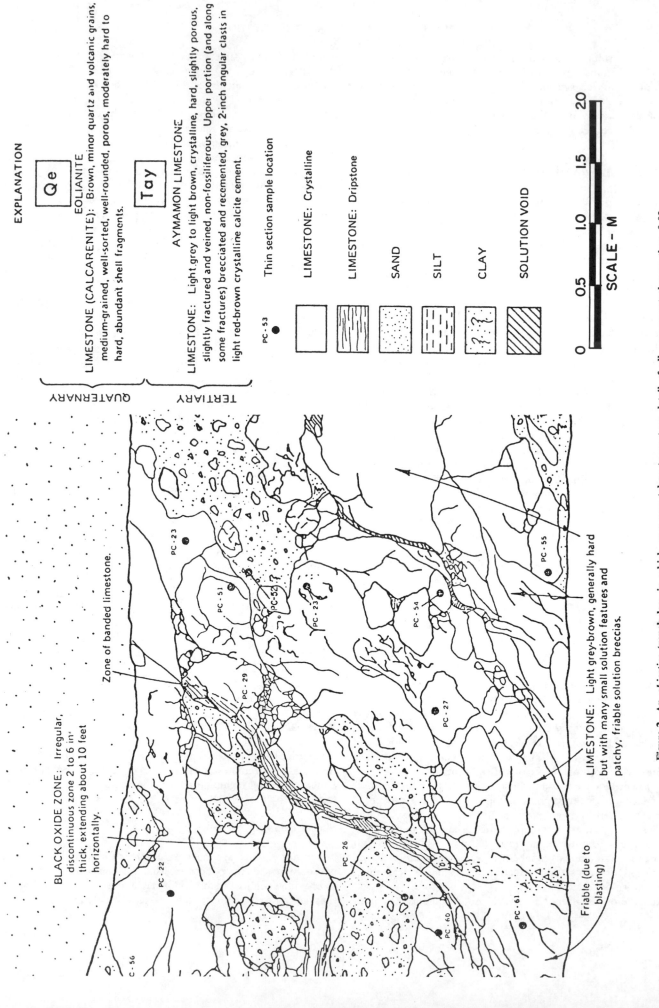

EXPLANATION

QUATERNARY

Qe

EOLIANITE

LIMESTONE (CALCARENITE): Brown, minor quartz and volcanic grains, medium-grained, well-sorted, well-rounded, porous, moderately hard to hard, abundant shell fragments.

TERTIARY

Tay

AYMAMON LIMESTONE

LIMESTONE: Light grey to light brown, crystalline, hard, slightly porous, slightly fractured and veined, non-fossiliferous. Upper portion (and along some fractures) brecciated and recemented, grey, 2-inch angular clasts in light red-brown crystalline calcite cement.

PC-53 ● Thin section sample location

LIMESTONE: Crystalline

LIMESTONE: Dripstone

SAND

SILT

CLAY

SOLUTION VOID

SCALE – M

0   0.5   1.0   1.5   20

Figure 2. An *objective* trench log, in which care was taken to portray detail of all components larger than 0.03 m, within each grid square, without particular attention to adjacent detail. Mapped in tropical marine limestones of Puerto Rico by J. K. Stowe, under direction of A. W. Hatheway (from Docket 50376-57, 1975).

BLACK OXIDE ZONE: Irregular, discontinuous zone 2 to 6 in. thick, extending about 10 feet horizontally.

Zone of banded limestone.

LIMESTONE: Light grey-brown, generally hard but with many small solution features and patchy, friable solution breccias.

Friable (due to blasting)

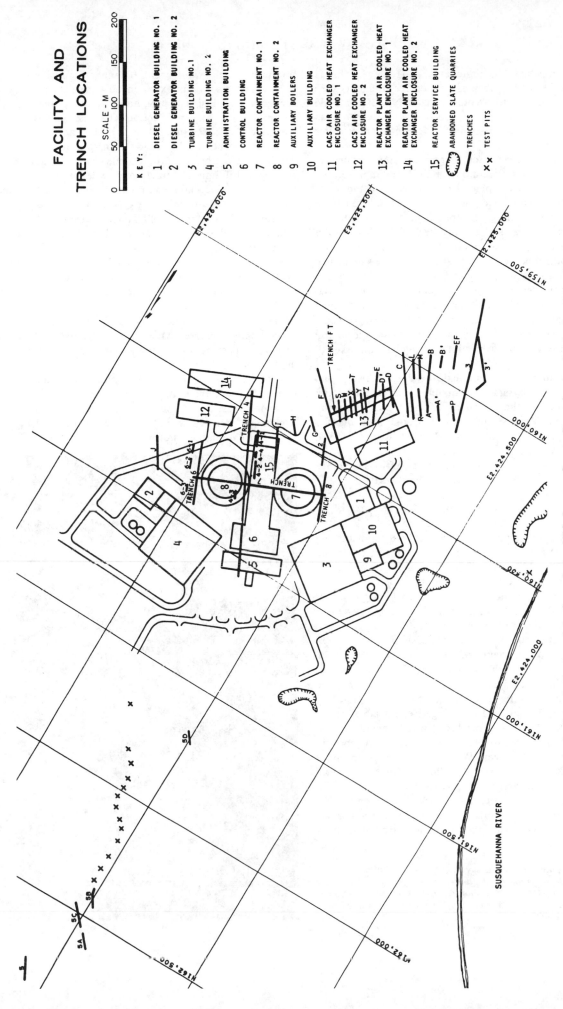

Figure 3. General site plan of the Susquehanna NPS, Luzerne County, Pennsylvania, showing locations of exploratory trenches placed to explore category I structure foundations and to investigate minor shear zones, breccia, slickensides, and calcite-healed fractures mainly discovered during foundation excavation work (from Docket 50387-76, 1974).

cal signature logging may be unnecessary. However, this is not always the case, and quality assurance requirements (see McClure and Hatheway, this volume) usually call for a tie to the site survey net for vertical and horizontal control, as a basis for stratigraphic control and for future re-entry, after closing, if necessary.

Survey requirements for trench logging are not exhaustive; narrow trenches need be staked along one side only, preferably at 2-m stations, with stakes placed not so close to the walls as to be affected by minor sloughing. In potentially unstable soil units, it is best to shore the trench prior to installation of the survey line so that stakes may be laid in close to the walls without fear of loss. We recommend that nuclear plant trench survey control be at ±0.03 m and tied to the site survey grid. It will generally be necessary to correlate profile horizons between the trench area and nearby boreholes. These correlations are used to establish the nature of any stratigraphic indicators that are used in explaining the trench geologic environment. Survey control consists of establishing a nearby bench mark and extending a baseline parallel to the axis of the trench.

It is generally sufficient to establish the desired end points of the trench location by staking, implement excavation, and then returning to stake the alignment of the trench along the crown of one wall. Vertical stationing is transferred into the trench by geologists, with the use of stout strings affixed to the sidewalls by large box nails.

The vertical string control at 2-m horizontal stations becomes the basis of the reference grid of the logging effort.

Excavation

The method of excavation that proves to be least disturbing to the host soil and/or rock will also likely prove to be the least expensive. Shallow trench depths are attained ordinarily with the use of backhoe-type equipment, whereas deeper excavations generally require slope-stabilized bench configurations and a width sufficient to allow working space for bulldozer-type equipment. Figure 4 illustrates a combination upper-level bulldozer cut and lower-level backhoe trench excavation, placed to a total depth of 15 m.

By the time trench excavation is contemplated at the site, sufficient insight into the engineering properties of site geologic units should be available to guide the basic choice of machine excavation versus blasting and mucking. Recent advances in high-pressure hydraulics have produced a new generation of large backhoes that are capable of excavating trenches in competent materials. However, Weaver (1975) has devised a matrix of physical properties and indicators that are useful in determining the best method of excavation.

When blasting is used in competent rock, it is essential that presplitting techniques be utilized to produce nearly vertical face walls without overbreak and to avoid introducing blast fracturing in the wall rock. Blasting is considered by many to be a blaster's art, but experienced geologists or civil engineers can generally design a program so that optimal delay times, patterns, hole and production charges, and stemming are specified—all based on rock structural character. A good blast round should be capable of loosening a metre or more of rock depth per blast level, without undesirable residual fracturing. Improper drill-hole alignment and overshooting in general can be avoided. Blast-induced fractures (Fig. 5) are unnecessary and sometimes difficult to explain in terms of origin. The California Department of Transportation (McCauley and others, 1974) has released an excellent guide to presplit rock excavation.

Shoring commonly consists of a framework of wood or metal posts braced at intervals by horizontal strut braces (Fig. 6). This shoring should be designed or reviewed by a registered civil or structural engineer and spaced in accordance with the lateral loads to be resisted. Hydraulically set aluminum shoring is sometimes preferred when the trench must not be maintained open for longer periods of time; investment costs are relatively high.

Trenches dug in questionable material should be sloped or benched in a manner that will minimize the hazard of caving. In some cases, a wide bulldozer trench can be deepened with a backhoe trench excavated less than 1.5 m in depth as a means of eliminating shoring.

Figure 4. Combination trench excavation in which bulldozers have cut away access for mapping of the upper level, to maximum stable height, with lower-level access via shored backhoe trench. Combined depth of exposure is 15 m; in tropical marine limestone, near Manati, Puerto Rico (Docket 50376).

Figure 5. Blast-induced fracturing (denoted by upright pen) in Quaternary eolianite overlying limestone. Such fractures fortunately did not extend downward into the limestone and were the result of differential elastic response to blasting Punta Chivato, Puerto Rico.

Generally, benches are excavated by a bulldozer for a deep trench and are set back at least half the height of a single face. Faces are sloped 1:1, providing adverse geologic conditions do not require flatter slopes.

All trenches should be properly flagged so that they can be identified by those approaching the area. In addition, spoil piles should be placed a safe distance from the trench to prevent ravelling and masking of the trench walls. This is generally at least 1 m for trenches more than 1.5 m in depth. Operators of trench excavation equipment should be instructed to place spoil piles in safe positions that do not surcharge potentially unfavorable walls, provide ravelling potential, and conceal cracks that might form upslope of a marginally safe trench wall. In sloping ground, the spoil pile is generally placed on the downhill side.

The logger and recorder must be protected from failure of these trench walls during logging operations. Shoring is the principal protection, but additional precautions must be taken. A safety checklist should be reviewed before every project, and no member of the team should enter a deep trench until it is properly shored and inspected for signs of distress, caving, or seepage. Safety precautions include wearing secured hard hats and football shoulder pads, particularly when friable cobbles or boulders and highly sheared rock can spall from above waist level in the trench. These zones should be dug out to sufficiently remove the hazard and shored as wide areas as shown in Figure 6.

Environmental and Safety Regulations

Environmental regulations necessitate application for clearances from appropriate State or Federal agencies in whose jurisdiction the site rests. It will be well to declare several alternate locations should complications arise concerning proper excavation, maintenance, dewatering, or definition of geologic conditions. Agency approval can result in waiting periods of 30 days or more for penetration of successive bureaucratic layers. In order to ensure that the request for approval of the environmental regulatory agency is forthcoming, it is best to clearly define the necessity for construction of the trench, to plan for as narrow a band of disruption as possible, to make the trench no longer or deeper than absolutely necessary, and to calculate accurately the bulking factor of waste, to accommodate for its interim storage, and to have plans for replacement of waste as backfill and to dispose of the remainder appropriately.

Federal regulations (U.S. OSHA, 1974) specify that trenches excavated deeper than 2.5 m be designed with safety features such as mechanical shoring, appropriate open widths, or sloping walls (Fig. 6). Because few trenches will show appropriate exposures in less than 2.5 m of depth, the safety features are nearly always mandatory. Where applicable, many organizations also prefer to utilize the trench safety guidelines of the California Department of Industrial Relations (1972) or the *Trenching and Shoring Manual* of the California Department of Transportation (1977). Particularly adverse trenching conditions include uncontrolled fill, unconsolidated alluvium and colluvium, seepage areas, caving sands, and otherwise unstable ground. Thompson and Tannenbaum (1977) have compiled statistics showing that some 100 workers die each year in the United States in construction trench failures. In California alone, at least two geologists have perished in exploratory trench or test pit failures in the past few years.

Dewatering

Probably more exploratory trenches for nuclear plant siting have been excavated in wet ground than in dry. Excavations made in temperate and tropical climates nearly always require dewatering, especially since the majority of offsite investigations for remote-image linears involve some sort of locally depressed geomorphic landform—a natural collection system for surface water. Water flowing into the trench under even low head constitutes not only a nuisance, but a direct threat to sidewall stability. Prior to excavation, a few shallow borings should be placed in an appropriate area around the trench location; tabulated ground-water levels may be related to the rudimentary stratigraphy being developed in the first geologic proof borings and an estimate made of the need for dewatering and the extent to which it will be required. Seldom are wellpoints warranted for trench dewatering, on the basis of cost and the relatively short life of the excavation, rather a plan for

Figure 6. Shored backhoe trench constructed to specifications of U.S. OSHA (1974) and California Department of Industrial Relations (1972). The trench is drained by gasoline-driven suction pumps.

portable sump pumps and over-the-bank collection drainage systems is usually appropriate.

In the trenching of urban areas, for non-nuclear, safety-related construction, the geologist should endeavor to locate buried utilities before laying out the trench. Most utility companies wish to assist in this identification in order to avoid damage to their system and interruption of service. It is also useful to know the locations of shutoff valves. Some geologists carry tapered wooden plugs and plumbing tools, especially when trenching in agricultural areas known to have a high density of irrigation pipes.

Protection from ground water and surface water is an essential aspect of trench maintenance throughout the logging effort as well as during the regulatory agency review visit. Protection of subtle relationships is of prime importance. It is only after panoramic photographs and trench logs are compared at the logged face by the review party that the trench can be backfilled and the site returned to its former state. The entire process of excavation of an unshored rock trench, for instance, a few hundreds of metres in length, may require a month for blasting, mucking, surveying, and fencing; an additional month for logging and in-house review; and another month for visitation and consultation by the regulatory agency party. Thus, the trench generally is left open for as much as three months, even for ideal weather and local labor conditions, and provision must be made for handling inflow of water during that period.

TECHNIQUES OF TRENCH LOGGING

The subtle detail illuminated by trench logging is the fabric that enables reading the geologic record. Does a fault pass through the trench area? Are two different earth formations juxtaposed? What type of landslide or other surficial debris is exposed? Trench logging generally serves two purposes: (1) presenting raw field data to scale and (2) delineating lithologic units and geologic structures.

Logging will always benefit from judicious application of the aforementioned steps of proper planning and siting. In the same way that an order of priority must be established for excavation of the trenches, an order of priority needs to be established for logging the trenches. Each trench should have primary and secondary geologic objectives assigned that can be borne in mind during both excavation and logging. Should these objectives not be met, final logs may reveal the need for additional trenching, either in new locations or by deepening or lengthening the existing trenches.

Trench logs are made to objectively portray the fabric of geologic features visible in each excavation. As such, they should show all features that are important to the physical constitution of the country rock—all of this, but without the myriad of gradational hues and tones that complete the view in a color photographic record. Trench logging is an onerous task requiring infinite patience, unusual talents of observation, precision, decisive judgment, an eye for detail, a very broad geologic base of knowledge, and not a little artistic ability. The correct blend of these facets and talents are used to bring out and record what is essential and to subdue what is unessential or confusing in lack of contrast. Good and poor

logs are instantly separable. Experienced engineering geologists, especially those of the regulatory review committee, will be prone to judge the relative worth of each set of trench logs long before they are displayed at the trench wall for evaluation and comparison. It is for this reason that proper techniques are the essential basis of worthwhile trench logging. When weighed against the costs involved and the effect of inspection and review times, the necessity for a proper logging effort becomes clear.

Preparation

Equally important in the logging process is the person responsible, *the logger,* and the product, *the log.*

Efficiency in trench logging demands attention by both an experienced geologist (*logger*) and a field assistant (*recorder*). Major attributes of the logger are (1) experience in geologic mapping on a large scale, (2) an eye for subtle details, and (3) precision in graphic representation of geologic features. The witches of *Macbeth* prophesied the logging problems of the geologist with their "Double, double, toil and trouble." The geologist must clearly differentiate between what is known and what is inferred, first on the walls of the trench and then on the trench log. Based on the features and conditions mapped, he can, with a proper degree of scientific detachment, draw objective conclusions and exercise critical judgment. But every portion of the trench must be examined in detail, and mapped details must be double checked for their precision and significance.

Teamwork is essential between the geologist and the recorder. Keeping in mind the experience of the recorder, the geologist feeds information deciphered as rapidly as possible. The geologist encircles representative attitudes for plotting on the geologic map and completes the graphic portion of the log. Summary procedures are presented in Appendix 1.

The recorder is responsible for serving as chauffeur, liaison, equipment manager, photographer, and record keeper. He should be viewed as a budding geologist. It is desirable that the recorder review all abbreviations, trench locations, and equipment items before leaving for the field, based on a checklist provided by the geologist (Appendix 1). Emphasis should be placed on his developing an eye for detail and abilities to accurately locate and portray all of the features so exposed. The recorder should be able to stake out trench locations plotted by the geologist and manage excavation work in accordance with a table showing the numbered trenches, their configuration, and their location.

Shoring, in accordance with governmental standards for trenches in excess of 1.5 m, should be installed as soon as the trench is excavated and before the recorder enters the trenches to first clean the trench walls. The recorder precedes the geologist to each trench, cleaning the trench walls with the large blade of a mattock for soft but cohesive earth materials and with a whisk broom for less cohesive materials such as alluvium. It is important to remove entirely the coating or smear commonly left by excavating equipment and to illuminate contact or structural features by indentation with the mattock point or blade.

During his recording of data, the recorder generally keeps

a sample completed log in front of him and inscribes descriptive items on a trench log report checklist (Fig. 7).

A grid system should be provided for each trench. This can consist of a tape placed along the top or bottom of the trench or a more detailed "hub and string" reference grid that is spaced to coincide with the degree of detail sought. The survey position of the trench must be tied in with the reference grid. Generally, survey hubs at the ends of each trench are flagged and represent the termini of the base line for the trench. Deviations in elevation at the top and bottom of trenches can be accommodated by hand leveling, and deviations from the vertical can be accommodated with a plumb line.

It is common to project data from the trench floor to the trench wall, or to log the floor of the trench on a separate sheet. The recorder may find color pencils useful in plotting fractures, joints, faults, clay seams, and other special features.

The outline of the trench is traced on standard-sized sheets, allowing overlap at the end of each sheet. It is helpful to provide heavier coordinates on grid paper located every 3 m for ease of plotting. A tape stretched out on the floor of the trench can be used for measuring distances and pinpointing locations. For most purposes, locations between 3-m marks can be judged by eye with an error of 25 cm or less. If a feature must be more exactly located, a smaller hand tape can be used.

Polaroid pictures provide instant replicas of trench walls and should be taken from the surface, without entry, before shoring is completely installed. Because bulldozer trenches can be photographed more readily than backhoe trenches, and often do not require shoring, they deserve priority in critical areas. Panoramic photography is necessary to provide a lasting record. Cameras of 35-mm or larger format should be used from a tripod mount to provide continuous coverage, with overlap for preservation of critical detail at the lowest degree of radial distortion possible.

Correlation

Trench correlation and the compilation of a geologic map are natural steps following trench logging. The objective is, of course, to identify and trace earth units from one trench to others. Trench logs thus serve as windows in a continuous panel diagram produced by correlation techniques. These techniques include defining marker features and other correlation indicators and identifying lithologic similarity and stratigraphic-geomorphic position.

Once contact and facies relationships have been determined in each trench, tectonic-lithologic relationships and geomorphic-pedologic history of the site become more apparent. Commonly, this work involves review of the regional geology and consideration of subsurface data gathered from outside site boundaries. A second stage of trenching may be needed to erase multiple explanations of correlation problems.

Resource Requirements

Since the need for trenching often hinges on what is being found on a day-to-day basis in the general exploration program,

SPOT-REPORT CHECKLIST FOR TRENCH LOGS
(To be used for each typical occurrence of soil and/or rock conditions)

Trench No. _____ Station No. _____ Logged by/Date _____
Trench bearing _____ Project No. _____ Reviewed by/Date _____
Wall logged _____ Project name _____ Photographed _____
Scale _____

1. Unit name _____
2. Lithologic name _____
3. Munsell color _____
4. Particle constituents _____
5. Grain size (U.S.C.S.*) _____
6. Particle shape _____
7. Degree of sorting _____
8. Cementation _____
9. Weathering _____
10. Bedding or foliation _____
11. Discontinuities _____
12. Lithologic contacts _____
13. Deformational characteristics _____
14. Mineralization _____
15. Fossils or organic matter _____
16. Moisture and/or ground water _____
17. Samples extracted _____
18. Remarks _____

*Unified Soil Classification System (U.S. Army, 1953).

Figure 7. Example of spot-report checklist for trench logs. This form is used to record observations made at key locations along the mapped face.

the project team may well decide, on very limited notice, to proceed with such an excavation. Resource requirements should be identified at once and the client and applicant utility notified at once as to cost estimates and necessary clearances so that the trench may be opened, logged, photographed, sampled, reviewed, and backfilled on schedule.

Estimation of resource requirements is best based on previous project management experience. However, wide variations in rock and soil type and rock structural condition can be expected. In addition, those operating in new or foreign geographic areas will find that local climatic and socioeconomic conditions may precipitate order-of-magnitude scheduling complications. For excavation planning, earth materials can be classified into four basic types: (1) soil—light equipment required; (2) jointed or weathered crystalline rock—heavy equipment required; (3) unjointed, bedded sedimentary rock—light to medium equipment required; and (4) sound crystalline or cemented sedimentary rock—blasting required.

In the absence of on-site experience in exploratory trenching, or experience in similar rock and under like conditions, the production rates for trench excavation listed in Table 3 may be used as a basis for planning. The units represent a variety of ground conditions in an objective logging effort undertaken by geologists experienced in trench logging.

LOGGING IN SOIL

The Unified Soil Classification System (U.S. Army, 1953) is generally used in logging soil; this classification is a standard link in communication between the geologist, geotechnical

TABLE 3. RESOURCE REQUIREMENTS FOR EXPLORATORY TRENCHING

Type of effort	Production rates
1. Excavation: soil, backhoe, 1.2-m (4-ft) width, 3.0-m (10-ft) depth	7.5 m^3/h (10 yd^3/h)
2. Excavation: soil, using bulldozer, average width 6.1 m (20 ft) one free face, spoil stockpiled within 60 m	115 to 230 m^3/h (150 to 300 yd^3/h)
3. Blasting: line-drilled on 0.6-m (2-ft) centers for presplit face, production drilled for remainder, 3.7-m (12-ft) depth, stemmed, per wagon drill, medium-velocity sound rock	115 to 305 m^3/d (150 to 400 yd^3/d)
4. Mucking of blast waste: bulldozer, spoil placed within 61 m (200 ft) of excavation	455 to 600 m^3/d (600 to 800 yd^3/d)
5. Surveying: four-man crew, no brushing involved, non-inclement weather: Initial grid control Trench stationing, 3.0-m (10-ft) station, single face (wall)	1 to 2 d 122 m/d (400 ft/d)
6. Shoring: standard 1.2-m (4-ft) width, backhoe trench, to 3.0-m (10-ft) depth, meets OSHA standards, using wood supports, six-man crew	15 m/h (50 ft/h)
7. Fencing: 4-strand barbed wire, metal posts, braced wood-post corners, wire-stretched, four-man crew	105 m/d (350 ft/d)
8. Face-cleaning (wall, face, headwall): per assistant	75 m^2/d (800 ft^2/d)
9. Installation of string reference grid 1.5 × 1.5-m points (5 × 5 ft): by hand level, ±0.03 m (0.1 ft), geologist and assistant	140 m^2/d (1,500 ft^2/d)
10. Compilation of graphic log: at the face, per geologist, for 1:10 scale	18.5 m^2/d (200 ft^2/d)
11. Panoramic photography: tripod mount, overlapping, one individual	1 trench/d
12. Preparation of lithologic supporting notes: per geologist	185 m^2/d (2,000 ft^2/d)
13. On-site review and discussion with project geologist: test hypotheses, modify logging, per geologist and supervisor	95 m^2/d (1,000 ft^2/d)
14. Office review by logging geologist: comparison with panoramic photographs, review of log-specific and supportive notes	370 m^2/d (4,000 ft^2/d)
15. Review and discussion with project geologist: two geologists (logging and supervisor)	1 trench/d
16. Drafting for PSAR use: single draftsman Simple profile Complicated profile	2 trenches/d 0.2 to 0.5 trench/d

engineer, and laboratory personnel (Fig. 8). Within this classification, soil units are also classified as to their genetic nature, namely *alluvial* (stream-deposited), *colluvial* (related to mass-wasting), *residual* (weathered), and *artificial soils* (for example, fill).

Criteria for differentiating alluvium and colluvium relate chiefly to understanding running-water processes and the features they produce compared to mass-wasting processes and the features they produce. These criteria are listed in Table 4.

Differentiating fill from natural earth materials is of critical importance in trench logging. These criteria are summarized in Table 5.

Paleosols, buried soils of the geologic past, are commonly exposed by trenching. These buried soils can retain many of their original characteristics, particularly in the youthful sediments of California. Some serve as excellent marker horizons, others as recent indications of faulting and landsliding. Organic material contained in the soil may be useful in age-dating

geologic events depicted in the trench, as in the Oak Hill trench, San Fernando, California (Bonilla, 1973).

Recognition of Faulting

The most widespread, identifiable basis for assessing active fault movements appears to be disruption of the soil overburden and of Holocene deposits. One of the best ways to assess this recency of disruption is the detailed geologic logging of trenches (Fig. 9, Table 6).

Subsurface trenching programs have demonstrated that faults can be logged in trenches within surficial deposits. Bonilla (1973) found that 9 of 11 trenches showed evidence of pre-1971 faulting in Quaternary deposits along the San Fernando, California, fault system.

Evidence of active faulting can commonly be detected in trenches, whereas they are commonly camouflaged by younger natural processes at the ground surface. Features such as drag,

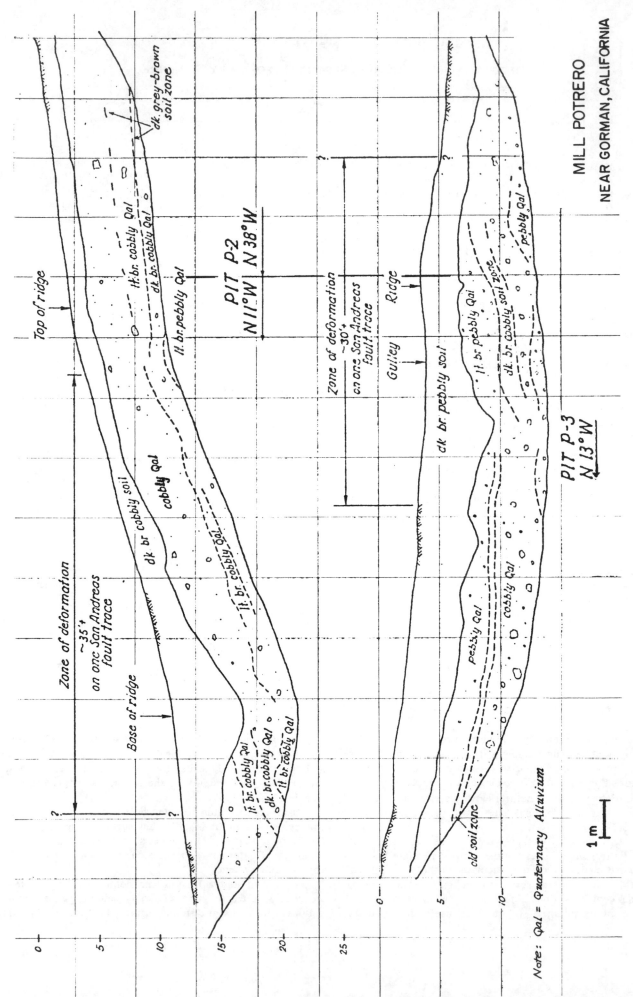

Figure 8. Trench logs in earth units (soil), Mill Potrero, California. Prepared during a study of the San Andreas fault, by E. G. Heath and F. B. Leighton, 1970.

Logged by *HEATH*
Notes by _____
Type of Rig *24" Backhoe*

Project *Active Faults*
Tract *Lopez Canyon*
Date *3-30-71*

GEOLOGIC PIT LOG NO. *1*

Northern Trace - Lopez Canyon

Pit Location

ATTITUDES	ENGINEERING GEOLOGY DESCRIPTION	PHYSICAL CONDITION	COMMENTS
	Qal & Sw , alluvium and slope wash, silty sand with angular clast of Slt + Ss and well rounded pebbles. Well bedded sand at base, stream deposits with some pebbles and cobbles at base.	soft - friable	none
Bedding ① N 77°W, 74 N	*Slt* , siltstone, med. gry., iron stain - mass. - highly fractured	firm	
Bedding plane fault ② N 80°W, 75 N	*Ss + Slt* , sandstone with thin siltstone interbeds well bedded, beds up to 4' thick.	firm - hard	
Fault ③ N 75°W, 62 N	*Cg + Ss* , conglomerate and sandstone matrix - white, clean, ig. & meta. clast up to 3"	firm - hard	
			NATURAL SLOPE
			none

GRAPHIC REPRESENTATION

Pit Trend = *North* →

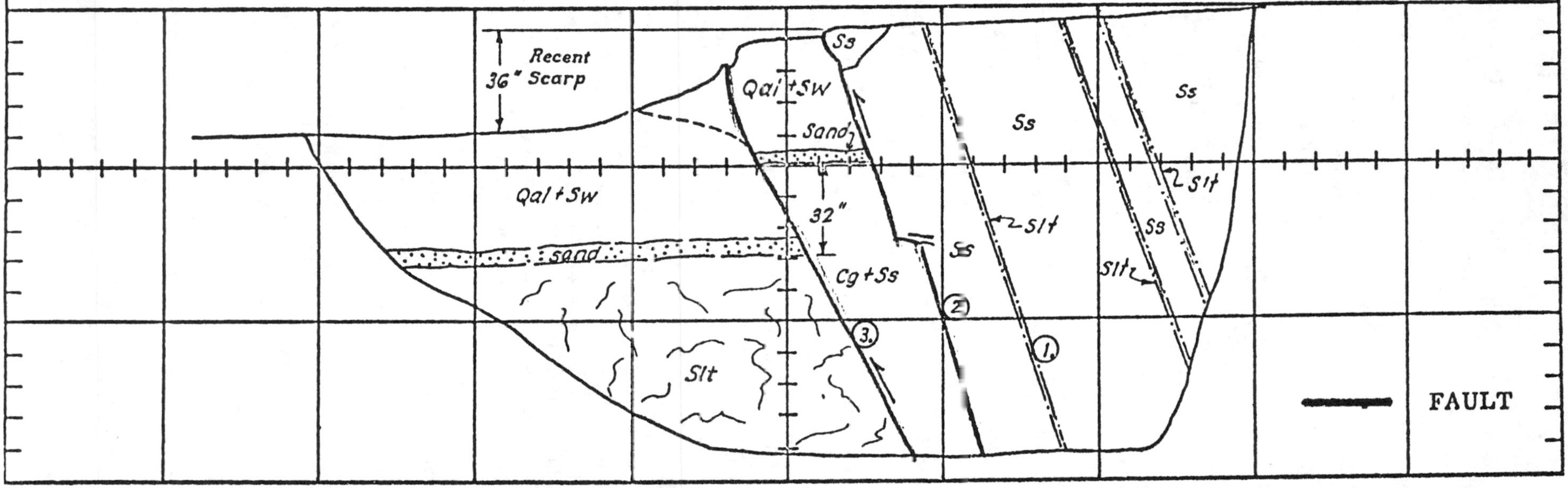

Scale - 1" = 5'

FAULT

Figure 9. Trench log of the active branch of the Tujunga fault, following the San Fernando, California, earthquake of 1971. Prepared by E. G. Heath.

TABLE 4. SELECTED FIELD CRITERIA FOR DIFFERENTIATING ALLUVIUM FROM COLLUVIUM

Parameter	Alluvium	Colluvium*
Geomorphic occurrence	Fluvial areas; stream channels and flood plains	Flanks of gentle hillslopes; interfingers with alluvium at toe of slope
Agent of deposition	Running water; either continual, episodic, or ephemeral	Gravity (downslope creep) and sheet-flow erosion
Grain size	Sand and gravel, some silt and boulders	Clayey matrix and variable rock fragments; often poorly sorted
Lithology	Highly varied lithology of entire drainage area	Directly related to lithology of underlying bedrock
Sedimentary structures	Scour and fill, graded bedding, cross bedding, imbricate structure	Often massive except for soil profile(s). Heterogeneous distribution of angular rock chips
Angularity of clasts	Subrounded to rounded	Subangular to angular
Matrix	Generally unconsolidated with low cohesion; fines are usually winnowed out	Very high clay content in cohesive matrix
Color	Generally tan to brown	Often dark brown to black-brown
Organic content	Low, except in soil profile on older alluvium	Often high, especially in A horizon of soil profile(s)
Soil profile	Absent in most alluvium; some A and B horizons in older alluvium	Well-developed A, B, and C horizons; often with caliche patchwork. Frequent repetitive or buried soil horizons
Bedrock contact	Usually abrupt (scour channel)	Usually well-developed C horizon
Gross stability	Generally stable except for local scour structures	Frequently involved in landslides

*Some of these features can occur in both deposits, but they are more common in colluvium.

gouge, buried scarplets, chaotic structures, shear and fracture patterns, clastic dikes, soil in-fillings, and disturbed zones have all been distinguished in known active fault zones. Such indicators can be applied to zones whose activity is under investigation.

Fault detection in trenches excavated in certain types of deposits is difficult. For example, trenching across the 1971 San Fernando, California, faults in loose and coarse alluvium has revealed only chaotic zones as evidence of faulting (Heath and Leighton, 1973).

Faults are generally also subtle where they extend upward into the soil zone. The hairline cracks that often represent faults near the ground surface may not appear until the excavated soils dry out.

One serious problem in trench logging is that of differentiating faults from cracks associated with vibratory ground motion and consequent ground disturbance. These cracks may be associated with mass wastage phenomena as well. They commonly develop on hillsides or in bottomlands underlain by alluvial deposits and represent surficial cracking. In the San Fernando, California, earthquake of 1971, it was possible to distinguish most surface ruptures of tectonic origin from those related to ground shaking and ground failure by trenching deeper, to about 3.5 to 4.5 m.

Glacial Deposits

Glacial and glaciofluvial deposits present some of the most difficult trench logging media. Not only are such units extremely heterogeneous, but they are notably discontinuous in lateral and vertical extent and are prone to retain a variety of disturbing nontectonic fault features (Fig. 10). The Central Maine Power Company site at Sears Island, Maine, was diverted in purpose from a nuclear plant site to that of a large fossil fuel–fired station in 1977 because the applicant was unable to conclusively prove a nontectonic, glacial rebound origin for faults found in glacial deposits. The applicant had contended glacially induced, base shear deformation of incompetent, weathered, Paleozoic phyllites. Trenching at the site by Gerber and Rand (1978) disclosed evidence of deformation caused by the passage of a final and localized Wisconsinan ice advance. The evidence was not accepted as being conclusive by regulatory officials.

During the conduct of a preliminary nuclear plant siting effort in Burt County, Nebraska, for the Nebraska Public Power District, as well as the PSAR field work for the Fort Calhoun unit 2 expansion of the Omaha Public Power District (Docket 50548-93, 1976), both geotechnical consultants were alerted to the presence of suspicious faultlike features (Fig. 11) in glaciofluvial deposits near Murray Hill, Iowa. The Murray Hill features were truly faults, nontectonic in origin, and were shown to be so by detailed studies in connection with the Fort Calhoun PSAR. Trenching at the site revealed three units, river-bluff, glaciofluvial, and outwash deposits, chaotically displaced as mass wastage blocks, separated by the "faults." The complex nature of the disturbed ground required support work in the form of large-scale topographic and detailed geologic mapping. Plastic deformation of younger tills were also found in the form of small diapirs. Till units were differentiated on the

TABLE 5. SELECTED FIELD CRITERIA FOR
DIFFERENTIATING ARTIFICIAL FILL FROM NATURAL EARTH MATERIALS

I. Essentially conclusive evidence of fill

1. Buried trails, tracks, and artifacts of machines and humans, including imprints from sheepsfoot compaction equipment
2. Plants and animals buried alive, with fresh remains of these
3. Fill benches
4. Sediment not native to watershed
5. Freshly broken and angular bedrock fragments in same zone with well-rounded fragments of similar size
6. Freshly buried soil zones

II. Circumstantial evidence of fill

1. Horizontal banding of layers
2. Randomly oriented fragments within layers
3. Caliche flecks without veinlets and patchwork
4. Odor of decaying organic debris
5. Scattered blue-gray unoxidized zones
6. Preferential vegetation line at cut-fill boundary
7. Preferential burrowing by rodents favoring fill over natural materials

III. Essentially conclusive evidence of natural material

1. Bedding alternating with cross bedding
2. Caliche capping (and caliche beds)
3. Graded bedding
4. Steeply tilted bedding
5. Imbricate structure
6. Jointing
7. Folding and faulting
8. Unoxidized zones
9. Gypsum seams
10. Clastic dikes
11. Dense, unbroken lattice work of root hairs
12. Liesegang banding (diffusion phenomenon)

IV. Circumstantial evidence of natural materials

1. Cavity fillings
2. Oriented buried ventifacts
3. Scour and fill structures
4. Caliche patchwork
5. Cemented zones or concretions
6. Lack of animal burrows except in old soil zones

---

basis of pebble counts, and paleosols and volcanic ash prevalent in the mid-central states) provided the Illinoian-Yarmouthian boundary (600,000 yr timeline).

LOGGING IN ROCK

Rock presents a medium for logging that is perhaps less predictable in character and detail than soil. In igneous and metamorphic rocks, evidence of stratigraphy is often obscured or nonexistent. Added to this is the fact that rock units are naturally considerably older than soil units. The effect of aging on earth materials is familiar to all of us: development of weathered profiles, diagenetic changes, mineralized zones and veins, complicated shear planes, overlapping joint sets, pockets of chemically or physically degraded material, and so on.

The obvious intent of trench logging in rock is to carefully record as much detail as is warranted by the objectives of the particular study. To leave detail unrecorded is defeating. As has been discussed under the section dealing with siting of trenches, special attention must be given to selecting the orientation, position, and dimensions of each trench. Some considerations are purely physical and relate solely to the layout and dimensions of the power plant. Other considerations are determined by what is known about the subsurface geologic details of the plant site.

When it becomes necessary to prepare the more detailed or objective trench logs at a particular power plant site, the following sequence of ideal actions will help to produce optimal results based on objective trench logging:

1. Discuss the general lithologic nature of all important rock units observed in the trench walls and floor (a standard form such as that of Fig. 7 is helpful).

2. Begin to assess the various types of planar features: faults,

joints, fractures, lineations, foliations, cleavages, veins, dikes, sills, and others.

3. Note general types of physical and chemical distress indicators: chemical alteration, gouge, slickensides, brecciation.

4. Select an appropriate logging scale sufficient to portray the smallest level of detail that appears to be relevant.

5. Record all components of trench geology that appear within each log sheet grid square; the key is to avoid concern with elements outside of the particular grid square within which you are currently drawing geologic components (the authors prefer a 0.5- to 1-m square).

6. Measure geometric components of all planar features within each grid square; record by grid square coordinates for possible later stereographic analysis.

7. Diagnose obvious chronologic relationships between components in adjacent grid squares.

8. Sample representative components: whole rock, individual minerals, gouge, and vein filling.

9. Complete the process for the entire trench; usually one wall will be sufficient unless particularly complex or rewarding segments are detected on the opposite wall.

10. Now view the trench log in its entirety, associating grid square with adjacent grid square, making the truest possible associations of lithologic units and geometric elements from square to square. This process of connection should be accomplished *in the trench,* viewing the geologic display at the same time.

11. Attempt to divide gross trench-wall components on bases of similarities in lithology, color, fabric, structures, degree of weathering, and residual soil bodies.

12. Attempt to identify rock units that exhibit recognizable regional stratigraphic affinities.

13. Establish the petrogenesis of host rocks and chronology of structural features.

14. Using results of age-determination studies on appropriate trench-wall samples, attempt to relate suites of structural features and episodes of regional deformation.

15. Attempt to establish the rates and effects of physical denudation in terms of geothermometric determinations of the original pressure-temperature environment.

Steps 13, 14, and 15 will require attention outside of the trench, as well as the results of office and laboratory studies.

Level of Maximum Detail

The first inspection of a freshly excavated rock trench must bring a decision from the project geologist as to what will be shown and to what degree it will be portrayed graphically. The level of maximum detail that is chosen for portrayal will constitute the component parts of a reconstructed jig-saw puzzle and the degree to which the graphic log faithfully represents ground conditions. The lowest discernable level of rock structural detail should be shown: foliation, lineation, major porphyroblasts, inclusion, schlieren, boudinage, vugs, cavities, veins, stringers, dikelets, and so forth. The logging team should be instructed to record the primary macroscopic structural components of the rock mass in any given grid space. The authors have found that a resolution diameter of about 0.03 m is generally adequate.

Fractures, joints, and faults are generally discontinuous features identified primarily by their presence as breaks in the elements of macroscopic detail of the logs, rather than as continuous linear traces drawn across the reference grids of the logs. It is important to note each sequential element of the discontinuity, as it is encountered in logging of each log grid space. As the fractured, broken, or truncated rock structural elements are outlined in the course of logging, even the most subtle become evident discontinuities. In this method of identifying discontinuities by their components, important details of the nature and origin of such features become apparent also and can be noted on the log. These annotations will become the basis for evaluating the origin and importance of each of the discontinuities noted. In rock, it is essential that no natural discontinuity go unevaluated as to its nature and origin.

An example of the philosophy of logging to maximum detail is shown in Figure 2, logged by James K. Stowe, at Punta Chivato, Puerto Rico (Docket 50376-57, 1975). Stowe carefully and faithfully reproduced all lithologic matrix details larger than 0.03 m, and in doing so, he portrayed the real physical and structural character of the limestone rock.

Assessing the Log

Following complete graphic representation, attention must be given to interrelationships, such as contacts and boundaries, three-dimensional bodies and planes, and the more subtle variations of fracture and color needed to separate the component geologic and/or lithologic bodies in the trench and to evaluate the nature of the interfaces between such bodies. The evaluation is not commonly complete, however, until any planar structural elements have been reduced to stereographic plots (usually poles to planes) and examined for spatial relationships and lithologic affinities. Because geologic rock units often

TABLE 6. GUIDELINES FOR TRENCHING IN
ACTIVE FAULT AREAS

1. Consider all near-regional evidence for faulting to determine if any fault strands can be projected into the site area (8-km radius).

2. Prepare and log trenches where photogeologic evidence of faulting, such as lines of seepage, ground-water barriers or vegetation changes, or other linear features appear.

3. Prepare two or three trenches along the hypothetical path of a suspected fault in order to establish with certainty the presence or absence of faulting; this is called the "blocking technique" of creating an obstacle of negative evidence to the entry of faults.

4. Attempt to locate trenches at critical locations, for example, where the apparent fault trace crosses a contact between surficial deposits and bedrock or between surficial deposits of two different types or ages.

5. Extend trenches from loose and coarse sediments into the better preservation environment of fine-grained sediments, or prepare new trenches where fine-grained sediments might be expected (Heath and Leighton, 1973; Bonilla, 1973).

6. Clean trench walls in minute detail, and map in the same detail (Bonilla, 1973).

7. Ensure that the trenches are long enough and deep enough (Bonilla, 1973).

Figure 10. Nontectonic faults produced by gravity-induced mass wastage in Wisconsinan-aged kame delta sands near Bridgewater, Massachusetts. Nontectonic faults are extremely common in glacial materials of all varieties.

Figure 11. Apparent reverse-sense fault-type displacements produced by rotational slumping in Pleistocene glaciofluvial sands bordering the Missouri River at Murray Hill, Iowa (Docket 50548-93, 1976).

bear the physical evidence or imprint of regional stress history, their physical characteristics generally give witness to similar response to the differing levels of strain associated with each regional stress episode. Some of the most strikingly different stress-related physical effects are the shear zones often found in older metasedimentary rocks, such as slates and phyllites. Differences such as these were instrumental in developing a capability assessment of the Peach Bottom fault zone at Fulton NPS, Pennsylvania (Docket 50463-86, 1975).

Importance of Mineralogical Analyses

When the graphic mapping is complete and the results of the preliminary assessment are at hand, the trench log will depict a network of planar or quasiplanar features intersecting defined geologic units. Some of the relationships will have been solved directly by the doctrine of superposition of structural elements. But when difficult questions remain, such as the origin of suspect faults, shear zones, and shear surfaces, mineralogical studies may provide a satisfactory solution.

During the earlier days of nuclear plant siting, an informal doctrine of "Quaternary overburden" came to the front and was used successfully in a number of instances. When a site

contained a continuous or nearly continuous blanket of Quaternary geologic material in the age range of more than 35,000 to 500,000 yr, there was a ready means at hand to demonstrate the unbroken time-stratigraphic cover over identified faults. Definitive mineralogical analyses were not required, and perhaps an undue amount of dependence was placed on the presence of Quaternary deposits. However, in 1973 the Central Aquierre NPS site near Ponce, Puerto Rico, was abandoned in the construction phase largely because of discovery of faulting in the foundation excavation. The advice of a third-party geological review to the applicant was that the site safety was not provable due to the absence of a Quaternary-related means of age determination. At about the same time, foundation excavations at the North Anna NPS, Virginia (Docket 50404-53, 1973), also exhumed a suspect fault. With only a discontinuous saprolite layer at hand for comfort, personnel of the geotechnical consultant sought out other rationales for salvaging the site (see McEldowney and Pascucci, this volume). This has been, by no means, the only example of looking to the small macroscopic and microscopic levels to develop a complete assessment. Rather, it heralded extensive use of mineralogical analyses in dating trench-exposed faults.

Many crystalline rocks, especially tabular units such as dikes and sills, can be distinguished by peculiar mineral assemblages, crystal size, zoning and resorption, and so forth.

Quartz is a useful mineral in many ways. At the Limerick NPS (Docket 50352-70, 1974) site in Pennsylvania, fragile, undamaged quartz crystals were used to demonstrate a lack of movement along the fault since their formation. Furthermore, the quartz crystals were found to contain fluid inclusions that yielded estimates of the pressure-temperature regime of formation, and hence, an estimate of the original depth of burial. This depth-of-burial estimate, when coupled with estimates of erosional denudation, based on other geologic and geomorphic evidence, gave minimal ages of latest activity on the otherwise unassessable fault—this in the face of nonexistent Quaternary deposits.

Clay minerals, long the mainstay of stratigraphic continuity studies (see Crosby and Scott, this volume), have presented diagnostic relative-age determination evidence for faulting, such as at Fulton NPS, Pennsylvania (Docket 50463-86). At Fulton, the following clay suites were useful: black clay, an original depositional feature; yellow clay, a weathering product along faults; and red clay, random deposition, as coatings or fillings along fractures.

When carefully sampled and laboratory-separated, many of the clay minerals are excellent K-Ar dating specimens (Lyons and Snellenburg, 1971; Murphy and others, this volume). The three-layer clays (illite, montmorillonite, and the smectites), the regular mixed-layer clays (including vermiculite and chlorite), and random mixed-layer associations of the above are especially useful assemblages. The clay mineral identification was made during foundation excavation mapping for the FSAR at the Millstone NPS, Connecticut (Docket 50423-109, 1975), and furnished datable K-Ar specimens.

Difficulties Associated with Sedimentary Sequences

Sedimentary sequences often exhibit low shear resistance to regional stress and are widely deformed into a variety of folds and other warped structures. Where pronounced, such structures do not, themselves, present unusual problems to the objectives of trenching. It is when deformational stresses have been of a low magnitude or extremely localized that sedimentary rock presents unusual challenges to exploratory trenching.

Not the least of these challenges are those presented by linears, the straight-line tonal and textural anomalies commonly found on aerial photographs and other remote imagery (McEldowney and Pascucci, this volume). Shallow glacial and loess mantles in the mid-central states offer literally hundreds of such linears, notably in the terrain underlain by the Dakota sandstone. Farther south, in the gulf coast region, growth faults and ground-water withdrawal-induced subsidence fractures are the bane of nuclear plant investigations. Trenching was attempted in conjunction with the Allens Creek NPS (50466-34, 1974) in Texas to explore the existence of linears detected by the Texas Bureau of Economic Geology. Few doubt the presence of such linears, but extensive trenching in the very

stratigraphically variable Beaumont Formation clay soil units did not detect any tangible evidence of the linears. Many linears are believed to be associated with the location of ancient river channels and point bar deposits on the gulf coast plain.

Microfossils have provided an indication of the presence or absence of faulting in sedimentary rocks at the North Coast NPS, Puerto Rico (Docket 50376-57, 1975; Osborne and others, this volume), and at Diablo Canyon NPS, California (Jahns, 1969—Docket 50323-3). Plastic deformation of the microfossils is generally related to primary folding and flexure; elastic breaks are related to later folding and faulting.

Deformation of marginally competent sedimentary units is common in the north-central states, formerly covered by Pleistocene glaciation. At the Perry NPS, Ohio (Murphy, 1974—Docket 50440-58), foundation excavation work exposed small thrust faults in the Chagrin Member of the Ohio Shale. These features exhibited 0.5 to 1 m of displacement, with only small amounts of gougelike accumulations along the thrust planes. Mapping of the exposures and similar nearby features in backhoe-scraped outcrops produced evidence of glacially induced surficial deformation. All thrust planes were shallow and curved to near-horizontal orientations within a few metres of the uppermost exposures.

AGE DETERMINATION

Should trench logging and correlation bring to light features that cannot be explained unequivocally as being nonhazardous, a reasonable estimate of age is the last of a series of steps that have located the feature, described its physical and geometric characteristics, and sampled and identified its integral parts. Mineral and whole-rock sampling provides material for the following studies related to age determinations:

1. *Petrographic analyses:* Identify minerals in the fault zone or key stratigraphic horizon; seek evidence of postformational strain representing possible fault reactivation; note paragenetic relationships among minerals; deduce diagenetic and/or weathering effects; define the sequential history of the feature.

2. *Quartz inclusion studies:* Seek quartz or other crystals containing dissimilar included materials; determine the range of temperature of formation; seek to locate more than one included mineral for determination of pressure of formation; estimate temperature and depth conditions of formation.

3. *Clay mineralogical analyses:* Define precise mineralogical assemblage in clay-sized fraction; estimate percentages present for effect on age-determination techniques; detect presence of potassium-bearing minerals to act as possible K-Ar radiometric contaminants.

4. *Radiometric analyses:* Determine absolute age range for constituent materials.

Techniques of age determination for fault-activity determination are discussed in detail by Murphy and others (this volume).

SUMMARY

Trenching programs must produce optimal excavations, faithful graphic logs, and realistic interpretations of these logs.

They also must produce lasting records of the geologic conditions observed.

The trench log is a single document that can record more aspects of subsurface geology than can be effectively depicted in nearly any other fashion. Interpretations of the logs must be so thoroughly and graphically documented that they are conveyed in as unequivocal manner as possible to the regulatory officials involved in nuclear plant siting. From these interpretations, the geotechnical conditions in the trench can be understood and appraised in "safe" or "unsafe" terms.

ACKNOWLEDGMENTS

We recognize the contributions of the dozens of geologists who performed the nuclear plant trench logging reported herein. As is the custom, reports to applicant electric utilities rarely acknowledge the work of individuals; hence, it is not possible to extend proper credit other than by reference to appropriate source materials. The sources, portions of PSARs furnished by the applicant utilities to the NRC, are in the public domain and are readily obtainable from the National Technical Information Service, U.S. Department of Commerce, Springfield, Virginia (see McClure and Hatheway, this volume).

The manuscript has been critically reviewed by Manuel G. Bonilla, William V. Conn, Ellis L. Krinitzsky, Richard Lung, and Robert Sydnor. Their comments have been both penetrating and helpful. We especially value Robert Sydnor's comments in connection with compilation of Table 4. The authors, however, accept full responsibility for content, especially its philosophical considerations.

APPENDIX 1. FIELD PROCEDURE FOR EXPLORATORY TRENCHING AND TRENCH LOGGING[1]

Purpose

Exploratory trenches are excavated and logged in detail by engineering geologists in order to fully investigate subtle relationships dealing with geologic structure and soil and/or rock fabric. In nuclear plant siting, detailed trench logging places an emphasis on determining the presence and relative age of faults.

Equipment

1. Operational Requirements, issued by project geologist for subject trench
2. Sheets, fade-out grid, metric base
3. Scale, engineer's
4. Ruler, carpenter's, 2-m
5. Rod, stadia, 2-m
6. Tape, flagging, surveyor's, white
7. Tape, cloth, 50-m
8. Shovel, short, D-handle
9. Shovel, short, military entrenching type
10. Whisk broom, one per geologist

11. Nails, box, eightpenny
12. Tags, white, waterproof, with string
13. Hammer, geologist's
14. Plumb bob
15. Bags, sample, small
16. Pens, indelible
17. Pencils, drafting
18. Eraser, soft
19. Clipboard, one per geologist
20. Level, hand
21. String, white, waxed

Operational Requirements

1. Operational Requirements will be issued by the project geologist, in written form, covering the desired physical characteristics of each exploratory trench to be excavated during the project work. These requirements will be reviewed and approved by the chief geologist, with the concurrence of the project manager.
2. Operational Requirements will contain the following specifications:
   a. End points, turning points, approximate elevations (at end and turning points), approximate bearing of the long axis, width, minimum desired depth, slope inclination, and bench configuration
   b. Anticipated mode of excavation: bulldozer, backhoe, explosive, and so forth
   c. Objective of the trenching and subsequent logging
   d. Personnel to be assigned
   e. Desired initiation and completion dates
   f. Scale of log
   g. Method of photographic recording
   h. Selected subcontractors: excavation, shoring, fencing, survey, and photographic
   i. Scheme of sampling, numbering, transfer, and shipment
   j. Plan of exploratory trenching will conform to the Operational Requirements or as amended, in writing, by the project geologist
3. Conduct of exploratory trenching will conform to the Operational Requirements or as amended, in writing, by the project geologist.

Documentation

1. A separate set of file folders will be kept for each exploratory trench excavated and logged.
2. The subject file folders will contain the following data:
   a. Subcontract agreements for excavation, surveying, and other construction-type support services
   b. Operational Requirements statement for the subject trench
   c. Original trench logs and supporting field notes and lithographic or petrographic summaries
   d. Photographic negatives and prints for the subject excavation
   e. Survey and grid control notes
   f. Letters of transmittal and laboratory reports and expert opinions regarding samples removed from the trench
   g. Minutes of meetings, memorandums to file, and other written summary data concerning the trench

Excavation and Shoring—General Remarks

1. Excavation will commence only at direction of an authorized staff member, according to the specifications of the Operational Requirements statement of the project geologist. The staff member will ensure that location and orientation of the trench are correct. An effort will be made to ensure that the location is end-staked

---

[1]Modified from procedures developed by Haley & Aldrich, Inc., Cambridge, Massachusetts.

(nonsurveyed) and inspected by the project geologist prior to initiation of excavation.

2. Entry on property will be undertaken only after appropriate notification of the client's landman or field representative. The staff member in charge should carry a Letter of Authorization from the client utility. Every effort will be made to meet any local resident of the property to explain presence and ask for reverification of permission to enter.

3. Utility companies should be contacted to verify presence and location of utility lines if they are anticipated.

4. The staff member in charge will mentally note the condition of entry roads, gates, drainage pipes, cattle guards, and so forth, so that repair of damages may be effected.

5. Excavation will not commence without appropriate arrangements having been made for suitable shoring, if this is indicated.

6. Excavation spoil will be placed not closer than 0.6 m to the edge of backhoe trenches, placed equally to either side on flat ground, and placed to the downhill side on sloping ground.

7. Shoring will be installed, according to OSHA standards, by the authorized contractor, for trench depths in excess of 1.5 m, and before other individuals are allowed to enter such trenches.

8. Prior to entry, the trench will be inspected for signs of distress in the walls and floor. Potentially unstable areas of the trench wall shall be further stabilized to the degree of satisfaction of the authorized project representative, prior to entry of technical personnel.

9. The trench will be fenced as soon as excavation equipment has ceased to work at the trench site.

10. Walls will be made as nearly vertical as practicable.

Excavation and Shoring—Bulldozer Trenches

1. The remarks of the preceding section will apply, except as noted below.

2. Shoring provisions, if deemed necessary, will be provided by the project geologist, in discussion with the project engineer and project manager.

3. Excavation width will be limited as much as possible to minimal working dimensions of the contemplated equipment.

4. Excavation spoil will be spread as much as possible in the areas about the ends of the trench. Provisions will be made to maintain natural drainage in the area and to prevent ponding of rainfall or development of inflow conditions.

Maintenance of Open Trenches

1. Each trench must remain open for on-site inspection and review by the project geologist, project manager, project engineer, and certain other team members as directed by the project manager. In addition, it is important that the client's representative, members of the licensing management contractor, other parties to the project, officials from State regulatory agencies, and the NRC and its supporting consultants be given the opportunity to inspect the trench at a time when the project field logs are available in final form.

2. The immediate surface surrounding the trench shall be graded so as not to collect and direct surface runoff into the trench.

3. Portable pumping provisions will be maintained in a manner so as to keep the collection of infiltration (from the floor and walls) to a depth of preferably less than 0.3 m during the time that the trench remains open.

4. The project manager will endeavor to schedule review authority visits in a timely fashion so that maintenance efforts will be kept to a minimum and so that the trench may be closed at the earliest possible time.

5. Prior to the arrival of official visitors, the trench will be inspected for general stability and conditions of safety and will be pumped as dry as possible.

6. Open trenches will be surrounded by a continuous wire barrier sufficient to exclude entry by domestic livestock and to prevent inadvertent entry by persons not parties to the siting project.

Documentary Photography

1. Each trench will be documentarily photographed as a permanent record. In the narrower trenches, requiring shoring, interim photographs should be made from a safe position on the edge, prior to installation of shoring.

2. Each wall will be photographed, in an overlapping sequence, from the interior of the trench (if width so permits) or from the opposite wall, so that the focal plane of the camera remains essentially parallel to the subject face.

3. At the completion of photography, the ensuing negative should be amenable to production of a continuous panorama of each trench face.

4. The method of photography will be chosen at the discretion of the project manager: 35-mm or larger, color transparency or color print film.

5. The trench will not be filled until photography has been completed, the film developed, and the results found acceptable to the project geologist.

Logging Effort

1. The logging effort begins at the time when both walls have been hubstaked on 3-m stations (at the ground surface), the walls have been cleaned, the loose excavation waste has been removed (by laborers) from the floor, and the trench has been shored (if deemed necessary).

2. Brush the face to be logged, with minimal appropriate effort, using whisk broom, hand broom, paint brush, tooth brush, or damp toweling.

3. Affix the initial horizontal string reference line on an even-increment spacing about mid-depth on the subject face. Anchor at 0.3- or 0.6-m intervals (or as appropriate) around a box nail placed in the soil or rock matrix. Extend the reference line by use of a carpenter's level and vertical measurements (as necessary). The string reference grid spacing is to be specified by the project geologist.

4. Install additional horizontal reference lines at 0.3-m vertical intervals (or as specified by the project geologist).

5. Install the vertical string reference lines at 2-m spacing (or more frequently, as directed by the project geologist) and at points corresponding with the surveyed trench-wall stationing. Using a plumb bob, keep these lines vertical, and anchor to the trench wall around box nails.

6. Tag each vertical station reference line (at one point) by a suitably identified, waterproof, string-tied label and indelible ink. Anchor the tag, if possible, to the trench wall rather than to the reference vertical string.

7. In cases of irregular bottom (floor) topography, be prepared to adjust the initial, mid-height, horizontal reference line in order to maintain this datum for graphical purposes.

8. Measure the distances from the top and bottom interfaces of each face to the mid-height horizontal string line. This will compensate for deviations in top and bottom horizontally. Place these measurements in a tabulated form in notes for future reference.

9. Place the horizontal string reference line on the log grid, noting vertical adjustments of the reference line.

10. Sketch in the top and bottom interfaces of each face, using the tabulated measurements noted above.
11. Enter the stationing on the gridded logging paper.
12. Draw on the log in as much detail as possible every feature, cobble, boulder, fragment, fossil, and so forth, that is more than 0.03 m in diameter.
13. Draw *only what can be seen in particulate detail*. Avoid placing any linear conjectural contacts or other features that reasonably seem to separate rock or soil units. This approach is essential to maintenance of the objective nature of logging. Features such as fractures, joints, and veins can be objectively recorded, however.
14. Record the presence and magnitude of features such as glacial striations, slickensides, and displacements (of veins, joints, fractures, obvious faults, bedding, and so forth). Note the salient features of each offset or displacement, to include bearing, plunge, strike and/or dip.
15. Record accurately any areas of the face that are obscured from photographic view by shoring materials.
16. Establish a trench-related notation station symbol and apply it to taking notes of any typical or unusual features. Record them in the field notebook (or on spot report checklist, Fig. 7) against location numbers as shown on the field log, for example,

> T4-23: Polished, glacially striated, granodiorite prophyry boulder; 18-cm diameter; in polished clay till shell; striations bearing S45°E, plunge 15°.

17. Maintain lithologic and/or petrologic descriptions in the manner discussed in appropriate field procedures dealing with visual-manual identification of soils and of rock. Entries are to be made in the individual field notebook and referenced to stations as in step 16 above.
18. Note areas or locations sampled; include sample number assigned.
19. At completion of the basic graphic sketch work of both faces, review the lithologic descriptions in the light of known site-specific geologic data. Attempt to define probable correlations between tentative trench stratigraphic units and those known to the site or area under investigation.
20. Write a comprehensive description of each tentative soil and/or rock unit detected and proposed for the trench. Review this scheme with the project geologist. Attempt to place correlative nomenclature for recognized geologic units known in the site area or for units being tentatively recognized by the project team as a by-product of exploration of the site or surrounding area.
21. Now, draw in the most probable contacts separating soil and/or rock units recognizable after step 20 above. Do this at the trench site in a position to test subdivision and/or contact schemes.

Filling the Trench

1. The trench will be filled at the direction of the project manager, as soon as is practicable. Authorization to do so will be obtained, by the project manager, from the client or his authorized representative.
2. At the direction of the client, shoring materials will be removed.
3. Spoil will be returned to the trench in workable lifts and compacted according to the direction of the project manager and project engineer, taking into consideration the past and future use of the trench site and its immediate vicinity.
4. The immediate area will be returned to a clean and graded condition, conforming as much as possible to its previous appearance. Pre-existing drainage patterns will be restored, and all debris, both vegetative and construction, will be removed from the immediate area to a designated disposal site (per directions of the project manager).
5. The site will be visited by the project geologist, project engineer, or project manager, and the appearance of the site will be verified for the file in writing.

REFERENCES CITED

Adair, M. J., 1979, Geologic evaluation of a site for a nuclear power plant, *in* Hatheway, A. W., and McClure, C. R., Jr., eds., Geology in the siting of nuclear power plants: Geological Society of America Reviews in Engineering Geology, v. IV (this volume).

Bonilla, M. G., 1973, Trench exposures across surface fault ruptures associated with San Fernando earthquake, *in* Murphy, L. M., ed., San Fernando, California earthquake of February 9, 1971: Washington, D.C., U.S. Department of Commerce, v. III, p. 173–182.

Burwell, E. B., Jr., and Moneymaker, B. C., 1950, Geology in dam construction, *in* Paige, Sidney, chairman, Application of geology to engineering practice (Berkey volume): Boulder, Colorado, Geological Society of America, p. 11–43.

California Department of Industrial Relations, 1972, Extracts from State construction safety orders, Title 8: Sacramento, Division of Industrial Safety, Excavations and Trenches, State Printing Office.

California Department of Transportation, 1977, California trenching and shoring manual: Sacramento, Division of Structures, 180 p.

Crosby, J. W., III, and Scott, J. D., 1979, Borehole geophysics in nuclear power plant siting, *in* Hatheway, A. W., and McClure, C. R., Jr., eds., Geology in the siting of nuclear power plants: Geological Society of America Reviews in Engineering Geology, v. IV (this volume).

Docket 50344-38, 1973, PSAR, Trojan NPS, Columbia County, Oregon, Volume 1, Geology, seismology and foundation engineering: Portland, Oregon, Portland General Electric Company, 652 p.

Docket 50352-70, 1974, PSAR, Limerick NPS, Montgomery County, Pennsylvania, Additional information on geologic data: Philadelphia, Pennsylvannia, Philadelphia Electric Company, 6 p.

Docket 50352-79, 1974, PSAR, Limerick NPS, Montgomery County, Pennsylvania, Geologic studies, supplementary information: Philadelphia, Pennsylvania, Philadelphia Electric Company. 489 p.

Docket 50354-171, 1976, PSAR, Hope Creek (Newbold) NPS, Burlington County, New Jersey, Post excavation soils investigation: Newark, New Jersey, Public Service Electric and Gas Company.

Docket 50369-9, 1971, PSAR, McGuire NPS, Mecklenburg County, North Carolina, Volume 2: Charlotte, North Carolina, Duke Power Company, 442 p.

Docket 50376-57, 1975, PSAR, North Coast NPS, Barrio Islote, Puerto Rico, Volume 2, Geology, sesimology and foundation engineering: San Juan, Puerto Rico, Puerto Rico Water Resources Authority, 655 p.

Docket 50387-76, 1974, PSAR, Susquehanna NPS, Luzerne County, Pennsylvania, Report on geologic dating of the Susquehanna site: Allentown, Pennsylvania, Pennsylvania Power and Light Company, 9 p.

Docket 50400-4, 1971, PSAR, Shearon Harris NPS, Wake and Chatham Counties, North Carolina, Vol. 2, Geology, seismology, and foundation engineering: Raleigh, North Carolina, Carolina Power and Light Company.

Docket 50404-53, 1973, PSAR, North Anna NPS (Units 3–4), Louisa County, Virginia, Supplemental geologic data: Richmond, Virginia, Virginia Electric & Power Compnay, 158 p.

Docket 50413-2, 1972, PSAR, Catawba NPS, York County, South Carolina, Volume 1, Appendix 2C, Report on detailed study of test trenches: Charlotte, North Carolina, Duke Power Company, 461 p.

Docket 50413-13, 1973, PSAR, Catawba NPS, York County, South

Carolina, Ammendment No. 5: Charlotte, North Carolina, Duke Power Company, 243 p.

Docket 50413-107, 1975, PSAR, Catawba NPS, York County, South Carolina, Summary of meeting held on September 16, 1975, to discuss geologic faults: Washington, D.C., U.S. Nuclear Regulatory Commission, 13 p.

Docket 50413-108, 1975, PSAR, Catawba, NPS, York County, South Carolina, Staff position of proposed geologic investigations: Washington, D.C., U.S. Nuclear Regulatory Commission, 4 p.

Docket 50413-115, 1975, PSAR, Catawba NPS, York County, South Carolina, Final geologic report on brecciated zones 2 and 3: Charlotte, North Carolina, Duke Power Company, 219 p.

Docket 50413-120, 1976, PSAR, Catawba NPS, York County, South Carolina, Final geologic report on brecciatred zones: Charlotte, North Carolina, Duke Power Company, 219 p. (revision of 50413-115).

Docket 50413-122, 1975, PSAR, Catawba NPS, York County, South Carolina, Final geologic report on brecciated zones, attachment 1, Geologic investigation of auxiliary building excavation: Charlotte, North Carolina, Duke Power Company, 87 p.

Docket 50423-109, 1975, FSAR, Millstone (Unit 3) NPS, New London County, Connecticut, Report of geologic mapping of bedrock surface: Hartford, Connecticut, Millstone Point Company.

Docket 50423-144, 1976, FSAR, Millstone (Unit 3) NPS, New London County, Connecticut, Fault uncovered in warehouse No. 5—unit 2 condensate polishing facility: Hartford, Connecticut, Millstone Point Company, 30 p.

Docket 50440-136, 1975, PSAR, Perry NPS, Lake County, Ohio, Report on geologic investigation of a portion of the PNPP foundation: Cleveland, Ohio, Cleveland Electric Illuminating Company, 78 p.

Docket 50440-154, 1976, PSAR, Perry NPS, Lake County, Ohio, Addendum to geologic investigation of a portion of the PNPP foundation: Cleveland, Ohio, Cleveland Electric Illuminating Company, 32 p.

Docket 50440-165, 1976, PSAR, Perry NPS, Lake County, Ohio, Second addendum to geologic investigation of a portion of the PNPP foundation: Cleveland, Ohio, Cleveland Electric Illuminating Company, 37 p.

Docket 50463-5, 1973, PSAR Fulton NPS, Lancaster County, Pennsylvania, Volume 1: Philadelphia, Pennsylvania, Philadelphia Electric Company, 578 p.

Docket 50463-10, 1973, PSAR, Fulton NPS, Lancaster County, Pennsylvania, Volume 6: Philadelphia, Pennsylvania, Philadelphia Electric Company, 435 p.

Docket 50463-75, 1975, PSAR, Fulton NPS, Lancaster County, Pennsylvania, Safety evaluation report: Washington, D.C., U.S. Nuclear Regulatory Commission, 415 p.

Docket 50463-86, 1975, PSAR, Fulton NPS, Lancaster County, Pennsylvania, Supplementary geological investigation of the Fulton Generating Station, Appendix B9-2: Philadelphia, Pennsylvania, Philadelphia Electric Company, 771 p.

Docket 50466-34, 1974, PSAR, Allens Creek NPS, Austin County, Texas, Amendment No. 8, Appendix B (Sec. 2.5), Site-related studies of the potential for surface faulting: Houston, Texas, Houston Lighting and Power Company, p. 2.5–B1–B25.

Docket 50466-85, 1974, PSAR, Allens Creek NPS, Austin County, Texas, Request for additional information on site analysis (geology and seismology): Washington, D.C., U.S. Nuclear Regulatory Commission, 5 p.

Docket 50466-95, 1974, PSAR, Allens Creek NPS, Austin County, Texas, Amendment No. 24, Appendix D (Sec. 2.5), An evaluation of aerial photographic tonal anomalies: Houston, Texas, Houston Lighting and Power Company, 109 p.

Docket STN-50491-139, 1977, Safety evaluation report, Cherokee NPS, Cherokee County, South Carolina: Washington, D.C., U.S. Nuclear Regulatory Commission, NUREG-0189.

Docket 50496-4, 1974, PSAR, Montague NPS, Franklin County, Massachusetts, Volume 3: Hartford, Connecticut, Northeast Nuclear Energy Company, 272 p.

Docket 50496-34, 1974, PSAR, Montague NPS, Franklin County, Massachusetts, Interim report on site structure and fault offset: Hartford, Connecticut, Northeast Nuclear Energy Company.

Docket 50514-94, 1975, PSAR, Pebble Springs NPS, Gilliam County, Oregon: Portland, Oregon, Portland General Electric Company.

Docket STN-50522-100, 1972, PSAR, Skagit NPS, Skagit County, Washington, Ammendment 8: Belleview, Washington, Puget Sound Power and Light Company, 970 p.

Docket STN-50528-12, 1974, PSAR, Palo Verde NPS (Units 1–3), Maricopa County, Arizona, Volume 2, Appendix 2L: Phoenix, Arizona, Arizona Public Service Company, 501 p.

Docket 50548-93, 1976, PSAR, Fort Calhoun NPS, Washington County, Nebraska, Amendment No. 10: Omaha, Nebraska, Omaha Public Power District, 496 p.

Docket 50582-12, 1975, PSAR, Sundesert NPS, Riverside County, California, Volume 2, Chapter 2 (Sec. 2.5): San Diego, California, San Diego Gas & Electric Company, 348 p.

Gerber, R. G., and Rand, J. R., 1978, Late Pleistocene deformations of bedrock and till, Sears Island, Searsport, Maine [abs.]: Geological Society of America, Abstracts with Programs, v. 10, no. 2, p. 43–44.

Heath, E. G., and Leighton, F. B., 1973, Subsurface investigation of ground rupturing during San Fernando earthquake, in Murphy, L. M., ed., San Fernando, California, earthquake of February 9, 1971: Washington, D.C., U.S. Department of Commerce, v. III, p. 165–172.

Jahns, R. H., 1969, Geologic reports of December 1966, January 1967, July 1967, and June 1968: San Francisco, California, Pacific Gas and Electric Company (Docket 50323-3, PSAR, Diablo Canyon NPS, unit 2, San Luis County, California, App. B).

Lapworth, H., 1911, The geology of dam trenches: Institute of Water Engineers Transactions, v. 16, p. 25.

Louderback, G. D., 1950, Faults and engineering geology: in Paige, Sidney, chairman, Application of geology to engineering practice (Berkey volume): Boulder, Colorado, Geological Society of America, p. 125–150.

Lyons, J. B., and Snellenburg, J. W., 1971, Dating faults: Geological Society of America Bulletin, v. 82, p. 1749–1752.

McCauley, M. L., Hoover, T. P., and Forsyth, R. A., 1974, Presplitting, a final report: Sacramento, California Department of Transportation, Report CA-DOT-TL-2955-4-74-32, 32 p.

McClure, C. R., Jr., and Hatheway, A. W., 1979, An overview of nuclear power plant licensing, in Hatheway, A. W., and McClure, C. R., Jr., eds., Geology in the siting of nuclear power plants: Geological Society of America Reviews in Engineering Geology, v. IV (this volume).

McEldowney, R. C., and Pascucci, R. F., 1979, The application of remote sensing data to nuclear power plant site investigations, in Hatheway, A. W., and McClure, C. R., Jr., eds., Geology in the siting of nuclear power plants: Geological Society of America Reviews in Engineering Geology, v. IV (this volume).

Murphy, James L., 1974, Superficial deformation in the Chagrin and Bedford Formations of Lake County, Ohio: Case Western Reserve University (Docket 50440-58, PSAR, Perry NPS, Lake County, Ohio, Amendment No. 11, Appendix 2L, Part 2, Cleveland Electric Illuminating Company, Cleveland, Ohio, 4 p. illustrations).

Murphy, P. J., Briedis, J., and Peck, J. H., 1979, Age determination techniques in fault investigations, *in* Hatheway, A. W., and McClure, C. R., Jr., eds., Geology in the siting of nuclear power plants: Geological Society of America Reviews in Engineering Geology, v. IV (this volume).

Taylor, C. L., and Cluff, L. S., 1973, Fault activity and its significance assessed by exploratory excavation, *in* Kovach, R. L., and Nur, A., eds., Proceedings of the Conference on Tectonic Problems of the San Andreas Fault System: Stanford University Publications, Geological Sciences, v. 13, p. 239–248.

Thompson, L. J., and Tannenbaum, R. J., 1977, Survey of construction related trench cave-ins: American Society of Civil Engineers Proceedings, Journal of the Structural Division v. 103, no. CO3, p. 501–512.

U.S. Army, 1953, The unified soil classification system: Vicksburg, Michigan, U.S. Army, Corps of Engineers, Waterways Experiment Station Technical Memorandum no. 3-357, v. 1, 30 p.

——1975, Geologic mapping procedures, open excavations: Washington, D.C., Office of Chief of Engineers, Engineering Technical Letter no. 1110-2-203.

U.S. Occupational Safety and Health Administration (OSHA), 1974, Construction standards and interpretations (chg. 2) Subpart P, Excavations, trenching, and shoring: Washington, D.C., Government Printing Office, p. 157–164.

Weaver, J. M., 1975, Geological factors significant in the assessment of rippability: Die Siviele Ingenieur in Suid Afrika, Capetown, p. 313–316.

Manuscript Received by the Society July 13, 1978
Manuscript Accepted November 13, 1978

Geological Society of America
Reviews in Engineering Geology, Volume IV
1979

Geophysics as related to siting of nuclear power plants

V. J. MURPHY
T. F. SEXTON
E. N. LEVINE
Weston Geophysical Corporation, Westboro, Massachusetts 01581

ABSTRACT

The safe siting of nuclear power plants requires knowledge of foundation conditions and faulting. Geophysical surveys and measurements are necessary to provide needed data in the early stages of a siting program, in order to supplement geologic studies. Later, detailed licensing studies may require additional geophysical measurements to supplement geotechnical engineering studies.

Seismic methods are most commonly used for exploring localized geologic and foundation conditions at and near a plant site; gravity and magnetic measurements are often helpful in regional geologic studies.

Other geophysical exploration techniques are usually reserved for specialized applications such as the search for subsurface cavities, determination of stratigraphy, slope stability studies, hydrogeology, and locating construction materials. Special seismic techniques are employed to determine dynamic elastic properties.

INTRODUCTION

Nuclear power plant siting requires a multidisciplined exploration program, which includes the use of geophysics for both regional and site-specific considerations. For about 20 yr, and especially for the past 5 to 10 yr, an ever increasing utilization of geophysics is evident from even a cursory examination of Preliminary Safety Analysis Reports (PSARs); a special need for geophysics is evident for solving licensing problems (see McClure and Hatheway, this volume).

The Nuclear Regulatory Commission (NRC) requires that nuclear power plant applicants include geophysical surveys and measurements in compiling their PSAR submissions. These studies are among the first phases of exploration to be implemented in a siting program.

Although seismic techniques are generally the most widely used and the most applicable for plant siting, specific site needs often dictate the use of an additional geophysical method and sometimes multiple methods.

Applications vary from regional considerations, such as delineation of large or extended geologic structures, to site-specific considerations, such as thicknesses of overburden and weathering. Land, marine, and sometimes airborne coverage can be effected both on-site and in the region about a site (Murphy, 1978).

ROLE OF GEOPHYSICS

The findings of geophysical surveys that are used for the siting of nuclear power plants are basic for both geological and engineering considerations; each discipline has its own needs, and geophysics appears to be able to satisfy both the geological and the engineering requirements, but not always at the same time.

For regional considerations, the early evaluation of available geophysical data (gravity and magnetic maps) and seismic profiling (including proprietary data banks) can help to eliminate "problem" sites and define the most favorable candidate sites.

The evaluation of several sites and/or the study of a specific site require investigations that are both comprehensive and timely. Problems, or geologic "surprises," must be identified at the earliest possible opportunity so that economic decisions can be made regarding the viability of sites. Geophysics helps greatly to fulfill those requirements.

A paramount concern for siting is that of faulting. The definition of other structural relationships and the mapping of areal extent of rock units are also necessary for suitable compliance with regulatory requirements. All these objectives are subject matter for geophysical surveys. Water-covered areas adjacent to or surrounding plant sites are especially well suited for geophysical surveys, which may be the only means of determining the existence and recency of faulting. A common and primary question is, Do faults that exist near a site extend upward to, or near to, the sea floor?

For the assessment of vibratory ground motion, the essential questions concern depth and engineering properties of rock on the one hand and the possibility of overburden liquefaction on the other. Geophysical profiling and in situ measurements provide much of the data needed for final decisions in power-block locationing. In conjunction with test-boring programs at the selected power-block location, geophysical profiling provides a firm basis for the strategic placement of individual confirmatory drill holes. In this fashion, uniform subsurface conditions that extend over large sections of a plant site can be verified, and anomalous zones can be further identified positively by other direct methods of exploration.

TECHNIQUES AND OBJECTIVES

Geophysical methods are well-known exploration techniques that are documented in many well-known textbooks and journals. Most techniques were developed for petroleum and mining applications and subsequently adapted to the solution of engineering and ground-water problems (Murphy, 1978).

The detection and delineation of faulting, as well as the differentiation and identification of geologic materials, such as overburden and bedrock, have always been primary objectives of geophysical surveys.

For nuclear siting considerations, geologic and engineering objectives are sometimes equal for siting studies. The dual considerations of capable faulting and vibratory ground motion can separately or together eliminate or favor locations for siting nuclear plants. Localized site conditions, such as zones of softer material, cavity occurrences, and bedrock "lows," are always of concern.

The following sections deal with the different, standard geophysical techniques and specific cases that we have been involved with.

Seismic Refraction

The seismic refraction method allows for measurement of seismic-wave velocity values and calculations of depths to discontinuities or interfaces, such as bedrock, formational or unit contacts, and the water table. This method is especially suitable for comparing the engineering aspects of one site with another, and optimizing plant facility locations within a specific site (see McClure and Hatheway, this volume, Table 1). It is the geophysical technique that has been used on virtually every nuclear power plant site study throughout the world. The seismic energy source can be either explosives (contained in shallow shotholes) or weight drops (heavy hammers). The use of multiple channel (12 or more) instrumentation and geophone spread lengths of 200 to 2,000 ft (50 to 600 m) is common practice. Data "stacking" and tape recording provide for sophisticated analyses in complex areas. At the Charlestown, Rhode Island, site of New England Electric Company, refraction profiling determined an optimal area of shallow, competent bedrock where the power block could be positioned.

A more recent use for the velocity data determined during refraction profiling is the identification of seismic reflecting horizons. Such data were obtained during offshore investigations for the Jamesport, Long Island, nuclear site in order to identify deep and intermediate reflections as "top of bedrock" and the upper surface of Cretaceous sediments, respectively.

One of our recent studies in California resulted in detection and delineation of active, shallow faulting of the Calaveras fault. Even the lowest velocity layers were offset—a certain indication of the recency of faulting.

Seismic Reflection

The seismic-reflection method is uniquely suited for exploration of offshore areas and for some land sites. Land-reflection surveys are useful, generally to a depth greater than 600 ft (~200 m). The high-resolution technique of over-water profiling, utilizing such devices as "boomers," "air guns," and "sparkers" can cover literally miles of profiling per day. The detection of both shallow and deeply occurring faults and other structures is a routine application. Offshore profiling near a California nuclear plant site disclosed fault displacements in a deep sedimentary regime that occurs several miles west of the offshore extension of the San Andreas fault.

For land applications, the use of the Vibroseis seismic-reflection technique has been somewhat successful for fault and basement-rock detection in areas where the reflecting horizons of interest are greater than about 600 ft (~200 m) below ground surface. Profiling with this technique, near the Douglas Point, Maryland, site, disclosed Triassic faults within the underlying sedimentary basin.

In Situ Velocity Measurements

A stringent regulatory emphasis on seismic design has resulted in a need for the most comprehensive site-specific seismic parameters that can be obtained. Seismic P (compressional)- and S (shear)-wave velocity values are used to determine the seismic wave transmission characteristics of the site. Accordingly, in situ velocity measurements, which involve the use of an array of boreholes, are usually drilled to depths of about 200 ft (~60 m) below foundation level (shallower, if high-velocity bedrock exists at shallow depth).

Both P- and S-wave velocities are measured directly to allow calculation of the shear modulus G and other dynamic moduli.

An advantage of in situ measurements of such an important parameter as the shear modulus is obvious; the foundation rock and/or soils are studied in a truly undisturbed condition. Shear-wave velocity values that exceed 4,000 ft/s (1,200 m/s) are indicative of rocklike material; velocity values that are in the range of 2,000 to 4,000 ft/s (600 to 1,200 m/s) usually correlate with materials that are very compact and/or contain some amount of cementation. Velocity values less than 2,000 ft/s (600 m/s) usually correlate with overburden material.

Electrical Resistivity

This method has rather widespread application to ground-water studies for such engineering projects as reservoirs, tunnels, and dams; its application to nuclear siting has been less common.

Areas where solutioning is suspected are ideally suited for resistivity profiling and for detection of such features at shallow depths. In this particular geologic environment, flat-lying or steeply dipping carbonate rock, cavity size, and depth will have a direct bearing on the successful use of any electrical method. A good rule-of-thumb is that, if the cavities (voids) occur at depths in excess of 10 times their average diameter, they probably cannot be detected. The geophysicist's experience and judgment must be relied upon for application at a particular site; confirmatory test drilling should follow the geophysical program to verify the interpretation.

Gravity and Magnetics

Use of gravity and magnetic studies for regional siting considerations is widespread. The association of magnetic anomalies with earthquake epicenters has been a matter of recent discussion, especially in New England. Here, high-resolution airborne magnetic profiling disclosed large-amplitude anomalies, of nearly circular shape, that were identified geologically as mafic plutons of late Mesozoic age and which correlated spatially with the occurrences of the largest historical earthquakes in the region.

In addition to the detection of plutons, regional geologic structural trends can be extended from mapped features on land into offshore areas.

Airborne magnetic surveys with close flight-line intervals (0.8 to 1.6 km) and at low levels (190 to 450 m above ground) can be readily and economically augmented by land or marine operations. Dual-level coverage helps to evaluate the shape and depth of the "body" or structure causing the anomaly.

Gravity surveys are usually restricted to further defining the causes of magnetic anomalies and for checking and verifying a common data base for existing gravity survey data.

Total Bouguer-anomaly map data can be processed to separate residual anomalies from regional ones. Because the data value at any station location is due to the contribution of localized as well as regional geologic conditions, it should be evident that separation of the residual from the regional anomalies is highly desirable. The recently submitted amendment to the Washington Public Power Supply System units 1 and 4 PSAR, at a site located on the Hanford Reservation, included a regional gravity-anomaly map for the northwest United States–southwestern Canada area. This compilation disclosed broad, regional gravity anomalies and well-defined steep gravity gradients that help to further understand the geologic structural relationships of this large area. Of particular interest was the striking spatial correlation of earthquake epicenters with steep gravity gradients.

Data for both gravity and magnetic surveys are usually presented by means of contour maps. In the case of gravity data, both regional and residual maps are often prepared at the same scale as available geologic maps.

Borehole Logging

Geophysical logging is especially useful for correlating stratigraphy from one borehole to another and across a series of holes. The usual logging tools are resistivity, self-potential, natural gamma, and one or more of the "active" nuclear tools. If a marker bed can be identified, then the presence or absence of faulting can often be demonstrated with high confidence.

GEOPHYSICAL CONSIDERATIONS FOR A SUITABLE SITE

Geophysical techniques provide a number of methods that help to assure safe siting of nuclear power plants.

The absence of faulting, as demonstrated by the lack of offsets of horizons, and the presence of firm foundation materials, as demonstrated by velocity measurement data, are readily ascertained. Where faulting does exist, the age-lack of capability can oftentimes be demonstrated by determining, with seismic surveys, the existence of overlying, undeformed sediments.

Depths to rock, overburden conditions, and moduli values are critical information and necessary data for PSAR preparation. The routine application of geophysical surveys provides data for siting and later design phases that can demonstrate uniformity of foundation conditions and the absence of significant anomalous zones beneath critical structures. Correlation borings are useful and sometimes essential where subsurface conditions are variable over short distances.

Regional or localized gravity and magnetic anomalies should be avoided whenever possible; the anomalies require further exploration and identification that may be time consuming and costly. Sites are preferable in areas where both the magnetic and gravity contour maps display gentle trends and where steep gradients are absent.

ACKNOWLEDGMENTS

We express our gratitude for the review provided by Allen W. Hatheway, a co-editor of this volume.

REFERENCES CITED

McClure, C. R., Jr., and Hatheway, A. W., 1979, An overview of nuclear power plant siting and licensing, *in* Hatheway, A. W., and McClure, C. R., Jr., eds., Geology in the siting of nuclear power plants: Geological Society of America Reviews in Engineering Geology, v. IV (this volume).

Murphy, V. J., 1978, Geophysical engineering investigative techniques for site characterization, state-of-the-art paper *in* Proceedings, 2nd International Conference on Microzonation, San Francisco, California.

MANUSCRIPT RECEIVED BY THE SOCIETY JULY 13, 1978
MANUSCRIPT ACCEPTED NOVEMBER 13, 1978

Geological Society of America
Reviews in Engineering Geology, Volume IV
1979

Measurement of in situ dynamic properties in relation to geologic conditions

T. L. DOBECKI
Sandia Laboratories, Instrumentation Development Division 4733, Albuquerque, New Mexico 87185

ABSTRACT

Evaluation of nuclear power plant sites from a material stability standpoint requires measurement of in situ dynamic properties. These are derived from measurement of shear-wave propagation velocity in subsurface materials by utilizing either the seismic downhole or seismic cross-hole techniques, or both. The downhole technique is rapid and less expensive than the cross-hole survey but is limited in maximum survey depth and resolution of thin, higher velocity beds. The cross-hole test, although less subject to depth and resolution limitations, requires more boreholes and is therefore more expensive. This test is also more exacting because of borehole drift considerations and timing corrections that may or may not be required for the particular energy source used.

Actual field cross-hole examples for several sites of varied subsurface geology illustrate the variation of shear velocity versus material make-up and condition. High shear-wave velocities are characteristic of massive crystalline rock, whereas fractured rock and unconsolidated sediments show progressively reduced values.

The combination of the dynamic model with a proposed design earthquake event produces the basic data upon which site evaluation from an engineering standpoint may be made. An example from a deep sand sediment site shows the increased potential for liquefaction as the strength of the design earthquake is increased.

INTRODUCTION

The entire process of nuclear power station (NPS) site selection, evaluation, and regulatory licensing encompasses many complementary investigations involving geologic, hydrologic, seismologic, demographic, and engineering analyses. The immediate impact of surface rupture along an active fault passing through a candidate site is obvious, as is the lack of an adequate cooling-water supply. More subtle are those characteristics of the site subsurface that dictate the surface and subsurface response of soil and rock materials to the loading of vibrations impressed by proposed governing earthquake events determined through geologic and seismologic investigations.

To adequately investigate the potential effects of such phenomena as liquefaction and site amplification, which are principally engineering considerations, an understanding of the dynamic elastic nature of subsurface materials, their individual thicknesses, and configurations is required. Mechanical tests may be performed in exploratory boreholes, but these determinations are limited to the narrow cylinder of material immediately adjacent to the borehole wall, and this has certainly been affected by the drilling process. Laboratory tests on borehole samples, such as the resonant column test (Hardin, 1970), provide direct measure of such elastic parameters at selectable rates of strain. These tests, however, are performed on samples from a single subsurface point that again has been affected by the drilling process. In the case of unconsolidated sediments, these samples are often remolded for laboratory analysis. Also, the laboratory conditions of overburden pressure and cementation, while variable and selectable, are not exactly as they exist for the given depth and subsurface conditions from which the sample was obtained. It is desirable, therefore, to be able to determine these elastic characteristics in situ.

Geophysical measurements at candidate NPS sites provide a more intimate link between earth science investigations and actual plant engineering and safety than any other source of data. Standard geophysical surveys, such as seismic reflection or refraction and electrical resistivity, provide the measure of thickness and attitude of subsurface units required for construction of the geometry of a subsurface model. Specific geophysical techniques, such as the seismic cross-hole and downhole surveys, provide the measure of in situ elastic character of the individual subsurface units required as input to dynamic analyses performed for an engineering evaluation of the candidate site.

The use of seismic techniques in the determination of the dynamic elastic properties of subsurface materials relies on the fact that seismic techniques measure the passage of a low-level elastic deformation through a given material, and that the manner in which this deformation passes through this material depends upon its inherent elastic nature. Specifically, by measuring the propagation velocities of shear (V_s) and compressional (V_p) deformations through a given material, the various elastic moduli of the material may be described according to the following equations (Griffiths and King, 1965):

$$G = \rho V_S^2, \tag{1}$$

$$\sigma = \frac{\left[1 - 2\left(\dfrac{V_S}{V_P}\right)^2\right]}{\left[2 - 2\left(\dfrac{V_S}{V_P}\right)^2\right]}, \tag{2}$$

and

$$E = 2G(1 + \sigma), \tag{3}$$

where G = shear modulus (rigidity), ρ = mass density, V_S = shear-wave velocity, V_P = compressional-wave velocity, σ = Poisson's ratio, and E = Young's modulus.

A field program may commonly consist of the determination of V_P versus depth (for example, by seismic refraction) with the shear-wave velocity being determined from this by assuming a value of σ. This practice, however, is not encouraged, as the range of σ, as experienced by me and by others (Mooney, 1974), is large, ranging typically from $\sigma = 0.25$ for dense, crystalline rock to $\sigma = 0.49$ for saturated, unconsolidated sediments. Therefore, a direct measure of in situ shear-wave velocity versus depth is required. This wave is not easily determined by general seismic methods. Seismic sources dominantly produce compressional energy that masks shear-wave arrivals. Also, compared to the compressional wave, the shear wave is generally more rapidly attenuated. This is the rationale behind the development of the seismic cross-hole and downhole tests.

Several other papers, notably those by Beeston and McEvilly (1977), Stokoe and Woods (1972), Mooney (1974), and Ballard and McLean (1975), have described various in situ techniques of measuring shear-wave velocity. In this paper I present the history of the development of these techniques and include examples of their application.

INSTRUMENTATION AND FIELD PROCEDURES

Seismic Downhole Survey

The seismic downhole survey involves (1) the generation of shear-wave and compressional-wave energies at ground surface, (2) recording the arrivals of these waves at a detector within a borehole, and (3) analyzing the traveltimes and paths to provide a description of V_S and V_P versus depth by varying the depth of the detector. The instrumental requirements are, then, a source capable of producing distinct P and S waves, a triaxial geophone detector, and a recording unit (for example,

seismograph, magnetic tape recorder, storage oscilloscope) capable of precise time measurements.

Compressional-wave energy sources are numerous and include simple weight drops or hammer blows, dynamite explosions, gas or compressed air guns, and vibratory sources (Barbier and others, 1976). The generation of shear waves requires a source that produces distinct shearing energy while producing a minimum of compressional-wave energy, as the latter, if strong, tends to mask the arrival of the shear wave. Therefore, the S-wave sources tend to be more exotic and highly directional in nature. Examples include (1) the striking of the ends of a heavily weighted plank to produce horizontal shear (Beeston and McEvilly, 1977) as in Figure 1, (2) a horizontal, mortarlike device (Jolly, 1956), and (3) the use of lengths of primacord to produce directed shear.

Generally, detection of the compressional waves is accomplished by using the vertical detector of the triaxial phone, whereas the shear waves are accentuatated on the horizontal detectors. To ensure recording of direct shear waves, it is necessary that the geophone be pressed against the borehole sidewall. This is made possible by using a mechanical wedge or a geophone with a spring-loaded arm or with a hydraulic packerlike sleeve. The sidewall contact necessitates the use of casing in unconsolidated sections or in soil sites. This requires the use of low-velocity casing material such as polyvinylchloride (PVC) plastic so that interference by waves traveling along a high-velocity casing does not confuse the recorded wave train. It is often necessary to grout the annular space

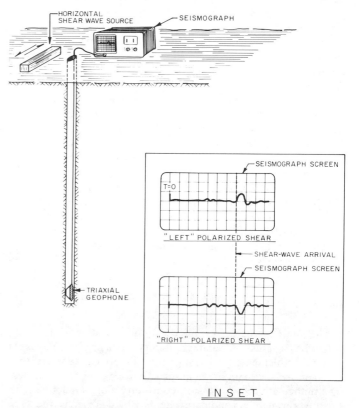

Figure 1. Field setup for seismic downhole velocity survey. Representation of waveform data (inset) illustrates 180° phase reversal made possible by striking opposite ends of the energy source.

between the casing and the sediments to avoid water or air gaps. Such gaps would reduce the possibility of transmission of direct shear waves.

The down-hole survey (Fig. 1) is performed by first positioning the geophone at the first of a series of desired depths of investigation. The energy source is initiated providing a time break to the recording system, and the output of the triaxial detector is recorded. Traveltimes of the P and S waves are picked directly from the record. If the energy source is located near the borehole, the slant path taken by the waves is very close to the vertical depth of the geophone. Therefore, the average compressional velocity V_P of the section from the surface to the depth of the geophone and, similarly, the average shear-wave velocity V_S may be calculated as follows:

$$\overline{V}_P = \frac{d}{t_P}, \ \overline{V}_S = \frac{d}{t_S}, \tag{4}$$

where d = depth of the geophone and t_P and t_S = the traveltime of the P and S waves, respectively.

Interval velocities (V_{int}) may be determined by analyzing the traveltimes recorded at the top and bottom of an interval.

$$V_{int\,1,2} = \frac{d_2 - d_1}{t_2 - t_1}, \tag{5}$$

where 1,2 signify the top and bottom of the interval, respectively.

Thus, performing downhole tests at numerous depth points along the length of the borehole enables the construction of average velocity $\overline{V}$ and interval velocity V_{int} versus depth distributions for both V_S and V_P such as shown in Figure 2.

This technique has possible pitfalls and shortcomings that should be noted. As the survey becomes deeper, more energy is required at the source. This limits the maximum depth of the survey by the power of the source and the attenuation characteristics of the section. However, the recent development of the signal enhancement seismograph has enabled stacking (adding) of several lower-energy impulses to provide the net effect of a single, larger impulse.

In sections of dominantly high velocity rock, such as most limestone or other competent crystalline rock, the time differences between successive depths may be so small as to be nonreadable, depending on the timing precision of the recording medium. If such is the case, the survey resolution is limited to larger subsurface intervals, with the net result that thin layers may not be sufficiently described.

The volume sampled by the downhole method is limited to the very near vicinity of the borehole, which may have been altered as a result of the drilling process. However, the survey is done quickly without the need for additional equipment such as on-site drilling rigs that might be required for other seismic surveys.

Seismic Cross-Hole Survey

For determination of in situ elastic properties in support of major construction projects, such as NPSs, dams, and sports and housing complexes, the seismic cross-hole survey has become the dominant technique. Originally developed for analysis of foundations in soil (for example, Stokoe and Woods, 1972), the method is currently applied to soil, rock, or combination soil-rock sites to provide an accurate measure of V_S and V_P versus depth. The seismic cross-hole survey consists of the generation of shear and compressional waves at depth within a given borehole and detecting and recording the transmitted waves at geophones placed in other nearby boreholes at the same depth. Whereas the downhole survey measures average velocity over a highly varied path length, the cross-hole survey determines true velocity at the depth of the test measured over a nearly constant path length given by the separation of the holes.

Numerous energy sources are currently in use for cross-hole surveys; however, these may be conveniently grouped into two categories—explosive and mechanical.

Explosive source types include dynamite, gas ignition, and compressed air (air gun) sources. Each of these provide the high level of energy required for boreholes that are separated by several tens of metres. However, in producing a nearly spherical compressional energy radiation pattern, these sources generally lack directionality. Therefore, the source produces a great amount of compressional energy, and the clarity of the shear-wave arrival suffers as a result. Computer analysis of recorded waveforms aids final interpretation, but field results are sometimes confusing. This problem may be reduced by orienting the geophone to minimize sensitivity to the P wave. An additional problem is that an explosive source can render the borehole useless for re-testing at the same depth at a later date.

Mechanical sources, although low in energy output, are highly directional and produce energy dominated by shear waves along these specific directions. Several types have been developed. Among these are (1) a simple hammer blow to the top of a drill rod that is transmitted to the subsurface at the drill bit and (2) a vibratory source linked by in-hole rods to the depth point (Ballard and McLean, 1975). Another commonly used source is a sliding hammer that may be lowered to any depth within a borehole and wedged to the borehole wall by using a mechanical packer. By pulling the sliding hammer up or letting it fall, one may generate vertically polarized shear waves with 180° phase differences (up or down), depending on the direction of impact. This fact provides an additional criterion for shear-wave identification between upward and downward hammer blows. In each case of these mechanical sources, the energy transmitted in the horizontal plane of the test elevation is dominantly a vertically polarized shear wave. The maximum component of compressional energy in the plane of the source and receiver is radially away from the source, or horizontally polarized. Therefore, a single, vertically sensitive geophone placed in the receiving borehole at the same depth as the source should receive a maximized shear wave and a minimal compressional wave. This facilitates the separation of P- and S-wave energies and provides highly accurate determination of the onset of each of these phases. Velocity is calculated by simply dividing the separation distance of the source and receiver by the respective P- and S-wave traveltimes taken from the record.

It should be noted that, as schematically shown in Fig. 3, the receiving and impact boreholes should be reasonably close together to avoid problems with refracted compressional waves from stiffer soil or rock horizons that may lie above or below the level of the test.

To illustrate a possible procedure for performance of the cross-hole test, the mechanical source utilizing a hammer blow to the top of a drill rod, as discussed earlier, will be used. This technique involves minor corrections for traveltime from the impact point, through the drill rod, to the drill bit. In-hole sources do not require such corrections. As indicated in Figure 4, this cross-hole technique consists of drilling or coring a receiving borehole to the deepest horizon to be investigated. Again, for soil sites, this borehole is cased with a PVC pipe, and the annular space between the borehole wall and the casing is grouted with a light cement and bentonite grout pumped through a small-diameter pipe. The grout is pumped until all water, bentonite, mud, and/or debris flow to the surface; this assures a rigid coupling between the casing and the adjacent subsurface materials. If water or air remained in the annular space, direct shear waves would not be transmitted.

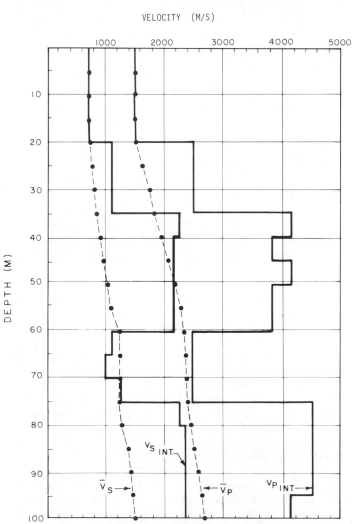

Figure 2. Example of shear-wave and compressional-wave velocity profiles determined by the seismic downhole technique.

The next step is to drill or core an "impact borehole" adjacent to the receiving borehole. When the impact borehole reaches a subsurface horizon where seismic velocities are to be measured, drilling is abruptly halted to assure a tight contact between the drilling bit and the subsurface material. A vertical velocity transducer (geophone) is installed in the receiving borehole at this same elevation. The geophone is coupled to the casing with a wedge to provide direct connection between the geophone and the casing. The drilling bit (via the drill rod) is then struck vertically with a hammer at ground surface; this triggers a storage oscilloscope and sends a compressional impulse down the drilling rod. At the drilling bit, body waves in the form of compressional waves and vertically polarized shear waves are generated in the subsurface. The arrival of these body waves is sensed by the geophone in the receiving borehole and are displayed on the oscilloscope screen, where a polaroid photograph of the record is obtained (Fig. 5). Figure 5 shows three separate impacts played back at increasing oscilloscope sweep rates to emphasize (1) the entire wave train, (2) the shear-wave arrival, and (3) the compressional-wave arrival. A low-amplitude, high-frequency P-wave trace and a lower-frequency, high-amplitude S-wave trace are obtained on the display. This provides the geophysicist with a clear definition of the arrival of the individual waves. When a particular horizon has been investigated to the satisfaction of the field geophysicist, the impulse rod (drill stem) is advanced to the next depth where the cross-hole data are required, the receiving geophone is relocated to this depth, and this procedure is repeated.

As the triggering device is located at ground surface, the total traveltime recorded on the oscilloscope screen includes the time for the compressional wave to travel down the impulse rod, as well as the time for the body waves to travel between the boreholes. The traveltime in the rod must be subtracted from the total time to determine the correct travel-time of the body waves through the medium from the impact borehole to the receiving borehole. The body-wave velocities are then calculated by dividing the distance traveled by the corrected traveltime. To correctly account for this traveltime within the rod, it is required that the drilling rod be calibrated in the field, as shown in Figure 6. Consistent with the elastic constant for steel in compression, the P-wave velocity in the rod is about 5.2 km/s. In the case of a source triggered within the borehole at test depth, such as a sliding hammer, this correction is unnecessary.

As mentioned above, the body-wave velocities are calculated by dividing the distance traveled between the boreholes by the corrected traveltime. If the two boreholes deviate from true verticality, their separation at a given test level may be significantly different from that measured at the ground surface. The accuracy of the survey depends on knowing their true separation along the entire length of the tested section. Therefore, after the cross-hole survey, all test boreholes should be checked for verticality by using any of the number of commercially available magnetic or gyroscopic borehole survey systems. The results of this check, as shown in Figure 7, then give the accurate separation of the impact and receiving boreholes at every test level of the cross-hole survey. An example of cross-hole survey results before and after correction for borehole verticality is given in Figure 8. Note that prior

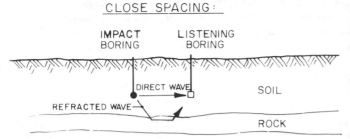

CLOSE SPACING:

IMPACT BORING   LISTENING BORING

DIRECT WAVE   SOIL

REFRACTED WAVE   ROCK

DISTANT SPACING

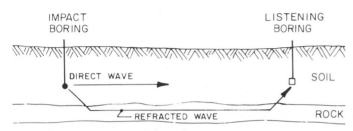

IMPACT BORING   LISTENING BORING

DIRECT WAVE   SOIL

REFRACTED WAVE   ROCK

Figure 3. Possible interference of direct and refracted waves as source-receiver spacing is increased.

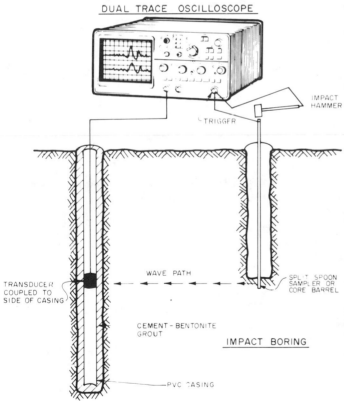

DUAL TRACE OSCILLOSCOPE

IMPACT HAMMER

TRIGGER

TRANSDUCER COUPLED TO SIDE OF CASING

WAVE PATH

SPLIT SPOON SAMPLER OR CORE BARREL

CEMENT-BENTONITE GROUT

IMPACT BORING

PVC CASING

RECEIVING BORING

Figure 4. One possible field setup for performing a cross-hole velocity survey utilizing a nonexplosive source.

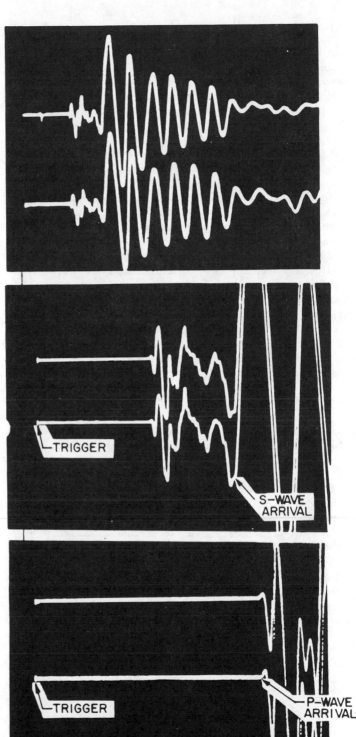

TRIGGER

S-WAVE ARRIVAL

TRIGGER

P-WAVE ARRIVAL

Figure 5. Example of compressional- and shear-wave arrivals recorded using the seismic cross-hole technique. Beginning with the general definition of wave arrivals (top), the three photographs represent the same waveforms observed with increasing sweep rate on the oscilloscope (waveform expansion).

to correction, the velocity distribution shows a decrease with increasing depth. These corrections, then, are extremely important to maintain the survey accuracy, because a 10% error in the determination of V_S results in a 21% error in the determination of G, shear modulus.

In addition to problems already mentioned regarding refraction effects for widely separated impact and receiving boreholes and variations from true verticality, there are a few possible complications that could develop. Those surveys utilizing a rod for connection of the energy source with ground surface may have problems with spurious compressional waves generated where the rod contacts the sidewall in the section between surface and source. These compressional waves may interfere with or even precede the true compressional wave generated at the drill bit, depending on the velocity of the slant path from the point of spurious generation to the geophone. The problem is not a factor in low-velocity sediments nor does it affect the accuracy of V_S determinations. Its effect on V_P measurements may be minimized in rock sections by using insulating standoffs to minimize rod-sidewall contact as suggested by Ballard and McLean (1975). To recognize that this problem may be occurring, the operator should look for signs of interference (changes in P-signal amplitude, frequency, or phase shifts) on observed waveforms and should make preliminary field calculations of V_P. Unusually high V_P values for the type material at test level may signal interference problems of this nature.

OBSERVED VELOCITY DISTRIBUTIONS FOR VARIOUS SOIL–ROCK CONDITIONS

This section presents the results of measurements of in situ compressional and shear-wave velocity distributions in the site subsurface for several proposed NPSs. For the measurements, I used the cross-hole velocity technique as detailed in this paper. The representative examples show such distributions for (1) thick, unconsolidated sediments, (2) unconsolidated

sediments over rock, (3) "hard" rock with occasional fractured intervals, and (4) "soft" rock sites. The accompanying descriptions also denote difficulties encountered with field procedure for each and significant observations in the resulting data.

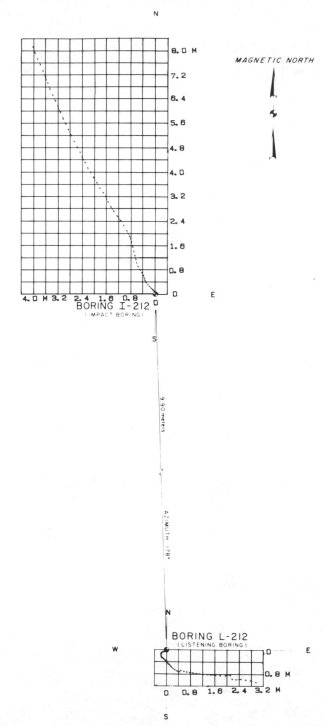

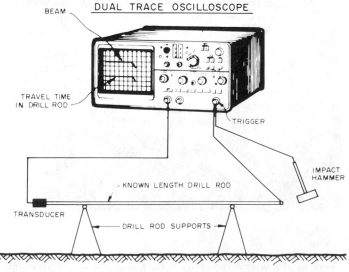

Figure 6. Generalized field technique showing calibration of drill rod used for seismic cross-hole survey.

Figure 7. Typical example of a borehole directional (verticality) survey for two boreholes. Borehole I-212 has drifted north and west from its surface location, whereas borehole L-212 has drifted to the south and east. The two boreholes, which were 9.90 m apart at ground surface, are 20.4 m apart at 93-m depth.

Thick, Unconsolidated Sediments

The subsurface section at this proposed NPS site, as determined from exploratory boreholes and regional geological data, consists of a minimum of 185 m of dense, fine-to-medium sand overlying soft, Tertiary sandstone. A cross-hole survey was performed to a total depth of 91.5 m by utilizing a single impact borehole and a pair of orthogonally situated receiving boreholes (for evaluation of horizontal anisotropy), as depicted on the inset in Figure 9. The results of the velocity determinations are also presented in Figure 9. The most notable item observed in the data is that V_S generally increases smoothly with depth at a gradient of 3.3 m/s per metre except for two zones of higher V_S at depth intervals from 30.5 to 36.5 m and 67.1 to 73.1 m. The observed gradient is the result of increased compaction of the sands with depth. The two observed intervals of increased velocity cannot be explained by lithologic change (such as gravel beds), as the only related observation made during the sampling of the borehole was a noted increase in penetration resistance to a Standard Penetration Test (SPT) over these same intervals. This would indicate that these two intervals represent zones of higher than normal density. It is also appropriate to note that similar measurements made in a thick, dominantly clay section at another site showed a linear shear-wave velocity gradient of 4.25 m/s per metre over a 49-m test section. This is in accordance with results presented by Hardin and Drnevich (1972). They stated that the change in maximum shear modulus (equivalently, shear velocity) with confining pressure (depth) is greater for an overconsolidated clay than for sand.

Generally, discrimination of P waves and S waves is most easily accomplished in saturated, unconsolidated sections because of the large differences in V_P and V_S. Records are, therefore, quite easy to interpret and allow for precise measurement. The major consideration in performing the field test is ensuring that the energy source is securely coupled to the unconsolidated materials. This is often accomplished, for example, by rotating the bit without circulating water for a few centimetres or by using a driven SPT sampler as the source. If an in-hole mechanical source (sliding hammer or vibratory source) is used, care must be taken to ensure a rigid connection to the casing and a rigid (grouted) connection between the casing and the unconsolidated materials.

Unconsolidated Sediments Over Rock

This is a very common geologic configuration for proposed NPSs, as their requirements for a cooling-water source often find prospective sites located on coastal plains or near large rivers. The section given in this example, as shown in Figure 10, consists of 22.9 m of silt, silty clay, and sand overlying Paleozoic bed rock consisting of limestone, shale, and claystone. The shear-wave distribution in the overburden materials shows an increase with increasing depth, but the absolute values of observed V_S (152 to 213 m/s) are lower than those presented for the unconsolidated sediments in the preceding section. This indicates that the unconsolidated sediments in this particular example are looser than those dense sands observed in the previously discussed example. Below the top of rock, there is

a dramatic increase in both V_S and V_P attesting to the increased rigidity of the rock. It is also apparent that individual rock units show appreciable variation, as higher values of V_S are recorded in limestone than in the shale and claystone.

The only additional precaution required for field procedures under conditions presented in this geologic situation is to be alert to the possibility of recording spurious P waves at test levels below the top of rock. These arise from drill rod–sidewall contacts when using the drill rod to transmit the input energy from ground surface to test levels. As stated previously, the use of an in-hole source or insulating standoffs significantly reduces this effect.

Hard Rock with Occasional Fractured Zones

The data presented in Figure 11 represent one of three separate cross-hole investigations performed at a single NPS site. Earlier borehole investigations revealed significant lateral variation in rock quality across the site area which, therefore, required dynamic analyses at each area of significant difference. The site subsurface consists, dominantly, of hard quartzose sandstones and siltstones that have been intruded by dikes of varied composition. Several of the dikes observed are extremely hard, whereas others are significantly decomposed. The cross-hole results (Fig. 11) show that beneath the upper 3 m of boulder fill material, the strength of the rock increases (as shown by increasing shear-wave velocity) in the depth interval from 3 to 12 m. The lower values of V_S (610 to 1,220 m/s) in this interval indicate the fractured nature of the rock. Below 12 m and down to 36.6-m depth, the rock is quite uniform in shear-wave velocity, which indicates that, although fractured, rock strength is higher. This is probably because secondary calcite filled the fractures, as observed in recovered core samples. A final observation is the apparent slight divergence in V_S for the two given data sets over the interval from 36.6 to 42.7 m. Velocities in this interval are about 30% slower between boreholes 2-17 and 2-37 than between boreholes 2-17 and 2-36. In this interval, a decomposed sample of mafic intrusive material was recovered from one cross-hole borehole but not from the other two; this would suggest that the material in this depth interval between 2-17 and 2-36 is probably different from the material between 2-17 and 2-37. Therefore, rather than evidence of apparent anisotropy, the velocity difference observed over this interval is more likely attributable to a steeply dipping weathered dike that lies between boreholes 2-17 and 2-37 but not between 2-17 and 2-36.

No significant problems with field procedure should be expected when testing at rock sites, other than those that have been described in the preceding sections.

"Soft" Rock

The following example represents measurements taken in a section of tropical marine limestone that is quite heterogeneous and contains karst features as well as hard and soft zones. A detailed analysis of this particular survey is presented by Yang and Hatheway (1976). The heterogeneity of this unit makes it particularly adaptable to geophysical testing, as laboratory tests performed on individual samples cannot adequately

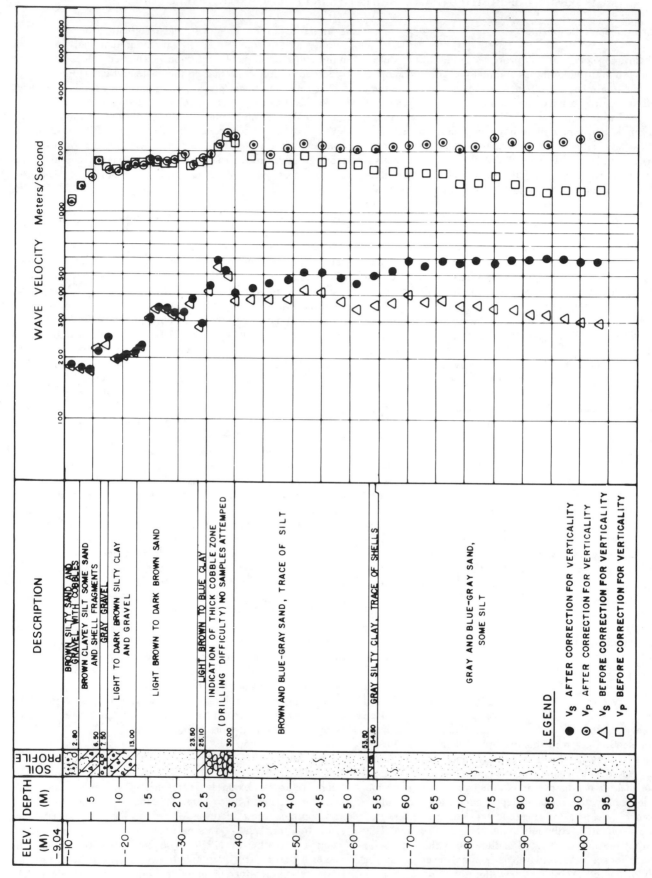

Figure 8. Results of a seismic cross-hole survey before and after correcting for deviation from true borehole verticality. Error in velocity determination ranges from zero at ground surface to greater than 40% at hole bottom when comparing corrected and uncorrected values.

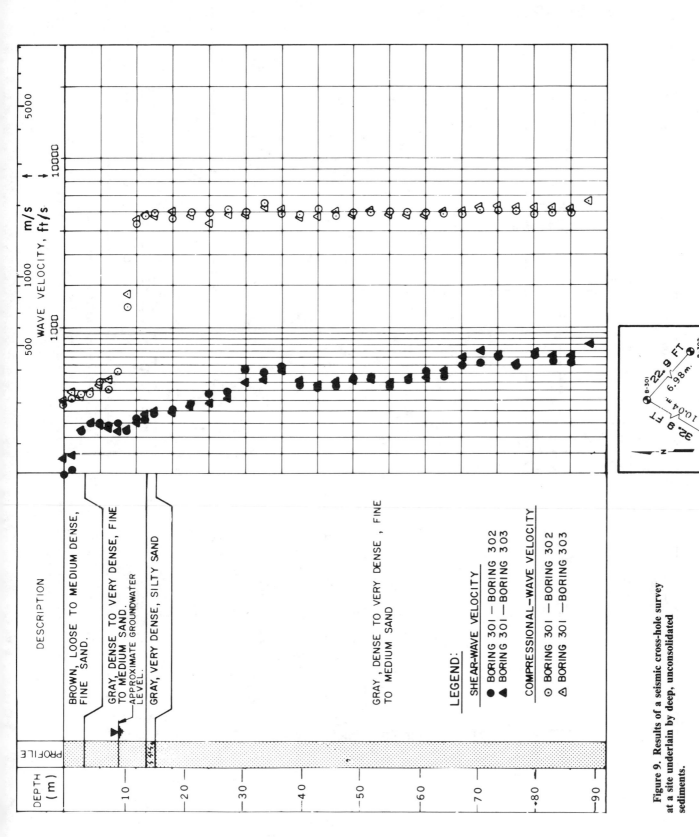

Figure 9. Results of a seismic cross-hole survey at a site underlain by deep, unconsolidated sediments.

percolating waters have deposited radioactive salts. Arguments in favor of stratigraphic control, however, include the lateral persistence of the features, the relatively constant distance between the peaks, the consistent relationships of the natural gamma features occurring between the peaks, and the relatively constant thickness of the features themselves (Siems and others, 1974). The natural gamma peaks also were noted to coincide with zones of iron-stained carbonate rocks recognizable in cores and cuttings.

Studies by Osborne and Seiglie (1974) and Osborne and others (this volume) demonstrated that the natural gamma spikes were attributable to bismuth[214], a daughter product of uranium. They have suggested that the lowermost spike occurs at, or near, the Aymamon-Camuy contact and may be related to the unconformity in a process whereby carbonate recrystallization has resulted in uranium expulsion. The upper natural gamma spike may be associated with a diastem or unconformity produced when rates of marine sedimentation were greatly reduced.

Lithologic and paleontologic evidence (Osborne and Seiglie, 1974; Osborne and others, this volume) similarly corroborated the stratigraphic validity of the gamma-ray data. Biostratigraphic discontinuities between ecozones across the Aymamon-Camuy contact, coupled with pronounced mineralogic and petrologic differences, clearly define the contact and demonstrate that it corresponds, within sampling error, to the gamma-ray spike.

Osborne and Seiglie (1974) and Osborne and others (this volume) have further shown that the uppermost gamma-ray spike closely parallels ecozones in the Camuy Formation. This factor, together with the inclusion of the spike within an iron oxide–rich horizon, which itself appears to be stratigraphically controlled on the basis of geochemical models, is convincing stratigraphic evidence.

The Islote site is one of the few studied in which virtually all of the geophysically significant data were contained in a single log. Little of the other geophysically derived data offered much substantiation of the gamma-ray data. Neither did other logs appear to provide significant stratigraphic data themselves. Without gross supporting geologic evidence, it would be necessary to view the geophysical data with considerable doubt. Only borehole logs that are internally consistent when analyzed in composite are normally considered to have true geologic significance. The Islote site illustrates how geophysical information, correctly interpreted and well documented by supporting geologic evidence, can be extremely valuable in complex geologic investigations.

Sundesert Nuclear Project

The Blythe site of the Sundesert Nuclear Project is located in the southeastern Mojave Desert area of California about 15 mi (24.1 km) southwest of the city of Blythe. Additional sites are included in the Sundesert project, but discussion herein will be limited to the Blythe site, as conditions elsewhere are similar.

Basement rocks in the Blythe area are composed of intrusive igneous, metamorphic, and volcanic rocks of Precambrian to Tertiary age. These are well exposed in the rugged block mountains within and around the site area. Intervening valleys are filled with lacustrine and alluvial materials of late Tertiary to Quaternary age. These include fanglomerates, derived from the surrounding mountains, which are overlain by marine estuarine deposits of the Bouse Formation. The youngest rocks are alluvial-fan materials and fluviatile deposits of the Colorado River.

Stratigraphically, the Pliocene Bouse Formation is of particular interest to the siting studies because of its determined age of at least 3 m.y. This formation consists of marine- to brackish-water accumulations of limestone, sand, silt, clay, and tufa and is fossiliferous. It is readily recognized in exposures, and its distinct lithology would lead one to believe that its geophysical signature would also be diagnostic. However, this is not necessarily so, as most of the Bouse Formation and its contact with the overlying Colorado River fluviatile sediments are difficult to identify in the logs. Only the basal sandy limestone, which is seldom penetrated by the exploratory drill holes, has a unique response.

Figures 8 and 9 (Summers and others, 1975) show natural gamma and neutron-epithermal neutron correlation suites, respectively, of a series of holes at the Blythe site. The strata here are divided into geophysical units according to dominant lithologic characteristics of the sediments. Features of the logs to note are the gross similarities between individual holes, the correspondence of certain detailed features, and the close agreement between geophysical sequences. Natural gamma correlations are substantiated by neutron-neutron responses and by neutron-gamma and gamma-gamma responses, although these latter logs are not illustrated. Units N, O, and P are defined on the natural gamma log but have not been differentiated on the neutron-neutron log because of the change in physical conditions associated with the water surface in the test holes. Wherever the water surface occurs at or near a lithologic boundary, the boundary will be obscured or obliterated on the induced-radiation logs.

The uppermost sediments, represented by unit N, are largely sands and gravels representative of the latest stage of Colorado River activity. Units O and P are composed, generally, of finer-grained materials and probably represent alluvial-fan and flood-plain deposits. Unit Q consists of sand and gravel deposited in alluvial fans that overlie the Bouse Formation. Unit S is diagnostic of a transitional sandy portion of the upper Bouse Formation, whereas unit T is composed of interbedded sand, silt, and clay layers most typical of Bouse Formation stratigraphy.

CONCLUSIONS

Borehole geophysical methods in their application to nuclear power plant siting are not a substitute for sound, comprehensive geological investigations. They can, however, greatly aid and facilitate the work of the geologist by pointing out features of the lithology and stratigraphy that warrant his concentrated effort.

Project costs can be reduced by the use of rotary-drill wash borings rather than extensive coring. Detailed lithologies and stratigraphy can be established in a relatively few core holes

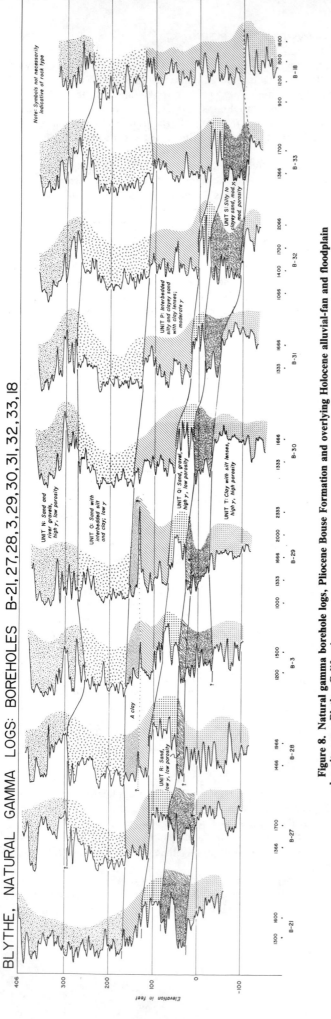

Figure 8. Natural gamma borehole logs, Pliocene Bouse Formation and overlying Holocene alluvial-fan and floodplain deposits, near Blythe, California.

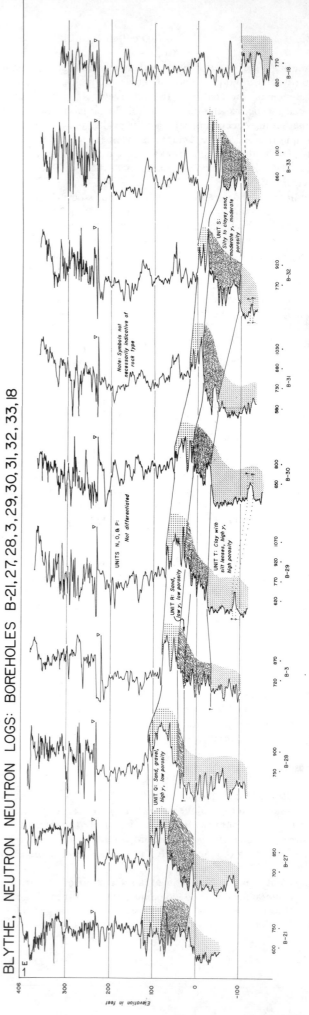

Figure 9. Neutron-neutron borehole logs, Pliocene Bouse Formation and overlying Holocene alluvial-fan and floodplain deposits, near Blythe, California.

and projected laterally with the geophysical methods. The geophysical methods can be supplemented by as much additional information as possible from the rotary-drill wash cuttings. In some environments it will be found that the geophysical information, which represents a response to chemical and physical parameters, will be well defined, whereas lithological variations are megascopically indistinct. Lithologic contacts established by geophysical logging are sometimes sharper than any the geologist may wish to define based solely on his judgment. Accordingly, they can offer a higher measure of resolution, which is important in site structural evaluation. On the other hand, if the chemical and physical properties of the examined media are continuously changing in an incremental fashion, no borehole geophysical technique will indicate sharp contacts and should not be expected to enhance resolution.

To be of maximum benefit, geophysical investigations may commence shortly after the completion of the first exploratory boreholes. Preliminary studies should be directed to the evaluation of any geophysical signatures that may have value in areal stratigraphic correlation. If present, the diagnostic features should be called to the attention of project management in order that geologic efforts be directed to evaluating their stratigraphic significance. If good geophysical markers are not evident, recourse must be taken to geophysical events characterized by less well developed contacts or to events or sequences of events of limited areal extent. In the latter cases, stratigraphic continuity must be demonstrated by virtue of overlap of correlating units in different parts of the study area.

Investigations at nuclear power sites are best accomplished with miniaturized equipment using amplification factors that will resolve minor differences in lithologies. Radiation logging methods are the preferred procedures because of the restrictions on logging inherent to the drilling and completion measures, the normally unconsolidated nature of site materials, the relatively shallow exploratory holes utilized, and the relative position of the water or mud surface in the holes. The radiation logs normally are affected by the time constants employed, and resolution is reduced accordingly. In the equipment utilized in the described studies, radiation is incrementally sampled and the data are computer-smoothed to reduce radiation statistics. This procedure is useful in gaining a greater measure of lithologic resolution.

ACKNOWLEDGMENTS

The authors appreciate critical reviews provided by Howard A. Coombs, W. Frank Scott, and Allen W. Hatheway.

REFERENCES CITED

Croft, M. G., and Gordon, G. V., 1968, Geology, hydrology, and quality of water in the Hanford-Visalia area, San Joaquin Valley, California: U.S. Geological Survey Open-File Report.

Crosby, J. W., III, Siems, B. A., Anderson, J. V., and Weber, T. L., 1973a, Geophysical borehole investigation: Richland, Washington, Washington Public Power Supply System (Docket 50460, PSAR, WPPSS NPS, Unit 1, Benton County, Washington).

Crosby, J. W., III, Siems, B. A., and Weber, T. L., 1973b, Interpretation of geophysical logs: Pullman, Washington, Washington State University, College of Engineering Research Report 73/15–92 (City of Los Angeles, Department of Water and Power, ESRR, San Joaquin NPS, Kern County, California, v. 2, App. 2.5A).

Crosby, J. W., III, Anderson, J. V., Lane, G. B., and Weber, T. L., 1974, Geophysical borehole investigations: Richland, Washington, Washington Public Power Supply System (Docket 50460, PSAR, WPPSS NPS, Units 1 and 4, Benton County, Washington, App. 2K, Amendment 9).

Docket 50528-12, 1974, PSAR, Palo Verde NPS, Maricopa County, Arizona: Phoenix, Arizona, Arizona Public Service Company.

Frink, J. W., and Kues, H. A., 1954, Corcoran clay—A Pleistocene lacustrine deposit in the San Joaquin Valley, California: American Association of Petroleum Geologists Bulletin, v. 38, p. 2357–2371.

Osborne, R. H., and Seiglie, G. A., 1974, Stratigraphic continuity report for the NORCO nuclear power plant site: San Juan, Puerto Rico, Puerto Rico Water Resources Authority, Preliminary Report, 101 p. (Docket 50376-59, PSAR, North Coast NPS, Barrio Islote, Puerto Rico, v. 3, App. 2.5C).

Osborne, R. H., Junge, W. R., and Seiglie, G. A., 1979, Application of microfacies analysis to the identification of stratigraphic marker beds in the Tertiary strata of northern Puerto Rico, in Hatheway, A. W., and McClure, C. R., Jr., eds., Geology in the siting of nuclear power plants: Geological Society of America Reviews in Engineering Geology, v. IV (this volume).

Siems, B. A., Anderson, J. V., Weber, T. L., and Castleberry, J. S., 1974, Interpretation of downhole geophysical logs: San Juan, Puerto Rico, Puerto Rico Water Resources Authority, Preliminary Report, 26 p. (Docket 50376-59, PSAR, North Coast NPS, Barrio Islote, Puerto Rico, v. 3, App. 2.5F).

Summers, K. V., Castleberry, J. S., and Crosby, J. W., III, 1975, Geophysical borehole investigations: San Diego, California, San Diego Gas and Electric Company, various pages (Docket 50582-12, PSAR, Sundesert NPS, Riverside County, California).

Swanson, D. A., Wright, T. L., Hooper, P. R., and Bentley, R. D., 1979, Revisions in stratigraphic nomenclature of the Columbia River Basalt Group: U.S. Geological Survey Bulletin 1457 (in press).

Manuscript Received by the Society July 13, 1978
Manuscript Accepted November 13, 1978

Geological Society of America
Reviews in Engineering Geology, Volume IV
1979

Ground-water studies for nuclear power plant siting

CLIFFORD R. FARRELL
Bechtel Incorporated, 50 Beale Street, San Francisco, California 94119

JOHN W. HARSHBARGER
Harshbarger & Associates, 1525 E. Kleindale Road, Tucson, Arizona 85719

ABSTRACT

Ground-water studies for nuclear power plant sites call for extraordinary and extensive effort in comparison to site investigations for more conventional, large engineering structures, primarily to assure the stability and safe operation of the plant. Providing that assurance may require unusually complex design solutions to foundation problems. Basic data collection must be extensive and thorough in response to the requirements of the Safety Analysis Report (SAR) for a detailed and well-documented description on the occurrence and movement of ground water in the site vicinity. The ground-water studies presented in the SAR must demonstrate that normal operation of the plant will not have a serious impact on the ground water and that water levels will not rise to a height that might affect the stability of plant foundations. Further, the studies must be thorough enough to assure that any accidental spill of radioactive fluid will either be dispersed harmlessly or will be intercepted by a monitoring system before the spill could percolate to a usable off-site aquifer.

studies must (1) demonstrate that normal operation of the plant, including any use of ground water, will not have a serious impact on the ground-water resources of the area; (2) determine the direction of movement and possible impact of a postulated serious spill of radioactive fluid infiltrating and reaching a ground-water reservoir; (3) show the maximum rise of the ground-water table that could occur in order to aid in design of hydrostatic loading and in evaluating the possible liquefaction of foundation materials during earthquakes; and (4) include the design of a monitoring system to detect accidental spills of radioactive waste (radwaste) fluid that might reach the ground-water table. A system to control or intercept ground water impaired by a spill may be required.

A detailed analysis of ground-water conditions on-site as well as a description of the regional ground-water system must be included in the SAR to support the conclusions related to these study requirements. The data are to be presented in tabulated form and as ground-water contour maps, hydrographs, and special graphs to demonstrate that safety criteria for licensing a nuclear power plant are satisfied.

OBJECTIVES OF GROUND-WATER STUDIES

When a plant site is first considered, studies should be directed to the general characteristics of the hydrologic regimen. Factors that could make development of a site difficult or preclude its licensing should be identified as early as possible. For example, a site underlain by limestone that is known to have solution cavities may require extensive tracer studies to identify the fluid flow paths of a postulated spill of radioactive fluids. An elaborate fluid-interceptor system might be required for such a site; the expense involved may make the site untenable. As another example, a site underlain by sand and silt layers that are susceptible to liquefaction could require an extensive and permanent dewatering system to assure the stability of the foundation.

To fulfill the requirements of the Safety Analysis Report (SAR) for a proposed nuclear plant site, the ground-water

BASIC DATA COLLECTION FOR SAR

Investigation of any proposed nuclear plant site requires collection of comprehensive basic data on ground-water conditions to meet SAR requirements. For most areas, published ground-water studies provide much of the information needed to describe the regional hydrologic system. Published material may provide some of the more detailed on-site information required, but intensive field work and site investigation must be done to provide much of the data needed. As a guideline, all water wells within a radius of about 3 mi (5 km) of the site and all municipal or public wells within 20 mi (32 km) of the site must be identified and their condition documented.

Collection of water-level data from these local and regional wells provides important information on the potentiometric surfaces in the area, depth to the water table, and direction of ground-water movement. An extensive network of observation wells will be constructed to closely define the occurrence and characteristics of ground water within the immediate site area. Thirty, or more, small-diameter observation wells or piezometers are not unusual for a site investigation. The monitoring network will provide detailed definition of the potentiometric surfaces of perched water tables and aquifers immediately underlying the site area. Water samples are obtained for chemical analysis, and the wells are monitored to determine short-term as well as long-term water-level fluctuations.

Thorough borehole exploration tests to determine the hydrologic characteristics of the materials underlying the site are coordinated with the geologic, geophysical, and soils explorations. Packer tests are performed in exploratory holes to provide permeability measurements (U.S. Bureau of Reclamation, 1968, Designation E-18), and many of the required observation wells can be selected from these exploratory holes. Proper understanding of the direction and movement of ground water from the plant site is needed to evaluate the consequence of a postulated accidental spill. Ground-water monitoring wells are essential in the down-gradient area.

It may be necessary to construct test wells and several observation wells to obtain adequate data to determine the aquifer characteristics of an area. This is especially important where it is planned to use ground water as a source of supply for operation of the plant. Extensive pumping tests will be needed to fully support the designed system. Long-term productivity of the aquifer to yield the necessary water supply without seriously interfering with other users must be thoroughly demonstrated.

Water-level measurements from the on-site observation-well network are a minimum to document short-term fluctuations. The installation of a continuous water-level recorder for each aquifer monitored should be considered. These data, correlated with available long-term well hydrographs and precipitation data, are especially important to determine the maximum ground-water level and to evaluate any potential liquefaction problems. For water-supply considerations, these data are needed to demonstrate aquifer productivity, recharge, discharge, and surface-water relationships.

ACCIDENTAL SPILL ANALYSIS

Probably the most critical aspect of ground-water studies for each site concerns the disposition of contaminants following a postulated accidental spill of radioactive liquid. Parameters affecting the migration of the spill are similar to those for other waste fluids, except that with radwaste the contaminant is radioactive. Dilution of the contaminant radionuclides as they migrate through an aquifer is affected by hydrodynamic dispersion and by adsorption onto the solid particles. Decay of the radionuclides also reduces the radioactivity with time.

The basic data collection as discussed is commonly adequate to demonstrate no threat to usable ground water by spills of radioactive fluids. Analyses of movement of the spilled fluid from the radwaste building (or site of the postulated spill) to the nearest off-site user of ground water can be based on simple Darcian flow of ground water, $V = Kl/\phi$, where $V =$ average velocity of ground water, $K =$ hydraulic conductivity of the porous media, $l =$ hydraulic gradient, and $\phi =$ effective porosity of the aquifer. This relationship provides a first approximation of the time required for the spill to travel through the aquifer to the nearest water user. When the time is sufficient to allow decay of all radionuclides to less than the MPC (maximum permissible concentrations), further investigation may not be necessary. For MPC standards, refer to Title 10, *Code of Federal Regulations* (1978), Part 20, "Standards for Protection against Radiation." On the other hand, more sophisticated flow models will be required when a simple ground-water flow system does not indicate sufficient time for radioactive decay or when the aquifer system is not in porous media (that is, the ground water flows through widely spaced fractures or solution channels).

Commonly, it can be recognized early in the site study whether or not the transit time of simple ground-water movement will be adequate to decrease the radionuclide concentration of the spilled radwaste fluids, or if more detailed information on the parameters affecting the migration of radionuclides is needed. It should be determined if the endangered aquifer can be studied with analytic methods that have been developed for porous media. If the aquifer permeability is due to fractures or the aquifer is cavernous, these methods may not be valid, and quantitative prediction of the effects of a radioactive fluid spill may be made only with tracer tests. Such tests may be required, even with porous media, to measure directional hydraulic conductivity, dispersivity, and the distribution coefficient of the aquifer.

Dispersion of a fluid within an aquifer occurs primarily because of differing lengths of the flow paths. A characteristic length, termed the "dispersivity," describes the geometry that affects this dispersion. Although dispersivity can be estimated from laboratory tests or from empirical relations to grain size (Harleman and others, 1963), field dispersivity is commonly several orders of magnitude greater than laboratory-measured or empirical values (Mercado, 1967). Large-scale inhomogeneities, such as stratification and jointing, apparently dominate the dispersion process in the field. If dispersion is to be relied on for significantly decreased radionuclide concentration, field tracer tests will be needed to measure the dispersivity of the aquifer.

The adsorptive property of the aquifer may also be considered in reducing the radionuclide concentration in ground water. This reaction is characterized by the distribution coefficient K_d, which is the ratio of the amount of contaminant adsorbed on the solid aquifer to the amount remaining in the ground water. This process effectively reduces the velocity of the contaminant and thus allows more time for radioactive decay. The reduced velocity is expressed quantitatively by the equation (Kaufman, 1973), $V_r = V/[1 + (K_d P_b)/n]$, where $V_r =$ average velocity of the radionuclide, $P_b =$ bulk density of the formation, and $n =$ porosity of the formation

Laboratory measurements of the distribution coefficient can be representative of field conditions. The basic method is to treat an aquifer sample with a solution containing the ions of interest (for example, strontium and cesium) and the ambient ground water. After the system reaches equilibrium, the reduction of ionic concentration in the liquid phase is measured. This procedure has been used on disturbed (batch method) and undisturbed samples, and both have been found to provide effective values of the aquifer distribution coefficient, provided the aquifer is a porous media (Kaufman, 1963). Because the distribution coefficient depends on the surface area of the solid material, disturbed samples may allow erroneously high values in laboratory measurements. This factor is acute with indurated rocks where flow of ground water is through fractures; in such an aquifer, field tracer tests may be the only acceptable method to measure the retardation of radionuclides by adsorption.

When dispersion, adsorption, and radioactive decay are all considered, the travel of a contaminant spill, considered as a pulse injection in one-dimensional ground-water flow, can be described by the following equation (Grove, 1970):

$$c/c_o = \frac{1}{2}\exp(-\lambda t)\left[\text{erf}\left(\frac{X - V_r t'}{2\sqrt{D_m V_r t'}}\right) - \text{erf}\left(\frac{X - V_r t}{2\sqrt{D_m V_r t}}\right)\right],$$

where c = concentration at point X and time t, c_o = original concentration of contaminant, X = distance from initial spill location, t = time since initial migration of pulse, $t' = (t - \Delta t)$ where Δt is the time necessary for the fluid to flow one pulse width, V = average interstitial ground-water velocity, D_m = longitudinal dispersivity, λ = radioactive decay constant = 0.693 divided by the radioactive half-life, and erf = error function:

$$\text{erf } X = \frac{2}{\sqrt{\pi}}\int_0^\infty e^{-t^2} dt.$$

This (or a similar) solution of the general partial differential equations for movement of ground water and mass transport require simplifying assumptions to reduce the analysis to one-dimensional migration. The conditions of ground-water occurrence and movement must be thoroughly understood to demonstrate that such assumptions render a conservative result; that is, calculated arrival times of spilled waste fluids and resulting dilution are less than would actually occur. Two-dimensional models may be required in some complex cases. Although the three-dimensional flow models can be developed, large computer core requirements and the common lack of adequate input data usually preclude the feasibility of such precise description. Finally, it must be borne in mind that all of these models are only for porous media.

Secondary permeability conditions may be simulated in approximately the same way as porous media if the fracturing and jointing of the rock is closely spaced. However, where flow is through widely spaced fractures or channels, field tracer tests will probably be required to determine directly the movement and dilution of fluids. An example of tracer-test field measurement is described by Webster and others (1970). A major factor in planning field tracer tests is the time required; it may take 1 yr or more of field testing to measure an adequate sample.

SPECIAL DESIGN ASPECTS

As the site investigation progresses and design of the proposed plant evolves, problems or needs may be identified that could require unusual or new design methods. Commonly, such design is in response to very conservative safety criteria. For example, should ground water be considered for the emergency cooling-water supply, the well field to supply the water could be classified as seismic category 1 (plant structures directly related to plant safety in the event of an earthquake), and design and construction of it will need to meet the very strict criteria required by that classification.

Ground-water conditions at some sites have required the design of blanket drains or permanent relief wells to prevent undesirable uplift pressures and to control corrosive and/or thermal ground water. Land subsidence due to withdrawal of ground water in the Houston, Texas, area has required close analysis of this problem followed by effective design of the area's nuclear plants to preclude serious differential settlements of the plant buildings. Potential liquefaction of foundation materials has resulted in permanent dewatering systems being proposed for at least two nuclear plant sites. The objective is to maintain the water table at a depth that will preclude liquefaction of underlying sand layers.

Probably each nuclear plant site has required some extraordinary effort in ground-water studies, either because of the effect of the plant operation on ground water or because of ground-water conditions that affect the design of the plant. The following examples are submitted for illustration.

GROUND–WATER UTILIZATION AT NUCLEAR POWER PLANT A

In the early phases of site investigation for nuclear power plant A, it was recognized that a large and dependable water supply was available from the underlying Cretaceous aquifer system. This was determined to be the most feasible source of supply during normal operation to provide for the nuclear service needs (for example, the reactor cooling system), for plant demineralized water treatment, and for the domestic water supply. The adjacent large river was planned as the source of makeup water (that is, the amount of water lost by evaporation) for the turbine plant cooling towers, the largest use of water during normal operation. The water uses and requirements are summarized in Table 1.

Safety considerations require that a 30-d supply of reactor cooling water be available for emergency shutdown of the reactor unit, in case the normal operation source of supply is not available. As a safety assurance, standby nuclear service water wells are provided to assure that the emergency water supply is maintained. For nuclear plant A, the design of these standby wells was analyzed to determine its capability to withstand a Safe Shutdown Earthquake (SSE), and construction of the wells will meet seismic category 1 criteria. The original plans submitted in the Preliminary Safety Analysis Report (PSAR) comprised four 1,100-MW generating units. However, present scheduling calls for only two of the units to be completed. The following, based primarily on information contained in the PSAR, describes the investigations performed.

Capacity of the Cretaceous Aquifer System

The plant site is on a broad coastal plain which is underlain by a thick and extensive series of alternating beds of sand, clay, marble, and limestone that dip gently toward the coast only slightly more than the regional ground slope. The permeable sand and limestone units are major aquifers, utilized by municipalities and individuals throughout the coastal plain. The Cretaceous sand forms one of the largest and most extensive of these aquifer systems. The aquifer contains fresh water in a belt 60 mi (97 km) wide and 400 mi (644 km) long. It ranges from several feet (1 m) to more than 300 ft (91 m) thick in the outcrop area along the inland boundary of the coastal plain and increases to 1,100 ft (335 m) thick downdip. To demonstrate that the aquifer is capable of yielding the expected water supply at the plant site, a test well and five observation wells were drilled and pumping tests were performed. The test well at the plant site penetrated 550 ft (168 m) of the formation.

The site area is immediately underlain by sand and clay units of Eocene age and younger. About 40 ft (12 m) of blue-gray marl occurs at a depth of 100 ft (30 m) or less and forms an extensive impermeable unit. Unconfined ground water is present in the sand units above the marl. These upper sand units are relatively unconsolidated, and the plant design requires excavation and recompaction of all materials above the marl aquiclude. The latter is referred to as the plant-foundation–bearing unit. Beneath the marl to a depth of about 470 ft (143 m) are silt and fine sand beds with some more permeable sand beds that could yield moderate amounts of water to wells. Below 470 ft are the permeable Cretaceous sand beds that form the confined aquifer system.

TABLE 1. WATER REQUIREMENTS PER UNIT

Users	Normal flow (gpm)	Normal shutdown (gpm)	Emergency shutdown (gpm)
Nuclear service cooling towers			
Evaporation and drift losses to atmosphere	203	540	
Blowdown to river outfall	65	60	
Total	268	600	(30-d supply)
Turbine plant cooling towers			
Evaporation and drift losses to atmosphere	16,500		
Blowdown to river outfall	5,500		
Total (maximum)	22,000	0	0
Plant demineralized water treatment	220	0	0
Potable water	~2	~10	~2*

*Stored in plant.

Aquifer Test Program

Drilling of the test well and five observation wells commenced with a pilot hole to a depth of 928 ft (283 m). Wash samples were taken at 10-ft (3-m) intervals, and measurements were made of the electrical resistivity and self-potential, gamma-ray intensity, and acoustical velocities of the materials. From these data, calculations of elastic moduli, bulk density, and Poisson's ratio were made. The results are shown with a log of the hole in Figure 1. On the basis of logging of the pilot hole and grain-size analysis of samples, intervals were selected for screening, and the hole was reamed for construction of the test well. It was decided to construct the well as one of the standby nuclear service wells (well 1, Fig. 2). Depth intervals at which wire-wrapped well screens were placed include 503 to 538, 558 to 588, 698 to 708, 730 to 750, and 820 to 850 ft (153 to 164, 170 to 179, 213 to 216, 223 to 229, and 250 to 259 m).

The observation wells were drilled to the depth of the aquifer to be tested and were completed by placing 2-in. (5-cm) black pipe, with selected intervals of slotted (screen) sections. To assure connection with the aquifer, the wells were pumped with an air-lift system until the water produced was clear.

After the test-well array was completed, a constant-discharge pumping test was performed at a rate of 1,200 gpm (76 l/s) for 48.5 h. Pumping was then increased to 1,800 gpm (114 l/s) for 4 h. From the water-level data at the observation wells, the hydraulic characteristics of the aquifer were determined by using methods based on the nonequilibrium theory of flow to a well. The results of the analyses are summarized in Table 2.

Ground elevation surveys were made in the area of the test well before and after the pumping test to detect any subsidence caused by the cone of depression. Repeated elevation surveys were made for 2 months before the pumping test; these surveys established a base reference to an accuracy of 0.003± ft (0.9 mm). Elevation measurements following the test indicated that a possible maximum subsidence of 0.012 ft (3.5 mm) may have occurred; this supports the calculated expected subsidence of 0.017 ft (5 mm). The result assumes that all water is released from storage by compression of the soil skeleton and that

TABLE 2. SUMMARY OF AQUIFER CHARACTERISTICS CALCULATIONS

Method of analysis	Observation point(s)	Calculated transmissivity (gpd/ft)	Storage coefficient
Straight-line distance, drawdown	Pumping well	158,000	
Type-curve, time-drawdown	1	196,000	6.6×10^{-4}
Type-curve, time-drawdown	2	160,000	3.3×10^{-4}
Type-curve, time-drawdown	3	163,700	3.5×10^{-4}
Type-curve, time-drawdown	4	153,000	2.1×10^{-5}
Type-curve, time-drawdown	5	229,200	3.9×10^{-4}

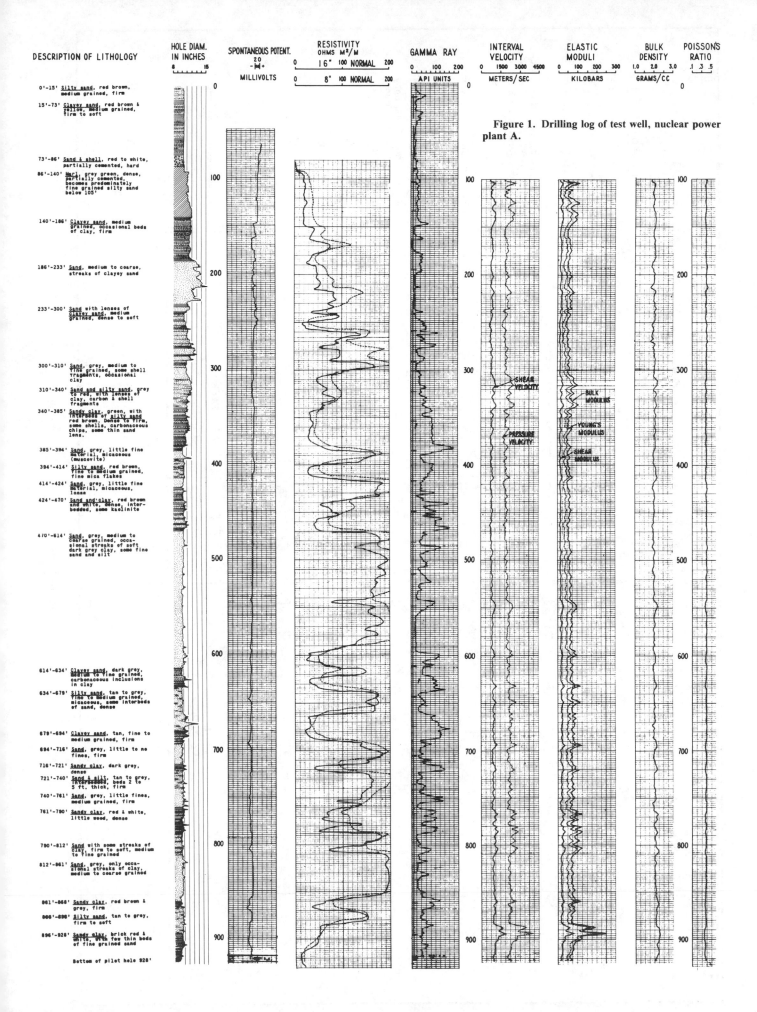

Figure 1. Drilling log of test well, nuclear power plant A.

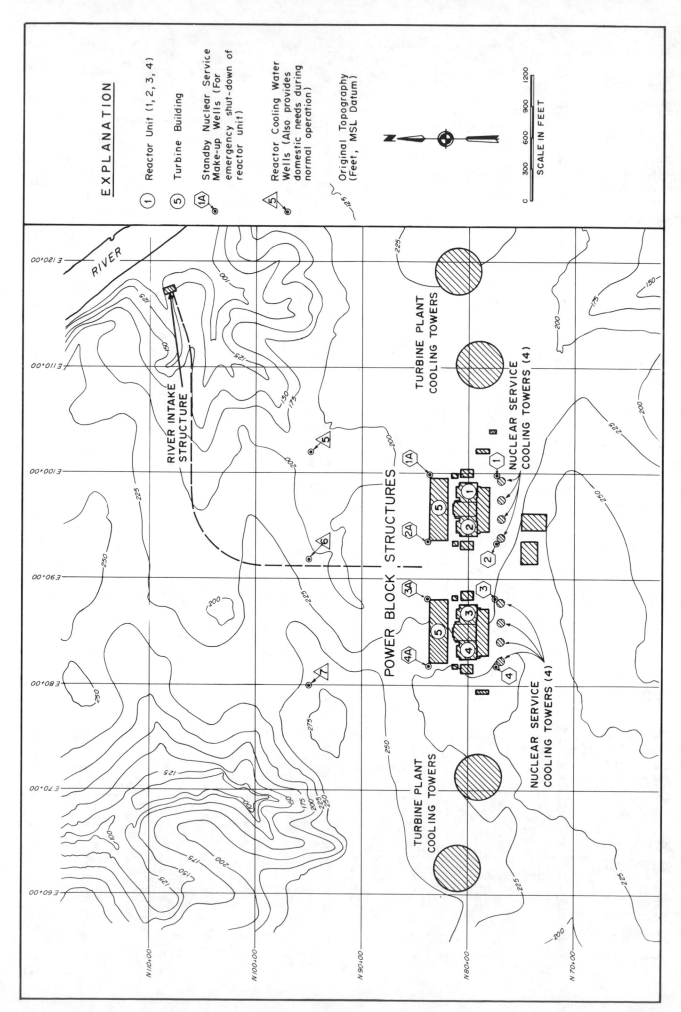

Figure 2. General layout of facilities of nuclear power plant A.

the average storage coefficient is 0.0004. Maximum differential subsidence beneath the plant area, if a storage coefficient variation is assumed, was estimated to be less than 0.032 ft (less than 1 cm).

Well Field Design

The well field (Fig. 2) was designed on the basis of aquifer characteristics determined from the pumping tests. The parameters used were a transmissivity of 150,000 gpd/ft (1,860 m^2/d) and a storage coefficient of 0.0004. The three normal-operation wells were each designed with a pumping capacity of 2,000 gpm (126 l/s); this provided redundant standby capacity for the water makeup and domestic needs. Locations of the normal-operation wells were selected to minimize subsidence effects beneath the power block. In the event the normal wells should fail, eight standby nuclear service wells are available, each capable of producing 1,000 gpm (63 l/s). The only function of the standby wells is to supply water to the dual nuclear service–cooling tower basins of each generating unit, should normal well water be insufficient.

Seismic Category 1 Wells

Because the eight standby nuclear service makeup wells are expected to withstand the SSE, they are classified as seismic category 1 structures and are required to meet design and quality-assurance criteria in accordance with that classification. Design of the wells to survive the SSE was done in a three-step approach. First, an analysis was made of the kinds of damage that have occurred to wells during past major earthquakes. From this study, preventative measures and design criteria to avoid such damage were determined. Then a well design was prepared by applying these criteria to the site and calculating the imposed earth pressures and seismic stresses of the SSE on the well structure.

Investigation of water-well damage by earthquakes was done primarily through review of the literature and by interviews with well drillers, well service companies, and ground-water hydrologists and geologists. From this review of water-well performance, summarized in Table 3, three main factors in the design of wells can be recognized: (1) well-site considerations, (2) the critical outage or downtime during and immedi-

TABLE 3. SUMMARY OF EARTHQUAKE DAMAGE RELATED TO WATER WELLS

	San Fernando, California 2/9/71	Alaska 3/27/64	Lake Hebgen, Montana 8/17/59	Arvin Tehachapi California 7/21/52	Charleston, Virginia 8/31/89	San Francisco, California 4/18/06	Long Beach, California 3/10/33
Intensity (modified Mercalli)	VIII	XI	X	XI	X	XI	IX
Number of wells in area of major structural damage	200+	100+	50±	200+	Many	Many	200±
Destroyed wells							
Earth displacement (shearing) or slides	None	7	None	None	None	None	None
Collapse of casing or rupture in drilled wells	1	None	None	None	None	None	None
Collapse of dug wells	None	(?)	Many	None	(?)	None	None
Wells rendered inoperable, but repairable							
Distortion or bending of casing	2	None	1	10±	None	None	None
Submersible pump cable break	1	None	None	None	. .	. .	. .
Sanding or mudding of wells	None	5±	None	None	None	Many	None
Collapse of well house	None	1	None	None	None	None	None
Damaged but operable wells							
Misalignment of pump column	3±	5±	2	(?)	None	1	None
Sanding or mudding of wells	10±	Few	Many	(?)	(?)	. .	None
Pollution of ground water	4(?)	None	None	None	None	(?)	None
Other effects (wells continued to operate)							
Reduction in well capacity	3	(?)	10±	(?)	(?)	Few	None
Semipermanent changes in water levels	Many	Many	Many	Many	(?)	Many	Few
Fluctuations in water levels or overflow of water	Many	Many	Many	Many	Many	Many	Many
Displacement of pump base and/or soil consolidation	10±	10±	2	Few	(?)	1	None
Indirect effects (supplying ground water)							
Disruption of water-distribution systems	Many	Many	Few	Many	(?)	(?)	(?)
Electric power failure	Many	Many	Few	Many	. .	(?)	(?)

Note: Values are reported number of affected wells.

ately following the earthquake when power would be shut off, and (3) the earthquake-induced ground-motion effects. A fundamental siting consideration is that it is not practical to design wells to resist ground displacement caused by such features as faults, steep slopes (possible landslides), or shallow saturated sand layers susceptible to liquefaction.

On the basis of these guidelines, earthquake-resistance criteria for the wells were determined as follows: (1) Each well shall be able to provide an adequate water supply in case of an emergency. (2) The minimum specification for the wells shall be the American Water Works Association Standard for Deep Wells (Standard AWWA A-100). (3) The wells shall be within the excavated and stabilized backfill areas of the plant site to avoid low-density soils. (4) The well screens shall be of wire-wound type, of sufficient strength to carry the stress loads anticipated to occur during the SSE and shall be of stainless steel. (5) The water wells shall be fully lined, using stainless steel casing. Stainless steel shall also be used for the discharge pipe and connections. The material shall have a minimum yield strength of 42,000 psi (290 MPa) and modulus of elasticity of 28×10^6 psi (193 GPa). Corrosion allowance of $1/16$ in. (0.16 cm) shall be considered in analyzing the well casing, discharge pipe, and components. (6) Concrete used for the access pit and the annular space around the casing shall have a minimum yield strength of 3,000 psi (20.7 MPa) in 28 d. (7) The well casing and screen assembly shall be designed to withstand earthquake-induced acceleration loads of 0.2g lateral soil pressure (g = acceleration of gravity); and seismic wave–induced stresses based on an average compressional wave velocity of 6,700 ft/s (2,042 m/s) and a shear-wave velocity of 1,800 ft/s (549 m/s). (8) Allowance shall be provided in the well screen and casing column for the hydrodynamic response of the well-aquifer system caused by earthquake-induced stresses. (9) An automatic power shutoff switch that is activated by a strong-motion earthquake shall be included on the power line to each well.

Criteria for earthquake-resistance design were also prepared for the well access pit, discharge line, and other conveyance features. In accordance with these criteria, analysis was made of the capability of the well casing to withstand stresses caused by seismic waves traveling through the soil (Nazarian, 1973). It was assumed that the casing is sufficiently flexible to conform to the free-field soil deformations. Expansion joints or separations were provided at interface locations such as the base slab of the access pit and the horizontal discharge pipe. Figure 3 illustrates the procedure used in computing stresses on the well casing.

The discharge pipe and pump were analyzed for dynamic loads as a separate system inside the casing. A finite-element model was used to represent the system where the pipe and pump are divided into beam elements related to the leaf springs attached to the discharge pipe and pump for stabilizing within the well column. A dynamic analysis of the model was made based on the response at each spring to a time-history of one-dimensional seismic wave propagation in the soil. The frequencies, mode shapes, and critical stresses in the discharge pipe and pump were obtained. Design of the components met these calculated stresses. Analysis of the hydrodynamic effects of seismic waves causing water levels in the well to fluctuate

(Cooper and others, 1965) indicated that the level changes would be small and that surges would not damage the well.

Planned Additional Testing

The normal makeup water wells have been constructed, and an additional testing program is to be performed. The first test will be a sequence of step-drawdown tests. The already constructed standby makeup well (well 1, Fig. 2) will be used as the pumping well during the step-drawdown tests, and the normal makeup wells will be used as observation points. The second test will be a multiple-well, constant-discharge test. It is proposed to use standby well 1 and makeup well 5 as pumping wells and the rest of the wells as observation wells. The increments of discharge for the step-drawdown are proposed as 400, 800, and 1,600 gpm (25, 50.5, and 101 l/s), with the first two increments to continue for 24 h and the last increment for 5 to 10 d. Duration will be determined by reaching or approaching "equilibrium." A primary objective of the multiple-well test is to verify the degree of well interference calculated from the initial test. The test will continue for 30 d (cooling-water supply period specified by the U.S. Nuclear Regulatory Commission [NRC]) unless equilibrium conditions are definitely reached before that time.

GROUND–WATER CONTROL AT NUCLEAR POWER PLANT B

In addition to the structure complex of three 1,100-MW generating units for nuclear power plant B, other facilities at the site will include a large cooling-water reservoir (80 acres [0.324 km^2]) and an evaporation pond covering in excess of 200 acres (0.809 km^2) (final design has not been determined at this writing). A plan of the facilities is shown in Figure 4.

During the site investigations, a shallow perched water zone was found to occur below the plant site area. Initial studies suggest that sand layers present beneath the site could be susceptible to liquefaction if the perched water table rose significantly. The stability of those sand layers could not be assured. It was apparent that stability analyses were critical, and closer, more detailed study including careful soil sampling and testing was needed. Because it was realized that these studies might indicate that the foundation would be unstable with high ground-water levels, a second, parallel study was also begun to develop a ground-water control system. The investigation first required an understanding of the occurrence of ground water beneath the site. The following description was developed as part of the basic studies required for the SAR.

Ground-Water Occurrence

The site is located within the Basin and Range province. It is a structural basin filled with thick sequences of sedimentary units that overlie crystalline basement. The stratigraphic units present in the basin are shown in Figure 5. The regional aquifer is the thick sequence of volcanic and sedimentary rocks older than 16 m.y. They do not crop out in the site area. At depth

NOTES

1. MINUS SIGN IS COMPRESSION AND PLUS SIGN TENSION USED WITH STRESSES.

2. THE COMPRESSIONAL WAVE VELOCITY "v_p" AND SHEAR WAVE VELOCITY "v_s" ARE AVERAGE VALUES FOR THE SITE.

3. GRAPHICAL DESCRIPTION OF APPLIED STRESSES.

3.a RADIAL PRESSURE

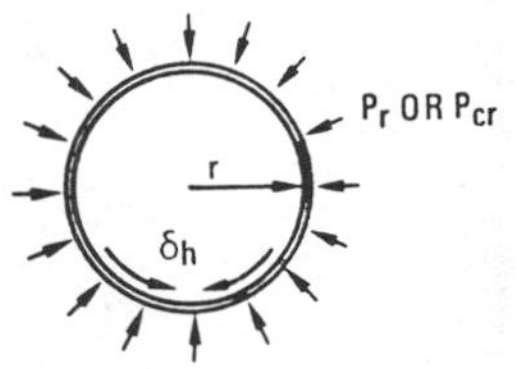

3.b CASING ELEMENT UNDER APPLIED STRESSES.

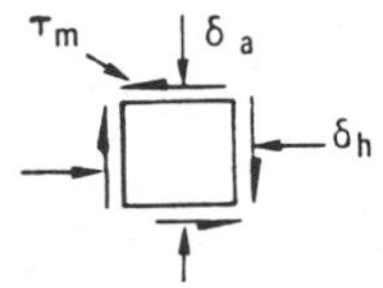

3.c SHEAR DEFORMATION OF SOIL.

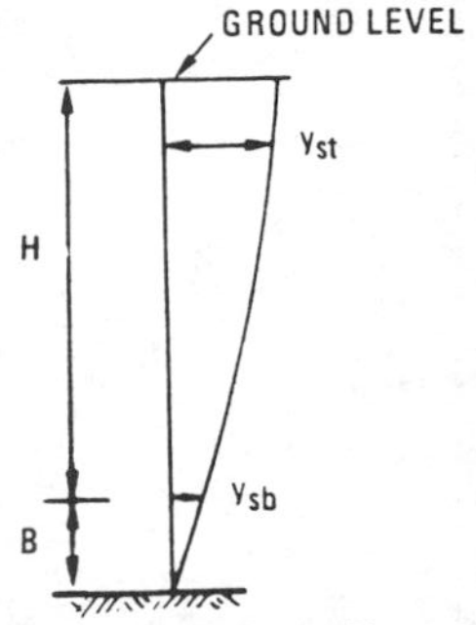

4. THE COMBINED STRESSES FOR THE SCREEN ARE THE MAXIMUM STRESSES AND ARE NOT PRINCIPAL STRESSES.

STEPS	DESCRIPTION	SYMBOL	RELATIONS AND FORMULAS	MATERIAL PROPERTIES AND NUMERICAL DATA	16φ CASING	10φ CASING	10φ SCREEN	REMARKS
1	HOOP STRESS DUE TO RADIAL SOIL PRESSURE	δ_h	$P_r = 62.4\, h_a + K_h(h_1\gamma_s + h_2\gamma_b)$ $\delta_h = \dfrac{P_r r}{t}$	$\gamma_s = 120$ pcf, $\gamma_b = 57.6$ pcf $h_1 = 50$ FT, $h_1^1 = 200'$, $h_2^1 = 750'$ $K_h = 0.7$, $h_a =$ DIFF HYDROSTATIC HEAD $t = 0.312$ IN., $t^* = 0.25$ IN. (SCREEN) $r =$ CASING RADIUS	3851	4875	6685	*THE THICKNESS IS AN EQUIVALENT THICKNESS OF THE HORIZONTAL WIRES h_1^2 FOR 16"φ; h_2^2 FOR 10".
2	AXIAL STRESS DUE TO COMPRESSIONAL SEISMIC WAVES	δ_{ac}	$\delta_{ac} = E_s\left(\dfrac{1}{2\pi}\cdot\dfrac{TA}{v_p}\right)$	$E_s = 28 \times 10^6$ PSI $T = \dfrac{L}{v_p} = 0.12$ SEC $v_p = 6700$ FPS $A = 6.44^\dagger$ FT/SEC²	±515	±515	±515	† THE MAXIMUM ACCELERATION IS ASSUMED 0.2g.
3	AXIAL STRESS DUE TO SEISMIC SHEAR WAVES	δ_{as}	$\delta_{as} = E_s(3CH^{n-1})$ (H IS IN FEET).	$E_s = 28 \times 10^6$ PSI $C = 1.0 \times 10^{-7\ddagger}$ $H = 800$ FT $n = 1.86^{\ddagger}$	±2638	±2638	±2638	‡ THE VALUES C AND n ARE FOR LOOSE SAND AND SOFT CLAY.
4	SHEAR STRESS DUE TO DISTORTION OF SOIL	τ_m	$\tau_m = Y_m G$ $Y_m = \dfrac{5}{2}\dfrac{(H+B)}{v_s^2}$	$G = 10.5 \times 10^6$ PSI $H = 800$ FT $B = 100$ FT $v_s = 1800$ FPS	7298	7298	7298	
5	COMPRESSIONAL HOOP STRESS DUE TO INERTIA LOADS.	δ_c	$\delta_c = 0.798\sqrt{\dfrac{P\dfrac{(D_1 - D_2)}{D_1 D_2}}{\dfrac{1-\mu_1^2}{E_1} + \dfrac{1-\mu_2^2}{E_2}}}$	$D_1 = 20$ IN., $D_2 =$ CASING DIAM. $\mu_1 = 0.42$, $\mu_2 = 0.27$ $E_1 = 2.7 \times 10^3$ PSI, $E_2 = 28 \times 10^6$ PSI $P = 50$ LB/IN.	36	72	72	
6	COMBINED STRESSES A. PRINCIPAL SHEARS B. MAXIMUM PRINCIPAL TENSION C. MAXIMUM PRINCIPAL COMPRESSION	τ_P δ_1 δ_2	$\tau_P = \sqrt{\left(\dfrac{\delta_a - \delta_H}{2}\right)^2 + \tau_m^2}$ $\delta_1 = \dfrac{\delta_a + \delta_H + \tau_P}{2}$ $\delta_2 = \dfrac{\delta_a + \delta_H - \tau_P}{2}$	τ_m (STEP 4) $\delta_a = \delta_{ac} + \delta_{as}$ $\delta_H = \delta_h + \delta_c$	$\begin{cases}8103\\7307\end{cases}$ +7736 -10927	$\begin{cases}8346\\7353\end{cases}$ +7449 -11403	7298 +3153 -6685	THE PRINCIPAL STRESSES ARE DERIVED USING δ_a FIRST AS TENSION THEN AS COMPRESSION
7	CRITICAL EXTERNAL PRESSURE AT WHICH YIELDING IN THE EXTREME FIBERS BEGINS	P_{yp}	$P_{yp}^2 - \left[\dfrac{\sigma_{yp}}{m} + (1+6mn)P_{cr}\right]P_{yp} + \dfrac{\sigma_{yp}}{m}\cdot P_{cr} = 0$ $P_{cr} = \dfrac{1}{4}\left(\dfrac{E_s}{1-\mu^2}\right)\dfrac{t^3}{r^3}$	$n = 0.02$ $m = \dfrac{r}{t}$ $R =$ RADIUS OF PIPE $\sigma_{yp} = 42{,}000$ PSI $P_{cr} =$ CRITICAL PRESSURE ASSUMING PERFECT ROUNDNESS	227	656	312	2% OUT-OF-ROUNDNESS IS ASSUMED

Figure 3. Sample computation of stresses in well casing.

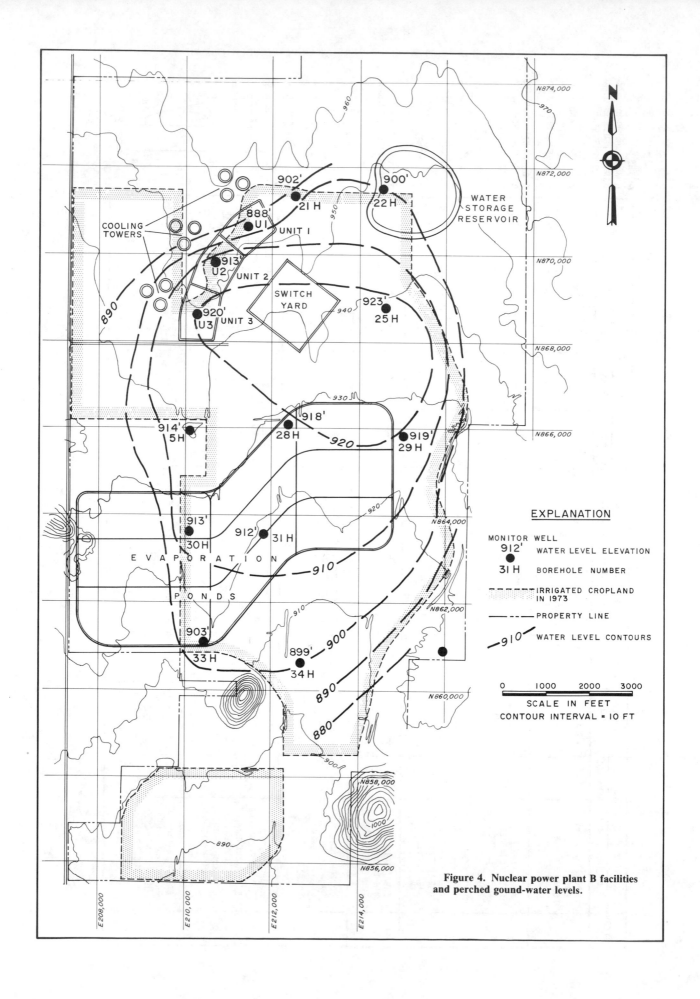

Figure 4. Nuclear power plant B facilities and perched gound-water levels.

within the basin the volcanic rocks are known, from water-well logs, to consist of fractured andesite and basalt with interbedded tuffaceous sandstone, claystone, and conglomerate. The maximum thickness of the aquifer is not known because no wells have penetrated the full thickness of the section. Logs of water wells to the west of the site indicate a thickness of at least 1,400 ft (427 m). The thick andesite flows near the top of this sequence seem to form a confining layer for parts of the regional aquifer. Artesian conditions prevail in the site area, but water-table conditions are present in the western part of the site. The confining layer is not everywhere impermeable.

Unconformably overlying the basalt and andesite sequence is as much as 300 ft (91 m) of fanglomerate and, in most areas, the lower silt, sand, and gravel deposits. Permeability of these units is low, and apparently they are not everywhere saturated. Above these units is a calcareous clay unit. It is generally 80 to 100 ft (24 to 30 m) thick with known maximum thickness of 136 ft (41 m). The known area of this continuous clay layer extends over 40 mi^2 (104 km^2). The clays are nearly impermeable and restrict the downward movement of percolating waters.

Perched ground water is present in the materials above the calcareous clays, including the upper silt which is 150 to 200 ft (46 to 61 m) thick. The upper contact of this unit is not everywhere well defined; the silt grades into the surficial upper sand and gravel deposits, which range from 25 to 53 ft (8 to 16 m) thick. Some thin erosional remnants of younger fan deposits occur in the immediate site area.

Ground-water movement in the regional aquifer is generally north to south, except in the vicinity of depression cones developed by wells for irrigation. Ground water is discharged from the aquifer via underflow to the south, by pumpage from irrigation wells, and by evapotranspiration. The principal source of recharge is via underflow from the valley north of the site area. Infiltration of surface runoff is a small fraction of the natural recharge. An estimated 25% of the water pumped for irrigation, or about 20,000 acre-feet per year (about 0.25 km^3/yr), is returned to the ground-water reservoir via vertical percolation. The calcareous clay restricts this percolation, and a perched ground-water mound has developed beneath this site area.

Perched Water Zone

The irrigation wells in this site area penetrate the regional aquifer to depths in excess of 1,000 ft (305 m); consequently, hydrologic data pertaining to the upper sediments have been scant. Measurements made in the initial site exploratory holes indicated that water levels in and adjacent to the irrigated cropland were significantly higher than in the existing irrigation wells. The borehole water levels ranged to within 5 ft (1.5 m) of the land surface, whereas water levels in irrigation wells ranged from 200 to 225 ft (61 to 69 m) below the land surface. To better define the ground-water conditions in the perched water zone, additional boreholes were constructed. The boreholes were drilled to shallow depths (50 to 70 ft [15 to 21 m] below the land surface) to detect the uppermost level of perched water in the sediments. Because of the variable nature of irrigation patterns and the occurrence of partially saturated materials of low permeability, the perched water table is irregular. However, a general ground-water mound was defined as shown in Figure 4.

The mound lies beneath the central part of the irrigated cropland. Discharge from the perched water zone is via underflow in a general direction radially outward from the center of the irrigated cropland and by downward leakage through the calcareous clay. It was recognized that once construction of the plant begins, the irrigation and return flow that developed the ground-water mound would cease. It could be expected that water levels in the perched zone would decline. However, when the plant is completed and operations commence, new sources of recharge to the mound would be present—the plant water-storage reservoir and the evaporation ponds.

It can be expected that water levels in the perched zone will rise beneath these ponds, but the extent will be small and should not cause levels beneath the power blocks to rise significantly. However, in the early studies, conservative parameters were necessarily used. The initial results suggested that during the life of the plant, water levels beneath power block unit 3 might rise as high as 920-ft (280-m) elevation and to lesser elevations beneath the two other units. At that time, foundation-stability analyses were not complete, but preliminary work suggested that liquefaction of some underlying soils might be possible with water levels about 904 ft (276 m). The more complete soil analyses showed that soil liquefaction would not occur during a SSE with ground-water levels as high as 920-ft (280-m) elevation. Nevertheless, the possibility that ground-water levels would require close control had been considered, and a preliminary design for a permanent dewatering system was developed.

Dewatering System Design

The proposed permanent dewatering system would maintain the water level beneath the power block units 2 and 3 to 900-ft (274-m) elevation or below. The purpose is to remove the perched ground water from granular soil above an elevation of 904 ft. A design objective of the dewatering system is to ensure that the depressed water levels would not recover above the 904-ft elevation in less than 30 d in the remote possibility of a total well-system failure. This allows sufficient time to restore operation or to allow an emergency shutdown of the plant before soil instability would occur.

Pumping tests were conducted with specially constructed wells located at the sites of power block units 2 and 3 to obtain data for the determination of coefficients of transmissivity, hydraulic conductivity, and water storage in sediments of the perched water zone. The parameter values determined from these tests were used to prepare the projected drawdown analysis and design of the dewatering system. At each unit site, a test array comprising a pumping well and observation wells was constructed, and constant-discharge tests were performed. Analysis of the tests was by the Theis nonequilibrium equation and the modified nonequilibrium graphic procedures.

A 24-in. (0.61 m) hole was drilled to a depth of 65 ft (20 m) for the test pumping well at the unit 3 site. It was equipped with 10-in. (0.254 m) casing and screen, and the annular space

LITHOLOGIC UNIT	AGE	THICKNESS	LOCATION	DESCRIPTION	LITHOLOGIC SYMBOL
Young Fan Deposits	Holocene-Pleistocene	8 to 15 feet	North and east of site	Brown gravel in a loose to medium dense silt and sand matrix, poorly sorted moderately stratified Volcanic, granitic, and metamorphic clasts.	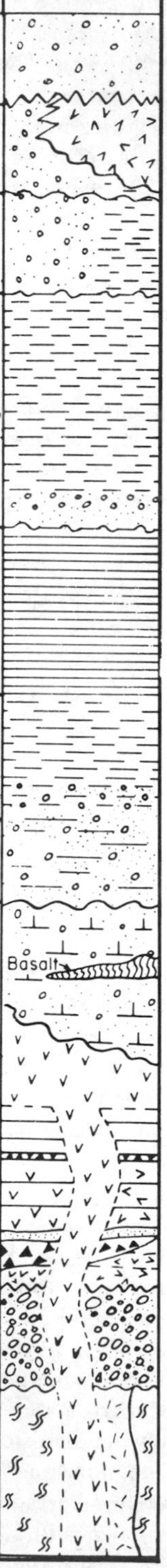
Basalt Flow	2 m.y. (Best K-Ar date)	5 to 200 feet (estimate)	South of site	Dark gray, hard, slightly porphyritic olivine basalt.	
				──────── UNCONFORMITY ────────	
"Upper" Sand and Gravel	> 2 m.y.	Up to 50 feet	Basin	Brown, medium dense silty sand and gravel; predominantly quartz sand with volcanic gravel; weathered mica common; locally calcareous.	
				──────── PARACONFORMITY ────────	
"Upper" Silt L-10 Horizon	> 2 m.y. to 2.8 m.y.	150 to 200 feet	Basin and south and southeast of site	Brown, medium dense to dense silt and clayey silt with generally minor interbedded fine sand, scattered fine weathered mica common, local calcareous cement; coarse sand and gravel locally at base of unit. Series of paleosols developed near upper contact	
				──────── PARACONFORMITY ────────	
Clay	2.8 m.y. at top	0 to 136 feet	Basin and south and southeast	Red-brown, very stiff, calcareous, silty clay; interbedded clastic wedges near west edge of basin Paleosols developed at upper contact.	
"Lower" Silt	> 3 m.y.	0 to 97 feet	Basin and south and southeast	Brown to red-brown, stiff to very stiff, sandy and clayey silt, locally grading to sand and gravel at base of unit.	
"Lower" Sand & Gravel	> 3 m.y.	0 to 30 feet	Basin	Brown, dense, silty and clayey sand and gravel of volcanic origin, poorly sorted	
				──────── UNCONFORMITY ────────	
Indurated Fanglomerate	16.7 ± .3 m.y. (K-Ar date of interbedded basalt)	0 to 285 feet	Basin	Brown, moderately to well cemented fanglomerate composed of volcanic clasts derived from underlying bedrock; local interbed of dark gray, hard basalt	Basalt
				──────── MAJOR UNCONFORMITY ────────	
Volcanic Bedrock Sequence	17.7 to 20.3 m.y. (K-Ar dates)	6,000 to 7,000 Feet	Hills west of site	Miocene volcanic sequence includes interbedded basalt, andesite and tuff, Tvb differentiated basalt, Tvu undifferentiated basalt and andesite, Tvt tuff and tuffaceous sandstone	
				──────── UNCONFORMITY ────────	
Arkosic Conglomerate	Unknown	148 Feet	Subsurface	Arkosic conglomerate, granite andesite and basalt clasts	
				──────── MAJOR UNCONFORMITY ────────	
Granitic and Metamorphic Basement	Precambrian	Unknown	Subsurface	Granite, granitic gneiss and metamorphosed volcanic and sedimentary rocks	

Figure 5. Stratigraphy of basin underlying nuclear power plant B.

backfilled with a sand filter; no. 40 slot Johnson "Irrigator" screen was placed between depths of 40 to 45 and 50 to 60 ft (15 to 18 m). A submersible pump with a capacity ranging from 2 to 18 gpm (0.1 to 1.1 l/s) was installed with the intake at a depth of 62 ft (19 m). Six small-diameter observation wells were drilled at distances from the pumping well ranging from 20 to 250 ft (6 to 76 m). Pumping of the well during the test continued for a period of 6.05 d (8,715 min). The well was pumped at 17.5 gpm (1.1 l/s) for the first 20 h, 15 gpm (0.95 l/s) for the next 7 h, and at an average of 12.5 gpm (0.789 l/s) for the remainder of the test. The discharge was adjusted to maintain maximum drawdown without breaking suction. Water levels remained unchanged (no drawdown) in observation wells beyond a distance of 100 ft (30 m) from the pumped well. At the end of the test, drawdown in the pumped well and at 100 ft (30 m) away from it was 0.37 ft (0.11 m).

At the unit 2 site, the test pumping well was drilled to a depth of 86 ft (26 m) and equipped similarly to that at the unit 3 site. Well screen was placed between depths of 50 and 75 ft (15 to 23 m). Five small-diameter observation wells were drilled at distances ranging from 20 to 500 ft (6 to 152 m). The pumping of the test well at the unit 3 site continued for a period of about 3.5 d (the test terminated owing to equipment failure). The pumping rate was 6 gpm (0.38 l/s) for the first 10 h and averaged 5 gpm (0.32 l/s) thereafter. As with the other test, the pumping rate was adjusted to prevent a break in pump suction. Drawdown in the pumped well was 35 ft (11 m) after 10 h of pumping and remained at approximately that level. Maximum drawdown in the observation wells was 0.81 ft (0.25 m) at a distance of 50 ft (15 m) from the pumping well and 0.24 ft (0.07 m) at a distance of 120 ft (37 m).

From the results of these tests, the coefficients of transmissivity and storage were estimated to be, respectively, 100 gpd/ft (1.24 m²/d) and 0.20 at unit 2, and 1,500 gpd/ft (18.6 m²/d) and 0.20 at unit 3. The higher transmissivity beneath unit 3 is due to the presence of a 10-ft (3-m) zone of sand, sandy clay, clayey sand, and clayey gravel that are the most permeable sediments encountered in the saturated zone to a depth of 65 ft (20 m) below the power-block units.

A projected drawdown analysis using these parameters indicates that the water levels beneath units 2 and 3 could be lowered to the 900-ft (274-m) elevation in about 5 yr with 52 wells, as shown in Figure 6. Five of the wells are located inside the boundary of units 2 and 3, and the remaining wells are on a 100-ft (30-m) spacing along the boundary. The wells are to be gravel-pack design, 100 ft (30 m) deep, with 6-in. (0.152-m) diameter casing and screen. There is to be at least 60 ft (18 m) of wire-wrapped or louvred screen, and the average capacity of each well is 5 gpm (0.32 l/s).

Drawdown analyses indicate that dewatering in less than 5 yr is not practical. For example, it would take about 200 wells distributed throughout the area of units 2 and 3 to dewater it in 1 yr. In addition to the expense, such an array would pose unacceptable construction problems. Water produced from the dewatering system will be pumped to either the evaporation pond or the water storage reservoir.

After the foundation is initially dewatered beneath units 2 and 3, perched ground water outside the units will move toward them. Therefore, some of the dewatering wells will need to be maintained to intercept this ground-water flow. A flow-net analysis indicates that about 40 of the wells may be required to continue pumping permanently. Observation wells will be located inside the boundary at units 2 and 3 to monitor the water level.

Computations were made to estimate the rise in water level under the units, should the total well system fail. The equation and parameters used in the analysis are

$$H = H_1 \left(1 - \mathrm{erf} \frac{x}{\sqrt{\dfrac{4K\bar{\bar{H}}t}{n}}} \right),$$

where H = increase in water level under the units; H_1 = excess hydraulic head (20 ft [6-m]—static level, 920-ft [280-m] elevation, less dewatered level, 900-ft [274-m] elevation); H_0 = initial head of perched water table, 150 ft (46 m); $\bar{\bar{H}} = H_0 + H_1$ = 150 + 20 = 170 ft (52 m); K = hydraulic conductivity = 1,000 ft/yr (305 m/yr) (based on average transmissivity of the two pumping tests and a saturated thickness of 40 ft [12.2 m]); n = porosity = 0.39; x = distance from well line to units = 500 ft (152 m); t = time = 30 d (use 0.1 yr); and erf = error function.

This analysis assumes the dewatering wells affect only water levels within units 2 and 3 area; immediately outside the line of wells ground water is at 920-ft (280-m) elevation. With this conservative assumption, the water level rise under the units,

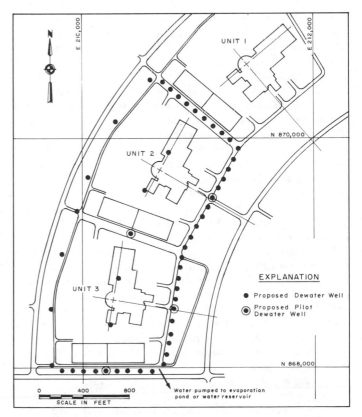

Figure 6. Proposed dewatering system, nuclear power plant B.

after 30 d of no pumping, would be 1.8 ft (0.55 m). If a worse condition were assumed of flow from two directions, the increase could not be more than twice the unidirectional flow, or 3.6 ft (1.1 m). This is less than the 4 ft (1.22 m) required to exceed the design water level of 904-ft (276-m) elevation. Considering its conservativeness, the analysis model provides additional assurance that the system meets the design objectives.

System analyses are based on conservative values of hydrogeologic parameters as derived from the two initial pumping tests, and the number of wells in the dewatering system is also considered to be conservative. Should the system be implemented, additional testing is proposed to provide data for optimum well-field design. The test program would include four pilot dewatering wells at the locations shown in Figure 6. With an observation well 100 ft from each pilot dewatering well, long-term pumping tests will be performed at each pilot well. Concurrently, water-level measurements will be taken monthly in existing shallow boreholes and monitor wells. The data obtained from the pilot dewatering wells and pumping tests will enhance the development of an optimum well array to dewater units 2 and 3. Water-level measurements in existing shallow boreholes and monitor wells would enable an assessment of the impact of irrigation termination on the perched water levels beneath the site.

GROUND-WATER CONTROL, NUCLEAR POWER PLANT C

Two power-generating units are being constructed for nuclear power plant C, which is on a coastal site of moderately rugged relief. The site is about 450 m from the shoreline on the lee side of stable sand dunes. Ground surface at the site was originally 12- to 15-m elevation. Immediately inland of the site, mountainous terrain begins with steep-sided ridges and deeply incised drainages. The power-block units are excavated in bedrock, a moderately indurated complex of sandstone, shale, siltstone, and mudstone, all with low permeability.

During the original exploration, warm, sulfurous ground water was reported in one deep drill hole at a depth of 75 m. At that time, the site was being used for flood irrigation, so the hole was capped, and no tests were performed on the water. At a later date, when access was available, several holes were drilled to investigate the ground-water conditions in detail. However, no warm, sulfurous waters were encountered.

The bedrock itself is nearly impermeable, but fractures provide permeable pathways. Because ground-water levels were shallow and because deeper, confined thermal water had been reported, it was recognized that ground-water control would need to be considered. However, the quality of the ground water encountered at foundation grade was good, and would present no problems to the plant structures.

Ultimately, site excavation uncovered the original hole (D-11) in which sulfurous waters were found, and poor-quality ground water began flowing into the excavation. Sulfate- and sulfite-bearing water was then found flowing from other drill holes and from fractures in the rock. Because this warm, aggressive water is potentially detrimental to concrete, a thorough evaluation was begun.

Ground-Water Occurrence

The foundation material of the site is a sedimentary complex of the central portion of the "M formation" of Miocene age (Fig. 7). Although some streaks of carbonaceous material were found in cored holes, coal beds of commercial quality and thickness occur only in stratigraphically higher rocks than those beneath the site. The rocks are moderately indurated, and from laboratory measurements of strength, they were determined sufficiently strong to carry the plant design loads. The bedrock is overlain by about 10 m of loosely consolidated alluvial clay, silt, sand, and some gravel. To the northeast, the site is bordered by stabilized sand dunes that separate it from the shoreline. The stratigraphic column for the site is shown in Figure 8.

Shallow, unconfined ground water is within 5 m of the ground surface at the site during exploration, or at approximately 10-m elevation above mean sea level. Samples from water wells in the area indicate that the water is of mixed quality; it contains approximately 350 mg/l total dissolved solids, but has an unusually high content of iron and magnesium. The water will present no problem to the structures. The water table is at slightly higher elevations beneath the sand dunes to the northwest; this suggests a ground-water mound recharged by infiltration of precipitation on the dunes. Exploration indicates that this shallow ground water extends to approximately 50-m depth within the bedrock.

The excavation uncovered the early exploratory hole, D-11, which apparently provided the initial pathway by which deep, confined waters permeated the shallow fractured zones and began seeping onto the floor of the excavation. These waters are warm; temperature measured in drill hole D-11 at a depth of 42 m was 40.2°C. These waters were found seeping from at least 19 other drill holes or rock fractures. More than 50 samples were taken from seeps shown in Figure 9. The analyses indicate that most waters entering the excavation are in the neutral pH range (6 to 8) and contain less sulfate than 200 mg/l (Table 4). However, several seeps were markedly acidic (pH of 3±) and contained as much sulfate as 2,600 mg/l. Flow at most of the seeps was too small to measure, but several flowed at a rate of 1 to 2 gpm (0.063 to 0.126 l/s).

The site is at the northeast end of a geothermal belt of hot springs and fumaroles associated with a Pliocene-Pleistocene group of volcanic rocks including andesitic and basaltic lava flows and pyroclastic and detrital material. Three distinct types of hot springs can be identified in the belt, of which the first type, an acid sulfate-chloride water has apparently traveled from the geothermal area by way of open joints, bedding planes, and fractures to eventually intersect with the exploration holes and the excavated area. Most of the energy for migration is provided by the hydraulic gradient between the source and the site. However, additional energy is provided by the temperature gradient. The drilling of holes and the excavation have increased that gradient.

Remedial Measures

It had been recognized early that control of the shallow ground water would be required to reduce uplift pressures at the foundation base. However, the warm, sulfurous waters presented a potentially more serious problem—chemical attack

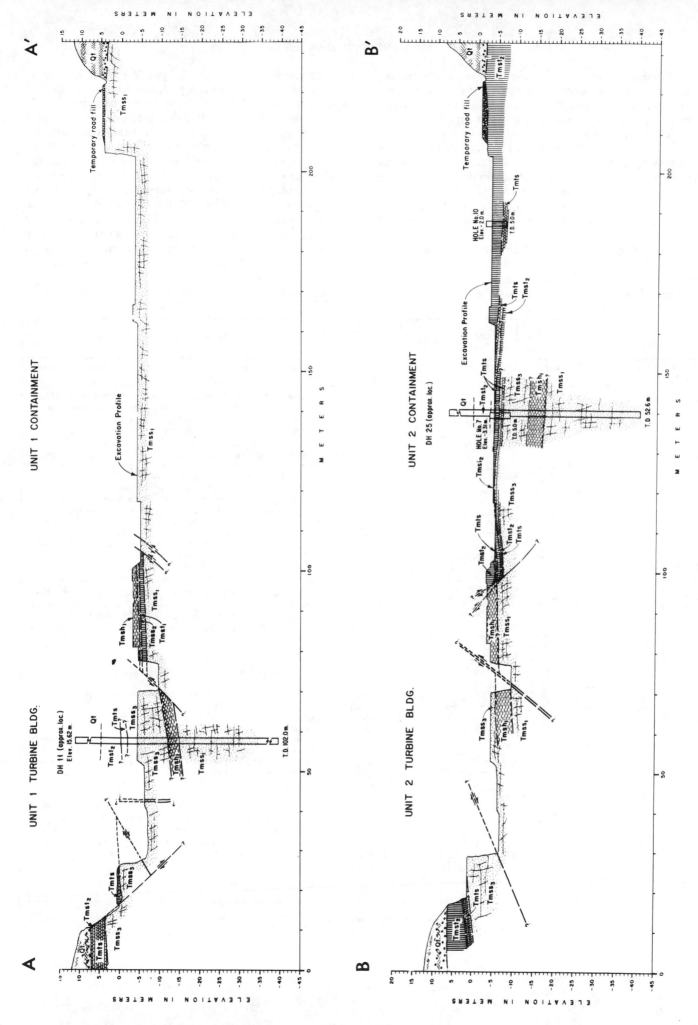

Figure 7. Geologic sections, nuclear power plant C.

on the foundation structure. Because there is no feasible way to completely eliminate or divert the source, it was recommended that protection of the foundation be provided in three ways: (1) reduce seepage into the area by pressure-grouting unsealed drill holes and areas where seepage along joints and fractures is occurring, (2) retard and minimize deterioration of the foundation by the use of sulfate-resistant cement and by waterproofing, and (3) prepare a permanent dewatering system to intercept inflow of sulfurous waters that may start in new locations after the grouting is complete, as well as maintain the ground water at an acceptable level below grade.

Grouting and Concrete Protection from Sulfate Attack

Basic techniques for minimizing attack of sulfate-bearing waters on concrete are to use cements that form compounds which do not react with sulfate (type V cement, or use of pozzolans as an admixture) and to design a concrete mix that will produce a more dense and impermeable concrete.

Grout holes were 3½-in. (8.9 cm; EX) diameter and were drilled to varying depths and angles that depended on the nature of the seepage and rock conditions. Grout consisted of type II cement with 15% to 20% replacement with fly ash. Initially, the water/cement ratio was about 4 to 1, and then the grout was thickened progressively on each hole. Grout pressures were less than 10 kg/cm^2 (9.8×10^5 Pa). If grouting of the initial hole failed to reduce the seepage, additional holes were drilled and grouted until seepage was reduced to an acceptable amount. When completed, the grouting reduced seepage in the power-block area from 200 gpm (12.6 l/s) to less than 40 gpm (2.5 l/s).

The concrete for the foundation includes TCC type II cement

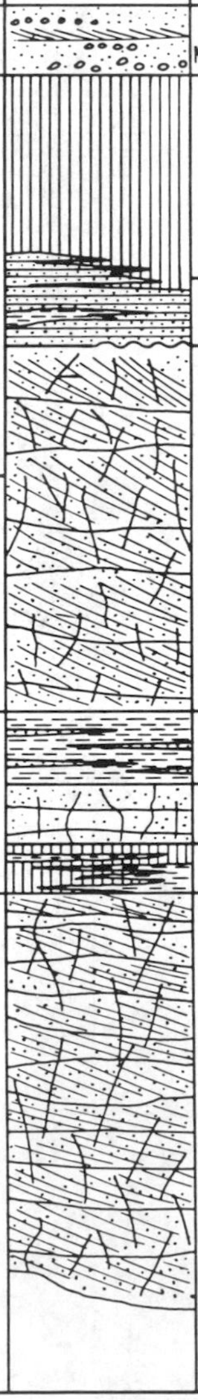

SYSTEM	SERIES	SYMBOL	LOC. OF MEASURED SECTION	COLUMNAR SECTION	THICKNESS (m)	DESCRIPTION
QUATERNARY	RECENT	Qt	NOT MEASURED		NOT MEASURED	Undifferentiated clay, silt, sand, and gravel including dune sand on north side of power block
TERTIARY	MIOCENE	$Tmst_2$	South bank of powerblock from east to west		6 +	Siltstone / Mudstone - black to dark gray; massive; jointed with blocky fracturing; locally finely laminated; exhibits conchoidal fracture; carbonaceous with locally abundant leaf imprints; secondary euhedral pyrite crystals found in some joint spaces and inside spheroidal inclusions (nodules ?); interfingers with thin sandstone near base especially in Unit 2 reactor containment and auxiliary building areas
		Tmts	South bank of powerblock from east to west		2 ±	Sandstone - gray; thin-bedded; quartz-rich; cemented; jointed perpendicular to bedding; wavy beds; marked variations in thickness of unit and individual beds; thin seams of black, glassy coal; abundant carbon streaks along bedding surfaces; locally alternates with thin shale beds; local unconformity with $Tmss_3$; interfingers with $Tmst_2$ and $Tmsh_2$
		$Tmss_3$	South bank of powerblock from east to west; Unit 1 turbine bldg. intake-east side		10.7 ±	Sandstone - light gray; thick-bedded to massive; quartz-rich; fine- to coarse-grained; generally well sorted; grains-angular to subangular; poorly to well cemented; extensively cross-bedded with abundant thin sinuous carbon streaks outlining the cross-bedding; local thin lenses and pockets of coal with vitrain texture; jointed and fractured across the bedding; iron and sulphur stains locally present on weathered surfaces and joint faces; contains spheroidal and elongate inclusions of cemented silt and clay with secondary euhedral pyrite; unit is very friable where disturbed by shear zones
		$Tmsh_1$	Unit 1 turbine bldg. discharge-south side		2.1 +	Shale - brown to brownish gray; alternates with thin beds of gray sandstone; laminated; fissile; varies markedly in thickness and sand content across site
		$Tmss_2$	Unit 1 turbine bldg. discharge-south side		1.8 ±	Sandstone - white to light gray; thin- to thick-bedded with local thin shale beds; jointing approx. perpendicular to bedding; quartz-rich; cemented; slightly friable; dense
		$Tmst_1$	Unit 1 turbine bldg. discharge-south side		1.4 ±	Siltstone / Shale - brown to brownish gray siltstone interfingering with shale; siltstone has a banded appearance - especially in Unit 1; thin sand lenses are abundant; parting parallel to bedding well developed where shaly; thickness varies markedly
		$Tmss_1$	Unit 1 auxiliary and fuel bldgs -west side		12 +	Sandstone - light gray; thick-bedded to massive; quartz-rich; fine to coarse-grained; generally well sorted; grains-angular to subangular; moderately to well cemented; jointed and fractured approx. perpendicular to bedding; locally cross-bedded with thin sinuous carbon streaks along the cross-bedding; iron and sulphur stains on weathered surfaces and in joint spaces

Figure 8. Stratigraphy underlying power block, nuclear power plant C.

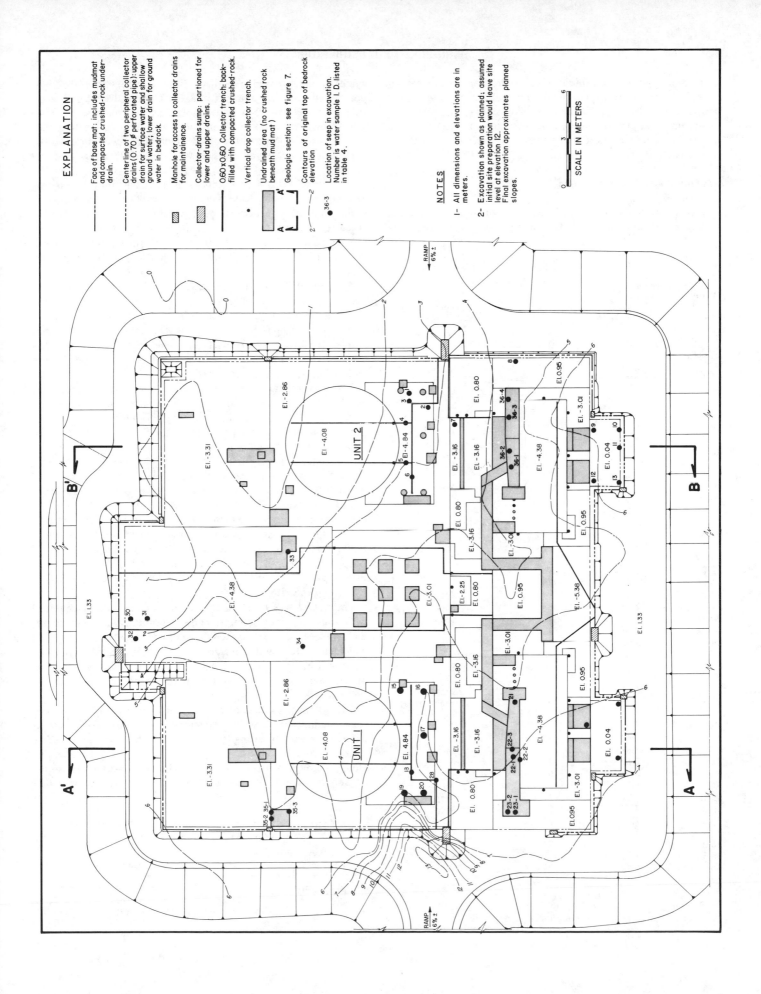

with 25% fly-ash replacement. The production and placement of it followed procedures applicable to nuclear power plant construction. Finally, Vandex (a proprietary water-proofing compound that penetrates the concrete and combines with free lime to increase the sulfate resistance) was placed on all exterior surfaces below grade.

Ground-Water Control System

Several methods or systems had been considered to provide a permanent drainage including a closely spaced deep-well system; a deep peripheral gravel-filled trench with embedded, perforated pipe and connecting laterals; free draining, gravel-filled trenches on a 2-m grid under class 1 structures and 30-m grid elsewhere; a porous concrete pad; and, the system that was selected, a 30-cm-thick bed of crushed, well-compacted, free-draining aggregate beneath the mud-mat throughout the foundation.

The objective of the drainage is to keep uplift pressures at acceptable levels. However, to accomplish this, the system must (1) intercept a maximum number of joints and rock fractures, (2) be constructed with a minimum disruption of the foundation rock, and (3) minimize the distance to less than 1 m between any point beneath class 1 structures and a drain.

A major difficulty in selecting a system was the need to leave the foundation rock undisturbed. The concept of drain trenches on a 1-m grid was desirable, except that it was found to be nearly impossible to dig the trenches, even by hand, without seriously disturbing the intervening rock. Finally, the crushed aggregate met these requirements; it was permeable and provided a dense, firm mat.

The crushed-aggregate source was coarse gravels from the nearby river channel. After having been subjected to sulfurous water, these gravels met the following durability tests: In seven runs of an abrasion test (ASTM Design–C131-69), the average loss of material by weight was less than 20%. In the modified wetshot (Deval) test (AASHTO Design–T 4-35), after 1,000 revolutions with one abrasive charge, 674 g of aggregate material lost less than 12% material by weight. After the sodium sulfate soundness test (ASTM Design–C 88-73), the weighted loss of aggregate samples was less than 10%. The petrographic analysis revealed that the aggregate was composed of ±35% relatively fresh, nonporous pyroxene andesite; ±55% slightly altered, porous pyroxene-hornblende andesite; and ±10% weathered porous pyroxene-hornblende andesite. Other characteristics are listed in Table 5.

The gravel was crushed to provide a free-draining material with high angle of friction. The maximum size was 5 cm, and no more than 15% passed through a #4 screen. The material was compacted with vibratory compactors to 85% relative density. Finally, a layer of gunite or stiff concrete was placed on the aggregate before the concrete mud-mat was laid to prevent clogging.

The 30-cm-thick bed of compacted aggregate placed on the rock foundation serves as a subdrain that carries water to collector trenches along the flanks of the base slabs. The collector trenches drain to the lower of two perforated pipes along the power-plant periphery. The two perforated pipes are separated by the restraint slabs. The lower pipe is connected

TABLE 4. WATER SAMPLE ANALYSIS, POWER PLANT C

Sample* no.	pH	SO_4 (ppm)	Estimated flow (gpm)
1	5.90	180	1
3-1	6.64	134	0.5
8	7.20	93	1
9	6.61	178	Seep
10	5.84	88	Seep
11	5.55	170	Seep
12	7.73	184	Seep
13	9.03	270	Seep
14	6.68	55.4	Shallow ground water
15	12.20	20	Seep
16	11.82	300	Seep
17	11.47	129.2	Seep
18	6.80	129.6	Seep
19	10.53	188.4	Seep
20	10.33	181.2	Seep
21	7.22	198	2
22-1	7.40	248.4	2
22-2	6.62	78.8	2
22-3	6.00	89.6	2
23-1	7.48	229	2
23-2	8.06	95.5	2
24-1	3.10	930	Seep
24-2	5.14	316	Seep
24-3	2.98	2,376	Seep
24-3A[†]	3.07	2,440	Seep
24-3B[†]	3.04	2,592	Seep
24-3C[†]	3.02	2,464	Seep
24-4	3.28	690	Collector sump
25-1	6.92	116	Seep
25-2	6.98	70.2	0.5
26	6.61	88	Shallow ground water
28	6.88	118.4	Collector trench; total inflow, 4 gpm
29	6.72	147.0	2
30	7.44	174.0	Seep
31	7.61	192.0	Seep
32	7.69	131.0	1
33	6.88	201.0	1
34	8.04	152.0	1
35-1	7.21	37.2	Seep
35-2	7.35	35.0	Seep
35-3	7.39	37.2	Seep
36-1	5.50	172.0	Seep
36-2	6.70	73.5	Seep
36-3	7.32	70.8	Seep
36-4	6.94	79.4	4

Note: 1 gpm = 0.0633 l/s.
*Sample points shown in Figure 9.
[†]Check samples taken following initial sample analysis.

TABLE 5. CHARACTERISTICS OF FIVE SAMPLES OF RIVER AGGREGATE

Parameter	High	Low	Average
Specific gravity	2.69	2.11	2.44
Porosity	14.83%	2.61%	7.36%
Water absorption	6.41%	0.97%	3.03%

to the subdrain and the collector trenches to carry away the sulfurous waters mixed with shallow ground water within the bedrock. The upper perforated pipe collects shallow ground water draining from the alluvium surrounding the power block and thus keeps those waters separate from the poorer-quality water beneath the plant foundation.

Because of the wide variations in base slab elevations, it is impractical to provide a continuous run of pipe for the lower collector pipes. Therefore, all elevation changes of the collector pipes from each base slab are made at sumps or manholes. The manholes facilitate inspection and cleaning of the drain pipes (Fig. 9).

The perforated pipes around the periphery of the power block drain to four sumps. Each sump is provided with two 10-horsepower pumps, each with a capacity of 450 gpm (28 1/s). If necessary, additional pumps may be installed. The present rate of inflow is estimated to be less than 400 gpm (25 1/s). The perforated reinforced concrete pipe is constructed locally. It is of sufficient strength to carry the design loads and is 70.0-mm diameter to facilitate inspection. Mixing of the sulfurous waters with shallow ground water from the bedrock occurs in the aggregate layer to neutralize the waters before reaching the concrete pipe.

The crushed-aggregate blanket provided the following advantages for a permanent drainage-control system: (1) rapid and simplified placement; (2) little to no disturbance of underlying foundation rock; (3) a dense, free-draining stable foundation that is resistant to sulfate attack; (4) sulfurous waters are mixed with good-quality water before reaching collector drains and sumps; and (5) a dry work area for construction and placement of the mud-mat.

SUMMARY

Ground-water conditions can impose serious design restrictions on a proposed nuclear power plant site in many different ways, as suggested by the above examples. It is important that conditions that may cause such restrictions be identified as early as possible in the site investigation. Data to evaluate the potential problem can then be collected in a timely and systematic manner to minimize design changes to meet any restrictions posed by such conditions.

ACKNOWLEDGMENTS

Reuben C. Newcomb and Allen W. Hatheway critically reviewed the manuscript.

REFERENCES CITED

Code of Federal Regulations, 1978, Title 10, Energy; Part 20 [10 CRF 20], Standards for protection against radiation: Washington, D.C., U.S. Nuclear Regulatory Commission.

Cooper, H. H., Bredehoft, J. D., Papadopules, I. S., and Bennet, R. R., 1965, The response of well-aquifer systems to seismic waves: Journal of Geophysical Research, v. 70, p. 3915–3926.

Grove, D. B., 1970, A method to describe the flow of radioactive ions in groundwater: Albuquerque, New Mexico, Sandia Laboratories, Report SC-CR-70-6139, 38 p.

Harleman, D.R.F., Melhorn, P. F., and Rumer, R. R., 1963, Dispersion-permeability correlation in porous media: American Society of Civil Engineers Proceedings, Journal of Hydraulics Division, v. 89, no. HY2, p. 67–85.

Kaufman, W. J., 1963, An appraisal of the distribution coefficient for estimating underground movement of radioisotopes (A preliminary report): Palo Alto, California, Hazelton-Nuclear Science Corp., 23 p.

——1973, Notes on radionuclide pollution of groundwaters: Course in ground-water pollution, Section IV: University of California, Berkeley, Water Resources Engineering Series, 14 p.

Mercado, A., 1967, The spreading pattern of injected water in a permeability stratified aquifer: International Association of Statistical Hydrologists, Symposium at Haifa, Israel, Proceedings, Publication no. 72, p. 23–36.

Nazarian, H. N., 1973, Water well design for earthquake induced motions: American Society of Civil Engineers Proceedings, Journal of Power Division, v. 99, p. 377–394.

U.S. Bureau of Reclamation, 1968, Earth manual: Washington, D.C., U.S. Government Printing Office, p. 541–562.

Webster, D. S., Proctor, J. F., and Marine, I. W., 1970, Two-well tracer test in fractured crystalline rock: U.S. Geological Survey Water-Supply Paper 1544-I, 22 p.

MANUSCRIPT RECEIVED BY THE SOCIETY JULY 13, 1978
MANUSCRIPT ACCEPTED NOVEMBER 13, 1978

Glossary of terms and abbreviations

ACRS   Advisory Committee on Reactor Safeguards

AEC   Atomic Energy Commission (discontinued with formation of ERDA and NRC on January 19, 1975)

ASLAB   Atomic Safety and Licensing Appeals Board

ASLB   Atomic Safety and Licensing Board

BWR   boiling water reactor

b.y.   billion years

cc   cubic centimetre(s)

CFR   *Code of Federal Regulations*

CP   Construction Permit

d   day(s)

DBE   Design Basis Earthquake

DOE   Department of Energy

EIR   Environmental Impact Report

EPA   Environmental Protection Agency

ERDA   Energy Research and Development Agency (discontinued; now DOE)

ESR   Early Site Review

ESRR   Early Site Review Report

FIND   Fiche Index to Nuclear Dockets

FOL   Full Operating License

FPC   Federal Power Commission

FSAR   Final Safety Analysis Report

γ gamma rays

g   gram(s)

g the acceleration of gravity ($9.81 \text{ m/s}^2 = 32.2 \text{ ft/s}^2$)

h   hour(s)

IAEA   International Atomic Energy Agency

ISC   International Seismological Centre

ISS   International Seismological Summary

km   kilometre(s)

kW·h   kilowatt hour(s)

LOL   Limiting Operating License

LWA   Limited Work Authorization

LWR   light water reactor

µg   microgram(s)

µm   micrometre(s)

m   metre(s)

m_b body-wave magnitude

mg   milligram(s)

M_L local magnitude

MM   modified Mercalli (scale of felt earthquake intensities)

mol   mole(s)

M_s surface-wave magnitude

mW   milliwatt(s)

MW   megawatt(s)

m.y.   million years

NEPA   National Environmental Policy Act

NOAA   National Oceanic and Atmospheric Administration

NPS   Nuclear Power Station

NRC   Nuclear Regulatory Commission (formerly part of AEC)

NSSS   nuclear steam supply system

NTIS   National Technical Information Service

OBE	Operating Basis Earthquake	SAR	Safety Analysis Report
POL	Possession Only License	SER	Safety Evaluation Report
ppb	parts per billion	SPT	Standard Penetration Test
ppm	parts per million	SRP	Standard Review Plan
PSAR	Preliminary Safety Analysis Report	SSE	Safe Shutdown Earthquake
psi	pounds per square inch	TIC	Technical Information Center
PWR	pressurized water reactor	WWSSN	World-Wide Standardized Seismograph Network
s	second(s)	yd	yard(s)
SAB	Site Analysis Branch	yr	year(s)

Index